A TREASURY
OF RIBALDRY

BOOKS BY LOUIS UNTERMEYER

POETRY

Challenge · These Times · The New Adam · Roast Leviathan
Burning Bush · Food and Drink · Selected Poems and Parodies

PARODIES

The Younger Quire · Including Horace
Heavens: A Book of Burlesques · and Other Poets

ESSAYS AND BIOGRAPHIES

American Poetry Since 1900 · Play in Poetry · Forms of Poetry
Heinrich Heine: Paradox and Poet
From Another World: An Autobiography
Makers of the Modern World

FICTION

Moses (a novel) · The Last Pirate (Tales from Gilbert and Sullivan)
Chip: My Life and Times · The Fat of the Cat and Other Stories
The Wonderful Adventures of Paul Bunyan
The Donkey of God and Other Stories

CRITICAL COLLECTIONS

Modern American Poetry · Modern British Poetry
American Poetry from the Beginning to Whitman
Early American Poets · An Anthology of New England Poets
The Book of Living Verse · A Treasury of Great Poems
A Treasury of Laughter
The Love Poems of Robert Herrick and John Donne
The Love Poems of Robert and Elizabeth Browning
The Prose and Poetry of Walt Whitman

COLLECTIONS OF POETRY FOR YOUNG PEOPLE

This Singing World · New Songs for New Voices · Stars to Steer By
Yesterday and Today · Doorways to Poetry · Rainbow in the Sky
The Magic Circle

A Treasury

of

RIBALDRY

EDITED, WITH CRITICAL NOTES AND

A RUNNING COMMENTARY, BY

Louis Untermeyer

HANOVER HOUSE

GARDEN CITY, NEW YORK

Library of Congress Catalog Card Number 56-13368

For many helpful reminders, I am grateful to Mel Evans, who first suggested the basic idea of the book, and also to George de Kay, Michel Farano, Juliette Rypinski, Ethel Everett, and Mort L. Nasatir. For editorial acuteness, creative research, and constant collaboration, I am happily indebted to my wife, Bryna Ivens.

Beneath the unregenerate lines,
Racy as talk and natural as food,
You touch the thing that laughs and shines,
Nourishing man's first need: the good
Accord of earth and all its certitude.

ACKNOWLEDGMENTS

The publisher has made every effort to trace the ownership of all copyrighted material contained herein. It is his belief that the necessary permissions from authors or their authorized agents have been obtained in all cases. In the event of any question arising as to the use of any material the publisher, while expressing regret for any error he has unconsciously made, will be pleased to make the necessary correction in future editions of this book.

Thanks are due to the following authors, publishers, publications and agents for permission to use the material indicated.

Abelard-Schuman, Inc., for "The Keeper of the Gelded Unicorn" from *Hopalong-Freud and Other Literary Characters*, by Ira Wallach. Copyright, 1951, by Abelard-Schuman, Inc. Also for "God's Little Best Seller" from *Hopalong-Freud Rides Again*, by Ira Wallach. Copyright, 1952, by Abelard-Schuman, Inc. Reprinted by permission of the publishers, Abelard-Schuman, Inc.

Conrad Aiken for his poem, *Limberick*, heretofore unpublished, and copyrighted as a part of this book.

Brandt and Brandt for "she being Brand" from *Poems: 1923–1954*, by E. E. Cummings, published by Harcourt, Brace and Company. Copyright, 1926, by Horace Liveright.

James Branch Cabell for the chapter from *Jurgen*, published by Robert M. McBride Company. Copyright, 1921, by James Branch Cabell.

Coward-McCann, Inc., for "The Ballad of Yukon Jake," by Edward E. Paramore, Jr. Copyright, 1921, 1924, 1948, by Edward E. Paramore, Jr. Reprinted by permission of Coward-McCann, Inc.

Doubleday & Company, Inc., for "Legend of the Crooked Coronet" from *Crooked Coronet*, by Michael Arlen. Copyright, 1937, by Doubleday & Company, Inc. Also for "Appearance and Reality" from *Creatures of Circumstance*, by W. Somerset Maugham, copyright, 1934, by W. Somerset Maugham, and for "Winter Cruise" from *Creatures of Circumstance*, by W. Somerset Maugham, copyright, 1943, by W. Somerset Maugham. Reprinted by permission of Doubleday & Company, Inc.

Faber & Faber (London) for "A Ballad of the Good Lord Nelson" from

Petronius, Furebaugh translation, The Black and Gold Library. Copyright, 1949, by Liveright Publishing Corporation. Reprinted by permission of Liveright Publishers, New York.

Harold Matson Company for "The Bedchamber Mystery," by C. S. Forester. Originally published in *Cosmopolitan Magazine*. Copyright, 1943, by C. S. Forester. For "Rope Enough," by John Collier. Originally published in *The New Yorker*, and collected in *Fancies and Goodnights*. Copyright, 1939, by John Collier. For "Season of Mists," by John Collier. Originally published in *Esquire, Inc.*, and collected in *Fancies and Goodnights*. Copyright, 1939, by Esquire, Inc. For "En la Noche," by Ray Bradbury. Originally published in *Cavalier Magazine* and collected in *The Golden Apples of the Sun*. Copyright, 1952, by Fawcett Publications, Inc. All the foregoing reprinted by permission of Harold Matson Company.

Ogden Nash for "Four Prominent So-and-So's," by Ogden Nash. Copyright, 1933, by Ogden Nash, and reprinted with permission of the author and Curtis Brown, Ltd.

Museum Press Limited (London) for a chapter from *The Best Butter*, by Jean Dutourd. Reprinted by permission of Museum Press Limited (London) and Simon & Schuster, Inc. (New York).

New Directions for "To Helidora," "Inscription for a Smyrna Outhouse," and "The Sober Companion" from *One Hundred Poems from the Palatine Anthology*, translated by Dudley Fitts. Copyright, 1938, by New Directions.

Peter Pauper Press for the selections from Voltaire's *Alphabet of Wit* (*Satirical Dictionary*), translated by Paul McPharlin. Copyright, 1945, 1954, by Peter Pauper Press.

Random House, Inc., for "Joey and the Calcutta Club" from *Pipe Night*, by John O'Hara. Copyright, 1940, by John O'Hara.

Juliette Rypinski for her translations from *The Memoirs of Casanova*, heretofore unpublished, and copyrighted as a part of this book.

Simon & Schuster, Inc., for a chapter from *The Best Butter*, by Jean Dutourd. Copyright, 1955, by Jean Dutourd. Reprinted by permission of Simon & Schuster, Inc., and Museum Press, Ltd. (London). Also for the selections from *The Scandals of Clochemerle*, by Gabriel Chevallier. Copyright, 1937, by Simon & Schuster, Inc. Reprinted by permission of Simon & Schuster, Inc., and Martin Secker & Warburg, Ltd. (London).

Martin Secker & Warburg, Ltd. (London), for selections from *The Scandals of Clochemerle,* by Gabriel Chevallier. Permission also from Simon & Schuster, Inc. (New York).

William Sloane Associates, Inc., for "The Captain's Pink Panties" from *All the Ship's At Sea,* by William J. Lederer. Copyright, 1950, by William J. Lederer, and reprinted by permission of William Sloane Associates, Inc.

The Society of Authors (London) for "When Adam Day by Day" from *The Collected Poems of A. E. Housman.* Copyright, 1940, by Henry Holt & Company, Inc. Permission granted by The Society of Authors as the literary representative of the trustees of the estate of the late A. E. Housman, and Jonathon Cape, Ltd. (publishers of A. E. Housman's *Collected Poems*), and Henry Holt & Company (New York).

Louis Untermeyer for his translations from *The Greek Anthology,* Aristophanes, Ovid's *Art of Love,* Petronius' *Satyricon,* and *The Poems of Catullus,* heretofore unpublished, and copyrighted as a part of this book.

The Viking Press, Inc., for "The Miller's Tale," "The Reeve's Tale," and "Prologue to the Wife of Bath's Tale," from *The Portable Chaucer,* translated by Theodore Morrison. Copyright, 1949, by Theodore Morrison. For "Indian Summer" and "The Little Old Lady in Lavender Silk" from *The Portable Dorothy Parker.* Copyright, 1926, 1931, 1944, by Dorothy Parker. For "Entrance Fee" from *The Portable Woollcott.* Copyright, 1934, by Alexander Woollcott; 1946, by The Viking Press, Inc. For "The Strength of God" from *Winesburg, Ohio,* by Sherwood Anderson, also included in *The Portable Sherwood Anderson.* Copyright, 1919, by B. W. Huebsch; 1947 by Eleanor Copenhaver Anderson. For Chapter XIII from *Tortilla Flat,* by John Steinbeck. Copyright, 1935, by John Steinbeck. All the foregoing are reprinted by permission of The Viking Press, Inc., New York.

A. P. Watt & Son (London) for "Appearance and Reality" and "Winter Cruise" from *Creatures of Circumstance,* by W. Somerset Maugham. Reprinted by permission of A. P. Watt & Son for the author, William Heinemann, Ltd. (London), and Doubleday & Company, Inc. (New York).

Ann Watkins for "Legend of the Coronet" from *Crooked Coronet,* by Michael Arlen. Copyright, 1937, by Doubleday & Company, Inc.

FOREWORD

Man—to begin with a thumping generality—has always staggered under pressures which have pushed him from one anxiety to another. He has tried to shoulder the lot with a philosophy of fortitude or accept it with the comfort of religion. But when the world seems not only too much with him but against him, he frequently thumbs his nose at it all and escapes by way of his irrepressible lust for life, his saving gift of gaiety, his very animal spirits.

It was the unregenerate animal spirit rather than the life of the spirit that always promised him the vastest range of pleasures. It made possible his frank delight in the five senses, especially touch and taste, and (until the censors made him aware of their "unwholesomeness") the wholesome fulfillment of his natural appetites. Even when he was afflicted with a sense of guilt he did not lose his enjoyment of lavish eating, drinking, and love-making—he was merely conditioned to relish his carnalities in secret or, in a kind of blithe overcompensation, to make fun of them.

In the broadest sense, the world's favorite humor has been a playful expression of primitive sensuality. It has, at times, been tinctured with self-mockery, a sort of protective derision, a comic exposure of what is condemned in public and gleefully practiced in private. The satisfactions of the body, from food to sex, are responsible for some of the wisest and wittiest as well as some of the most rollicking and ribald writing in literature.

Twenty-five hundred years ago, the Greeks (who had many words for it) treated love with a mixture of reverence and ridicule. Even while they worshiped the power of Priapus, fertile god of gardens as well as wives, his manifestations were also the subject of many a wanton jest. In the twentieth century, an important school of thought has persuaded its followers that sex is the prime mover and pure force behind man's behavior. The opposite attitude is revealed in the story credited (or discredited) to the Harvard professor who, explaining sex, said that the pleasure is transitory, the price is excessive, and the position is ridiculous. From the time of the Greeks to our own time, man's reactions to his large as well as little diversions have been incongruously mixed. Man has learned not only to laugh at sex but to laugh with it.

It is to the paradox of love and laughter that this volume is devoted. Here is a collection of literature that people have always enjoyed even when they were timid about reading it. If it shows up many of man's follies and frailties, it also discloses the complexity of his simple humanness. Proofs of his instinctive and sometimes irresponsible behavior are to be found in the earliest reflections of his culture—in (for a particularly brilliant example) *The Greek Anthology*, with which this treasury begins.

Much of this literature has been created by the most honored men of letters. Ovid, for example, has been rated by scholars as a model of elegiac poetry and a fabulist of the first order; yet his *Ars Amatoria* presents a surprisingly naturalistic attitude to love. Catullus, continually praised for his tender lyricism, also wrote with rude virility. Daniel Defoe, the first outstanding figure in English journalism, is beloved throughout the world for the children's romance, *Robinson Crusoe*; but he is equally famous for the complete realism of *Moll Flanders*. Proving that he was indeed "more universal than Newton or Voltaire," Benjamin Franklin, in addition to being a great statesman, homely philosopher, inventor, printer, and patriot, was an essayist who indulged in light and occasionally licentious prose. Honoré de Balzac, who documented and dramatized an entire society in his monumental *Human Comedy*, entertained himself (and countless others) with the lusty satire of *Droll Stories*. Such celebrated contemporaries as John Steinbeck and Erskine Caldwell leaven their serious social criticism with a rough and particularly earthy humor.

In this volume the ribald note is not extended to express the sniggering, the merely lewd, lascivious, or scatological. On the other hand, it includes the kind of ribaldry that is subtle as well as robust, bitter as well as bawdy, satirical, iconoclastic, wry, sometimes irreverent, and even outrageous. It should be added that practically nothing appears in these pages that has not been previously published and freely circulated. Moreover, everything included has won the approval of countless readers and is, in the editor's opinion, a work of literature.

Nothing, however, is more fluctuating than taste. What may offend a present-day guardian of the public morals was once a convention, completely acceptable to the devout clerics of the Middle Ages, severe queens like Margaret of Navarre, and the most high-minded citizens of the Renaissance. The swarming canvases of Breughel and the alternately grotesque and gorgeous pages of *The Canterbury Tales* rollick with raw humanity; neither the painter nor the poet was afraid to depict the normal and gross activities of ordinary men and women. The roaring coarseness of Rabelais is far healthier than the false reticence and indecent delicacy of the later "gentility." The Elizabethan playwrights shared their immense gusto and illimitable range of human passions with their listeners; the Restoration writers were no more squeamish about the details of everyday living than their readers. "Evil to him who thinks evil" is a proverb which has been popular for centuries.

Outspokenness suffered a decided setback during the nineteenth century. It was not only in America that to the Puritan all things seemed impure. In England what started as an era of "sweetness and light" became a blight of evasiveness and prudery that was worse than prurience. Mrs. Grundy, the symbol of censoriousness and the genteel tradition was, in many people's minds, synonymous with the righteous Queen Victoria herself. It was seriously suggested that a proper library would keep male and female authors on separate shelves—unless the authors were married.

Victorian standards were upheld by a smug code of conduct, an earnestness founded on stiff restraints and sanctimonious platitudes. Anything experimental or novel was attacked as immoral and, hence, taboo. It was not long before the artists and writers rebelled. "Show me," protested the essayist, Arthur Symons, "any commandment of the code of morals which you are at present obeying and I will show you the opposite among the commandments of some other code of morals which your forefathers obeyed . . . Is it for such a shifting guide that I am asked to forsake the sure and constant leading of art, which tells me that whatever I find in humanity (passion, desire, the spirit or the senses, the hell or heaven of man's heart) is part of the eternal substance which nature weaves in the rough for art to combine into beautiful and lasting patterns?"

The so-called "Nice Nellies" extended Victorianism into our own time. Throughout his life James Joyce had great difficulties getting published; James Branch Cabell fell afoul of the censors; D. H. Lawrence, writing with "the hot blood's blindfold art," found himself engaged in an endless battle with the authorities on both sides of the Atlantic. "What is obscene to one man," cried Lawrence in anguished protest, "is the laughter of genius to another."

What shocked us yesterday merely amuses us today. We are no longer living in the prim, equivocal days of Victoria, when a leg was an unmentionable limb and the word "woman" was a term of opprobrium. By a pleasant trick of chronology there is another Elizabeth in England, and we are again enjoying an Elizabethan freedom of utterance. Once more our speech is muscular, full of unhampered vigor, and we no longer call a spade "a common garden implement." The whispered heresies of one generation have become the candid commonplaces of another.

Nevertheless, the impulse to confuse obscenity and sex still persists in some quarters. There are those who think literature is shameful, let alone carnal, if it is probing or "unduly curious," and there are those who consider sophistication merely another word for sex. As for this manifestation, writes Louis Kronenberger in his introduction to *The Pleasure of Their Company*, "we are all familiar with it, and with its prime desire to titillate or shock. What we possibly overlook is that it has a much wider and less adolescent appeal than we might imagine. There is nothing surprising in that: sex is the common denominator of literature no less than life, and the basis for almost everybody's standards of worldliness . . . The trouble with sex at the merely concupiscent or exhibitionistic level, beyond what may be crude in treatment, is that it is made to exist without an exhilarating enough context, without reference to temperament or recourse to wit; and that after a time a lively mind finds its repetitions tiresome. Some guides to gallantry, some scandalous chronicles, manage to go on diverting us, and so to save themselves by their portrayal of manners."

It would be too much to claim that this volume is an encyclopedic study of social comedies. But comedy is one of its essential elements, and, by its very nature, the book becomes a running "portrayal of manners." Its chief aim, however, is amusement. In these pages, the studious mind can discover evidences of shifting fashions in taste, proofs of an ever-changing culture. But it is not aimed at the scholar. On the contrary, it is intended for that favorite consumer, the much-sought-after general reader who is looking for diversion rather than instruction. Such a reader will, so this compiler believes, discover echoes of a laughing world. He will relish the drolleries and enjoy the high-spirited and piquant humor which binds them together. Such at least is the earnest hope of the editor.

LOUIS UNTERMEYER

CONTENTS

FOREWORD, XV

THE ANCIENTS

FROM "THE GREEK ANTHOLOGY"
The Virgin-Mistress—*Paulus Silentiarius*, 2
Against Dawn—*Meleager*, 3
The False One—*Philodemus*, 3
Greatest Bliss—*Asclepiades*, 3
False Proverb—*Paulus Silentiarius*, 3
Cupid for Sale—*Meleager*, 4
Interrupted Study—*Marcus Argentarius*, 4
Disloyal Lamp—*Meleager*, 4
Moth and Bee—*Rufinus*, 5
To Heliodora: A Fretful Monody—*Meleager*, 5
Seduced Girl—*Hedylos*, 5
Only Human—*Rufinus*, 6
Unfortunate Artist—*Lucilius*, 6
Precedent for Promiscuity—*Paulus Silentiarius*, 6
Golden Girl—*Antipater*, 6
Alas!—*Rufinus*, 7
Strictly for the Gods—*Bassus*, 7
Marital Hostility—*Palladas*, 7
To a Pompous Censor—*Palladas*, 7
Ungathered Sweets—*Author unknown*, 7
Pessimist—*Author unknown*, 7
A Libertine's Epitaph—*Simonides*, 8
Epitaph for a Model—*Simonides*, 8
The Proffered Gift—*Plato*, 8
The Old Courtesan—*Plato*, 8
On Professor Dryasdust—*Author unknown*, 9
Unforgiven—*Ammianus*, 9
Defeat into Victory—*Ammonides*, 9
The Bitter Man Bitten—*Demodocus*, 9
The Quack and the Dead—*Nikarchos*, 9
On a Singer—*Nikarchos*, 10
Inscription for a Smyrna Privy—*Agathias Scholastikos*, 10

ANACREON (CIRCA 500 B.C.)
The Drunkard, 11
Drinking, 11
Beauty, 12
Heat, 12
To His Young Mistress, 13
Bathyllus, 13
The Bull, 15
Design for a Bowl, 16

ARISTOPHANES (CIRCA 450–380 B.C.)
From "Lysistrata", 17

CATULLUS (84?–54 B.C.)
To Mamurra's Mistress, 25
To Lesbia, on Her Falsehood, 25
To Aufilena, 25
The Rendezvous, 26
Farewell to Lesbia, 26

HORACE (65–8 B.C.)
Growing Old Disgracefully, 28
Tears, Idle Tears, 29
The Passing of Lydia, 30
The Teasing of Xanthias, 30
A Happy Ending, 31
Horace Loses His Temper, 32
The Female of the Species, 32
Speaking from Experience, 33

OVID (43 B.C.–A.D. 17)
From "The Art of Love", 34
Afternoon Diversions, 50
The Protective Eunuch, 51
The Pleasures of Promiscuity, 52
The Cuckold-Maker, 53
Shameful Impotence, 54
The Deception Denied, 56
The First Hermaphrodite, 58

PETRONIUS (?–CIRCA A.D. 66)
From "The Satyricon", 60
The Widow of Ephesus, 71

MARTIAL (A.D. 40?–104)
The Wife's Companion, 73
Ex-Slave, 74
The Incentive, 74

Insufficient Vengeance, 74
To Cloe, 74
To His Book, 75

JUVENAL (A.D. 55?–135?)
From "The Sixth Satire", 76

APULEIUS (CIRCA A.D. 120–?)
From "The Golden Ass"
How Apuleius Fell in Love with Fotis, 83
How Fotis Brought Apuleius to See Her Mistress Enchant, 88
The Deceits of a Woman, 91
The Stories of Barbarus and the Baker's Wife, 92

LUCIAN (A.D. 120–200)
The Lesbian, 98
A Curious Deception, 99

THE RENAISSANCE

GESTA ROMANORUM
Of Hanging, 105
Of Maintaining Truth to the Last, 105
Of Women, Who Not Only Betray Secrets but Lie Fearfully, 106
Of Women, Who are Not To Be Trusted, 106
Of the Execrable Devices of Old Women, 107
Of Absence of Parental Restraint, 109

FROM "THE ARABIAN NIGHTS"
Story of King Shehriyar and His Brother, 111
Sherkan and the Lady Wrestler, 115
The Scavenger and the Noble Lady of Baghdad, 121
The Confectioner, His Wife, and The Parrot, 124

GIOVANNI BOCCACCIO (1313–1375)
From "The Decameron"
The Monk, the Abbot, and the Girl, 126
Adventures of the Sultan of Babylon's Daughter, 128
The Not-So-Dumb Gardener and the Convent of Women, 140
Putting the Devil in Hell, 145
The Nightingale, 148
The False Phantom, 151
The Wife Who Did the Impossible Three Times, 153
The Wife Who Sold Herself Cheaply, 158
The Reasonable Vengeance, 159

GEOFFREY CHAUCER (1340?–1400)
From "The Canterbury Tales"
The Miller's Tale, 162
The Reeve's Tale, 177
Prologue to the Wife of Bath's Tale, 186

MASUCCIO (1420–1476)
From "The Novellino"
The Miraculous Breeches, 205
The Carpenter's Wife and Her Three Lovers, 211
The Neighbors Who Had Everything in Common, 216

FRANÇOIS VILLON (1431–1463?)
Complaint of the Fair Armoress, 220
Ballade of Villon and Fat Margot, 222
Ballade of Ladies' Love, 223
Ballade of the Fair Helm-Maker to the Light o' Loves, 224
Ballade of Ease, 225

MARGARET, QUEEN OF NAVARRE (1492–1549)
From "The Heptameron"
The Pleasure of the Innocents, 227
The Too-Clever Countess, 229
The Man Who Made Himself a Cuckold, 232
The Desperate Remedy, 235
The Hypocritical Mistress, 236
The Remarkably Solicitous Wife, 239

FRANÇOIS RABELAIS (1495?–1553)
From "The Book of Gargantua"
How Gargantua Was Carried Eleven Months in His Mother's
Belly, 241
How Gargamelle Did Eat A Huge Deal of Tripes, 242
How Gargantua Was Born in a Strange Manner, 243
How They Appareled Gargantua, 245
How Gargantua Paid His Respects to the Parisians, 247
From "The Book of Pantagruel"
Of the Origin and Antiquity of Pantagruel, 248
How Panurge Served a Parisian Lady a Trick, 250
How Pantagruel Departed from Paris, 252

MIGUEL DE CERVANTES (1547–1616)
From "Don Quixote"
What Happened to Don Quixote at the Inn, 254

THE ELIZABETHANS AND THE AGE OF WIT

WILLIAM SHAKESPEARE (1564–1616)
 Ophelia's Song, 260
 From "Venus and Adonis", 261
 From "The Passionate Pilgrim", 266
 Spring Song, 267

THE DELIGHTS AND DANGERS OF DRINKING
 The Thirsty Soul—*Author unknown*, 268
 The Sober Companion—*Author unknown*, 268
 Live My Follies O'er Again—*Anacreon*, 268
 Away With Rules—*Anacreon*, 269
 In Praise of Ale—*John Still*, 270
 A Song for Drinking—*Author unknown*, 270
 Ballade of Good Doctrine—*François Villon*, 270
 A Merry Ballade of Vintners—*François Villon*, 271
 The Discourse of the Drinkers—*François Rabelais*, 272
 Shakespeariana, 273
 Memoirs and Letters, 274
 Husband and Wife—*Claudius Quillet*, 276
 Three Epitaphs, 277
 John Barleycorn—*Robert Burns*, 277
 Five Reasons for Drinking—*Henry Aldrich*, 279
 Afterwards—*Eugene Field*, 279

ROBERT HERRICK (1591–1674)
 Upon Julia's Washing Herself in the River, 280
 Clothes Do But Cheat and Cozen Us, 280
 To Electra: The Vision, 280
 To Julia: The Night-Piece, 281
 Upon the Nipples of Julia's Breast, 281
 To Dianeme, 282
 To Perenna, 282
 What Kind of Mistress He Would Have, 282
 To His Mistresses, 282
 The Vine, 283
 To the Virgins, To Make Much of Time, 283

JEAN DE LA FONTAINE (1621–1695)
 From "Tales and Novels"
  The Gascon Punished, 285
  The Kiss Returned, 287
  The Pack-Saddle, 288
  The Ear-Maker and the Mould-Mender, 288

JOHN AUBREY (1626–1697)
 From "Brief Lives", 294

WILLIAM WYCHERLEY (1640–1716)
From "The Country Wife", 299

DANIEL DEFOE (1660–1731)
From "Moll Flanders"
Liaison in Bath, 312

LOVERS AND LIBERTINES
A LITTLE ANTHOLOGY OF AMOROUS POEMS
O Western Wind—*Author unknown*, 317
Beauty's Self—*Author unknown*, 317
O Stay, Sweet Love—*Author unknown*, 318
Maid and Mistress—*Mellin De Saint-Gelais*, 318
Against Fulfillment of Desire—*Author unknown*, 318
The Forsaken Lover—*Sir Thomas Wyatt*, 319
It Fell on a Summer's Day—*Thomas Campion*, 319
I Care Not for These Ladies—*Thomas Campion*, 320
Fain Would I Wed a Fair Young Man—*Thomas Campion*, 321
Come, My Celia—*Ben Jonson*, 321
To His Mistress Going to Bed—*John Donne*, 322
Song—*John Donne*, 323
From "A Rapture"—*Thomas Carew*, 324
To Phyllis: A Plea for Promiscuity—*Edmund Waller*, 326
The Constant Lover—*Sir John Suckling*, 326
The Rejected Offer—*Sir John Suckling*, 327
To His Coy Mistress—*Andrew Marvell*, 328
Alice—*Charles Cotton*, 329
Margaret—*Charles Cotton*, 329
Beneath a Myrtle Shade—*John Dryden*, 330
Whilst Alexis Lay Prest—*John Dryden*, 331
Love's Fancy—*John Dryden*, 331
Beneath a Cool Shade—*Aphra Behn*, 332
Indian Summer—*N. Berthelot*, 332
Upon Leaving His Mistress—*John Wilmot, Earl of Rochester*, 333
The Imperfect Enjoyment—*John Wilmot, Earl of Rochester*, 333
Man is for Woman Made—*Peter Anthony Motteux*, 335
Tell Me No More—*William Congreve*, 336
All or Nothing—*William Congreve*, 336
The Geranium—*Richard Brinsley Sheridan*, 336
A Lamentable Case—*Charles Hanbury-Williams*, 338
Sodger Laddie—*Robert Burns*, 339
Godly Girzie—*Robert Burns*, 339
The Cautious Struggle—*Author unknown*, 340
A Logical Song—*Author unknown*, 340
The Disappointed Maid—*William Pattison*, 341
The Penitent Nun—*John Lockman*, 342

VOLTAIRE (1694–1778)
    From "Candide"
      How Candide was Brought up in a Splendid Castle, 343
      The Adventures of the Old Woman, 345
    From the "Philosophical Dictionary"
      Adultery, 349
      Impotence, 350
      Incubi, 351
      Love, 352
      Nakedness, 353

BENJAMIN FRANKLIN (1706–1790)
    Advice on the Choice of a Mistress, 355
    What are the Poor Young Women to Do?, 356
    On Perfumes, 358

A BUNDLE OF BALLADS
    The Courteous Knight, 361
    The Fire-Ship, 362
    A-Roving, 363
    It's the Same the Whole World Over, 364
    The Eddystone Light, 364
    Venezuela, 365
    The Foggy, Foggy Dew, 365
    The Saga of Rex, 366

HENRY FIELDING (1707–1754)
    From "Tom Jones"
      The Affair with Lady Bellaston, 369

LAURENCE STERNE (1713–1768)
    From "A Sentimental Journey"
      The Temptation, 378
      The Case of Delicacy, 379
    From "Tristram Shandy"
      How I Was Begot, 382

OLD EPITAPHS AND EPIGRAMS
GIACOMO CASANOVA (1725–1798)
    From "The Memoirs of Casanova"
      I Forget Angela and Discover Her Pretty Cousins, 390
      My Passion for the Mistress of the Count, 395
      The Martyrdom of Damiens and Its Consequences, 397
      A Droll Encounter on My Way to Constantinople, 404

THE QUESTION OF BUNDLING (CIRCA 1770)
    The Whore on the Snow Crust, 406
    A New Bundling Song, 409

THE NINETEENTH CENTURY

GEORGE GORDON, LORD BYRON (1788–1824)
    From "Don Juan", 415

HEINRICH HEINE (1797–1856)
    You Love Me Not, 420
    Laocoön, 420
    Body and Soul, 421
    Passion, 421
    Quandary, 421
    The Morning After, 421
    A Woman, 422
    Surfeit, 422
    The Efficient Housewife, 423

HONORÉ DE BALZAC (1799–1850)
    From "Droll Stories"
        The Reproach, 423
        How the Pretty Maid of Portillon Convinced Her Judge, 430
        Concerning a Poor Man Who was Called Le Vieux Par-Chemins, 434
        Odd Sayings of Three Pilgrims, 440

ÉMILE ZOLA (1840–1902)
    From "Nana"
        Nana's Debut, 444

ANATOLE FRANCE (1844–1924)
    From "Penguin Island"
        The First Clothes, 458

GUY DE MAUPASSANT (1850–1893)
    The Signal, 462
    Rose, 466
    That Pig of a Morin, 470
    A Sale, 478
    The False Gems, 482
    The Spice of Life, 487

OSCAR WILDE (1856–1900)
    Twenty Aphorisms, 491

THE MODERNS

W. SOMERSET MAUGHAM (1874–   )
  Winter Cruise, 494
  Appearance and Reality, 508

A HANDFUL OF LIMERICKS
SHERWOOD ANDERSON (1876–1941)
  The Strength of God, 523

JAMES BRANCH CABELL (1879–   )
  From "Jurgen"
    About a Cock That Crowed Too Soon, 529

H. L. MENCKEN (1880–1956)
  Twenty Sententious Maxims, 533
  From "In Defense of Women"
    The Libertine, 534
    The Lure of Beauty, 536

FRANKIE AND JOHNNY, 539

DAMON RUNYON (1884–1946)
  Sense of Humor, 541

A SAMPLER OF MODERN RIBALD VERSE
  The Ruined Maid—*Thomas Hardy*, 548
  The Dark-Eyed Gentleman—*Thomas Hardy*, 549
  Oh, See How Thick the Goldcup Flowers—*A. E. Housman*, 550
  Oh, When I Was in Love With You—*A. E. Housman*, 550
  Adam and Eve—*A. E. Housman*, 551
  The Ladies—*Rudyard Kipling*, 551
  See-Saw—*Owen Meredith, Earl of Lytton*, 553
  The Rehearsal—*Author unknown*, 554
  A Rondeau of Difference—*Author unknown*, 556
  The Old Backhouse—*James Whitcomb Riley*, 557
  Little Willie—*Eugene Field*, 558
  King David and King Solomon—*James Ball Naylor*, 559
  Almost—*Louis Untermeyer*, 559
  Equals—*Louis Untermeyer*, 560
  The Little Old Lady in Lavender Silk—*Dorothy Parker*, 560
  Indian Summer—*Dorothy Parker*, 561
  she being Brand—*e. e. cummings*, 561
  Four Prominent So-and-So's—*Ogden Nash*, 562
  A Ballad of the Good Lord Nelson—*Lawrence Durrell*, 565
  The Ballad of Yukon Jake—*Edward E. Paramore, Jr.*, 566

ALEXANDER WOOLLCOTT (1887–1943)
Entrance Fee, 570

MICHAEL ARLEN (1895–1956)
Legend of the Crooked Coronet, 572

GABRIEL CHEVALLIER (1895–   )
From "The Scandals of Clochemerle"
A Few Words on the Curé Ponosse, 589
Joyful Acceptance of the Urinal, 594

C. S. FORESTER (1899–   )
The Bedchamber Mystery, 597

JOHN COLLIER (1901–   )
Rope Enough, 600
Season of Mists, 605

JOHN STEINBECK (1902–   )
From "Tortilla Flat"
Tortillas and Beans, 611

ERSKINE CALDWELL (1903–   )
Over the Green Mountains, 617
Meddlesome Jack, 621
August Afternoon, 630

JOHN O'HARA (1905–   )
Joey and the Calcutta Club, 637

GIOVANNI GUARESCHI (1908–   )
From "The Little World of Don Camillo"
A Baptism, 641
Out of Bounds, 643

WILLIAM J. LEDERER (1912–   )
The Skipper's Pink Panties, 648

IRA WALLACH (1913–   )
The Keeper of the Gelded Unicorn, 653
God's Little Best Seller, 658

JEAN DUTOURD (1920–   )
From "The Best Butter"
Léon Loses His Virginity, 663

RAY BRADBURY (1920–   )
En la Noche, 672

The Ancients

FROM: THE GREEK ANTHOLOGY

Several centuries before the Christian era, a Greek writer interested in curiosities made a collection of inscriptions which he found on public buildings and shrines: maxims, prayers, amatory verses accompanying votive offerings on temple walls and tombstones. Soon it became something of a pastime to collect short epigrammatic pieces by poets known and unknown. In 60 B.C. Meleager, himself a poet, made the first orderly arrangement of many of these lyrics and called his selection an anthology, literally a flower-gathering —anthos: a flower; legein: to gather.

Such "garlands" of verse became increasingly popular. Poets contributed to the ever-growing collection, and by the year 1000 there were thousands of these little Greek verses brought together in The Greek Anthology by Cephalas, a tenth-century scholar who is known only because of this work.

The gradually accumulating anthology was over fifteen hundred years in the making. There were countless additions and revisions—a fourteenth-century monk, Planudes, prepared an edition that satisfied the churchmen by omitting most of the erotic and, incidentally, the best verses. It was not until the eighteenth century that the entire opus, comprising some four thousand poems, was published in Germany. Meanwhile, fragments of the anthology had been discovered, translated, and put into English stanzas by such poets as Dryden, Cowper, Prior, Shelley, and, in one of his most characteristic sonnets, Shakespeare. Today they are part of the world's great poetic heritage.

The Greek Anthology is not conveniently divided into subject matter. Nevertheless, most of the poems fall into recognizable categories. A prevailing topic is the agony, as well as the ecstasy, of love. The exquisite longings and the bitter betrayals run like leading themes throughout the work. Dating from 700 B.C., they might have been uttered only yesterday.

THE VIRGIN-MISTRESS

Naked and breast to breast we lie;
   She kisses, coaxes, teases.
Her parted lips are eager—I
   Press on . . . and then she freezes.

She turns her mouth away, although
   My roving hand's unchided
Her body's soft and lithe, but so
   Frustratingly divided!

Part virgin-mistress and part whore,
  One half she gives to passion;
But oh, the half I hunger for
  She dedicates to caution.

PAULUS SILENTIARIUS, *translated by* L.U.

AGAINST DAWN

Oh, enemy of love, how slow you creep
Across the sky when she elects to sleep
With someone else. And oh, how fast you fly
When she is in my arms till night goes by.

MELEAGER, *translated by* L.U.

THE FALSE ONE

"You played me false before," I say; and she
Assents with kisses: "Yes, beware of me."
"I will! I hate you!" once again I say.
And once again she kisses—and I stay.

PHILODEMUS, *translated by* D. L. KELLEHER

GREATEST BLISS

Sweet in summer is the taste of snow for one athirst,
Sweet, after winter, is the air when the first bud has burst,
Sweet is the sight of land to sailors long at sea and loath—
But sweeter still, two lovers' lips when one cloak hides them both.

ASCLEPIADES, *translated by* L.U.

FALSE PROVERB

"Mockery murders love," they say; and she
  Laughed in my face last night and slammed the door.
I swore to stay away a year—but see,
  It's break of day, and here I am once more.

PAULUS SILENTIARIUS, *translated by* L.U.

CUPID FOR SALE

Let him be sold, I say, let him be sold!
  Why should I have to keep the impudent boy?
  He sports a poisoned arrow like a toy;
A threat to youth, a torture to the old,
      Let him be sold.

Mean even to his mother, wild and bold,
  He tricks the confident, betrays the coy
  With short-lived happiness, heart-breaking joy,
Turning to lead what promised to be gold.
      Let him be sold.

Let him be . . . Wait! He weeps and swears that he
  Will mend his ways and do as he is told,
  And keep my Zenophile from growing cold,
And always light new fires to kindle me—
      Oh, let him be!

                    MELEAGER, *translated by* L.U.

INTERRUPTED STUDY

Lifting my eyes from Hesiod's book,
  I saw young Pyrrha pass and nod,
Linger, and give another look—
  Good-by to dull old Hesiod!

                    MARCUS ARGENTARIUS, *translated by* L.U.

DISLOYAL LAMP

You were a witness, lamp, you saw him kneel
And swear he would be faithful, saw him seal
His urging kisses with a sacred vow.
        Where is he now?

You know whose arms are raised for his embrace,
Whose lips in semi-darkness seek his face,
You know the naked breast that rests his brow
        Where he lies now.

                    MELEAGER, *translated by* L.U.

MOTH AND BEE

Sweet is Europa's kiss, when she but dips
the wing of a moth that hovers as it sips.
But when she plunges like a bee, she hales
the very soul out by the fingernails.

RUFINUS, *translated by* HUMBERT WOLFE

TO HELIODORA: A FRETFUL MONODY

Well, well, my dear! So you thought you could cheat me!
You didn't, you see: I'm not blind; I know
All about it, and it's really no earthly good
Your calling on the gods to clear you.
                    "Alone"!
So you slept all alone, did you?
                    O shame of girls!
And that Kleon of yours, that frizzy darling,
Or if not Kleon, then—
                    But why waste words on you?
Get out of my bed, little bitch!
Get out of my house, and be off!
                    —But wait:
That's exactly what you're looking for, isn't it?
                    I know you're dying to see him.
Suppose you just stay where you are:
                    I'll be your jailer!

MELEAGER, *translated by* DUDLEY FITTS

Human frailty is seldom regarded with scorn. The Greek poets expressed the tribulations of the flesh not only with tolerance but with a rueful sympathy.

SEDUCED GIRL

With wine and words of love and every vow
    He lulled me into bed and closed my eyes,
A sleepy, stupid innocent. . . . So now
    I dedicate the spoils of my surprise:
The silk that bound my breasts, my virgin zone,
    The cherished purity I could not keep.
Goddess, remember we were all alone,
    And he was strong—and I was half asleep.

HEDYLOS, *translated by* L.U.

ONLY HUMAN

Reason has armed me well, and I
Can easily the god of love defy.
But if the wine-god helps him, I am through.
What can one mortal do against those two?

RUFINUS, *translated by* L.U.

UNFORTUNATE ARTIST

Eutychus, portrait-painter, had twenty sons,
And never got a likeness—no, not once.

LUCILIUS, *translated by* L.U.

PRECEDENT FOR PROMISCUITY

When I embrace Hippomenes
I think about Leander.
Held in Leander's arms
I dream of Xanthus.
Xanthus reminds me of Hippomenes.
And so it goes. . . .

Am I ashamed because I imitate
Venus herself who had many lovers?
Let those condemn me who are ugly, cold,
Or satisfied with a husband.

PAULUS SILENTIARIUS, *translated by* L.U.

Love may be a classic ideal, but it was not always idealized by the ancients. They were quick to pounce upon the commercial aspects of sex, marital hostility, the greed of desire, the disillusion after fulfillment, and other unromantic aspects of passion. That the poets were essentially singers did not prevent them from being cynics.

GOLDEN GIRL

This is the Golden Goddess. Friend is she
    To young and old, to bashful and to bold;
She gives herself with generosity
    For love—if love comes well equipped with gold.

ANTIPATER, *translated by* L.U.

ALAS!

> Once plighted, no men would go whoring;
> They'd stay with the ones they adore,
> If women were half as alluring
> After the act as before.

RUFINUS, *translated by* L.U.

STRICTLY FOR THE GODS

> Great Jupiter, for love or lechery,
> Became a bull, a swan, a shower, a ram.
> Such tricks delight the gods; but as for me,
> I pay my girl and stay the way I am.

BASSUS, *translated by* L.U.

MARITAL HOSTILITY

> No man regards his wife with pleasure, save
> Twice: In her bridal bed, and in her grave.

PALLADAS, *translated by* L.U.

TO A POMPOUS CENSOR

> Scornful of love, intolerably august,
> Remember, when cold dignity is dust,
> Your origin—be thankful, man—was lust.

PALLADAS, *translated by* L.U.

UNGATHERED SWEETS

> When your grapes grew round, you swore to save them;
> When they grew ripe, you passed me by;
> Yet anyone who asks can have them,
> Now that the grapes are shrunk and dry.

AUTHOR UNKNOWN, *translated by* L.U.

PESSIMIST

> My name is Dion. Here I lie,
> Beaten by life, a silly game.
> I had no wife nor child; and I
> Wish that my father had said the same.

AUTHOR UNKNOWN, *translated by* L.U.

Many of the little poems are elegiac in character, but thoughts of age and death cannot make them lugubrious or dull. Sometimes the mood is derisive, sometimes sadly resigned, yet the miniature pieces never lack the epigram's swift point.

A LIBERTINE'S EPITAPH

> I am so quiet now who once was roaring;
> Done with deceiving, drinking, dicing, whoring.

> SIMONIDES, *translated by* L.U.

EPITAPH FOR A MODEL

> "Who carved this mad Bacchante?" "Scopas, sir."
> "What drove her mad?" "Scopas. He jilted her."

> SIMONIDES, *translated by* L.U.

THE PROFFERED GIFT

> Accept this garland and the girl together;
> Enjoy them while in bloom, not when they wither.

> PLATO, *translated by* L.U.

THE OLD COURTESAN

> Now that I grow old, alas,
> And the sports of youth must pass,
> Venus, take my looking-glass.
>
> What from now on I must be
> Never, never, let me see.
> Venus, take the glass from me.

> PLATO, *translated by* L.U.

As though to balance the serious moments, hundreds of verses were devoted to mockery; beauty was extolled, but there was many a rowdy laugh at the expense of the body. Not a facet nor a function of the human condition was neglected. While not all ribald, the concluding selections indicate the range of a humor which is antique but not antiquated.

ON PROFESSOR DRYASDUST

This pedagogue deserves the highest heaven;
He never drank or diced or went with wenches.
His listeners are a small but loyal seven:
The four walls of his school and three old benches.

AUTHOR UNKNOWN, *translated by* L.U.

UNFORGIVEN

O Earth, lie light upon Nearchus, please—
So that the dogs may dig him up with ease.

AMMIANUS, *translated by* L.U.

DEFEAT INTO VICTORY

"Is there no one to beat the enemy?" "There's one:
Send naked Antipatra out—and see them run."

AMMONIDES, *translated by* L.U.

THE BITTER MAN BITTEN

A misanthrope one summer day
    Felt a fierce serpent strike his side.
He merely winced and went his way;
    The snake it was that died.

DEMODOCUS, *translated by* L.U.

THE QUACK AND THE DEAD

On Jove's own statue, Doctor Pill
    Chanced yesterday his hand to lay.
Though he is god, and marble, still
    Jove's funeral is today.

NIKARCHOS, *translated by* WALTER LEAF

ON A SINGER

> The gloom of death is on the raven's wing,
>   The song of death is in the raven's cries:
> But when Demophilus begins to sing,
>   The raven dies.

NIKARCHOS, *translated by* EDWIN ARLINGTON ROBINSON

INSCRIPTION FOR A SMYRNA PRIVY

> And so your head aches, friend? and so
> Your heavy body groans with sluggishness,
> And you must knead your paunch with both hands to dislodge
> The delicious work of your jaws?
>   What a fool!
> Then was the time to think of it when you lay,
> Most hog-like, gorging at table, in love with your own
> Capacity.
>   And so, well may you sit here now:
> The latter end of all your delight is this,
> That you pummel your belly for the sins your throat committed.

AGATHIAS SCHOLASTIKOS, *translated by* DUDLEY FITTS

ANACREON (circa 500 B.C.)

Born in Greece five centuries before the Christian era, Anacreon was one of the first—if not the very first—to sing the triple praise of Wine, Women, and Song. These were the subjects of all Anacreon's lyrics except one which was written to a beautiful boy named Bathyllus, with whom he was infatuated. Most of his poetry, however, was inspired by his mistress, Eurypile, and by Bacchus. "He never separated those two chief ingredients of an Epicurean's happiness: women and wine," wrote Abraham Cowley, Anacreon's most sympathetic translator. "To the latter of these he seemed to owe all the youthful vigor of his old age; he was so actuated, so enlivened with this, that when his own spirits decayed, those of wine became vital."

Anacreon's death, if the legend is to be trusted, was a piece of poetic injustice. In the eighty-fifth year of his life, he choked on a grape pit.

THE DRUNKARD

Fill the bowl with rosy wine,
Around our temples roses twine,
And let us cheerfully a while,
Like the wine and roses smile.
Crown'd with roses we contemn
Gyges' wealthy diadem.
Today is ours, what do we fear;
Today is ours, we have it here.
Let's treat it kindly, that it may
Wish at least with us to stay.
Let's banish business, banish sorrow.
To the gods belongs tomorrow.

Translated by ABRAHAM COWLEY

DRINKING

The thirsty earth soaks up the rain,
And drinks, and gapes for drink again;
The plants suck in the earth and are
With constant drinking fresh and fair.
The sea itself, which one would think
Should have but little need of drink,
Drinks ten thousand rivers up,
So fill'd that they o'erflow the cup.
The busy sun (and one should guess
By's drunken fiery face no less)
Drinks up the sea, and when h'as done,
The moon and stars drink up the sun.
They drink and dance by their own light,
They drink and revel all the night,
Nothing in nature's sober found,
But an eternal health goes round.
Fill up the bowl then, fill it high,
Fill all the glasses there; for why
Should every creature drink but I.
Why, men of morals, tell me why?

Translated by ABRAHAM COWLEY

BEAUTY

Liberal nature did dispense
To all things arms for their defense;
And some she arms with sinewy force,
And some with swiftness in the course;
Some with hard hoofs or forkèd claws,
And some with horns or tuskèd jaws.
And some with scales and some with wings,
Some with teeth and some with stings.
Wisdom to man she did afford—
Wisdom for shield and wit for sword.

But what for beauteous womankind?
What arms, what armor was she assigned?
Beauty is both, for with the Fair
What arms, what armor can compare?
What gold, what steel, what diamond
More impassible is found?
And what flame, what lightning e'er
Such great and active force did bear?

These are all weapon, and they dart
Like porcupines from every part
Who can, alas, their strength express,
Armed when they themselves undress,
Cap-a-pie with nakedness.

Translated by ABRAHAM COWLEY

HEAT

Fill, kind misses, fill the bowl
And let the wine refresh my soul.
For now the thirsty heat of day
Has almost drunk my life away;
Whole floods of sweat will not suffice—
It drinks, and still new floods arise:
It drinks till I myself grow dry
And can no longer floods supply.

Now my heat, I pray, relieve,
And now your cooling garlands weave,
Soothing garlands such as may
Invite refreshing winds to play
And chase the tyrant heat away.

But this I do perhaps, you'll guess,
Because I mean to love you less;
Or do't because I'd thus remove
All the flames and heat of love.

Foolish girls, perhaps you know
This to the body good may do.
But love can no abatement find—
Love's the high fever of the mind.

Translated by ABRAHAM COWLEY

TO HIS YOUNG MISTRESS

Because, forsooth, you're young and fair,
And fresher than the rose appear,
Gray hairs you treat with scornful eye
And leave me most unmannerly.

Sweetheart, these ashes do contain
Embers that strive to flame again.
And Etna that on top has snow
Feels warmth and constant fire below.

With roses white-haired lilies twine
And in a glowing garland shine;
They, locked in close embraces, lie
And kiss and hug most decently.

Translated by ABRAHAM COWLEY

BATHYLLUS

If painter thou true life canst draw,
Now, now, my fair Bathyllus show.
On's hair a charming blackness lies,
And ever thence a light does rise.
Make wand'ring little curls to dance
In a well-ordered negligence.
His high forehead bright as the morn
Black, narrow, eyebrows do adorn.
Through which, as from a bow that's bent,
Sharp arrows from his eyes are sent.
To my heart let them a passage bore,
And make me love him more.
Make fierce, black eyes, that thousands slew,
Yet make 'em kind and courteous, too.

This angry part by Mars was sent,
This mildness here by Venus lent.
That down th' admirer drives,
And this the criminal forgives.
His cheeks with youth and blushes drest,
By fairest apples are exprest.
Let modesty o'er all command,
Else the piece will blush to mend your hand.
His red, plump lips and little mouth
Will puzzle and torment us both.
Pretty, delicious—oh they've outgone
All Art, and all description.
But let sweet smiles around 'em play,
And there becoming moistures lay,
To them let eloquence be joined,
As if for rhetoric designed.
They must at least a motion make,
And even silence seem to speak.
Like that of the spheres let it be,
A sweet but unheard harmony.
And in this charming face, let all
Be stately and majestical.
O'er's slender, ivory neck I'll pass,
And with more joy do downwards hast.
His breast is full in every part,
For it contains Anacreon's heart.
Smooth are his hands, both long and white,
Which kisses must from all invite.
Here through blue veins pure blood does glide,
Here on it of't the soul does ride.
To this fair place o'erjoyed it runs,
Long stays it makes, and quick returns.
His large, big belly all approve,
'Tis in drunk'ness graceful and in love.
His thighs to marble I'd compare,
But that they soft and tender are.
Loose quivering flesh in whiteness lies,
And stiff cold age with fire supplies.
Let there be now a thin slight shade,
Or anything or nothing made.
An inward tickling only draw,
And love's first pleasant itchings show,
Even now let flowing nature try
To pass the bounds of chastity.

But see your Art is too unkind,
It does not show the charms behind,
Charms, that seem now lovelier far,
Because they hidden are.

On him I will not feet bestow.
For lovers never look so low.
I only this of you shall claim,
That you'd the piece Apollo name.
And if you e'er Apollo see,
Call't Bathyllus in effigy:
For both are gods, both loved by me.

Translated by ABRAHAM COWLEY

THE BULL

This bull, my boy, sure is some Jove,
Who in disguise is making love.
Methinks through his gilt horns I spy,
The brightness of the deity.
His front does no curl'd fierceness wear,
All heav'n does in his looks appear,
His very looks speak him a god,
Who now has left the blest abode.
Nay whence I more of credit take,
Europa's mounted on his back.
Europa who outshines by far
All his beauteous harlots there,
Though each harlot's made a star.
Methinks I see him now convey
The nymph, through the wond'ring sea,
Whose crystal waves swell here and there,
Seemingly proud of what they bear.
He now like oars his feet does ply,
And rows through the wat'ry sky,
'Tis Jove I mean, for sure no beast
Half so happy, half so blest,
Wafted a virgin o'er the seas,
And left his loving mistresses.
Nay none of all the Gods above,
But he, nor he were't not for love.

Translated by ABRAHAM COWLEY

DESIGN FOR A BOWL

Sculptor, wouldst thou glad my soul,
Grave for me an ample bowl,
Worthy to shine in hall or bower,
When springtime brings the reveler's hour.
Grave it with themes of chaste design,
Fit for a simple board like mine.
Display not there the barbarous rites
In which religious zeal delights;
Nor any tale of tragic fate
Which History shudders to relate.
No—cull thy fancies from above,
Themes of heaven and themes of love.
Let Bacchus, Jove's ambrosial boy,
Distill the grape in drops of joy,
And while he smiles at every tear,
Let warm-eyed Venus, dancing near,
With spirits of the genial bed,
The dewy herbage deftly tread.
Let Love be there, without his arms,
In timid nakedness of charms;
And all the Graces, linked with Love,
Stray, laughing, through the shadowy grove;
While rosy boys, disporting round,
In circlets trip the velvet ground.
But ah! if there Apollo toys,
I tremble for the rosy boys.

Translated by THOMAS MOORE

ARISTOPHANES (circa 450–380 B.C.)

An ironic dramatist who was also a dramatic critic, Aristophanes offset the terrifying if cathartic tragedies of Aeschylus, Sophocles, and Euripides by creating a series of uproarious satires on Greek life in the fifth century B.C. History tells us little about Aristophanes except that he was the son of Philippus and Zenodora, that he was born in Attica, that his first play was produced when he was barely eighteen, that he was prematurely bald, and that he lived until he was about seventy. His contemporaries considered him an unquestioned master of comedy. Plato never tired of his bland and roguish wit. "There has never been anything quite like it since, and regrettably there will never be anything quite like it again," wrote Eugene O'Neill,

Jr., *in his introduction to* The Complete Greek Drama. *"The effect of the initial impact of these plays is one of bewilderment. One rubs one's eyes and wonders whether it really can have happened. A closer acquaintance discloses a number of reasons for astonishment. The first of these is the absolute freedom of speech which the comic poet of the fifth century* B.C. *enjoyed . . . Equally astonishing is the pervading obscenity of the Old Comedy. This is so abundant and varied that it cannot be ignored or excised. It is so closely interwoven into almost every part of the plays that to expurgate is to destroy."*

An earlier editor, the learned Lord Neave, expatiated on the extreme coarseness of Aristophanes' speeches and, at the same time, the logic of such language. The plays were given at the Dionysia, the great Bacchic celebrations, so that "the wildest license was not only recognized as permissible but actually enjoined as part of the ceremonial at these festivals of Bacchus. It was not only in accordance with public taste, but was consecrated as a part of the national religion."

Although two of his early comedies are known to us only because of a few fragments, Aristophanes occupies a paramount position by virtue of almost a dozen remarkable survivals. The Frogs, The Birds, The Wasps, and The Clouds, are alive with brilliant portraits and swift disposals; but it is the war comedies which are the most diverting and also the most devastating. Of these Lysistrata is by far the most popular.

The following excerpts have been translated by the editor.

FROM: LYSISTRATA

[*The war between Athens and Sparta has been going on for some twenty years. The women, fearful that the war will never end, are almost hopeless. One of them, however, has a plan. She is Lysistrata, wife of one of the Athenian magistrates, and, at the beginning of the play, she is standing alone, waiting impatiently for other women she has summoned.*]

LYSISTRATA: If they had been invited to a Bacchanalian orgy or a festival for Pan or Aphrodite, they'd have come quickly enough. The streets would have been crowded with people drumming and dancing. But now—not a woman to be seen. Wait—here comes one, my neighbor, Calonice. Good morning, my friend.

CALONICE: Good morning, Lysistrata. What's the matter? You look gloomy. Knitting your dark eyebrows doesn't make your face pretty.

LYSISTRATA: Oh, Calonice, my heart is troubled. Not only for myself but for my sex. Men say we women are sly and subtle——

CALONICE: And so we are.

LYSISTRATA: Yet, though I told them to be here for their own good and for a matter of great importance, they stay home, probably still sleeping.

CALONICE: Oh, they'll come, dear heart. It's not easy, you know, for women to get away from the house. One has to fuss about her husband; another must keep after the servant; another has to put the child to sleep or wake him up or wash him. . . .

LYSISTRATA: But the thing for which I've summoned them is more urgent than anything else.

CALONICE: But, Lysistrata, why *have* you summoned us?

LYSISTRATA: It's something big.

CALONICE: Really? How big?

LYSISTRATA: Very big indeed.

CALONICE: You'd think that would bring them!

LYSISTRATA: Oh, if it were *that*, they'd all be here fast enough. No, it's something else. It's something that's kept me turning this way and that way during many sleepless nights.

CALONICE: Well, if it kept you tossing and turning, it can't have been so unpleasant.

LYSISTRATA: Unpleasant or not, it means just this: Greece can be saved by its women.

CALONICE: By its women!

LYSISTRATA: Yes, everything depends on us.

CALONICE: But how can we do anything so difficult? How can we accomplish anything political, we who sit at home, dressed in diaphanous robes, tricked out with saffron silk and dainty little slippers?

LYSISTRATA: Those are the very things that will save us—the diaphanous robes, the saffron silks, the dainty little slippers, *and* the paints and the perfumes . . . No man will lift his lance against another——

CALONICE: I'll get my saffron silk from the dyer's at once.

LYSISTRATA: —or brandish his shield——

CALONICE: I'll put on my most diaphanous robe.

LYSISTRATA: —or draw his sword.

CALONICE: I'll put on my dainty little slippers this very minute.

LYSISTRATA: So then, don't you think the women should have come?

CALONICE: Come? They should have flown here!

[*After a little further conversation the women begin to arrive. They have come from all parts of the country. One of them, Lampito, hails from Sparta, and the dramatist achieves some extra humor by having her speak in rough Doric. Modern translators have given Lampito various regional inflections. One makes her talk in broad Scots; another puts her speeches in the idiom of the Deep South.*]

MYRRHINE: Are we late, Lysistrata? What's it all about?

LYSISTRATA: You certainly took your time getting here.

MYRRHINE: I couldn't find my girdle in the dark. But if the thing is so pressing, tell us now.

CALONICE: No; let's wait until the others arrive.

MYRRHINE: Perhaps it would be better. Isn't that Lampito approaching?

LYSISTRATA: Welcome, Lampito. How well you look. And what muscles! Those wrists could strangle a bull.

LAMPITO: I bet they could. I'm tough because I keep in training. I'm always practicing the hardest dance—the one where you kick your bottom with your heels.

LYSISTRATA: And what firm breasts!

LAMPITO: Hey! Don't prod me like a beast that's going to be sacrificed.

[*Other women arrive from Boeotia, Corinth, and other parts of Greece.*]

CALONICE: Now will you tell us what this very important business is about?

LYSISTRATA: I will. First, let me ask you a simple question. Do you miss your husbands, the fathers of your children, who are away with the army?

CALONICE: My husband has been away for the last five months—far away, in Thrace.

MYRRHINE: Mine has been stationed seven long months in Pylos.

LAMPITO: As for my man, soon as he finishes one term of service, he signs up for another.

LYSISTRATA: No husbands to speak of. Not so much as the shadow of a lover. Or any satisfactory artificial substitute. Tell me, if I find a way to end this war, will you all help?

CALONICE: We will! We will! I swear I'll help even if I have to pawn my best gown.

MYRRHINE: I will, too. I'd be willing to be split in two like a flatfish—and give half for peace.

LAMPITO: For peace I'd climb to the rugged top of Mount Taygetus.

LYSISTRATA: Good. Now I'll tell you. Women! Sisters! If we want the war to end, there's just one way. We can compel our husbands to declare peace if we abstain——

MYRRHINE: Abstain from what?

LYSISTRATA: But will you?

MYRRHINE: Of course we will, even though we die.

LYSISTRATA: Well, then, we must abstain from going to bed with our husbands. Hah! You turn away from me. Where are you going? You look pale; you bite your lips; you shake your heads. Come, let's face it. Will you do it, or won't you?

CALONICE: I won't. Let the war go on.

MYRRHINE: I won't either. Let the war go on.

LYSISTRATA: My little flatfish, didn't you just say that you'd be willing to be split in two?

CALONICE: Ask me anything but that! Ask me to walk through the fire. But don't ask me to give up the best thing in the world. You know there's nothing like it, Lysistrata darling.

LYSISTRATA: What a sex we women are! No wonder the poets write tragedies about us. It seems that we are good for nothing but bed and babies. But you, my friend, you from tough Sparta—if you and I combine, we might succeed. Stand by me, won't you?

LAMPITO: It's a hard thing to ask a girl, by the two goddesses it is! It's not easy for a woman to sleep alone—in a big bed with no man in it. But anything for peace.

LYSISTRATA: Oh, my dear, my darling, my best friend! You deserve the name of woman.

CALONICE: But suppose we do everything you ask. Suppose—the gods forbid—we give up what you say. Would we get peace any quicker?

LYSISTRATA: Much quicker. All we have to do is to sit at home, prettily made up, wearing our most transparent gowns, reeking of perfume—and the men will be wild to get at us. That is the time to say no, and to keep on saying no until they end the war.

LAMPITO: It sounds plausible. They say that Menelaus threw his sword away when he saw Helen's naked breasts.

CALONICE: What if they use force and try to pull us into the bedroom?

LYSISTRATA: Hold on to the door.

CALONICE: What if they beat us?

LYSISTRATA: Give in to them if you have to, but do it reluctantly. They won't like it; there's no pleasure without co-operation.

CALONICE: Very well, if that's the way you want it, we'll agree.

[*The women are told by Lysistrata that they and a body of older matrons will seize the Acropolis and take over the Public Treasury. First, however, Lysistrata makes them take a sacred vow over a sacramental bowl of wine.*]

LYSISTRATA: Lampito, and the rest of you, place your hands on the rim of the bowl and you, Calonice, speaking for all, repeat after me the following words: I will not give in to husband or lover . . .

CALONICE (*quavering and faintly*): "I will not give in to husband or lover . . ."

LYSISTRATA: . . . even when he says he'll die if he doesn't have me.

CALONICE (*still more weakly*): ". . . even when he says he'll die if he doesn't have me."

LYSISTRATA: I will not allow him to touch me . . .

CALONICE: "I will not allow him to touch me . . ."

LYSISTRATA: . . . but I will sit around in my transparent saffron gown . . .

CALONICE: ". . . but I will sit around in my transparent saffron gown . . ."

LYSISTRATA: . . . so that I may continue to arouse him . . .

CALONICE: ". . . so that I may continue to arouse him . . ."

LYSISTRATA: . . . refusing to give myself voluntarily . . .

CALONICE: ". . . refusing to give myself voluntarily . . ."

LYSISTRATA: . . . and if he takes me by force . . .

CALONICE: ". . . and if he takes me by force . . ."

LYSISTRATA: . . . I will remain as cold as ice and never move a muscle.

CALONICE: ". . . I will remain as cold as ice and never move a muscle."

LYSISTRATA: I will neither point my slippers toward the ceiling . . .

CALONICE: "I will neither point my slippers toward the ceiling . . ."

LYSISTRATA: . . . nor will I crouch like a carved lioness.

CALONICE: ". . . nor will I crouch like a carved lioness."

LYSISTRATA: If I keep this oath let my cup always be filled with wine . . .

CALONICE: "If I keep this oath let my cup always be filled with wine . . ."

LYSISTRATA: . . . but if I break it, let me drink nothing but water.

CALONICE: ". . . but if I break it, let me drink nothing but water."

[*The women occupy the Acropolis. The older Athenian men, those who are not at the war, attempt to oust them. But the hill is steep and they are short of breath; the torches they carry are no help, for the women not only put them out with buckets of water but drench the men thoroughly. Finally a member of the Public Committee comes forward to parley and tells Lysistrata that women should keep out of politics. Lysistrata ironically replies that, although women have always had the management of their husbands, they are supposed to be unfit for public affairs. They are continually told that war is a man's business. When the spokesman taunts her by saying that women contribute nothing to the conduct of war, Lysistrata scornfully replies that they contribute the sons to carry it on. Rejecting the axiom that woman's place is the home, she throws down her woman's gear and tells him to go home, where he should weave and card wool.*

For a while, Lysistrata is triumphant. But the women begin to backslide and threaten to desert. They use all sorts of excuses. One of them claims she must get home before the moths attack her fine Milesian wool. Another says she has to go back to strip her flax. A third swears she is about to give birth to a baby, although Lysistrata points out that she was not pregnant yesterday. A fourth insists that she cannot sleep in the Acropolis because it is too noisy. It is obvious that one and all are desperately in need of their men. A few remain steadfast. Myrrhine is one. She, too, is tempted when her husband, Cinesias, seeks her, but she remembers the sworn compact for peace.]

CINESIAS: Myrrhine, my darling little Myrrhine, come down to me. Come quick. I need you.

MYRRHINE: Not I.

CINESIAS: Please, Myrrhine. Hurry—please.

MYRRHINE: What for? You don't need me.

CINESIAS: Not need you! It's killing me.

MYRRHINE: Good-by . . .

CINESIAS: Myrrhine! Myrrhine! Don't go—if only for the sake of our child. Listen to him. (*To the child*) Boy, speak up.

CHILD: Momma! Momma! Momma!

CINESIAS: Listen to that! Have you no feeling for the child? He hasn't been fed or washed in six days.

MYRRHINE: Poor dear, his father neglects him.

CINESIAS: Come down then and take care of him.

MYRRHINE: Well, I suppose I must. Oh, what it is to be a mother! (*To the child*) You are as sweet as your father is brutal. Give me a kiss, my pet, my treasure.

CINESIAS: I'm not blaming you—you've let yourself be influenced by those other women. They have persuaded you to make me miserable—and you, too, are suffering. I know you are. (*He tries to fondle her.*)

MYRRHINE: Hands off!

CINESIAS: But everything in our house is going to pieces.

MYRRHINE: I don't care.

CINESIAS: But how about your knitting? The hens are pecking at it and unraveling every thread. Don't you care about that?

MYRRHINE: Not much.

CINESIAS: What about our vows to Aphrodite? Won't you fulfill them again? Won't you—come home?

MYRRHINE: No, I won't . . . Well, not unless you and the others stop fighting.

CINESIAS: All right. If you want it that much, we'll make a treaty.

MYRRHINE: Well and good. When you've done it I'll come home. But until then I'll stay where I am—I'm bound by an oath.

CINESIAS: Sure. But let me hold you in my arms for a little while. It's been such a long time.

MYRRHINE: No . . . I mean it . . . No! But don't think I don't love you.

CINESIAS: Well then, if you love me, lie down with me.

MYRRHINE: What! In front of the child.

CINESIAS (*to his slave*): Take the child home. . . . (*To Myrrhine*) There. The child's gone. Come to me now.

MYRRHINE: Don't be foolish . . . Where?

CINESIAS: Pan's cave is handy.

MYRRHINE: But how can I purify myself afterwards?

CINESIAS: You can wash in the nearby spring.

MYRRHINE: But—my oath. Must I perjure myself?

CINESIAS: Never mind the oath. I'll take care of it.

MYRRHINE: Well—I'll get a pallet.

CINESIAS: Don't bother. The ground will do.

MYRRHINE: No. Even though you are a wicked man, I won't let you lie on the cold earth. (*She goes back to the Acropolis.*)

CINESIAS: How she loves me!

MYRRHINE (*re-entering*): There now, lie down. I'm going to take my things off. But—oh dear, I must fetch a mattress.

CINESIAS: Damn the mattress. I don't need one.

MYRRHINE: Well, I do. Lying on coarse sacking is unpleasant.

CINESIAS: Give me a kiss.

MYRRHINE: Just a minute. (*She leaves.*)

CINESIAS: For God's sake, hurry.

MYRRHINE (*returning with a mattress*): Here it is. Lie down now. See, I'm taking off my clothes. . . . But wait—where's the pillow?

CINESIAS (*groaning*): A pillow!

MYRRHINE: We *must* have a pillow.

CINESIAS: I'm getting everything except what I want!

MYRRHINE (*re-entering with a pillow*): Lift your head, darling. (*To herself*) Is there anything more I can do?

CINESIAS (*misunderstanding her*): Nothing. I don't need a thing—except you.

MYRRHINE: Look—there goes my girdle. But remember what you promised—you know, about making peace.

CINESIAS: I will! I will!

MYRRHINE: But, oh dear, there's no coverlet.

CINESIAS: We don't need one. I'll cover you.

MYRRHINE (*leaving him*): I won't be a moment.

CINESIAS: That woman will be the death of me!

MYRRHINE (*coming back with a coverlet*): Up now.

CINESIAS: I'm up enough!

MYRRHINE: Oh, I forgot the perfume. We must have it.

CINESIAS: By Apollo, no!

MYRRHINE: By Aphrodite, yes! Yes! (*She goes out again.*)

CINESIAS: I can't stand it much longer!

MYRRHINE (*re-entering with a bottle of perfume*): Hold out your hand. Put some on.

CINESIAS: I don't like the smell of it.

MYRRHINE: Oh! I'm so stupid, I brought the wrong bottle.

CINESIAS: Let it go.

MYRRHINE: Certainly not. (*She exits.*)

CINESIAS: Damn the man who invented perfume!

MYRRHINE (*re-entering with another flask*): Here's the right one.

CINESIAS: I've had the right one here all the time . . . We don't need another thing, darling. Come to bed!

MYRRHINE: I'm coming. See, there go my slippers. . . . And you *will* vote for peace, won't you?

CINESIAS: I'll think about it. (*Myrrhine runs away.*) She's fooled me. She's run off and left me to my tortures . . . This poor neglected fellow! Somebody else will have to take care of him.

[*Just when it seems that the war will never end and the women will not succeed, an emissary arrives from Sparta. The Spartan men, like the Athenians, are suffering from a general strike of all wives. They* come to agreement on one point: they thoroughly believe the adage about women—already old in the days of Aristophanes—that "you can't live with them or without them." Therefore they have come to offer terms. A great entertainment ensues. The Athenians find the Spartans admirable drinking companions—Lysistrata fears that the men may get to like each other far too well—and it is suggested that hereafter all embassies should be well supplied with liquor before negotiations. So, amidst general hilarity, peace is finally established.]

CATULLUS (84?–54 B.C.)

The Greeks had a word for it; the Latins embroidered it with decorative symbols and double meanings. For the most part, however, the Roman writers treated love as a physical enjoyment, the fulfillment of a particularly pleasant and almost insatiable appetite. One of the meanings of love, according to The Oxford English Dictionary, is "the animal instinct between the sexes and its gratification." Writing about what the Romans usually meant by "amor," Professor F. A. Wright, in The Mirror of Venus, says: "Of platonic love, spiritual love, romantic love, they knew very little; love was for them almost entirely physical, a thing of the senses . . . To the ordinary Roman, love was one of the natural functions, like eating and drinking, and performed with as much vigor. In this spirit Plautus' old reprobate in The Girl from Casinum sings:

> "There's nothing in the world like love,
>   So delicate and flavory.
> The sweetest flower has not its power;
>   It is so soft and savory.
> I wonder why cooks do not try
>   To use it as a spice;
> A tiny trickle our tongues would tickle,
>   It is so very nice."

Of all the Roman poets, none wrote with more ease, wit, and sensual imagination than Gaius Valerius Catullus. He excelled in lyric grace, and, although he delighted in the flesh, Catullus made the reader aware of the struggle between flesh and spirit. He was born in Verona about 84 B.C. and brought up in comparative luxury. His father had often entertained Julius Caesar and, as soon as he came of age, young Catullus was sent to Rome. There he made many important acquaintances, but the great city kept him poor. His love affairs were spasmodic, expensive, and unhappy; although he devoted himself to poetry he had little time for it. He was dead at the age of thirty.

TO MAMURRA'S MISTRESS

Though splay thy feet, and snub thy nose,
Thy fingers short, and unlike sloes
  Thine eyes in hue may be;
Thy lip with driv'ling moisture dew'd,
  Thy language vulgar, manners rude,
  Yet wanton, hail to thee!

And does the province praise thy grace;
And e'en presume thy form and face
  With Lesbia to compare?
Then why should I thy charms dispraise?
'Mid vulgar fools, in tasteless days.
  'Tis useless to be fair.

Translated by GEORGE LAMB

TO LESBIA, ON HER FALSEHOOD

To me alone, thou said'st, thy love was true,
And true should be, though Jove himself might woo.
I loved thee, Lesbia, not as rakes may prize
The favorite wanton who has pleased their eyes;
Mine was a tender glow, a purer zeal;
'Twas all the parent for the child can feel.
Thy common falsehood now, thyself I know;
And though my frame with fiercer heat may glow,
Yet Lesbia's vile and worthless in my sight,
Compared with Lesbia once my heart's delight;
No wonder passion's unrestrained excess
Makes me desire thee more, but love thee less.

Translated by GEORGE LAMB

TO AUFILENA

I like girls, Aufilena, of consciences nice,
  For the favors they grant who are honestly paid;
But you, who have cheated, and taken the price
  Of the love you withhold, are an infamous jade.

'Tis an honest girl's part, what she's promised, to do;
  'Twere a modest one's not to have promised the deed:
But she who can jilt, while she pockets like you
  The money for favors she will not concede,

Commits a base fraud, which would shame and disgrace
The lowest and worst of the prostitute race.

Translated by GEORGE LAMB

THE RENDEZVOUS

My Hypsithilla, charming fair,
My life, my soul, ah! hear my prayer:
Thy grateful summons quickly send,
And bless at noon, with joy, thy friend.
And if my fair one will comply,
And not her sighing swain deny,
Take care the door be then unbarr'd,
And let no spy be on the guard.
And thou, the aim of my desire,
Attend at home my amorous fire.
Prepare thy bosom to receive
All that so much love can give:
Prepare to meet repeated joy,
Continued bliss without alloy;
Dissolving still in thy dear arms,
Still raised by thy reviving charms
To onsets fresh of sprightly pleasure,
Tumultuous joy beyond all measure.
But dally not with my desire,
Nor quash with thy delays my fire.
Bursting with love upon my couch I lie,
Forestalling with desire the distant joy.

Translator unknown

FAREWELL TO LESBIA

Catullus, you're a fool, I said;
What's lost is lost, what's dead is dead.
The game is over, that you know.
Oh, let the pretty strumpet go.

Never was woman held before
With such devotion as we swore.
Never was there a happier lover!
Never such nights! But that's all over.

Stop fretting, stop repining. It's
High time, my boy, to call it quits.
Look at the past without regretting;
Forget the way that she's forgetting.

So farewell to the girl. Good-by,
Good riddance, too, to her, say I.
This is the end; you might have seen it;
But tell her that you're through—and mean it.

Who'll fill her empty hours now?
Who'll praise her arms, her breast, her brow?
Who'll be the ever-welcome one to
Inspire, dream about, and run to?

Who'll give her what her mouth must miss:
Rapturous biting kiss for kiss?
There will be memories, even so.
But let her go, man, let her go.

Translated by L.U.

HORACE (65–8 B.C.)

*A typical man about town who was in love with the country, Horace gave
up the pleasures of the metropolis for the simplicities of his beloved Sabine
farm. Horace—or, to give him the dignity of his full name, Quintus Horatius
Flaccus—was born in 65 B.C. in the little south Italian town of Venusia.
Although the son of a nobody—his father was a freedman who had been a
hard-worked slave—Horace succeeded in getting a classical education in
Athens, the cultural center of the Mediterranean, as well as in Rome. He
was twenty-one when Julius Caesar was assassinated, after which Horace became involved in the civil war—on the wrong side—suffered with the defeat
of Brutus at Philippi, and, when his father died, lost all claims to the estate.*

*Fortunately he made friends easily; one of them, the wealthy Maecenas,
became his patron. Thanks to his benefactor, Horace was able to spend much
of his time enjoying—and satirizing—the lures of the wicked city. Later, he
compensated for his youthful dissipations by retiring to the quiet of his
Sabine retreat, where he died at fifty-seven, after enjoying a good-humored,
full-blooded, and carnally comfortable life.*

*Although his satires, intimate and informal, are among the finest conver-
sation pieces ever written, they have never attained the popularity of his
odes. The odes are light verse rather than serious poetry; but they hurl shafts
of irony, frank suggestiveness, outright anger, and ridicule. Horace tells us*

that he "lived for the girls," but he did not worry too much about them. An advocate of the golden mean, he took everything—especially women— with an inquiring interest, but he took nothing too much to heart. Unlike Catullus, Horace never permitted an emotion to overpower him. His poems imply that he was a great lover, but they also indicate he was a very limited one. He failed to appreciate women except in their most obvious and physical aspects. He never speaks of the qualities of their minds but always of the qualities of their bodies—their whiteness or redness, their sinuous arms and insinuating ankles, their gratifying warmth or their reprehensible frigidity. His is essentially the love poetry of the dabbler in passion, the erotic dilettante, the unmarried middle-aged man—a record of teasing memories, of restrained paganism, of humorous detachment and polite bawdiness. The note is always that of extreme sophistication; Horace is more concerned with the delights and disappointments of love affairs than with love itself. An amused spectator, he keeps his head and brings all he sees down—or up—to a level of gay urbanity.

GROWING OLD DISGRACEFULLY
(BOOK III, ODE XV)

> Wife of poor Ibycus, listen; a word with you.
>   How can you seem so outrageously gay?
> Think of your age! It is sad and absurd, with you
>   Acting this way.
>
> Truly, old lady, it's time that you ceased all this;
>   Here, with young girls, you should never be found.
> Stop those ridiculous antics; at least all this
>   Running around.
>
> It's all very well for a kitten like Pholoë
>   To smile at the lads who repay her in kind,
> But when *you* approach them, they rapidly stroll away.
>   Lord, are you blind!
>
> Strange, you won't see that the thing which delights a man
>   Is always the dancer and seldom the dance;
> A Thyiad with white hair and wrinkles affrights a man;
>   He looks askance.
>
> Roses and romance and wine-jars are *not* for you;
>   There is the loom and the raw wool to comb,
> Mending and baking and—oh, there's a lot for you
>   Right here at home!

Translated by L.U.

TEARS, IDLE TEARS
(BOOK III, ODE VII)

Why are you weeping for Gyges?
    Your lover, though absent, is true.
As soon as warm weather obliges,
    He'll come back to you.

At Oricus, snow-bound and grieving,
    He yearns for domestic delights.
He longs for the moment of leaving;
    He lies awake nights.

His hostess, a lady of fashion,
    Is trying to fan up a few
Stray flames of his fiery passion,
    Lit only for you.

With sighs and suggestive romances
    She does what a sorceress can.
But Gyges—he scorns her advances;
    The noble young man.

But you—how about your bold neighbor?
    Does he please your still lachrymose eye?
When he gallops past, flashing his saber,
    Do you watch him go by?

When he swims, like a god, down the river,
    Do you dry the perpetual tear?
Does your heart give the least little quiver?
    Be careful, my dear.

Be warned, and be deaf to his pleadings;
    To all of his questions be mute.
Do not heed any soft intercedings
    That rise from his flute.

Lock up when the day has departed,
    Though the music grows plaintive or shrill.
And though he may call you hard-hearted,
    Be obdurate still!

Translated by L.U.

THE PASSING OF LYDIA
(BOOK I, ODE XXV)

No longer now do perfumed swains and merry wanton youths
    Come flocking, loudly knocking at your gate;
No longer do they rob your rest, or mar the sleep that soothes,
    With calling—bawling love-songs until late.

No longer need you bar them out, nor is your window-pane
    Ever shaken, now forsaken here you lie.
Nevermore will lute strings woo you, nor your lover's voice complain,
    "'Tis a sin, dear, let me in, dear, or I die!"

The little door that used to swing so gaily in and out,
    Creaks on hinges that show tinges of decay.
For you are old, my Lydia, you are old and rather stout;
    Not the sort to court or sport with those who play.

Oh, now you will bewail the daring insolence of rakes,
    While you dally in an alley with the crones;
And the Thracian wind goes howling down the avenues and shakes
    Your old shutters as it utters mocking moans.

For youth will always call to youth and greet love with a will—
    And Winter, though you tint her like the Spring,
Beneath the artificial glow she will be Winter still—
    And who would hold so cold and old a thing!

Translated by L.U.

THE TEASING OF XANTHIAS
(BOOK II, ODE IV)

You never need blush, since your love for a hand-maid,
    Friend Xanthias, is known to—well, more than a few.
Conceal it no more. Here's a girl who is planned, made
        And fashioned for you.

Briseis, the slave-girl, with tints like the lily's,
    Her body a mingling of fire and snow,
Enraptured the noble and haughty Achilles—
        A thing that you know.

And Ajax, the fearless and well-known defier,
    Was snared by Tecmessa, the modest and grave;
Though he was a lord who could surely look higher,
        And she was his slave.

And as for your Phyllis who scorns your sesterces,
   Her family tree may be broad as an oak's.
Her people, I'm sure, though upset by reverses,
           Were eminent folks.

A girl so devoted, unlike any other
   Your arm may have had the occasion to crush,
Could never, believe me, be born of a mother
           For whom you need blush.

Her arms and the turn of her ankles enthuse me;
   Her face has the glamor that all men adore.
What! Jealous? You mean it? Go on—you amuse me!
           I'm forty—and more.

Translated by L.U.

A HAPPY ENDING
(BOOK III, ODE IX)

HORACE: Once (even twice) your arms to me would cling,
       Before your heart made various excursions;
     And I was happier than the happiest king
          Of all the Persians.

LYDIA: So long as I remained your constant flame,
       I was a proud and rather well-sung Lydia,
     But now, in spite of all your precious fame,
          I'm glad I'm rid o' ye.

HORACE: Ah well, I've Chloe for my present queen.
       Her voice would thrill the marble bust of Caesar;
     And I would exit gladly from the scene
          If it would please her.

LYDIA: And as for me, with every burning breath,
       I think of Calaïs, my handsome lover,
     For him not only would I suffer death,
          But die twice over.

HORACE: What if the old love were to come once more
       With smiling face and understanding tacit;
     If Chloe went, and I'd unbar the door,
          Would you—er—pass it?

LYDIA: Though he's a star that's constant, fair and true,
       And you're as light as cork or wild as fever;
     With all your faults I'd live and die with you,
          You old deceiver!

Translated by L.U.

HORACE LOSES HIS TEMPER
(BOOK III, ODE X)

Your husband is stern and you're adamant, Lyce,
　　Oh yes, there is not the least doubt of it.
But open the door, for the weather is icy;
　　　　Let me in out of it.

Oh, cruel you are to behold me, unweeping,
　　All huddled and drenched like a rabbit here;
Exposed to the pitiless snow and the sweeping
　　　　Winds that inhabit here.

The blast, like the sharpest of knives, cuts between us—
　　Ah, will you rejoice if I freeze to death?
Come, put off the pride that is hateful to Venus;
　　　　Come, ere I sneeze to death!

Your sire was a Tuscan—may Hercules club me
　　Or crush out my life like a mellow pea—
But who in Gehenna are you that you snub me?
　　　　You're no Penelope!

Forgive me. I know that I rail like a peasant—
　　But won't you be more than a friend to me?
Won't tears and my prayers—and the costliest present
　　　　Make you unbend to me?

Once more I implore; give my pleadings a fresh hold;
　　My soul in its torment still screams to you. . . .
What? Think you I'll lie down and die on your threshold?
　　　　Good night! And bad dreams to you!

Translated by L.U.

THE FEMALE OF THE SPECIES
(BOOK III, ODE XX)

Have you ever robbed a lioness of just one tiny whelp?
　　Have you ever felt the power of her claws?
Well, think of these, oh Pyrrhus, and before you cry for help,
　　Remember what a woman is—and pause.

The unfair sex, the one that is more deadly than the male,
　　Will never leave unturned a single stone,
She'll fight, she'll bite, she'll scorn the rules; she'll make a strong man
　　pale. . . .
　　So you'd better let Nearchus quite alone.

And meanwhile this Nearchus, the sweet and blushing prize,
  Conducts himself as umpire of the fray;
He shakes his scented locks; he smirks and rolls his pretty eyes—
  A tired semi-demi-god at play.

Oh let her have her perfumed youth—as she is sure to do,
  Although she break a senate full of laws;
Admit defeat; retreat from them—the virgin or the shrew.
  Remember what a woman is—and pause.

Translated by L.U.

SPEAKING FROM EXPERIENCE
(BOOK I, ODE V)

What perfumed, posy-dizened sirrah,
  With smiles for diet,
Clasps you, O fair but faithless Pyrrha,
  On the quiet?
For whom do you bind up your tresses,
  As spun-gold yellow—
Meshes that go with your caresses,
  To snare a fellow?

How will he rail at fate capricious,
  And curse you duly;
Yet now he deems your wiles delicious—
  You perfect, truly!
Pyrrha, your love's a treacherous ocean;
  He'll soon fall in there!
Then shall I gloat on his commotion,
  For *I* have been there!

Translated by EUGENE FIELD

OVID (43 B.C.–A.D. 17)

None of the ancients wrote so constantly of love as the Latin poet Ovid, whose full name was Publius Ovidius Naso. Born about forty-five years before the Christian era, Ovid lived some sixty years, during which he collected amatory tales, rewrote erotic legends, and analyzed the art of love in all its phases. The titles of his most representative work are significant: Amores, Ars Amatoria, and Metamorphoses.

A member of a wealthy family, he became a State Counselor, but he neglected the law for literature and seems to have suffered as a consequence. His finances were considerably improved when, after two divorces, he married a daughter of one of the wealthiest families of Rome. In his fiftieth year he was banished to a town on the Black Sea, where he died in A.D. 17. It is said that he was exiled because of the salacious nature of his books on love. But this is unlikely since the book was published more than a dozen years before his banishment and, besides, contemporary Roman morals and manners were not only sophisticated but thoroughly cynical. It is more probable, as Ovid himself hinted, that he knew too many secrets about the society which centered about the court and may have been involved in some of the scandals.

Ovid thought of himself not only as a poet but as a teacher. The advice given to men and women in The Art of Love is so precise as to seem pedantic. Every detail of dress, deportment, bodily care, technique of courtship, psychological attitude, and physical love-making is as plainly outlined as a primer. Ovid's book is actually a manual of seduction: it instructs young men how to win mistresses and shows girls how to hold their lovers. "Ovid," wrote F. A. Wright, "may be sensual, but he is not morbid; he may be vulgar, but he is not callous; he may be frivolous, but he is not sour. He may indeed have all the faults that have ever been attributed to him, but he has one virtue that redeems them all: he believes in love."

It is this belief that gives even the most trivial of Ovid's lines a communication which is timely as well as timeless. No writers of antiquity and few of any age have blended the warmly romantic and the coolly realistic with so direct, yet so detached, a sense of delight and, more than occasionally, with such tongue-in-cheek humor.

FROM: THE ART OF LOVE

[*The selection from Book One is the famous seventeenth-century rhymed translation by John Dryden. The selections from Book Two and Book Three are prose versions by the editor.*]

BOOK ONE

> In Cupid's school whoe'er would take degree,
> Must learn his rudiments, by reading me.
> Seamen with sailing arts their vessels move;
> Art guides the chariot; art instructs to love.
> Of ships and chariots others know the rule;
> But I am master in Love's mighty school . . .
>   You, who in Cupid's rolls inscribe your name,
> First seek an object worthy of your flame;
> Then strive, with art, your lady's mind to gain;
> And last, provide your love may long remain.

On these three precepts all my work shall move:
These are the rules and principles of love.
Before your youth with marriage is oppress'd,
Make choice of one who suits your humor best:
And such a damsel drops not from the sky;
She must be sought for with a curious eye . . .
The face of heav'n with fewer stars is crown'd,
Than beauties in the Roman sphere are found.
  Whether thy love is bent on blooming youth,
On dawning sweetness, in unartful truth;
Or courts the juicy joys of riper growth;
Here mayst thou find thy full desires in both.
Or if autumnal beauties please thy sight,
(An age that knows to give and take delight,)
Millions of matrons of the graver sort,
In common prudence, will not balk the sport . . .
But above all, the playhouse is the place;
There's choice of quarry in that narrow chase.
There take thy stand, and sharply looking out,
Soon mayst thou find a mistress in the rout,
For length of time, or for a single bout.
The theaters are berries for the fair:
Like ants on molehills, thither they repair;
Like bees to hives, so numerously they throng,
It may be said, they to that place belong.
Thither they swarm, who have the public voice:
There choose, if plenty not distracts thy choice.
To see and to be seen, in heaps they run;
Some to undo, and some to be undone . . .
  Nor shun the chariots, and the courser's race;
The Circus is no inconvenient place.
No need is there of talking on the hand;
Nor nods, nor signs, which lovers understand.
But boldly next the fair your seat provide;
Close as you can to hers, and side by side.
Pleas'd or unpleas'd, no matter; crowding sit,
For so the laws of public shows permit.
Then find occasion to begin discourse;
Enquire whose chariot this, and whose that horse:
To whatsoever side she is inclin'd,
Suit all your inclinations to her mind;
Like what she likes: from thence your court begin;
And whom she favors, wish that he may win.
But when the statues of the deities,
In chariots roll'd, appear before the prize;

When Venus comes, with deep devotion rise.
If dust be on her lap, or grains of sand,
Brush both away with your officious hand.
If none be there, yet brush that nothing thence;
And still to touch her lap make some pretense.
Touch anything of hers; and if her train
Sweep on the ground, let it not sweep in vain;
But gently take it up, and wipe it clean;
And while you wipe it, with observing eyes,
Who knows but you may see her naked thighs!
Observe who sits behind her; and beware,
Lest his incroaching knee should press the fair.
Light service takes light minds; for some can tell
Of favors won by laying cushions well:
By fanning faces some their fortune meet;
And some by laying footstools for their feet.
These overtures of love the Circus gives;
Nor at the swordplay less the lover thrives:
For there the son of Venus fights his prize;
And deepest wounds are oft receiv'd from eyes.
One, while the crowd their acclamations make,
Or while he bets, and puts his ring to stake,
Is struck from far, and feels the flying dart,
And of the spectacle is made a part . . .

Thus far the sportful Muse, with myrtle bound,
Has sung where lovely lasses may be found.
Now let me sing, how she who wounds your mind,
With art, may be to cure your wounds inclin'd.
Young nobles, to my laws attention lend;
And all you vulgar of my school, attend.
First then believe, all women may be won;
Attempt with confidence, the work is done.
The grasshopper shall first forbear to sing
In summer season, or the birds in spring,
Than women can resist your flattering skill:
Ev'n she will yield, who swears she never will.
To secret pleasure both the sexes move;
But women most, who most dissemble love.
'Twere best for us, if they would first declare,
Avow their passion, and submit to prayer.
The cow, by lowing, tells the bull her flame;
The neighing mare invites her stallion to the game.
Man is more temp'rate in his lust than they,
And, more than women, can his passion sway . . .

All women are content that men should woo;
She who complains, and she who will not do.
Rest then secure, whate'er thy luck may prove,
Not to be hated for declaring love.
And yet how canst thou miss, since womankind
Is frail and vain, and still to change inclin'd?
Old husbands and stale gallants they despise,
And more another's than their own they prize.
A larger crop adorns our neighbor's field;
More milk his kine from swelling udders yield.

First gain the maid; by her thou shalt be sure
A free access and easy to procure:
Who knows what to her office does belong,
Is in the secret, and can hold her tongue.
Bribe her with gifts, with promises, and pray'rs;
For her good word goes far in love affairs.
The time and fit occasion leave to her,
When she most aptly can thy suit prefer.
The time for maids to fire their lady's blood,
Is, when they find her in a merry mood;
When all things at her wish and pleasure move:
Her heart is open then, and free to love.
Then mirth and wantonness to lust betray,
And smooth the passage to the lover's way.
Troy stood the siege, when filled with anxious care:
One merry mood concluded all the war.

If some fair rival vex her jealous mind,
Offer thy service to revenge in kind;
Instruct the damsel, while she combs her hair,
To raise the choler of the injured fair,
And sighing, make her mistress understand
She has the means of vengeance in her hand.
Then, naming thee, thy humble suit prefer,
And swear thou languishest and diest for her.
Then let her lose no time, but push at all,
For women soon are raised and soon they fall.
Give their first fury leisure to relent,
They melt like ice, and suddenly repent.

T'enjoy the maid, will that thy suit advance?
'Tis a hard question, and a doubtful chance.
One maid, corrupted, bawds the better for't;
Another for herself will keep the sport.
Thy business may be furthered or delayed,
But by my counsel, let alone the maid;
Even though she should consent to do the feat,

The profit's little and the danger great.
I will not lead thee through a rugged road,
But where the way lies open, safe, and broad.
Yet if thou findst her very much thy friend,
And her good face her diligence commend,
Let the fair mistress have thy first embrace,
And let the maid come after in her place.
　　But this I will advise, and mark my words,
For 'tis the best advice my skill affords,
If needs thou with the damsel must begin,
Before the attempt is made, make sure to win,
For then the secret will be better kept,
And she can tell no tales when once she's dipt.
'Tis for the fowler's interest to beware,
The bird entangled should not 'scape the snare.
The fish, once pricked, avoids the bearded hook,
And spoils the sport of all the neighboring brook.
But if the wench be thine, she makes the way,
And for thy sake, her mistress will betray,
Tell all she knows, and all she hears her say . . .

　　All things the stations of their seasons keep;
And certain times there are to sow and reap.
Plowmen and sailors for the season stay,
One to plow land, and one to plow the sea:
So should the lover wait the lucky day.
Then stop thy suit, it hurts not thy design;
But think, another hour she may be thine.
When she's in humor, ev'ry day is good.
But than her birthday seldom comes a worse;
When bribes and presents must be sent of course;
And that's a bloody day, that costs thy purse.
Be stanch; yet parsimony will be vain:
The craving sex will still the lover drain.
No skill can shift 'em off, nor art remove;
They will be begging, when they know we love . . .

　　Invoke the god, and all the mighty powers,
That wine may not defraud thy genial hours.
Then in ambiguous words thy suit prefer,
Which she may know were all address'd to her.
In liquid purple letters write her name,
Which she may read, and reading find thy flame.
Then may your eyes confess your mutual fires;
(For eyes have tongues, and glances tell desires.)
Whene'er she drinks, be first to take the cup;

And, where she laid her lips, the blessing sup.
When she to carving does her hand advance,
Put out thy own, and touch it as by chance.
Thy service ev'n her husband must attend:
(A husband is a most convenient friend.)
Seat the fool cuckold in the highest place,
And with thy garland his dull temples grace.
Whether below, or equal in degree,
Let him be lord of all the company,
And what he says be seconded by thee.
'Tis common to deceive thro' friendship's name;
But, common tho' it be, 'tis still to blame:
Thus factors frequently their trust betray,
And to themselves their masters' gains convey.
Drink to a certain pitch, and then give o'er;
Thy tongue and feet may stumble, drinking more.
Of drunken quarrels in her sight beware;
Pot-valor only serves to fright the fair.
Eurytion justly fell, by wine oppress'd,
For his rude riot at a wedding feast.
Sing, if you have a voice; and shew your parts
In dancing, if endued with dancing arts.
Do anything within your power to please;
Nay, ev'n affect a seeming drunkenness:
Clip every word; and if by chance you speak ·
Too home, or if too broad a jest you break,
In your excuse the company will join,
And lay the fault upon the force of wine.
True drunkenness is subject to offend;
But when 'tis feign'd, 'tis oft a lover's friend.
Then safely you may praise her beauteous face,
And call him happy, who is in her grace.
Her husband thinks himself the man design'd;
But curse the cuckold in your secret mind.
When all are risen and prepare to go,
Mix with the crowd, and tread upon her toe.

This is the proper time to make thy court,
For now she's in the vein, and fit for sport.
Lay bashfulness, that rustic virtue, by;
To manly confidence thy thoughts apply.
On Fortune's foretop timely fix thy hold;
Now speak and speed, for Venus loves the bold.
No rules of rhetoric here I need afford;
Only begin, and trust the following word;

It will be witty of its own accord.
Act well the lover; let thy speech abound
In dying words, that represent thy wound.
Distrust not her belief; she will be mov'd;
All women think they merit to be lov'd.
Sometimes a man begins to love in jest,
And, after, feels the torments he profess'd.
For your own sakes be pitiful, ye fair;
For a feign'd passion may a true prepare.
By flatteries we prevail on womankind,
As hollow banks by streams are undermin'd.
Tell her, her face is fair, her eyes are sweet;
Her taper fingers praise, and little feet.
Such praises ev'n the chaste are pleas'd to hear;
Both maids and matrons hold their beauty dear . . .
Beg her, with tears, thy warm desires to grant;
For tears will pierce a heart of adamant.
If tears will not be squeez'd, then rub your eye,
Or noint the lids, and seem at least to cry.
Kiss, if you can: resistance if she make,
And will not give you kisses, let her take.
Fie, fie, you naughty man, are words of course;
She struggles, but to be subdued by force.
Kiss only soft, I charge you, and beware,
With your hard bristles not to brush the fair.
He who has gain'd a kiss, and gains no more,
Deserves to lose the bliss he got before.
If once she kiss, her meaning is express'd;
There wants but little pushing for the rest:
Which if thou dost not gain, by strength or art,
The name of clown then suits with thy desert;
'Tis downright dulness, and a shameful part.
Perhaps, she calls it force; but, if she 'scape,
She will not thank you for th' omitted rape.
The sex is cunning to conceal their fires;
They would be forc'd ev'n to their own desires.
They seem t' accuse you, with a downcast sight,
But in their souls confess you did them right.
Who might be forc'd, and yet untouch'd depart,
Thank with their tongues, but curse you with their heart.

This is the sex; they will not first begin,
But, when compelled, are pleased to suffer sin.
Is there who thinks that women first should woo,

Lay by thy self-conceit, thou foolish beau.
Begin, and save their modesty the shame;
'Tis well for thee if they receive thy flame.
'Tis decent for a man to speak his mind;
They but expect the occasion to be kind.
Ask, that thou mayst enjoy; she waits for this,
And on thy first advance depends thy bliss. . . .
   But if you find your prayers increase her pride,
Strike sail awhile, and wait another tide.
They fly when we pursue; but make delay,
And when they see you slacken, they will stay.
Sometimes it profits to conceal your end;
Name not yourself her lover, but her friend.
How many skittish girls have thus been caught?
He proved a lover who a friend was thought.

   Here I had ended, but experience finds
That sundry women are of sundry minds,
With various crotchets filled, and hard to please:
They therefore must be caught by various ways. . . .
So turn thyself, and imitating them,
Try several tricks, and change thy stratagem.
One rule will not for different ages hold:
The jades grow cunning as they grow more old.
Then talk not bawdy to the bashful maid;
Bad words will make her innocence afraid.
Nor to an ignorant girl of learning speak;
She thinks you conjure when you talk in Greek.
And hence 'tis often seen, the simple shun
The learned, and into vile embraces run.
Part of my task is done, and part to do;
But here 'tis time to rest myself and you.

BOOK TWO

   Don't trust your good looks too much; a handsome body is not enough.
Soft words and gentle ways have won more women than a mere show of
strength. No one is fond of the wolf that attacks timid lambs or the hawk
which pounces on its prey. A sweet tongue supplies the food of love, but a
quarrelsome voice will estrange the most intimate pair of lovers. Your mistress will listen only to persuasion, not to force. No law compelled her to
share her bed with you. For lovers, love is the only law.
   When your mistress is preoccupied or ungracious, do not be impatient.
It is a woman's way to change her mind often—patience will help her change

it in your favor. If a branch is held carefully, it will bend to your will; if it is seized roughly, it will break.

Let me put it simply: Whatever she says is correct, whatever she does is right. If she says a thing isn't so, be prepared to agree wholeheartedly. Laugh when she laughs, weep with her when she weeps. Be a mirror for all her moods. When you play games with her, be sure to let her win. Let her always think herself your superior.

When you go out with her, carry her parasol, and make a path for her through any crowd. Always be ready with a chair for her toilette and a footstool to help her into bed. When her hands are cold, warm them in your bosom even though you yourself are freezing.

If you have an appointment with her in the Forum, be sure to be there ahead of her. If she asks you to meet her somewhere else at the last minute, don't complain and don't let anything detain you. When she comes home tired and calls for a slave, if there is none available, offer yourself. If she is in the country and summons you, go at once even if there is no conveyance and you have to walk. Love is a state of war, a long and tough campaign—nothing for the faint-hearted soldier. If her door happens to be locked, do not knock and disturb her. Climb through her window or, if necessary, go down the chimney. Remember Leander who swam the Hellespont to prove he would do anything for the sight of his beloved.

Get into the good graces of her servants, even the lowest. Bring some little gift to each one of them and a particularly handsome present to her maid. It is not necessary to give your mistress only extravagant things. Sometimes a few flowers or a basket of fruit will show your thoughtfulness as well as your taste.

What about poetry? For heaven's sake, no. Poetry is a drug on the market. You may never sing her praises often enough to satisfy her, but she won't care for pretty sentiments in verse. She may listen to your poem when you read it to her, especially if it happens to be written in her honor, but she will like it better if it is accompanied by a trinket or two. Remember, we are living in a golden age, and the sound of gold is more musical than tinkling syllables.

Another piece of advice: Decide to do something that she will like, then make it appear that it was she who thought of it. If, for instance, you have made up your mind to free one of your slaves, let her ask you to do it as a favor. Probably she will feel that she can twist you about her finger. Let her think so; it is the surest way of getting what you want.

Never stop praising her physical charms. Tell her that her beauty is so dazzling it outshines the sun. If she dresses in Tyrian purple, tell her that purple is your favorite color. If she wears a gown of thin Coan material, tell her that nothing becomes her so well as this tissue. If she decks herself out in gold, tell her that, sparkling though it is, gold is less brilliant than she. When she wears furs, tell her that you wish it were always winter. If she appears in a transparent tunic, tell her that you hope she won't catch cold, but that she sets you on fire. If she wears her hair parted, insist that this is the most becoming way; but if she wears it curled, tell her that she is most adorable in curls.

When she dances, praise her arms. When she sings, be ecstatic about her voice. When she stops, complain that it ended so soon. When she welcomes you to her bed, tell her that her bed is the very center of heaven. If you act like this, even though she is more tyrannical than the terrible Medusa, she will grow soft and docile.

Let her feel that you are always at hand to do her services. Let her see no one but you. Let her hear you only. Be available night and day, whenever she needs you. Then, when you are confident that she has grown dependent on you, leave her for a while. Let your absence worry her a little. Remember how shrewd Ulysses proved his shrewdness by staying away from Penelope for a long time. But don't stay *too* long. Time cures everything, including anguish. Be on the safe side. When Menelaus left Helen for too protracted a period, she grew tired of her cold couch and warmed herself in the arms of her guest. It was all the fault of Menelaus. No one should blame Helen merely because she was afraid to sleep alone.

Don't be afraid that, like some strict censor, I will insist that you remain faithful to one mistress only. God forbid. Even a married woman could not keep such a promise of fidelity. Amuse yourself, but be discreet. Don't brag about your conquests. Don't give presents to some woman that another of your favorites will recognize as coming from you. Be careful of what you write. Most women read between the lines; they usually read there more than was intended.

If, in spite of all your efforts, your secret affairs are brought to light, deny them emphatically. Do not protest too much, and never be on the defensive. Be bold, always bold. In love's battle, this is the only way to achieve peace. Some people will advise you to increase your virility by taking certain stimulants—pepper mixed with thistle seeds, camomile steeped in old wine, savory, and other herbs. In my opinion these are not aphrodisiacs but poison. Nevertheless, the small white onions that come from Megara, mixed with eggs, honey, and apples, may prove helpful.

Although I advised you not to boast of your infidelities, there are times when it might be well to display your good luck in love affairs. A mistress often grows bored, and the threat of a rival will rouse her to new displays of affection. Even a fairly good fire will go out unless it is fed with fresh fuel. Sometimes a dash of sulphur will bring up new flames. Let your mistress worry a little. It is good for her and for you, too. Nothing makes a lover happier than to hear his mistress is weeping because he has been unfaithful. First she refuses to believe the news, then she grows pale, then her voice fails, then she raves and tears her hair. Finally, in a flood of tears, she forgives him—because, she says, she knows he cannot live without her. This is your triumph. Throw your arms around her neck, hold her sad face to your breast, kiss away her tears. When war is over between you, call for a truce. She will be glad to sign a treaty of peace in bed.

Sometimes you may be told that your mistress is out, when you know she is really at home. Never mind; tell yourself that she has gone out, that your eyes deceive you. Perhaps some night after she has promised to receive you, you find her door shut. Do not rage. Lie down on the ground, even if it is cold and damp, and wait. A sensible man will understand the whims of women and will put himself, rather than them, in the wrong.

But these are little things. Let us turn to more important subjects and more difficult situations. If you have a dangerous rival, put up with it. Believe me, this is not an easy thing to do; but once you accomplish it your success is assured. If your mistress makes secret signs to your rival, ignore them. If she writes to him, do not try to intercept her letters. Let her come and go wherever and whenever she likes.

Frankly, I confess that, in my own case, I have never achieved this state of perfection. Like many others, I have never been able to practice completely what I preach. My jealousy is so great that when one day I saw my mistress kiss her husband, I complained about it.

There is nothing reasonable about love. At the same time, a really clever man allows his mistress to hide her infidelities—if you make her confess them, she will only grow more adroit at duplicity.

Above all, do not try to surprise your mistress in the act nor shame her in public. The temple of love is sacred, and the mysteries practiced in it should never be disclosed. Even Venus is not without shame. Most of the statues show her modest hands covering her secret charms. Animals may copulate anywhere and in front of everyone, but, at the sight, the young girl will turn her head away. Men and women seek private places and closed doors for love-making; they cover their nudity with clothes. Even when we do not want complete darkness, we certainly ask something dimmer than broad daylight.

Don't whisper intimately with every young girl you meet, as though to say, "That's another one I have slept with." There are men who like to do this in the hope that it will give them a reputation for gallantry, even though it makes the woman an object of scandal. Such men want you to believe that no woman can possibly resist them. If they cannot really possess a woman, they can dishonor her by implication.

Whatever you do, never talk to your mistress about her faults. Don't even hint, however playfully, that she may have a single defect. Andromeda was so extremely swarthy as to be almost black, but to Perseus she was the fairest of the fair. Most people found Andromache too tall, but Hector considered her exactly the right height. If there is something about your mistress you do not like, get used to it. Nothing is offensive to love. If her skin is black as pitch, call her a brunette. If her hair is carrot-red, compare her to the auburn and august Minerva. If she is nothing but skin and bones, tell her she is elegantly slender. If her waist is thick, praise her for her rosy plumpness. If she is short, extol her daintiness.

Never ask her age; never notice that she is growing older; ignore the fact that she keeps pulling out gray hairs. Remember, older women are much more experienced and even more experimental in the art of love. They know how to vary the pleasures and postures of Venus; they can enhance your pleasure in a thousand different ways. All the pictures and statues, however voluptuous, cannot show so much diversity.

I dislike the embraces in which both sides do not consummate—that is why boys give me little pleasure. Nothing is more unrewarding than making love to a woman when she is thinking about her housework. On the other hand, nothing is more exciting than the voice of the beloved heard in little gasps of pleasure, imploring her lover to go more slowly so that her happiness may be prolonged. Nothing can be sweeter than to behold her, drunk with ecstasy, her eyes swimming with delicious languor, holding off your caresses, but increasing your desire.

Do not hurry. Do not come too soon to the climax of your pleasure. Learn, by skillful delayings, to reach the end with gentle urgency. When you have found the most blissful sanctuary do not let any stupid modesty arrest your hand. Then you will see her eyes tremble and shine; then you will hear soft protests, broken sighs, and gentle moans which freshly stimulate desire. But beware—not too fast! Row together to the port on a mounting wave. Do not put on too much sail and reach the harbor leaving your panting mistress behind. Nor let her outstrip you on the way to the final haven. Do not hasten the last pleasure. If, however, there is danger in delay, do not be cautious; dig deep into your courser's side and spur your way to victory.

I am now at the end of my task. Award me the palm, and crown my head with myrtle. Extol your poet, sing his praises; let him be acclaimed by lovers everywhere. May everyone who has ever triumphed over some reluctant Amazon with weapons he has received from me inscribe upon his trophies: "Ovid Was Our Master."

BOOK THREE

Having just, so to speak, armed the Greeks against the Amazons, it seems only fair to furnish a few weapons to the Amazons for their struggle against the Greeks. It would be unfair to leave them defenseless in the eternal conflict between the sexes—men would not relish a victory under such conditions.

At this point some man may object: "Is it necessary to supply venom to the viper?" My answer is that it is unfair to condemn the entire sex for the wrongdoings of a few. Virtue has always been depicted as a woman, not a man, and it is only proper that she should befriend her own sex. However, I do not presume to instruct the virtuous and superior souls. I address myself to the lighthearted; I shall teach only those women who want to make themselves well loved.

For the most part, women are unfortunately ill-equipped to hold their men: They lack skill in love-making. A great deal of cleverness, artfulness, and even art are required to keep a lover from growing bored. I do this at the express command of Venus. Lately she appeared to me and spoke: "What have these poor women done to you that you make things worse for them? You have devoted two books to instructing men how to win every victory on love's battlefield. It is only fair that you give some thought to my daughters. They, too, need your advice."

Therefore, since I am inspired by Venus, listen to me carefully. Women, remember that, although you may reject love today, there will come a time when you will long for lovers, and it will be too late. No roses will be strewn on your doorstep and, at the same time, the rose will fade from your cheeks. The dread wrinkles will come; the hair will lose its luster and, though you swear you are prematurely white-haired, no one will believe you. Only the snake which slips its skin and the stag which sheds its horns seem to retain their prime. It is better to pluck the flower than let it wither on the stem. The ancient goddesses were not backward when they fell in love. Venus pursued Adonis; Dawn carried off Cephalus; Phoebe was shameless about her passion for Endymion.

Even if you are betrayed by men, what have you lost? Although many may enjoy your charm, the charm is still there. Iron corrodes, stone thins down, but the part of you needed for love never wears out. A torch does not lose its brilliance merely because it is used to light another torch; the ocean does not shrink when water is drawn from it. You, too, lose nothing by giving yourself freely. You can be lavish with your gifts without ever growing poor. But this is only the beginning. I am still in the harbor; soon we will be borne by strong winds on the open sea.

First, consider your appearance. Beauty is a gift of the gods, but only a few receive this gift. Most of you must enhance nature with artful raiment. The rustic carelessness of our forefathers' dress has given way to subtly revealing garments and elaborate adornments. It is not, however, necessary, to drag down your ears with masses of pearls or make walking difficult with the weight of heavy brocades. Moderation, as well as fastidiousness, is more alluring than showiness.

Neither neglect your hair nor depend upon its natural state. It is glamorous only when properly coiffed. There are a thousand ways of dressing the hair, and you must find the one most flattering to you. Your mirror can tell you. If your face is long and oval, part your hair in the middle. If it is round, lengthen it with a topknot. Some women look most charming when they let their hair fall down to their shoulders, like the lyre-playing Apollo; others look best when they bind their tresses tightly like Diana, the chaste huntress. One girl delights us with little curls; another flattens her hair sleekly across the temples. Some women affect high tortoise-shell combs; others crown their heads with towering waves; still others arrange their coiffure in a seemingly casual manner. Real art often seems artless. Think how lucky you are. Sooner or later men grow bald and show their age. Women, however, can disguise age by dyeing their hair—often the artificial color is more attractive than the original shade. Even if your hair should thin, you can always obtain a thick head of hair with a little money.

Now about clothes. Do not go in for too much embroidery or gaudy Tyrian purples. There are many handsome colors which cost less. Besides, why show off all your riches at once? Even an ordinary blue will mirror the heavens, a sky clear of clouds. There is a green that is like sea water, worthy of the loveliest nymph. There is a saffron that might have come from the mantle of Aurora. There is the purple-fiery amethyst, the pale rose, the lively chestnut, the light almond. . . . There are as many colored wools as there are spring flowers. Choose your particular hue with care. Black is dramatic for a blonde; a brunette shows off best in white. There is a color for everyone.

Perhaps I should not go into too many intimate details, but I should warn you against the smell of perspiration. Be careful about washing your armpits, and do not let your legs grow unsightly with bristling hairs. I am not, of course, speaking to lowborn coarse Caucasian women; so it is scarcely needful to tell you to brush your teeth free of discoloration and wash your mouth out carefully every morning. You doubtless know how to whiten your skin with powders and redden your cheeks with carmine. You also know how to pencil your eyebrows, widen the space between them, and make your eyes shine brighter by applying saffron to the lids. These things will help cover the marks made by the years.

At the same time, be sure to hide all such subterfuges from your lover. Do not let him behold you repairing the ravages of nature or see your dressing table full of pigments, salves, lotions, and other beauty aids. No one could blame him for feeling uncomfortable if he suspected that the bloom on your cheeks might run down your neck. Avoid the Greek ointments which turn rancid, and be careful of the oils which are extracted from the malodorous fleece of sheep. Never clean your teeth in front of anyone. Although the end result is commendable, the process is slightly disgusting. It is, of course, true that the most beautiful objects have crude origins. The sculptors' masterpieces were once nothing but shapeless marble blocks. The exquisite ring of gold was fashioned from a metal lump. The finespun material you are wearing probably came from an evil-smelling ram. So, if your lover arrives while you are still beautifying yourself, have your maid tell him you are still sleeping. Do not let him see an unfinished and imperfect product.

There are many things which men need not know about—things which, if seen in their naked reality, would shock them. Observing the lifelike trappings which transform the stage, we do not want to know that they are only props, plain wood tricked out with gilt. The audience is not expected to examine them too closely. In the same way, your private audience should not discover how artificial are your properties.

On the other hand, I do not forbid you to have your hair done in his presence. Nothing is more enchanting than watching the waves of a woman's hair ripple down her back. Be co-operative with your hairdresser; do not make her afraid of you. If you abuse her, she will have her revenge by doing something hateful behind your back. One day I entered the boudoir of my mistress unannounced—in a flurry of excitement she put on her false hair all awry. May such an awkward accident happen only to those we hate. A mutilated animal, a meadow without grass, a tree without leaves, and a head without hair—all are ugly.

It is not to you, ravishing Semele or lovely Leda, that I speak; not to you, Europa, carried away on the back of an enraptured bull; nor to Helen, whom her husband, Menelaus, rightfully demanded and whom her seducer, Paris, understandably refused to return. Most of my pupils are average women. The great beauties need little of my advice, but the plain ones—the great majority—will benefit by it. There are few faces without blemishes—hide the flaws with skill and circumspection. Remedy the defects of your figure. If you are short, sit down most of the time; this way men will not be aware of your lack of height. If you are so small as to be almost a dwarf, lie down and throw something over your feet. If you are thin, wear bulky materials; when you go out, put on a loose mantle. If you do not have shapely feet, do not expose them in sandals but cover them with fetching shoes. If your neck is thick, veil it with a scarf. If your hands are large, restrain your gestures. If your bosom is flat, a few pads will help; if it is too large, wear a tight brassière. If your breath is unpleasant, do not come too near your lover; talk as little as possible when your stomach is empty. A woman whose teeth are discolored or too large should be very careful about laughing.

It is hard to believe, but women must learn *how* to laugh. Do not open your mouth too wide, and be sure that your lower lip covers the tips of your upper teeth. Do not laugh too heartily or too often. Whatever you do, do it in a sweet and feminine way, and you will do it successfully. Remember it is an art; there is no act in which art is not somehow involved. When you weep, weep attractively. If you have a slight stammer, capitalize upon it. If you have a slight lisp, use it coquettishly. A clever female can turn any defect into a delight.

The way of walking is particularly important; your movements either attract or repel. One woman, for example, walks with undulating hips, her gown swaying as though in a breeze. Another woman steps forward boldly with a peasantlike stride. Here, as in everything else, there is the golden mean.

If you are fortunate enough to have an unblemished skin, leave your shoulders and the upper part of your arms uncovered. I myself am always set on fire by such a sight, so much so that I want to cover all I see with kisses. Your voice can be a great lure; sound has as much enticement as sight. Ulysses had to pour wax into the ears of his companions to protect them against the seduction of the sirens' song. You, too, should learn to sing; a thrilling voice may compensate for the lack of other attractions. When you accompany yourself on the harp, you can show bare arms to great advantage. You should also learn to chant endearing verses—I might immodestly recommend certain passages from my own *Amores*. Dancing, dicing, playing games of every sort—none of these should be neglected . . .

But I am wandering. Let us get back to the main issue. When your maid, that clever go-between, has delivered a letter from your lover, read it carefully. But do not be in a hurry to reply. When you answer, do not encourage him too much, but do not really reject him. Suspense sharpens love. Rouse both his hopes and his fears, but do it gracefully. If you are married, be especially discreet in what you write. Young men love to preserve letters, so be careful not to put on paper anything incriminating.

No matter what the provocation, never lose your temper. Beasts may roar and rage; man must learn to control himself. Besides, anger shows you off at your worst; it swells the veins on your forehead, it makes your eyes pop, gives your face an ugly flush, and distorts the entire countenance. Look at yourself in the mirror during a fit of temper and you will scarcely recognize yourself . . .

Do not be avaricious. At least dissemble; try to keep your lover from finding out that you are greedy. You will lose a new lover if he suspects that you are setting a trap for him. What's more, do not treat a lover in the springtime of his youth the same way you treat an older man. The veteran will move more slowly and he will endure things that a young recruit will not. He won't try to break down your door; he won't tear your hair, maul your flesh, or scratch your cheeks till the blood comes. A mature man's love is a less leaping fire but a more lasting one.

Now let us put aside the lesser weapons and take up the naked sword, even though I may foolishly be instructing you against my own sex. When you have got your lover in your net, let him think he is the only one you care to capture. Once, however, you get him in bed, let him suspect a rival. This device always sharpens a man's ardor. A race horse makes better time when several other horses are competing with him rather than when he is running alone. Do not be too obvious about it. Pique him with stories of imaginary lovers; pretend that some man's emissary is always pleading at your door; if you are married, delude him into the belief that your husband is violently jealous and watchfully suspicious. There are times when, though he might enter naturally by the door, you should insist that he creep in stealthily by the window. You might even create a dramatic scene. At the proper moment, have your maid rush in and cry out, "We are discovered!" To make up for such alarms, let there be nights when he has every pleasure without disturbance.

I don't think it's necessary for me to tell a married woman how to deceive her husband. Certainly a wife should respect and fear her spouse—that is the law. But does this mean that she is a slave? If your husband had as many means of watching you as Argus has eyes, you could still outwit him. Can he stop you from writing a letter when you are in your bath? Can he prevent your maid from hiding the note in her bosom or inside her shoe? Lines written in milk are invisible, until read over charcoal. Even if he knows about such tricks, a few words can be scribbled on your maid's body; her flesh will serve as a living tablet.

What can a husband, or any guardian do when there are so many theaters, circuses, and festivals? He may watch outside the private baths, but there is nothing to stop your lover concealing himself within. It is significant that a skeleton key is called "An Adulterer" . . .

At a banquet or any other formal meal, be sure to arrive late. Remain dignified and do not carouse until the evening is well advanced; men who have been imbibing freely will find even a plain and modest girl alluring. Eat slowly and with delicacy. Handle the food only with the tips of your fingers. Do not leave greasy marks around your mouth; wipe your hands often. Drink, but only a little. Love and wine are natural companions, but no one likes to see a woman drunk. Don't fall asleep after the meal; a sleeping woman is an open invitation to rape.

I fear to go on, but Venus insists. "That which you hesitate to disclose," she says, "is the most important part of all." So . . . Learn what postures suit you best in the arena of love. If your face is pretty, lie upon your back; if your hips are shapely, show them off. If you are short, be your lover's jockey. If you are tall, kneel. Remember that love has countless ways and poses.

None of the oracles ever gave better advice than that which I have given you. Listen, then, to the end. Respond to your lover every moment; let pleasure penetrate to the marrow of your bones. Share with him every delight; whisper words of tenderness or words which, in their naughtiness, will increase excitement. If, as with some women, you feel no pleasure, pretend an answering thrill. Do not overdo it; time your exuberant cries and gasps of delight carefully.

I have done. The swans, hitched to my chariot, are ready to carry me to the skies. And now, my fair and promising pupils, do as the men, your lovers, have already done; inscribe upon your trophies: "Ovid Was Our Master."

AFTERNOON DIVERSIONS

It was a summer afternoon. The lattice by my bed,
One shutter closed, about the room a pleasant darkness shed,
Such as in forests oft you see, or when the twilight fades,
Or in the dusk of early dawn, well suited to fair maids
Who love to hide beneath its cloak their looks of modest shame:
And then it was, in tunic clad, Corinna to me came,
Her hair unbound about her neck, presage of future bliss,
More beautiful than Lais or Queen Semiramis.

At once I drew her tunic down—the fabric was so fine
That what it hid a lover's eye could easily divine—
She tried, 'tis true, to stay me; but 'twas very plain to see
That in our amorous strife she did not wish for victory;
And self-betrayed at last she stood, the tunic flung aside,
In all the flawless splendor of her beauty's naked pride.

I saw her shoulders and her arms and marked their liveliness;
I touched the apples of her breasts made for a fond caress;
I gazed upon her bosom and the smooth white plain below,
Her rounded flanks and slender thighs with youthful strength aglow.
But why say more, when every part alike was passing fair?
Unveiled I took her in my arms and held her captive there.
You know the rest. Worn out with love, wearied at length we lay.
Such afternoons as this I hope may often come my way.

FROM *Amores*, BOOK I, ELEGY V
Translated by F. A. WRIGHT

THE PROTECTIVE EUNUCH

Ay me, an eunuch keeps my mistress chaste,
That cannot Venus' mutual pleasure taste.
Who first deprived young boys of their best part,
With selfsame wounds he gave, he ought to smart.
To kind requests thou would'st more gentle prove,
If ever wench had made lukewarm thy love:
Thou wert not born to ride, or arms to bear,
Thy hands agree not with the warlike spear.
Men handle those; all manly hopes resign,
Thy mistress' ensigns must be likewise thine.
Please her—her hate makes others thee abhor;
If she discards thee, what use serv'st thou for?
Good form there is, years apt to play together:
Unmeet is beauty without use to wither.
She may deceive thee, though thou her protect;
What two determine never wants effect.
Our prayers move thee to assist our drift,
While thou hast time yet to bestow that gift.

FROM *Amores*, BOOK II, ELEGY III
Translated by CHRISTOPHER MARLOWE

THE PLEASURES OF PROMISCUITY

I mean not to defend the scapes of any,
Or justify my vices being many;
For I confess, if that might merit favor,
Here I display my lewd and loose behavior.
I loathe, yet after that I loathe I run:
Oh, how the burthen irks, that we should shun.
I cannot rule myself but where Love please;
Am driven like a ship upon rough seas.
No one face likes me best, all faces move,
A hundred reasons make me ever love.
If any eye me with a modest look,
I burn, and by that blushful glance am took;
And she that's coy I like, for being no clown,
Methinks she would be nimble when she's down.
Though her sour looks a Sabine's brow resemble,
I think she'll do, but deeply can dissemble.
If she be learned, then for her skill I crave her;
If not, because she's simple I would have her.
Before Callimachus one prefers me far;
Seeing she likes my books, why should we jar?
Another rails at me, and that I write,
Yet would I lie with her, if that I might:
Trips she, it likes me well; plods she, what then?
She would be nimbler lying with a man.
And when one sweetly sings, then straight I long,
To quaver on her lips even in her song;
Or if one touch the lute with art and cunning,
Who would not love those hands for their swift running?
And her I like that with a majesty,
Folds up her arms, and makes low courtesy.
To leave myself, that am in love with all,
Some one of these might make the chastest fall.
If she be tall, she's like an Amazon,
And therefore fills the bed she lies upon:
If short, she lies the rounder: to speak troth,
Both short and long please me, for I love both.
I think what one undecked would be, being drest;
Is she attired? then show her graces best.
A white wench thralls me, so doth golden yellow:
And nut-brown girls in doing have no fellow.
If her white neck be shadowed with black hair,
Why, so was Leda's, yet was Leda fair.
Amber-tress'd is she? then on the morn think I:

My love alludes to every history:
A young wench pleaseth, and an old is good,
Nay what is she, that any Roman loves,
This for her looks, that for her womanhood:
But my ambitious ranging mind approves?

FROM *Amores*, BOOK II, ELEGY IV
Translated by CHRISTOPHER MARLOWE

THE CUCKOLD-MAKER

If for thy self thou wilt not watch thy whore,
Watch her for me, that I may love her more.
What comes with ease, we nauseously receive,
Who but a sot would scorn to love with leave?
With hopes and fears my flames are blown up higher;
Make me despair, and then I can desire.
Give me a jilt to tease my jealous mind;
Deceits are virtues in the female kind.
Corinna my fantastic humor knew,
Play'd trick for trick, and kept her self still new:
She, that next night I might the sharper come,
Fell out with me, and sent me fasting home;
Or some pretense to lie alone would take,
Whene'er she pleas'd, her head and teeth would ache,
Till having won me to the highest strain,
She took occasion to be sweet again.
With what a gust, ye gods, we then imbrac'd!
How every kiss was dearer than the last!
  Thou whom I now adore, be edify'd,
Take care that I may often be deny'd.
Forget the promis'd hour, or feign some fright,
Make me lie rough on bulks each other night.
These are the arts that best secure thy reign,
And this the food that must my fires maintain.
Gross easy love does like gross diet pall,
In queasy stomachs honey turns to gall.
Had Danae not been kept in brazen tow'rs,
Jove had not thought her worth his golden show'rs.
When Juno to a cow turn'd Io's shape,
The watchman helpt her to a second leap.
Let him who loves an easy whetstone whore,
Pluck leaves from trees, and drink the common shore.
The jilting harlot strikes the surest blow,
A truth which I by sad experience know.

The kind poor constant creature we despise,
Man but pursues the quarry while it flies.
　　But thou, dull husband of a wife too fair,
Stand on thy guard, and watch the precious ware;
If creaking doors, or barking dogs thou hear,
Or windows scratcht, suspect a rival there.
An orange-wench would tempt thy wife abroad;
Kick her, for she's a letter-bearing bawd;
In short, be jealous as the devil in hell;
And set my wit on work to cheat thee well.
The sneaking city cuckold is my foe,
I scorn to strike, but when he wards the blow.
Look to thy hits, and leave off thy conniving,
I'll be no drudge to any wittall living;
I have been patient, and forborne thee long,
In hope thou wouldst not pocket up thy wrong:
If no affront can rouse thee, understand
I'll take no more indulgence at thy hand.
What, ne'er to be forbid thy house, and wife!
Damn him who loves to lead so dull a life.
Now I can neither sigh, nor whine, nor pray,
All those occasions thou hast ta'en away.
Why art thou so incorrigibly civil?
Doe somewhat I may wish thee at the devil.
For shame be no accomplice in my treason,
A pimping husband is too much in reason.
　　Once more wear horns, before I quite forsake her,
In hopes whereof I rest: thy cuckold-maker.

FROM *Amores*, BOOK II, ELEGY XIX
Translated by JOHN DRYDEN

SHAMEFUL IMPOTENCE

Either she was foul, or her attire was bad,
Or she was not the wench I wished to have had.
Idly I lay with her, as if I loved not,
And like a burden grieved the bed that moved not.
Though both of us performed our true intent,
Yet could I not cast anchor where I meant.
She on my neck her ivory arms did throw,
Her arms far whiter than the Scythian snow.
And eagerly she kissed me with her tongue,
And under mine her wanton thigh she flung,
Yea, and she soothed me up, and called me "Sir,"

And used all speech that might provoke and stir.
Yet like as if cold hemlock I had drunk,
It mocked me, hung down the head and sunk.
Like a dull cipher, or rude block I lay,
Or shade, or body was I, who can say?
What will my age do, age I cannot shun,
Seeing in my prime my force is spent and done?
I blush, that being youthful, hot, and lusty,
I prove neither youth nor man, but old and rusty.
Pure rose she, like a nun to sacrifice,
Or one that with her tender brother lies.
Yet boarded I the golden Chie twice,
And Libas, and the white-cheeked Pitho thrice.
Corinna craved it in a summer's night,
And nine sweet bouts had we before daylight.
What, waste my limbs through some Thessalian charms?
May spells and drugs do silly souls such harms?
With virgin wax hath some abased my joints?
And pierced my liver with sharp needle-points?
Charms change corn to grass and make it die:
By charms are running springs and fountains dry.
By charms mast drops from oaks, from vines grapes fall,
And fruit from trees when there's no wind at all.
Why might not then my sinews be enchanted?
And I grow faint as with some spirit haunted?
To this, add shame: shame to perform it quailed me,
And was the second cause why vigor failed me.
My idle thoughts delighted her no more,
Than did the robe or garment which she wore.
Yet might her touch make youthful Pylius fire
And Tithon livelier than his years require.
Even her I had, and she had me in vain,
What might I crave more, if I ask again?
I think the great gods grieved they had bestowed,
This benefit: which lewdly I foreslowed.
I wished to be received in, in I get me.
To kiss, I kiss; to lie with her, she let me.
Why was I blest? why made king to refuse it?
Chuff-like had I not gold and could not use it?
So in a spring thrives he that told so much,
And looks upon the fruits he cannot touch.
Hath any rose so from a fresh young maid,
As she might straight have gone to church and prayed?
Well, I believe, she kissed not as she should,
Nor used the sleight and cunning which she could.

Huge oaks, hard adamants might she have moved,
And with sweet words caused deaf rocks to have loved.
Worthy she was to move both gods and men,
But neither was I man nor lived then.
Can deaf ears take delight when Phaemius sings?
Or Thamyris in curious painted things?
What sweet thought is there but I had the same?
And one gave place still as another came.
Yet, notwithstanding, like one dead it lay,
Drooping more than a rose pulled yesterday.
Now, when he should not yet, he bolts upright,
And craves his task, and seeks to be at fight.
Lie down with shame, and see thou stir no more,
Seeing thou would'st deceive me as before.
Then cozenest me: by thee surprised am I,
And bide sore loss with endless infamy.
Nay more, the wench did not disdain a whit
To take it in her hand, and play with it.
But when she saw it would by no means stand,
But still drooped down, regarding not her hand,
"Why mock'st thou me," she cried, "or being ill,
Why bade thee lie down here against thy will?
Either thou art witched with blood of frogs new dead,
Or jaded cam'st thou from some other's bed."
With that, her loose gown on, from me she cast her,
In skipping out her naked feet much graced her.
And lest her maid should know of this disgrace,
To cover it, spilt water on the place.

FROM *Amores*, BOOK III, ELEGY VII
Translated by CHRISTOPHER MARLOWE

THE DECEPTION DENIED

Seeing thou art fair, I bar not thy false playing,
But let not me, poor soul, know of thy straying.
Nor do I give these counsel to live chaste,
But that thou would'st dissemble, when 'tis past.
She hath not trod awry, that doth deny it.
Such as confess have lost their good names by it.
And hidden secrets openly to bewray?
The strumpet with the stranger will not do,
Before the room be clear and door put-to.
Will you make shipwreck of your honest name,
And let the world be witness of the same?

Be more advised, walk as a puritan,
And I shall think you chaste, do what you can.
Slip still, only deny it when 'tis done,
And, before folk, immodest speeches shun.
The bed is for lascivious toyings meet,
There use all tricks, and tread shame under feet.
When you are up and dressed, be sage and grave,
And in the bed hide all the faults you have.
Be not ashamed to strip you, being there,
And mingle thighs, yours ever mine to bear.
There in your rosy lips my tongue entomb,
Practice a thousand sports when there you come.
Forbear no wanton words you there would speak,
And with your pastime let the bedstead creak;
But with your robes put on an honest face,
And blush, and seem as you were full of grace.
Deceive all; let me err; and think I'm right,
And like a wittol think thee void of slight.
Why see I lines so oft received and given?
This bed and that by tumbling made uneven?
Like one start up your hair tost and displaced,
And with a wanton's tooth your neck new-rased.
Grant this, that what you do I may not see;
If you weigh not ill speeches, yet weigh me.
My soul fleets when I think what you have done,
And through every vein doth cold blood run.
Then thee whom I must love, I hate in vain,
And would be dead, but dead with thee remain.
I'll not sift much, but hold thee soon excused.
Say but thou wert injuriously accused.
Though while the deed be doing you be took,
And I see when you ope the two-leaved book,
Swear I was blind; deny if you be wise,
And I will trust your words more than mine eyes.
From him that yields, the palm is quickly got,
Teach but your tongue to say, "I did it not,"
And being justified by two words, think
The cause acquits you not, but I that wink.

FROM *Amores*, BOOK III, ELEGY XIV
Translated by CHRISTOPHER MARLOWE

THE FIRST HERMAPHRODITE

No spear she ever holds, no painted quiver;
　　Never her time in hunting will she pass;
She bathes her comely limbs within her river
　　And has its water for a looking glass;
With boxwood comb she combs her flowing tresses
And wrapped in lucent robe the herbage presses.

Often she gathers flowers; and on that day
　　With picking posies she beguiled her leisure,
When she beheld the boy, and lo, straightway
　　Resolved to take her fill of amorous pleasure.
But first she pranked her dress and smoothed her face,
And called to help her all her beauty's grace.

Then thus did she begin: "A god in sooth,
　　And if a god, then Cupid here I see!
Happy thy mother and thy sister both;
　　Happy the nurse who gave her breast to thee,
But happier far than all thy promised bride
Whom thou shalt deign to welcome to thy side.

If such there be, let mine be stolen joy;
　　If not, let us in wedlock be united."
So spoke the naiad; but the timid boy
　　Blushed rosy red, his innocence despited—
For never yet of wedlock had he dreamed—
And as he blushed to her more lovely seemed.

As ofttimes in a sunny orchard close
　　Half-hid by leaves ripe apples we espy;
As painted ivories their whiteness lose;
　　As the moon reddens in the evening sky
When the loud cymbals clash to bring her aid;
So were the lad's soft cheeks like roses made.

"Give me at least," she cried, "a brother's kiss"—
　　And sought her arms around his neck to throw.
"Have done," said he, "I love not ways like this;
　　Have done, or I will leave this place and you."
The nymph, affrighted, feigned to go away,
And in a neighboring thicket hidden lay.

The boy imagined that he was alone,
　　And dipped his feet within the lapping wave;
And stripping naked, now that she was gone,
　　Prepared in the cool stream his limbs to lave.

Spellbound the maid upon his beauty looked
With eyes ablaze, and scarce concealment brooked.

Then with clapped hands he plunged into the pool
    And with alternate strokes began to swim.
An ivory statue set in crystal cool,
    A lily seems he on the river's brim.
"Victory!" the naiad cries, and diving down
All naked takes the intruder for her own.

In vain he strives. She holds him closely pressed,
    Stealing a kiss meanwhile, with arms thrown round him.
Fondly she touches his unwilling breast
    And will not let him go now she has found him.
E'en as a serpent in an eagle's hold
Seeks with soft coils her captor to enfold,

And borne aloft entwines his beating wings
    And wraps herself around his claws and head;
Or e'en as ivy to a tree trunk clings
    Or as a polyp on the ocean's bed
On every side puts greedy suckers out
And holds his prisoner compassed all about.

But yet the stubborn boy denies her will,
    Nor can she gain the joy wherefor she craves,
Until at last close-fastened to him still
    She draws him down beneath the placid waves
And cries: "Strive as you may, you shall not go.
Join him to me, ye gods, and keep us so."

Her wish was granted. Even as she prayed
    A change came over them; by heaven's might,
Of their two forms a single shape was made
    Which did their bodies twain in one unite. . . .
Both bodies in a glowing body mix—
A single body, but a double sex.

FROM *Metamorphoses*
Translated by F. A. WRIGHT

PETRONIUS (?–circa A.D. 66)

Nothing definite is known about the man who wrote the Satyricon *except
this work. It is not even certain what his first name may have been; it is*

sometimes given as Gaius, sometimes as Titus. The only contemporary evidence of his existence is a reference in Tacitus' Annals, where he is given the name of Petronius Arbiter, "one of the chosen circle of Nero's intimates." The title indicates that he was looked upon as "an absolute authority on questions of taste [arbiter elegantiae] in connection with the science of luxurious living . . . He spent his days in sleep, his nights in attending to his official duties or in amusement. He became as famous for his dissolute life as other men became for their lives of creative energy."

On the other hand, the Satyricon shows no lack of "creative energy"; it brims and overflows with gaiety and invention. Its artistry, however, did not prevent the author's downfall. According to tradition, Petronius was ruined by a jealous rival for Nero's favor and, to escape the disgrace of being put to death, committed suicide. He opened a vein, then bound it so that it bled slowly, while he continued to converse with friends.

The Satyricon, often called "the first realistic novel," is a collection of fragments, pieces of a larger work which gives a sardonic picture of the splendor, viciousness, and decay of the Roman Empire. It is a picaresque set of adventures in which the central characters are vagabonds, scholar-thieves, amoral rogues who, wrote Charles Whibley, "wander up and down the world, blatant and unashamed. There is no disaster but falls upon their backs; yet they make light of all things with an imperturbable serenity and leap lightly from crime to crime." These brawling beggars are contrasted with the puffed-up parvenu Trimalchio, the epitome of the new-rich and all their arrogance and grossness. The dinner in Trimalchio's house is a triumph of everything that is overwhelming and vulgar. An ignorant boor, Trimalchio has so much wealth that he does not know one tenth of the slaves who work for him; he mentions the classics but misquotes them; he recites his own fifth-rate compositions and rehearses the pageantry of his own pompous funeral. Few authors have delineated rascality and affectation with such irony, but it is obvious that Petronius enjoyed every one of the ridiculous episodes.

The Satyricon also contains the classic story of the widow of Ephesus, a fascinating tale that is both amatory and macabre, which has served as the plot of several plays, the most recent being by Christopher Fry (A Phoenix Too Frequent). The present translation is by the editor. "The Feast at Trimalchio's," the high light of the Satyricon, is an adaptation of the translation by W. C. Firebaugh.

FROM: THE SATYRICON

THE FEAST AT TRIMALCHIO'S

You would never believe that this was the dining room of a private gentleman, but, rather, that it was an exhibition of pantomimes. A very inviting relish was brought on, for by now all the couches were occupied save only that of Trimalchio, for whom, after a new custom, the chief place was reserved. On the tray stood a donkey made of Corinthian bronze, bearing panniers containing olives, white in one and black in the other. Two platters flanked the figure, on the margins of which were engraved Trimalchio's name and the weight of the silver in each. Dormice sprinkled with poppy seed and honey were served on little bridges soldered fast to the platter, and hot sausages on a silver gridiron, underneath of which were damson plums and pomegranate seeds.

We were in the midst of these delicacies when, to the sound of music, Trimalchio himself was carried in and bolstered up in a nest of small cushions, which forced a snicker from the less wary. A shaven poll protruded from a scarlet mantle, and around his neck, already muffled with heavy clothing, he had tucked a napkin having a broad purple stripe and a fringe that hung down all around. On the little finger of his left hand he wore a massive gilt ring, and on the first joint of the next finger a smaller one which seemed to me to be of pure gold, but as a matter of fact it had iron stars soldered on all around it. And then, for fear all of his finery would not be displayed, he bared his right arm, adorned with a golden arm band and an ivory circlet clasped with a pate of shining metal.

Picking his teeth with a silver quill, "Friends," said he, "it was not convenient for me to come into the dining room just yet, but for fear my absence should cause you any inconvenience, I gave over my own pleasure: permit me, however, to finish my game." A slave followed with a terebinth table and crystal dice, and I noted one piece of luxury that was superlative; for instead of black and white pieces, he used gold and silver coins. He kept up a continual flow of various coarse expressions. We were still dallying with the relishes when a tray was brought in, on which was a basket containing a wooden hen with her wings rounded and spread out as if she were brooding. Two slaves instantly approached, and to the accompaniment of music commenced to feel around in the straw. They pulled out some peahens' eggs, which they distributed among the diners. Turning his head, Trimalchio saw what was going on. "Friends," he remarked, "I ordered peahens' eggs set under the hen, but I'm afraid they're addled, by Hercules, I am. Let's try them anyhow and see if they're still fit to suck." We picked up our spoons, each of which weighed not less than half a pound, and punctured the shells, which were made of flour and dough, and as a matter of fact, I very nearly threw mine away for it seemed to me that a chick had formed already, but upon hearing an old experienced guest vow, "There must be something good here," I broke open the shell with my hand and discovered a fine fat figpecker, imbedded in a yolk seasoned with pepper.

Having finished his game, Trimalchio was served with a helping of everything and was announcing in a loud voice his willingness to join anyone in a second cup of honied wine, when, to a flourish of music, the relishes were suddenly whisked away by a singing chorus, but a small dish happened to fall to the floor, in the scurry, and a slave picked it up. Seeing this,

Trimalchio ordered that the boy be punished by a box on the ear, and made him throw it down again; a janitor followed with his broom and swept the silver dish away among the litter. Next followed two long-haired Ethiopians, carrying small leather bottles, such as are commonly seen in the hands of those who sprinkle sand in the arena, and poured wine upon our hands, for no one offered us water. When complimented upon these elegant extras, the host cried out, "Mars loves a fair fight; and so I ordered each one a separate table: that way these stinking slaves won't make us so hot with their crowding." Some glass bottles carefully sealed with gypsum were brought in at that instant; a label bearing this inscription was fastened to the neck of each one:

OPIMIAN FALERNIAN ONE HUNDRED YEARS OLD

While we were studying the labels, Trimalchio clapped his hands and cried, "Ah me! To think that wine lives longer than poor little man. Let's fill 'em up! There's life in wine and this is the real Opimian, you can take my word for that. I offered no such vintage yesterday, though my guests were far more respectable." We were tippling away and extolling all these elegant devices, when a slave brought in a silver skeleton, so contrived that the joints and movable vertebrae could be turned in any direction. He threw it down upon the table a time or two, and its mobile articulation caused it to assume grotesque attitudes, whereupon Trimalchio chimed in:

> "Poor man is nothing in the scheme of things
> And Orcus grips us and to Hades flings
> Our bones! This skeleton before us here
> Is as important as we ever were!
> Let's live then while we may and life is dead."

The applause was followed by a course which, by its oddity, drew every eye, but it did not come up to our expectations. There was a circular tray around which were displayed the signs of the zodiac, and upon each sign the caterer had placed the food best in keeping with it. Rams' vetches on Aries, a piece of beef on Taurus, kidneys and lambs' fry on Gemini, a crown on Cancer, the womb of an unfarrowed sow on Virgo, an African fig on Leo, on Libra a balance, one pan of which held a tart and the other a cake, a small sea fish on Scorpio, a bull's eye on Sagittarius, a sea lobster on Capricornus, a goose on Aquarius, and two mullets on Pisces. In the middle lay a piece of cut sod upon which rested a honeycomb with the grass arranged around it. An Egyptian slave passed bread around from a silver oven and, in a most discordant voice, twisted out a song in the manner of the mime in a musical farce. Seeing that we were rather depressed at the prospect of busying ourselves with such vile fare, Trimalchio urged us to fall to: "Let us fall to, gentlemen, I beg of you; this is only the sauce!"

While he was speaking, four dancers ran in to the time of the music, and removed the upper part of the tray. Beneath, on what seemed to be another tray, we caught sight of stuffed capons and sows' bellies, and in the middle, a hare equipped with wings to resemble Pegasus. At the corners of the tray we also noted four figures of Marsyas, and from their bladders spouted a highly spiced sauce upon fish which were swimming about as if in a tiderace. All of us echoed the applause which was started by the servants, and fell to upon these exquisite delicacies, with a laugh.

"Carver," cried Trimalchio, no less delighted with the artifice practiced upon us, and the carver appeared immediately. Timing his strokes to the beat of the music, he cut up the meat in such a fashion as to lead you to think that a gladiator was fighting from a chariot to the accompaniment of a water organ. Every now and then Trimalchio would repeat "Carver, carver," in a low voice, until I finally came to the conclusion that some joke was meant in repeating a word so frequently, so I did not scruple to question him who reclined above me. As he had often experienced byplay of this sort he explained, "You see that fellow who is carving the meat, don't you? Well, his name is Carver. Whenever Trimalchio says Carver, carve her, by the same word he both calls and commands!"

I could eat no more, so I turned to my whilom informant to learn as much as I could and sought to draw him out with farfetched gossip. I inquired who that woman could be who was scurrying about hither and yon in such a fashion. "She's called Fortunata," he replied. "She's the wife of Trimalchio, and she measures her money by the peck. And only a little while ago, what was she! May your genius pardon me, but you would not have been willing to take a crust of bread from her hand. Now, without rhyme or reason, she's in the seventh heaven and is Trimalchio's factotum, so much so that he would believe her if she told him it was dark when it was broad daylight! As for him, he don't know how rich he is, but this harlot keeps an eye on everything, and where you least expect to find her, you're sure to run into her. She's temperate, sober, full of good advice, and has many good qualities, but she has a scolding tongue, a very magpie on a sofa; those she likes, she likes, but those she dislikes, she hates! Trimalchio himself has estates as broad as the flight of a kite is long, and piles of money. There's more silver plate lying in his steward's office than other men have in their whole fortunes! And as for slaves, damn me if I believe a tenth of them know the master by sight. The truth is that these stand-a-gapes are so much in awe of him that any one of them would step into a fresh dunghill without ever knowing it, at a mere nod from him!"

We knew not what to look for next, until a hideous uproar commenced, just outside the dining-room door, and some Spartan hounds commenced to run around the table all of a sudden. A tray followed them, upon which was served a wild boar of immense size, wearing a liberty cap upon its head, and from its tusks hung two little baskets of woven palm fiber, one of which contained Syrian dates, the other, Theban. Around it hung little suckling pigs made from pastry, signifying that this was a brood sow with her pigs at suck. It turned out that these were souvenirs intended to be taken home. When it came to carving the boar, our old friend Carver, who had carved the capons, did not appear, but in his place a great bearded giant with bands around his legs and wearing a short hunting cape in which a design was woven. Drawing his hunting knife, he plunged it fiercely into the boar's side, and some thrushes flew out of the gash; fowlers, ready with their rods, caught them in a moment as they fluttered around the room, and Trimalchio ordered one to each guest, remarking, "Notice what fine acorns this forest-bred boar fed on," and as he spoke, some slaves removed the little baskets from the tusks and divided the Syrian and Theban dates equally among the diners.

Getting a moment to myself, in the meantime, I began to speculate as to why the boar had come with a liberty cap upon his head. After exhausting my invention with a thousand foolish guesses, I made bold to put the riddle which teased me to my old informant. "Why, sure," he replied, "even your slave could explain that; there's no riddle, everything's as plain as day! This boar made his first bow as the last course of yesterday's dinner and was dismissed by the guests, so today he comes back as a freedman!" I damned my stupidity and refrained from asking any more questions for fear I might leave the impression that I had never dined among decent people before. While we were speaking, a handsome boy, crowned with vine leaves and ivy, passed grapes around in a little basket, and impersonated Bacchus happy, Bacchus drunk, and Bacchus dreaming, reciting, in the meantime, his master's verses in a shrill voice. Trimalchio turned to him and said, "Dionisus, be thou Liber," whereupon the boy immediately snatched the cap from the boar's head and put it upon his own. At that Trimalchio added, "You can't deny that my father's middle name was Liber!" We applauded Trimalchio's conceit heartily, and kissed the boy as he went around . . .

"If the wine don't please you," he said, "I'll change it. You ought to do justice to it by drinking it. I don't have to buy it, thanks to the gods. Everything here that makes your mouths water was produced on one of my country places which I've never yet seen, but they tell me it's down Terracina and Tarentum way. I've got a notion to add Sicily to my other little holdings, so in case I want to go to Africa I'll be able to sail along my own coasts. But tell me the subject of your speech today, Agamemnon, for, though I don't plead cases myself, I studied literature for home use, and for fear you should think I don't care about learning, let me inform you that I have three libraries, one Greek and the others Latin. Give me the outline of your speech if you like me." "A poor man and a rich man were enemies," Agamemnon began, when "What's a poor man?" Trimalchio broke in. "Well put," Agamemnon conceded, and went into details upon some problem or other; what it was I do not know. Trimalchio instantly rendered the following verdict, "If that's the case, there's nothing to dispute about; if it's not the case, it don't amount to anything anyhow."

These flashes of wit, and others equally scintillating, we loudly applauded, and he went on. "Tell me, my dearest Agamemnon, do you remember the twelve labors of Hercules or the story of Ulysses, how the Cyclops threw his thumb out of joint with a pigheaded crowbar? When I was a boy, I used to read those stories in Homer. And then, there's the Sibyl: with my own eyes I saw her, at Cumae, hanging up in a jar; and whenever the boys would say to her 'Sibyl, Sibyl, what would you like?' she would answer 'I would like to die.'"

Before he had run out of wind, a tray upon which was an enormous hog was placed upon the table, almost filling it up. We began to wonder at the dispatch with which it had been prepared and swore that no cock could have been served up in so short a time; moreover, this hog seemed to us far bigger than the boar had been. Trimalchio scrutinized it closely and "What the hell," he suddenly bawled out, "this hog hain't been gutted, has it? No, it hain't, by Hercules, it hain't! Call that cook! Call that cook in here immediately!" When the crestfallen cook stood at the table and owned up that he had forgotten to bowel him, "So you forgot, did you?" Trimalchio shouted, "You'd think he'd only left out a bit of pepper and cummin, wouldn't you? Off with his clothes!" The cook was stripped without delay, and stood with hanging head between two torturers.

We all began to make excuses for him at this, saying, "Little things like that are bound to happen once in a while. Let us prevail upon you to let him off; if he ever does such a thing again, not a one of us will have a word to say in his behalf." But for my part, I was mercilessly angry and could not help leaning over towards Agamemnon and whispering in his ear, "It is easily seen that this fellow is criminally careless, is it not? How could anyone forget to draw a hog? If he had served me a fish in that fashion I wouldn't overlook it, by Hercules, I wouldn't." But that was not Trimalchio's way: his face relaxed into good humor and he said, "Since your memory's so short, you can gut him right here before our eyes!" The cook put on his tunic, snatched up a carving knife with a trembling hand, and slashed the hog's belly in several places. Sausages and meat puddings, widening the apertures by their own weight, immediately tumbled out.

The whole household burst into unanimous applause at this. "Hurrah for Gaius," they shouted. As for the cook, he was given a drink and a silver crown and a cup on a salver of Corinthian bronze. Seeing that Agamemnon was eying the platter closely, Trimalchio remarked, "I'm the only one that can show the real Corinthian!" I thought that, in his usual purse-proud manner, he was going to boast that his bronzes were all imported from Corinth, but he did even better by saying, "Wouldn't you like to know how it is that I'm the only one that can show the real Corinthian? Well, it's because the bronzeworker I patronize is named Corinthus, and what's Corinthian unless it's what a Corinthus makes? And so you won't think I'm a blockhead, I'm going to show you that I'm well acquainted with how Corinthian first came into the world. When Troy was taken, Hannibal, who was a very foxy fellow and a great rascal into the bargain, piled all the gold and silver and bronze statues in one pile and set 'em afire, melting these different metals into one; then the metalworkers took their pick and made bowls and dessert dishes and statuettes as well. That's how Corinthian was born; neither one nor the other, but an amalgam of all. But I prefer glass, if you don't mind my saying so; it don't stink, and if it didn't break, I'd rather have it than gold, but it's cheap and common now.

"But there was an artisan, once upon a time, who made a glass vial that couldn't be broken. On that account he was admitted to Caesar with his gift; then he dashed it upon the floor, when Caesar handed it back to him. The Emperor was greatly startled, but the artisan picked the vial up off the pavement, and it was dented, just like a brass bowl would have been! He took a little hammer out of his tunic and beat out the dent without any trouble. When he had done that, he thought he would soon be in Jupiter's heaven, and more especially when Caesar said to him, 'Is there anyone else who knows how to make this malleable glass? Think now!' And when he denied that anyone else knew the secret, Caesar ordered his head chopped off, because if this should get out, we would think no more of gold than we would of dirt." . . .

"Let's get to better business and start the fun all over again and watch the Homerists," said Trimalchio. A troupe filed in immediately, and clashed spears against shields. Trimalchio sat himself up on his cushion and intoned in Latin, from a book, while the actors, in accordance with their conceited custom, recited their parts in the Greek language. There came a pause presently, and "You don't any of you know the plot of the skit they're putting on, do you?" he asked. "Diomedes and Ganymede were two brothers, and Helen was their sister Iphigenia. They palmed off a doe on Diana in her place, so Homer tells how the Trojans and Parentines fought among themselves. Of course Agamemnon was victorious, and gave his daughter Iphigenia to Achilles for a wife: This caused Ajax to go mad, and he'll soon make the whole thing plain to you." The Homerists raised a shout as soon as Trimalchio had done speaking, and, as the whole familia stepped back, a boiled calf with a helmet on its head was brought in on an enormous platter. Ajax followed and rushed upon it with drawn sword, as if he were insane; he made passes with the flat, and again with the edge, and then, collecting the slices, he skewered them and, much to our astonishment, presented them to us on the point of his sword.

But we were not given long in which to admire the elegance of such service, for all of a sudden the ceiling commenced to creak and then the whole dining room shook. I leaped to my feet in consternation, for fear some ropewalker would fall down, and the rest of the company raised their faces, wondering as much as I what new prodigy was to be announced from on high. Then lo and behold! the ceiling panels parted and an enormous hoop, which appeared to have been knocked off a huge cask, was lowered from the dome above; its perimeter was hung with golden chaplets and jars of alabaster filled with perfume. We were asked to accept these articles as souvenirs.

When my glance returned to the table, I noticed that a dish containing cakes had been placed upon it, and in the middle an image of Priapus, made by the baker, and he held apples of all varieties and bunches of grapes against his breast, in the conventional manner. We applied ourselves wholeheartedly to this dessert and our joviality was suddenly revived by a fresh diversion, for, at the slightest pressure, all the cakes and fruits would squirt a saffron sauce upon us, and even spurted unpleasantly into our faces. Being convinced that these perfumed dainties had some religious significance, we arose in a body and shouted, "Hurrah for the Emperor, the father of his country!" However, as we perceived that even after this act of veneration the others continued helping themselves, we filled our napkins with the apples. I was especially keen on this, for I thought I could never put enough good things into Giton's lap.

After they had all wished each other sound minds and good health, Trimalchio turned to Niceros. "You used to be better company at dinner," he remarked, "and I don't know why you should be dumb today, with never a word to say. If you wish to make me happy, tell about that experience you had, I beg of you." Delighted at the affability of his friend, "I hope I lose all my luck if I'm not tickled to death at the humor I see you in," Niceros replied. "All right, let's go the limit for a good time, though I'm afraid these scholars'll laugh at me. But I'll tell my tale and they can go as far as they like. What t' hell do I care who laughs? It's better to be laughed at than laughed down."

These words spake the hero, and began the following tale: "We lived in a narrow street in the house Gavilla now owns, when I was a slave. There, by the will of the gods, I fell in love with the wife of Terentius, the innkeeper, you knew—Melissa of Tarentum, that pretty round-cheeked little wench. It was no carnal passion, so hear me, Hercules, it wasn't. I was not in love with her physical charms: No, it was because she was such a good sport. I never asked her for a thing and had her deny me, if she had an *as*, I had half: I trusted her with everything I had and never was done out of anything. Her husband up and died on the place, one day, so I tried every way I could to get to her, for you know friends ought to show up when anyone's in a pinch.

"It so happened that our master had gone to Capua to attend to some odds and ends of business and I seized the opportunity, and persuaded a guest of the house to accompany me as far as the fifth milestone. He was a soldier, and as brave as the very devil. We set out about cockcrow, the moon was shining as bright as midday, and came to where the tombstones are. My man stepped aside among them, but I sat down, singing, and commenced to count them up. When I looked around for my companion, he had stripped himself and piled his clothes by the side of the road. My heart was in my mouth, and I sat there while he watered a ring around them and was suddenly turned into a wolf! Now don't think I'm joking. I wouldn't lie for any amount of money, but as I was saying, he commenced to howl after he was turned into a wolf, and ran away into the forest. I didn't know where I was for a minute or two; then I went to his clothes, to pick them up, and damned if they hadn't turned to stone! Was ever anyone nearer dead from fright than me? Then I whipped out my sword and cut every shadow along the road to bits, till I came to the house of my mistress. I looked like a ghost when I went in, and I nearly slipped my wind. The sweat was pouring down my crotch, my eyes were staring, and I could hardly be brought around. My Melissa wondered why I was out so late. 'Oh, if you'd only come sooner,' she said, 'you could have helped us: A wolf broke into the folds and attacked the sheep, bleeding them like a butcher. But he didn't get the laugh on me, even if he did get away, for one of the slaves ran his neck through with a spear!' I couldn't keep my eyes shut any longer when I heard that, and as soon as it grew light I rushed back to our Gaius' house like an innkeeper beaten out of his bill, and when I came to the place where the clothes had been turned into stone there was nothing but a pool of blood! And moreover, when I got home, my soldier was lying in bed like an ox, and a doctor was dressing his neck! I knew then that he was a werewolf, and after that I couldn't have eaten a crumb of bread with him—no, not if you had killed me. Others can think what they please about this, but as for me, I hope your geniuses will all get after me if I lie."

We were all dumb with astonishment, when "I take your story for granted," said Trimalchio, "and if you'll believe me, my hair stood on end, and all the more because I know that Niceros never talks nonsense. He's always level-headed, not a bit gossipy. And now I'll tell you a hair-raiser, myself, though I'm like a jackass on a slippery pavement compared to him. When I was a long-haired boy, for I lived a Chian life from my youth up, my master's minion died. He was a jewel, so hear me, Hercules, he was—perfect in every facet: While his sorrow-stricken mother was bewailing his loss and the rest of us were lamenting with her, the witches suddenly commenced to screech so loud that you would have thought a hare was being run down by the hounds! At that time, we had a Cappadocian slave, tall, very bold, and he had muscle too—he could hold a mad bull in the air! He wrapped a mantle around his left arm, boldly rushed out of doors with drawn sword, and ran a woman through the middle about here, no harm to what I touch. We heard a scream, but as a matter of fact, for I won't lie to you, we didn't catch sight of the witches themselves. Our simpleton came back presently and threw himself upon the bed: His whole body was black and blue, as if he had been flogged with whips, and of course the reason of that was she had touched him with her evil hand! We shut the door and returned to our business, but when the mother put her arms around the body of her son, it turned out that it was only a straw bolster, no heart, no guts, nothing! Of course the witches had swooped down upon the lad and put the straw changeling in his place! Believe me or not, suit yourselves, but I say that there are women that know too much, and night hags, too, and they turn everything upside down! And as for the long-haired booby, he never got back his own natural color and he died, raving mad, a few days later."

Though we wondered greatly, we believed none the less implicitly and, kissing the table, we besought the night hags to attend to their own affairs while we were returning home from dinner. As far as I was concerned, the lamps already seemed to burn double and the whole dining room was going round, when "See here, Plocamus," Trimalchio spoke up, "haven't you anything to tell us? You haven't entertained us at all, have you? And you used to be fine company, always ready to oblige with a recitation or a song. The gods bless us, how the green figs have fallen!"

"True for you," the fellow answered. "Since I've got the gout my sporting days are over; but in the good old times when I was a young spark, I nearly sang myself into a consumption. How I used to dance! And take my part in a farce, or hold up my end in the barber shops! Who could hold a candle to me except, of course, the one and only Apelles?" He then put his hand to his mouth and hissed out some foul gibberish or other, and said afterwards that it was Greek.

Trimalchio himself then favored us with an impersonation of a man blowing a trumpet, and when he had finished, he looked around for his minion, whom he called Croesus, a blear-eyed slave whose teeth were very disagreeably discolored. He was playing with a little black bitch, disgustingly fat, wrapping her up in a leek-green scarf and teasing her with a half loaf of bread which he had put on the couch; and when from sheer nausea she refused it, he crammed it down her throat.

This sight put Trimalchio in mind of his own dog and he ordered Scylax, "the guardian of his house and home," to be brought in. An enormous dog was immediately led in upon a chain and, obeying a kick from the porter, it lay down beside the table. Thereupon Trimalchio remarked, as he threw it a piece of white bread, "No one in all my house loves me better than Scylax." Enraged at Trimalchio's praising Scylax so warmly, the slave put the bitch down upon the floor and sicked her on to fight. Scylax, as might have been expected from such a dog, made the whole room ring with his hideous barking and nearly shook the life out of the little bitch which the slave called Pearl. Nor did the uproar end in a dog fight; a candelabrum was upset upon the table, breaking the glasses and spattering some of the guests with hot oil.

As Trimalchio did not wish to seem concerned at the loss, he kissed the boy and ordered him to climb upon his own back. The slave did not hesitate but, mounting his rocking horse, he beat Trimalchio's shoulders with his open palms, yelling with laughter, "Buck! Buck! How many fingers do I hold up!" When Trimalchio had, in a measure, regained his composure, which took but a little while, he ordered that a huge vessel be filled with mixed wine, and that drinks be served to all the slaves sitting around our feet, adding as an afterthought, "If anyone refuses to drink, pour it on his head: business is business, but now's the time for fun."

. . . .

After a short interval, Trimalchio gave orders for the dessert to be served, whereupon the slaves took away all the tables and brought in others, and sprinkled the floor with sawdust mixed with saffron and vermilion, and also with powdered mica, a thing I had never seen done before. When all this was done Trimalchio remarked, "I could rest content with this course, for you have your second tables; but, if you've something especially nice, why bring it on. Meanwhile an Alexandrian slave boy who had been serving hot water, commenced to imitate a nightingale, and when Trimalchio presently called out, "Change your tune," we had another surprise, for a slave, sitting at Habinnas' feet, egged on, I have no doubt, by his own master, bawled suddenly in a singsong voice. When he had to quit, finally, from sheer want of breath, "Did he ever have any training?" Habinnas exclaimed. "No, not he! I educated him by sending him among the grafters at the fair, so when it comes to taking off a barker or a mule driver, there's not his equal; and the rogue's clever, too. He's a shoemaker, or a cook, or a baker—a regular Jack-of-all-trades, but he has two faults, and if he didn't have them, he'd be beyond all price: He snores and he's been circumcised. And that's the reason he never can keep his mouth shut and always has an eye open. I paid three hundred dinars for him."

Had not the dessert been brought in, we would never have gotten to the end of these stupidities. Thrushes made of pastry and stuffed with nuts and raisins, quinces with spines sticking out so that they looked like sea urchins. All this would have been endurable enough had it not been for the last dish that was served; so revolting was this that we would rather have died of starvation than to have even touched it. We thought that a fat goose, flanked with fish and all kinds of birds, had been served, until Trimalchio spoke up, "Everything you see here, my friends," said he, "was made from the same stuff." With my usual keen insight I jumped to the conclusion that I knew what that stuff was and, turning to Agamemnon, I said, "I shall be greatly surprised if all those things are not made out of excrement, or out of mud, at the very least: I saw a like artifice practiced at Rome, during the Saturnalia." . . .

Our hilarity was somewhat dampened soon after, for a boy who was by no means bad looking came in among the fresh slaves. Trimalchio seized him and embraced him lingeringly, whereupon Fortunata, asserting her rights in the house, began to rail at Trimalchio, styling him an abomination who set no limits to his lechery, finally ending by calling him a dog. Trimalchio flew into a rage at her abuse and threw a wine cup at her head, whereupon she screeched as if she had had an eye knocked out, and covered her face with her trembling hands. Scintilla was frightened, too, and shielded the shuddering woman with her garment. An officious slave presently held a cold-water pitcher to her cheek and Fortunata bent over it, sobbing and moaning. But as for Trimalchio, "What the hell's next?" he gritted out, "this Syrian dancing whore don't remember anything! I took her off the auction block and made her a woman among her equals, didn't I? And here she puffs herself up like a frog and pukes in her own nest; she's a blockhead, all right, not a woman.

But that's the way it is; if you're born in an attic you can't sleep in a palace! I'll see that this booted Cassandra's tamed, so help me my genius, I will! And I could have married ten million, even if I did only have two cents: you know I'm not lying! 'Let me give you a tip,' said Agatho, the perfumer to the lady next door, when he pulled me aside. 'Don't let your line die out!' And here I've stuck the ax into my own leg because I was a damned fool and didn't want to seem fickle. I'll see to it that you're more careful how you claw me up, sure as you're born, I will! That you may realize how seriously I take what you've done to me—Habinnas, I don't want you to put her statue on my tomb for fear I'll be nagged even after I'm dead! And furthermore, that she may know I can repay a bad turn, I won't have her kissing me when I'm laid out!"

It was not long before Stychus brought a white shroud and a purple-bordered toga into the dining room, and Trimalchio requested us to feel them and see if they were pure wool. Then, with a smile, "Take care, Stychus, that the mice don't get at these things and gnaw them, or the moths either. I'll burn you alive if they do. I want to be carried out in all my glory so all the people will wish me well." Then, opening a jar of lard, he had us all anointed. "I hope I'll enjoy this as well when I'm dead," he remarked, "as I do while I'm alive." He then ordered wine to be poured into the punch bowl. "Pretend," said he, "that you're invited to my funeral feast."

The thing had grown positively nauseating, when Trimalchio, beastly drunk by now, bethought himself of a new and singular diversion and ordered some hornblowers brought into the dining room. Then, propped up by many cushions, he stretched himself out upon the couch. "Let on that I'm dead," said he, "and say something nice about me." The hornblowers sounded off a loud funeral march together, and one in particular, a slave belonging to an undertaker, made such a fanfare that he roused the whole neighborhood; and the watch, which was patrolling the vicinity, thinking Trimalchio's house was afire, suddenly smashed in the door and rushed in with their water and axes, raising a riot all their own. We availed ourselves of this happy circumstance and, leaving Agamemnon in the lurch, we took to our heels, as though we were running away from a real conflagration.

THE WIDOW OF EPHESUS

Once, long ago, there dwelt in Ephesus a married lady who was so chaste that women came from neighboring cities merely to look at her. When she was widowed, her virtue and constancy were proven to the very utmost. She followed tradition by walking behind the funeral procession with her hair unbound, weeping and beating her naked breast. But she went much further; she followed the corpse into the tomb and, when the body had been placed there, she remained inside of the vault. In spite of the pleas of her parents and the admonitions of her dearest friends, she refused to stir, and it was evident that she had determined to starve herself to death. Even the elders could not persuade her to leave the tomb, and she was regarded by all as a perfect symbol of wifely devotion.

For five days she went without nourishment. Her maid, who brought oil for the lamp which the widow kept burning, argued with her mistress in vain. Men and women agreed that never before had there been such an example of unwavering love.

On the sixth night, a soldier who stood guard over the crosses so that none could take the bodies down for honorable burial, noticed the little light. His curiosity aroused, he left his post and, drawn by the sound of low sobbing, entered the tomb. His first emotion was one of fear. Seeing the beautiful woman, he thought he was beholding some apparition, some spirit from another world. As his eye grew accustomed to the surroundings, he saw the corpse and, struck by the young widow's lament, realized what had occurred.

Sensing that she was weak from hunger as well as sorrow, he brought his rations into the tomb and begged her to share them with him. She shook her head. He argued with her, pleaded that she should not persist in a futile grief, declaring that we are all creatures of fate and that no one should will his own death before his time.

The lady refused to listen. She continued to beat her bosom, tear her hair, and manifest a grief that was, if anything, greater than before. Nevertheless, the soldier did not cease but tried to cajole her into an acceptance of life as well as death. Her maid, who was unable to resist the proffered food, abetted him.

"Why should you want to destroy yourself?" asked the maid. "Whom will you benefit by your death? Will the dead man feel happier when you have died of starvation? Would you—if you could—recall the dead from what destiny has intended? If he could speak, the cold clay lying there would tell you that to live is not only your right but your very duty!"

Thus implored, the lady yielded. Although she gave in unwillingly, after a six-day fast she ate as avidly as did her maid. Warmed with the food and a little wine—and the resolution to live—she raised her eyes from prolonged contemplation. Her expression was still chaste, but she could not help seeing that the soldier was young and not lacking in good looks. When he offered further consolation, she did not refuse him too coldly. Having satisfied one hunger, he aroused, and then hoped to allay, another. It was not long before he succeeded.

The soldier and the widow remained together that night. They held each other close the night following and the night after that. The door of the tomb was closed, and anyone coming upon it would suppose that the most exemplary of wives had expired on the breast of her husband. The soldier, supplying his mistress not only with necessities but with luxuries, neglected his duties as guard.

Observing that the crosses were no longer under military surveillance, the parents of one of the crucified criminals removed their son's body and buried it that night. Next morning the soldier saw the empty cross. Terrified, he was fearful both of punishment for being derelict in duty and the disgrace which a soldier dreads even more than death. "Rather than face the humiliation of a court-martial," he cried to the widow, "I will kill myself with my own sword. Let me lie here! Let this tomb be the burial place of your lover as well as your husband!"

Merciful no less than virtuous, the lady looked at him with horrified eyes. "The gods forbid any such thing," she exclaimed. "The gods did not decree that I should tend the corpses of the two men who have meant most to me. Rather than see the living slain, I would sacrifice the dead."

Now it was the soldier who objected. But her remonstrances persuaded him, and together they lifted the dead man from the coffin and hung him on the empty cross.

Love and ingenuity had devised a strange but successful expedient. Only a few people wondered how a dead man had managed to crucify himself.

MARTIAL (A.D. 40?–104)

Marcus Valerius Martialis or, as he is better known, Martial, was one of the most disillusioned writers that ever lived. Born in Spain about A.D. 40, still a youth at the age of twenty-four, he went to Rome. What he saw there affected him profoundly and adversely. However, he quickly recovered from the shock and attached himself to the family of Seneca and other benefactors, on whom he seems to have lived. In his late fifties he returned to Spain, where he died a few years later.

Although Martial continually complained of being poor and of the difficulty of writing in poverty, he left a body of more than twelve hundred poems. Most of these are brilliantly pointed epigrams. With complete frankness they reveal the gaudy, gross, and wicked aspects of Rome. The poet, however, was not much exercised over corruption or brutality. He saw a culture that was both coarse and overrefined, ribald, tolerant, and proud of its worldliness. Martial accepted it all with nothing more than barbed comments and a shrug.

All the translations except the last two are by the editor.

THE WIFE'S COMPANION

Who is that pretty fellow—
The one that's always hanging around your wife?
The one that's always whispering sweet nothings in her ear,
Who leans against her chair

And casually touches her hair
With jeweled fingers?
"He works for my wife," you answer.
He does, does he? Listen, my friend:
That handsome boy does not do your wife's work.
He does yours.

EX-SLAVE

Dancing with such salacious gestures
In such transparent vesture
This girl could excite passion
In an ashen corpse or a paralyzed statue.
It's a brave story.
Her master tired of her, sold her as a slave,
And then bought her back as his mistress.

THE INCENTIVE

As long as you allowed her complete liberty
And she was free to live her life,
No one went near your wife.
Now that you guard her well it's another matter.
Everyone wants to get at her.

INSUFFICIENT VENGEANCE

You did right, injured husband, to ruin the face
Of the man who shamed you. You cut off
His ears and nose. What a disgrace!
In your case you did right. . . .
But did you cut off enough?

TO CLOE

I could resign that eye of blue
    Howe'er its splendor used to thrill me;
And even that cheek of roseate hue,
    To lose it, Cloe, scarce would kill me.

That snowy neck I ne'er should miss,
    However much I've raved about it;
And sweetly as that lip can kiss,
    I *think* I could exist without it.

In short, so well I've learned to fast,
    That, sooth my love, I know not whether
I might not bring myself at last,
    To do without you altogether.

Translated by THOMAS MOORE

TO HIS BOOK

To read my book the virgin shy
May blush while Brutus standeth by;
But when he's gone read through what's writ,
And never stain a cheek for it.

Translated by ROBERT HERRICK

JUVENAL (A.D. 55?–135?)

The writings of Horace and Juvenal furnish the greatest possible contrast. Horace was an intellectual whose tastes were delicate and whose nature was gentle; Juvenal was an emotional being, temperamentally violent, cynical in expression, and savage in his attacks on the social system of his day. Differing also from Horace, who was fairly explicit about his life, practically all we know of Juvenal is gleaned between the lines of his work. We gather that he was born about the middle of the first century A.D. and lived for about eighty years. The fact that he dedicated three epigrams to Martial indicates that he was a friend of that irascible poet. He, too, was bitter and truculent. "Indignation makes verse," he tells us, while he furiously inveighs against the criminalities of Rome, condemns the common people for their petty vices, and arraigns all womankind.

Although to the modern reader Juvenal is full of obscure allusions and remote references, his satires are so savage that they have come thundering down the years. Launched upon his diatribes, Juvenal does not scant an event or spare a person; the tone may be grim but the touch is brilliant if bizarre. According to Suetonius, Juvenal's scurrility offended those in power and, although he was nearly eighty, he was exiled to a remote part of Egypt. It was a heavy punishment for a light and jocular offense. Juvenal did not survive the disgrace or the climate. Within a very short time, says Suetonius "he died of vexation and disgust."

The Sixth Satire is one of the most vicious and, at the same time, one of the most brilliant attacks on women ever delivered, charging them with everything from gossip to murder. The translation by John Dryden adds a seventeenth-century sting to Juvenal's Latin scorn.

FROM: THE SIXTH SATIRE

In Saturn's reign, at Nature's early birth,
There was that thing call'd chastity on earth;
When in a narrow cave, their common shade,
The sheep, the shepherds, and their gods were laid:
When reeds, and leaves, and hides of beasts were spread
By mountain huswifes for their homely bed,
And mossy pillows rais'd, for the rude husband's head.
Unlike the niceness of our modern dames
(Affected nymphs with new affected names),
The Cynthias and the Lesbias of our years,
Who for a sparrow's death dissolve in tears;
Those first unpolish'd matrons, big and bold,
Gave suck to infants of gigantic mold;
Rough as their savage lords who rang'd the wood,
And fat with acorns belch'd their windy food.
For when the world was buxom, fresh, and young,
Her sons were undebauch'd and therefore strong;
And whether born in kindly beds of earth,
Or struggling from the teeming oaks to birth,
Or from what other atoms they begun,
No sires they had, or, if a sire, the sun.
Some thin remains of chastity appear'd,
Ev'n under Jove, but Jove without a beard;
Before the servile Greeks had learnt to swear
By heads of kings; while yet the bounteous year
Her common fruits in open plains expos'd,
Ere thieves were fear'd, or gardens were enclos'd.
At length uneasy Justice upwards flew,
And both the sisters to the stars withdrew;
From that old era whoring did begin,
So venerably ancient is the sin.
Adult'rers next invade the nuptial state,
And marriage beds creak'd with a foreign weight;
All other ills did iron times adorn,
But whores and silver in one age were born.

· · · · · ·

. . . You shall hear
What fruits the sacred brows of monarchs bear:
The good old sluggard but began to snore,
When from his side up rose th' imperial whore:
She who preferr'd the pleasures of the night
To pomps, that are but impotent delight;

Strode from the palace, with an eager pace,
To cope with a more masculine embrace;
Muffled she march'd, like Juno in a cloud,
Of all her train but one poor wench allow'd;
One whom in secret service she could trust,
The rival and companion of her lust.
To the known brothel house she takes her way;
And for a nasty room gives double pay;
That room in which the rankest harlot lay.
Prepar'd for fight, expectingly she lies,
With heaving breasts, and with desiring eyes:
Still as one drops, another takes his place,
And baffled still succeeds to like disgrace.
At length, when friendly darkness is expir'd,
And every strumpet from her cell retir'd,
She lags behind, and, ling'ring at the gate,
With a repining sigh submits to fate:
All filth without, and all a fire within,
Tir'd with the toil, unsated with the sin.
Old Caesar's bed the modest matron seeks;
The steam of lamps still hanging on her cheeks
In ropy smut: thus foul, and thus bedight,
She brings him back the product of the night.

   Now should I sing what poisons they provide,
With all their trumpery of charms beside,
And all their arts of death, it would be known
Lust is the smallest sin the sex can own;
Caesinia still, they say, is guiltless found
Of every vice, by her own lord renown'd:
And well she may, she brought ten thousand pound.
She brought him wherewithal to be call'd chaste;
His tongue is tied in golden fetters fast:
He sighs, adores, and courts her every hour;
Who would not do as much for such a dower?
She writes love letters to the youth in grace;
Nay, tips the wink before the cuckold's face;
And might do more; her portion makes it good;
Wealth has the privilege of widowhood.

   These truths with his example you disprove,
Who with his wife is monstrously in love:
But know him better; for I heard him swear,
'Tis not that she's his wife, but that she's fair.
Let her but have three wrinkles in her face,
Let her eyes lessen, and her skin unbrace,
Soon you will hear the saucy steward say:

"Pack up with all your trinkets, and away;
You grow offensive both at bed and board:
Your betters must be had to please my lord."
    Meantime she's absolute upon the throne;
And, knowing time is precious, loses none:
She must have flocks of sheep, with wool more fine
Than silk, and vineyards of the noblest wine;
Whole droves of pages for her train she craves,
And sweeps the prisons for attending slaves.
In short, whatever in her eyes can come,
Or others have abroad, she wants at home.
When winter shuts the seas, and fleecy snows
Make houses white, she to the merchant goes;
Rich crystals of the rock she takes up there,
Huge agate vases, and old China ware:
Then Berenice's ring her finger proves,
More precious made by her incestuous loves,
And infamously dear; a brother's bribe,
Ev'n God's anointed, and of Judah's tribe;
Where barefoot they approach the sacred shrine,
And think it only sin to feed on swine.

. . . . . .

    Thus the she-tyrant reigns, till, pleas'd with change,
Her wild affections to new empires range:
Another subject-husband she desires;
Divorc'd from him, she to the first retires,
While the last wedding feast is scarcely o'er,
And garlands hang yet green upon the door.
So still the reck'ning rises; and appears,
In total sum, eight husbands in five years.
The title for a tombstone might be fit,
But that it would too commonly be writ.
Her mother living, hope no quiet day;
She sharpens her, instructs her how to flay
Her husband bare, and then divides the prey.
She takes love letters, with a crafty smile,
And in her daughter's answer mends the style.
In vain the husband sets his watchful spies;
She cheats their cunning, or she bribes their eyes.
The doctor's call'd; the daughter, taught the trick,
Pretends to faint; and in full health is sick.
The panting stallion, at the closet door,
Hears the consult, and wishes it were o'er.
Canst thou, in reason, hope, a bawd so known

Should teach her other manners than her own?
Her int'rest is in all th' advice she gives:
'Tis on the daughter's rents the mother lives.
　No cause is tried at the litigious bar,
But women plaintiffs or defendants are;
They form the process, all the briefs they write;
The topics furnish, and the pleas indite;
And teach the toothless lawyer how to bite.
　They turn viragoes too; the wrestler's toil
They try, and smear their naked limbs with oil:
Against the post their wicker shields they crush,
Flourish the sword, and at the plastron push.
Of every exercise the mannish crew
Fulfills the parts, and oft excels us too.

．　　．　　．　　．　　．

　Behold the strutting Amazonian whore:
She stands in guard with her right foot before;
Her coats tuck'd up, and all her motions just;
She stamps, and then cries Hah! at every thrust:
But laugh to see her, tir'd with many a bout,
Call for the pot, and like a man piss out.
The ghosts of ancient Romans, should they rise,
Would grin to see their daughters play a prize.
　Besides, what endless brawls by wives are bred!
The curtain lecture makes a mournful bed.
Then, when she has thee sure within the sheets,
Her cry begins, and the whole day repeats.
Conscious of crimes herself, she teases first;
Thy servants are accus'd; thy whore is curst;
She acts the jealous, and at will she cries;
For women's tears are but the sweat of eyes.
Poor cuckold-fool, thou think'st that love sincere,
And suck'st between her lips the falling tear;
But search her cabinet, and thou shalt find
Each tiller there with love epistles lin'd.
Suppose her taken in a close embrace,
This you would think so manifest a case,
No rhetoric could defend, no impudence outface:
And yet even then she cries: "The marriage vow
A mental reservation must allow;
And there's a silent bargain still implied,
The parties should be pleas'd on either side;
And both may for their private needs provide.
Tho' men yourselves, and women us you call,

Yet *homo* is a common name for all."
There's nothing bolder than a woman caught;
Guilt gives 'em courage to maintain their fault.
    You ask from whence proceed these monstrous crimes.
Once poor, and therefore chaste, in former times,
Our matrons were: no luxury found room
In low-roof'd houses, and bare walls of loam;
Their hands with labor harden'd while 'twas light,
And frugal sleep supplied the quiet night;
While pinch'd with want, their hunger held 'em straight,
When Hannibal was hov'ring at the gate:
But wanton now, and lolling at our ease,
We suffer all th' invet'rate ills of peace.

                .   .   .   .   .

    The secrets of the goddess nam'd the Good,
Are even by boys and barbers understood:
Where the rank matrons, dancing to the pipe,
Gig with their bums, and are for action ripe;
With music rais'd, they spread abroad their hair,
And toss their heads like an enamor'd mare:
Laufella lays her garland by, and proves
The mimic lechery of manly loves.
Rank'd with the lady the cheap sinner lies;
For here not blood, but virtue, gives the prize.
Nothing is feign'd in this venereal strife;
'Tis downright lust, and acted to the life.
So full, so fierce, so vigorous, and so strong,
That looking on would make old Nestor young.
Impatient of delay, a general sound,
A universal groan of lust goes round;
For then, and only then, the sex sincere is found.
"Now is the time of action; now begin,"
They cry, "and let the lusty lovers in."
"The whoresons are asleep." "Then bring the slaves,
And watermen, a race of strong-back'd knaves."
    I hear your cautious counsel, you would say:
"Keep close your women under lock and key."
But, who shall keep those keepers? Women, nurs'd
In craft, begin with those, and bribe 'em first.
The sex is turn'd all whore; they love the game:
And mistresses and maids are both the same.

                .   .   . .   .   .

    Their endless itch of news comes next in play;

They vent their own, and hear what others say:
Know what in Thrace, or what in France is done;
Th' intrigues betwixt the stepdame and the son:
Tell who loves who, what favors some partake;
And who is jilted for another's sake:
What pregnant widow in what month was made;
How oft she did, and, doing, what she said. . . .

   The gaudy gossip, when she's set agog,
In jewels dress'd, and at each ear a bob,
Goes flaunting out, and, in her trim of pride,
Thinks all she says or does is justified.
When poor, she's scarce a tolerable evil;
But rich and fine, a wife's a very devil.

   She duly, once a month, renews her face;
Meantime, it lies in daub, and hid in grease:
Those are the husband's nights; she craves her due,
He takes fat kisses, and is stuck in glue.
But, to the lov'd adult'rer when she steers,
Fresh from the bath, in brightness she appears:
For him the rich Arabia sweats her gum,
And precious oils from distant Indies come,
How haggardly soe'er she looks at home.
Th' eclipse then vanishes; and all her face
Is open'd, and restor'd to ev'ry grace;
The crust remov'd, her cheeks, as smooth as silk,
Are polish'd with a wash of asses' milk;
And should she to the farthest North be sent,
A train of these attend her banishment.
But, hadst thou seen her plaster'd up before,
'Twas so unlike a face, it seem'd a sore.

   'Tis worth our while to know what all the day
They do, and how they pass their time away;
For, if o'ernight the husband has been slack,
Or counterfeited sleep, and turn'd his back,
Next day, be sure, the servants go to wrack.
The chambermaid and dresser are call'd whores,
The page is stripp'd, and beaten out of doors;
The whole house suffers for the master's crime,
And he himself is warn'd to wake another time.

   .   .   .   .   .

   The poorest of the sex have still an itch
To know their fortunes, equal to the rich.
The dairymaid inquires if she shall take
The trusty tailor, and the cook forsake.

Yet these, tho' poor, the pain of childbed bear;
And, without nurses, their own infants rear:
You seldom hear of the rich mantle, spread
For the babe, born in the great lady's bed.
Such is the pow'r of herbs; such arts they use
To make them barren, or their fruit to lose.
But thou, whatever slops she will have brought,
Be thankful, and supply the deadly draught;
Help her to make manslaughter; let her bleed,
And never want for savin at her need.
For, if she holds till her nine months be run,
Thou mayst be father to an Ethiop's son;
A boy, who ready gotten to thy hands,
By law is to inherit all thy lands;
One of that hue, that should he cross the way,
His omen would discolor all the day . . .

    For, weak of reason, impotent of will,
The sex is hurried headlong into ill;
And, like a cliff from its foundations torn
By raging earthquakes, into seas is borne.
But those are fiends, who crimes from thought begin;
And, cool in mischief, meditate the sin.

APULEIUS (circa A.D. 120–?)

Written in the second century A.D., The Metamorphoses of Lucius
Apuleius *became known as* The Golden Ass, *the story of a tragicomic transformation—"golden" because of its superb storytelling. It was not a new
story; the plot existed in at least two preceding versions. The basic idea and
many of the anecdotes were derived from* Lucius, *or* The Ass *by Lucian of
Samosata, who founded his book on a similarly titled work by Lucius of
Patrae. For more than a thousand years various incidents from the work
were retold by others, notably Boccaccio and Le Sage. But Apuleius did more
than enlarge and embroider the original tapestry of tales. He rewove the
materials into a new pattern, supplied a new style of artistry, and added an
exquisitely designed myth of his own, the story of Cupid and Psyche.*

The author, Lucius Apuleius, was born about A.D. 120 *in Madaura, a Roman colony near the border of what now is Tunis. A rich man's son, he was
educated at the University of Carthage but, a little later, left Africa to study
in Athens, where he was initiated into the mystical cult of Isis, and in Rome,
where he practiced law. After winning considerable fame as an attorney and
orator, he gave all his attention to philosophy, writing, and religion—he seems*

to have been a senator as well as a priest. Returning to Africa, he met and married a wealthy widow several years his senior; was sued after her death by her family who accused him of using sorcery to win her; and, acting as his own lawyer, delivered so well-reasoned and witty a speech that he was cleared of all charges.

Sorcery plays a prominent part in The Golden Ass. It is, in fact, the structural element which holds the parts together. Although Apuleius does not scruple to string together other men's stories popular in his day, much of his book is autobiographical. Into it he puts all the oddments picked up in his many studies, and, as one of his editors, F. J. Harvey Darton, wrote, "in it he becomes a man, full of recondite beliefs and strange customs, observant, a sympathizer with rogues, vagabonds and poor men, even with lewd women, a lover of beauty, but informed with a humor sometimes witty and often fierce, and a real authority on witchcraft and exotic religions."

The curiously religious strain—pagan but devout—has led many commentators to consider The Golden Ass a subtle allegory. It implies, they say, that nothing but harm will come to those who seek low company, associate with wrongdoers, and dabble in the supernatural. But the book has been enjoyed for almost nineteen hundred years, not because of its moral implications, but because of what its most noted translator called "pleasant and delectable jests written in a frank and flourishing style," a style that is also poetic, brilliant, and unabashedly ribald.

FROM: THE GOLDEN ASS

In the introduction to his sixteenth-century prose version of The Golden Ass, *William Adlington, its first and most colorful English translator, succinctly summarized the plot as follows: "How Lucius Apuleius, the author himself, traveled into Thessaly (being a region in Greece where all the women for the most part be such wonderful witches that they can transform men into the figure of beasts), where, after he had continued a few days, by the mighty force of a violent confection, he was changed into a miserable ass, and nothing might reduce him to his wonted shape but the eating of a rose which, after endurance of infinite sorrow, at length he obtained by prayer." Shortly after the book opens, the adventurous young Lucius comes to the house of Milo, where he meets not only Milo's wife, the sorceress Byrrhena, but the lovely slave girl Fotis.*

HOW APULEIUS FELL IN LOVE WITH FOTIS

When I was within the house I found my dear and sweet love, Fotis, mincing meat and making pottage for her master and mistress. The cupboard was all set with wines, and I thought I smelled the savor of some dainty meats. She had about her middle a white and clean apron, and she was girded about her body under her breast with a swathe of red silk, and she stirred the pot and turned the meat with her fair and white hands in such sort that it was in my mind a comely sight to see.

These things when I saw I was half amazed, and stood musing with myself, and my courage came then upon me, which before was scant. And I spoke to Fotis plainly, and said, "O Fotis, how trimly you can stir the pot, and how finely you can make pottage. Oh, happy and twice happy is he to whom you give leave and license but to touch you."

Then she, being likewise wittily disposed, answered, "Depart, I say, wretch, from me, depart from my fire, for if the flame thereof do never so little blaze forth, it will burn thee extremely: and none can extinguish the heat thereof but I alone."

When she had said these words, she cast her eyes upon me and laughed, but I did not depart from thence until such time as I had viewed her in every point. But what should I speak of others? I do accustom abroad to mark and view the face and hair of every dame, and afterward delight myself therewith privately at home, and thereby judge the residue of their shape, because the face is the principal part of all the body, and is first open to our eyes, and whatsoever flourishing and gorgeous apparel doth work and set forth in the corporal parts of a woman, the same doth the natural and comely beauty set out in the face. Moreover, there are some who (to the intent to show their grace and feature) will cast off their partlets, collars, habiliments, fronts, cornets, and crepines, and delight more to show the fairness of their skin than to deck themselves up in gold and precious stones. But because it is a crime to me to say so, and to give no example thereof, know ye that if you spoil and cut off the hair of any woman or deprive her of the color of her face, though she were never so excellent in beauty, though she were thrown down from heaven, sprung of the seas, nourished of the floods, though she were Venus herself, though she were accompanied with the Graces, though she were waited upon of all the court of Cupid, though she were girded with her beautiful scarf of love, and though she smelled of perfumes and musks, yet if she appeared bald, she could in no wise please, no, not her own Vulcan.

Oh how well doth a fair color and a shining face agree with glittering hair! Behold, it encounters with the beams of the sun, and pleases the eye marvelously. Sometimes the beauty of the hair resembles the color of gold and honey, sometimes the blue plume and azure feathers about the necks of doves, especially when it is either anointed with the gum of Arabia or trimly tufted out with the teeth of a fine comb; if it be tied up in the nape of the neck, it seems to the lover who beholds it as a glass yielding forth a more pleasant and gracious comeliness than if it were sparsed abroad on the shoulders of the woman or hung down scattering behind. Finally, there is such a dignity in the hair, that whatsoever she be, though she be never so bravely attired with gold, silks, precious stones, and other rich and gorgeous ornaments, yet if her hair be not curiously set forth, she cannot seem fair.

But in my Fotis her garments unbraced and unlaced did increase her beauty. Her hair hung about her shoulders, and was dispersed abroad upon her partlet, and on every part of her neck, howbeit the greater part was trussed up in her nape with a lace. Then I, unable to withstand the broiling heat I was in, ran upon her and kissed the place where she had thus laid her hair; whereat she turned her face, and cast her rolling eyes upon me, saying, "O scholar, thou hast tasted now both honey and gall; take heed that thy pleasure do not turn into repentance."

"Tush" (quoth I), "my sweetheart, I am contented, for such another kiss, to be broiled here upon this fire." Wherewithal I embraced and kissed her more often, and she embraced and kissed me likewise. Her breath smelled like cinnamon, and the liquor of her tongue was like sweet nectar. Wherewith when my mind was greatly delighted, I said, "Behold, Fotis, I am yours, and shall presently die, unless you take pity upon me." Which when I had said, she eftsoons kissed me and bid me be of good courage, and, "I will" (quoth she) "satisfy your whole desire, and it shall be no longer delayed than until night. Wherefore go your ways and prepare yourself."

Thus when we had lovingly talked and reasoned together, we departed for that time . . .

When noon was come, Byrrhena sent me a fat pig, five hens, and a flagon of old wine. Then I called Fotis and said, "Behold how Bacchus the egger and stirrer of love offers himself of his own accord. Let us therefore drink up this wine, that we may prepare ourselves."

It fortuned on a day that Byrrhena desired me earnestly to sup with her, and she would in no wise take any excuse. Whereupon I went to Fotis to ask counsel of her, as of some divine, who (although she was unwilling that I should depart one foot from her company) yet at length she gave me license to be absent for a while, saying, "Beware that you tarry not long at supper there, for there is a rabblement of common rioters and disturbers of the public peace that rove about in the streets, and murder all such as they may take; neither can law nor justice redress them in any case. And they will the sooner set upon you, by reason of your comeliness and audacity, in that you are not afraid at any time to walk in the streets."

Then I answered and said, "Have no care of me, Fotis, for I esteem the pleasure which I have with thee above the dainty meats that I eat abroad, and therefore I will return again quickly. Nevertheless I mind not to come without company, for I have here my sword, whereby I hope to defend myself."

After dining I arose from the table and took leave of Byrrhena. When I came into the first street my torch went out, and I could scarce get home by reason it was so dark and I had to move slowly, for fear of stumbling.

When I was well-nigh come to the door I saw three men of great stature heaving and lifting at Milo's gates to get in. And when they saw me they were nothing afraid, but essayed with more force to break down the doors, whereby they gave me occasion (and not without cause) to think that they were strong thieves. Whereupon I drew out my sword, which I carried under my cloak, and ran in among them, and wounded them in such sort that they fell down dead before my face. Thus when I had slain them all, I knocked, sweating and breathing at the door, till Fotis let me in. And then, full weary with the slaughter of these thieves, like Hercules when he fought against King Gerion, I went to my chamber and laid me down to sleep.

When I was abed I began to call to mind all the sorrows and griefs that I was in the day before, until such time as my love Fotis came into the chamber, not as she was wont to do, for she seemed nothing pleasant either in countenance or talk, but with a sour face and frowning look. She began to speak in this sort: "Verily, I confess that I have been the occasion of all thy trouble this day."

Therewithal she pulled out a whip from under her apron, and delivered it to me, saying, "Revenge thyself of me, or rather slay me. And think you not that I willingly procured this anguish and sorrow to you, I call the gods to witness. I had rather suffer my own body to be punished than that you should receive or sustain any harm by my means. That which I did was by the commandment of another, and wrought (as I thought) for some other, but behold, the unlucky chance fortuned on you by my evil occasion."

I, very curious and desirous to know the matter, answered, "In faith" (quoth I), "this most pestilent and evil-favored whip (which thou hast brought to scourge thee withal) shall first be broken in a thousand pieces than that it should touch or hurt thy delicate and dainty skin. But I pray you tell me, how have you been the cause and means of my trouble and sorrow? For I dare swear by the love that I bear to you (and I will not be persuaded, though you yourself should endeavor the same) that ever you went about to trouble or harm me. Perhaps sometimes you imagined an evil thought in your mind, which afterward you revoked; but that is not to be deemed as a crime."

When I had spoken these words, I perceived by Fotis's eyes being wet with tears, and well-nigh closed up, that she had a desire to pleasure, and specially because she embraced and kissed me sweetly. And when she was somewhat restored to joy, she desired me that she might first shut the chamber door, lest by the intemperance of her tongue in uttering any unfitting words there might grow further inconvenience. Wherewithal she barred and propped the door and came to me again, and embracing me lovingly about the neck with both her arms, spoke with a soft voice, and said, "I do greatly fear to discover the privities of this house, and to utter the secret mysteries of my dame. But I have a confidence in you and in your wisdom, by reason that you are come of so noble a line and endued with so profound sapience, and are further instructed in so many holy and divine things, so that you will faithfully keep silence, and whatsoever I shall reveal or declare unto you, you would close within the bottom of your heart, and never discover the same: for I assure the love that I bear to you enforces me to utter it. Now shall you know all the estate of our house; now shall you know the hidden secrets of my mistress, whom the powers of hell do obey, and by whom the celestial planets are troubled, the gods made weak, and the elements subdued; neither is the violence of her art in more strength and force than when she espies some comely young man who pleases her fancy, as oftentimes it happens. For now she loves one Boeotian, a fair and beautiful person, on whom she employs all her sorcery and enchantment; and I heard her say with my own ears yesternight that (if the sun had not then gone down, and the night come to minister convenient time to work her magical enticements) she would have brought perpetual darkness over all the world herself. You shall know that when she saw yesternight this Boeotian sitting at the barber's, when she came from the baths, she secretly commanded me to gather some of the hair of his head, which lay dispersed upon the ground, and to bring it home; which when I thought to have done, the barber espied me, and by reason it was bruited throughout all the city that we were witches and enchantresses, he cried out, and said, 'Will you never leave off stealing of young men's hairs? In faith, I assure you unless you cease your wicked sorceries I will complain to the justices.'

"With that he came angrily toward me, and took away the hair which I had gathered out of my apron, which grieved me very much, for I knew my mistress's manners, that she would not be contented, but beat me cruelly. Wherefore I intended to run away, but the remembrance of you put always that thought out of my mind, and so I came homeward very sorrowfully; but because I would not seem to come in my mistress's sight with empty hands, I saw a man shearing blown goat skins, and the hair that he had shorn off was yellow, and much resembled the hair of the Boeotian.

"I took a good deal thereof and, coloring the matter, brought it to my mistress. When night came, before your return from supper, she (to bring her purpose to pass) went up to a high gallery of her house, opening to the east part of the world, and, preparing herself according to her accustomed practice, she gathered together all her substance for fumigations. She brought forth plates of metal carved with strange characters, she prepared the bones of such as were drowned by tempest in the seas, she made ready the members of dead men, as their nostrils and fingers. She set out the lumps of flesh of such as were hanged, the blood which she had reserved of such as were slain, and the jawbones and teeth of wild beasts. Then she said certain charms over the hair, and dipped it in divers waters, as in well water, cow's milk, mountain honey, and other liquor, which, when she had done, she tied and lapped up together, and with many perfumes and smells threw it into a hot fire to burn.

"Then by the great force of this sorcery, and the violence of so many confections, those bodies (whose hair was burning in the fire) received human shape, and felt, heard, and walked, and (smelling the scent of their own hair) came and rapped at our doors instead of Boeotius. Then you, being well tippled, and deceived by the obscurity of the night, drew out your sword courageously, like furious Ajax, and killed, not as he did, the whole herd of beasts, but three blown skins."

When I was thus pleasantly mocked and taunted by Fotis, I said to her, "Verily, now may I for this achieved enterprise be numbered as Hercules, who by his valiant prowess performed the twelve notable labors, as Gerion with three bodies, and as Cerberus with three heads, for I have slain three blown goat skins. But to the end that I may pardon thee of that which thou hast committed, perform the thing which I shall most earnestly desire of thee—that is, bring me that I may see and behold when thy mistress goes about any sorcery or enchantment, and when she prays to the gods, for I am very desirous to learn that art, and as it seems to me, thou thyself hast some experience in the same. For this I know and plainly feel that (whereas I have always irked and loathed the embracings and love of matrons) I am so stricken and subdued with thy shining eyes, ruddy cheeks, glittering hair, and lily-white bosom, that I have mind neither to go home nor to depart hence, but esteem the pleasure which I shall have with thee above all the joys of the world."

Then quoth she, "O my Lucius, how willing would I be to fulfill your desire, but by reason she is so hated, she gets herself into solitary places and out of the presence of every person when she minds to work her enchantment. Howbeit, I regard more to gratify your request than I esteem the danger of my life, and when I see opportunity and time I will assuredly bring you word, so that you shall see all her enchantment, but always upon this condition, that you secretly keep close such things as are done."

So she came to bed, and we passed the night in pastime and dalliance, till by drowsy sleep I was constrained to lie still.

HOW FOTIS BROUGHT APULEIUS TO SEE HER MISTRESS ENCHANT

On a day Fotis came running to me in great fear and said that her mistress (to work her sorceries on such as she loved) intended, the night following, to transform herself into a bird, and to fly whither she pleased, wherefore she willed me privily to prepare myself to see the same. And when midnight came she led me softly into a high chamber, and bid me look through the chink of a door.

First I saw how Pamphiles put off all her garments, and took out of a certain coffer sundry kinds of boxes, of which she opened one and tempered the ointment therein with her fingers, and then rubbed her body therewith from the sole of the foot to the crown of the head. When she had spoken privily with herself, having the candle in her hand, she shook her body, and behold, I perceived a plume of feathers did burgeon out; her nose waxed crooked and hard, her nails turned into claws, and so she became an owl. Then she cried and screeched like a bird of that kind, and, willing to prove her force, moved herself from the ground by little and little, till at last she flew quite away.

Thus by her sorcery she transformed her body into what shape she would. Which when I saw I was greatly astonished, and although I was enchanted by no kind of charm, yet I thought that I seemed not to have the likeness of Lucius, for so was I banished from my senses, amazed in madness, and so I dreamed waking, that I felt my eyes to know whether I were asleep or no.

But when I was come again to myself, I took Fotis by the hand, and moved it to my face, and said, "I pray thee, while occasion serve, that I may have the fruition of the fruits of my desire, and grant me some of this ointment. O Fotis, I pray thee, make that in the great flames of my love I may be turned into a bird, so will I ever hereafter be bound to you and obedient to your commandment."

Then said Fotis, "Will you go about to deceive me now, and enforce me to work my own sorrow? Are you in that mind that you will not tarry in Thessaly? If you be a bird, where shall I seek you, and when shall I see you?"

Then answered I, "God forbid that I should commit such a crime; for though I could fly into the air as an eagle, or though I were the messenger of Jupiter, yet would I have recourse to nest with thee. And I swear, by the knot of thy amiable hair, that since the time that I first loved thee, I never fancied any other person. Moreover, this cometh to my mind, that if by virtue of the ointment I shall become an owl, I will take heed that I come nigh no man's house. I am not to learn how these matrons would handle their lovers if they knew that they were transformed into owls. Moreover, when they are taken in any place, owls are nailed upon posts, and so they are worthily rewarded, because it is thought that they bring evil fortune to the house. But I pray you (which I had almost forgotten) tell me by what means, when I am an owl, I shall return to my pristine shape and become Lucius again?"

"Fear not" (quoth she), "for my mistress has taught me the way to bring that to pass; neither think you that she did it for any good will or favor, but to the end I might help her, and minister some remedy when she returns home. Consider, I pray you, with yourself, with what frivolous trifles so marvelous a thing is wrought, for, by Hercules, I swear I give her nothing else, save a little dill and laurel leaves in well water, which she drinks and washes herself withal."

When she had spoken this she went into the chamber and took a box out of the coffer, which I first kissed and embraced, and prayed that I might have good success in my purpose. And then I put off all my garments and greedily thrust my hand into the box, and took out a good deal of ointment and rubbed myself withal.

After I had well rubbed every part and member of my body, I hovered with my arms, and moved myself, looking still to be changed into a bird, as Pamphiles was. Behold, neither feathers nor appearance of feathers did burgeon out, but verily my hair did turn into ruggedness, and my tender skin waxed tough and hard, my fingers and toes, losing the number of five, changed into hoofs, and I grew a great tail. Now my face became monstrous, my nostrils wide, my lips hanging down, and my ears rugged with hair. Neither could I see any comfort of my transformation, for my members increased likewise, and so without all help (viewing every part of my poor body) I perceived that I was no bird, but a plain ass.

Then I thought to blame Fotis, but, being deprived as well of language as of human shape, I looked upon her with my hanging lips and watery eyes.

As soon as she espied me in such sort she cried out, "Alas, poor wretch that I am, I am utterly cast away. The fear that I was in, and my haste, beguiled me, but especially the mistaking of the box deceived me. But it matters not much, since a medicine may be got for this sooner than for any other thing. For if thou couldst get a rose and eat it, thou wouldst be delivered from the shape of an ass and become my Lucius again. Would to God I had gathered some garlands this evening past, according to my custom. Then thou shouldst not continue an ass one night's space. But in the morning I will seek some remedy."

Thus Fotis lamented in pitiful sort. But I, now a perfect ass, and instead of Lucius a brute beast, yet retained the sense and understanding of a man. I devised a good space with myself, whether it were best for me to tear this mischievous and wicked harlot with my mouth, or to kick and kill her with my heels. But a better thought reduced me from so rash a purpose, for I feared lest by the death of Fotis I should be deprived of all remedy and help.

So, shaking my head and dissimulating my ire, and taking my adversity in good part, I went into the stable to my own horse. There I found another ass of Milo's (sometime my host). I did verily think that my own horse (if there were any natural conscience or knowledge in brute beasts) would take pity upon me, and proffer me lodging for that night, but it chanced far otherwise. My horse and the ass, as it were, consented together to work my harm, and, fearing lest I should eat up their provender, would in no wise suffer me to come nigh the manger, but kicked me with their heels from their meat, which I myself gave them the night before.

Then I, being thus handled by them and driven away, got me into a corner of the stable, where (while I remembered their uncourtesy, and how on the morrow I should be turned again to Lucius by the help of a rose, when I might revenge myself of my own horse) I fortuned to espy, in the middle of a pillar sustaining the rafters of the stable, the image of the goddess Hippone, garnished and decked round about with fair fresh roses.

In hope of present remedy I leaped up with my forefeet as high as I could, and, stretching out my neck, with my lips coveted to snatch some roses. But in an evil hour did I go about that enterprise, for behold, the boy to whom I gave charge of my horse came in, and finding me climbing upon the pillar, ran threateningly toward me and said, "How long shall we suffer this vile ass, that not only eats up his fellows' meat, but also would spoil the images of the gods? Why do I not kill this lame thief and weak wretch?"

Therewithal, looking about for some cudgel, he espied a faggot of wood, and choosing out a crabbed truncheon of the biggest he could find, never ceased beating of me (poor wretch) until such time as by great noise and rumbling he heard the doors of the house burst open, and the neighbors crying in lamentable sort, which enforced him (being stricken in fear) to fly his way.

By and by a troop of thieves entered in, and kept every part and corner of the house with weapons. As men resorted to aid and help those who were within doors, the thieves resisted and kept them back, for every man was armed with his sword and target in his hand, the glimpses whereof did yield out such light as if it had been day.

Then they broke open a great chest with double locks and bolts, wherein was laid all the treasure of Milo, and ransacked the same; which when they had done they packed it up, and gave everyone a portion to carry. But when they had more than they could bear away, yet were they loath to leave any behind. So they came into the stable, and took us two poor asses and my horse, and loaded us with greater trusses than we were able to bear.

When we were out of the house, they followed us with great staves, and bade one of their fellows tarry behind and bring them tidings what was done concerning the robbery; and so they beat us forward over great hills out of the highway.

THE DECEITS OF A WOMAN

There was a man dwelling in the town, very poor, who had nought but that which he got by the labor and travail of his hands. His wife was a fair young woman, but very lascivious and given to the appetite and desire of the flesh.

It fortuned on a day that while this poor man was gone betimes in the morning to the field about his business, according as he accustomed to do, his wife's lover secretly came into his house to have his pleasure with her. And so it chanced that during the time that he and she were busking together, her husband, suspecting no such matter, returned home, praising the chaste continency of his wife; and he found his doors fast closed, wherefore, as his custom was, he whistled to declare his coming home. Then his crafty wife, ready with present shifts, caught her lover and covered him under a great tub standing in a corner; and therewithal she opened the door, blaming her husband in this sort, "Comest thou home so every day with empty hands, and bringest nothing to maintain our house? Thou hast no regard for our profit, neither providest for any meat or drink, whereas I, poor wretch, do nothing day and night but occupy myself with spinning, and yet my travail will scarce find the candles which we spend. Oh, how much more happy is my neighbor Daphne, who eats and drinks at her pleasure, and passeth the time with her amorous lovers according to her desire."

"What is the matter?" (quoth her husband). "Though our master hath made holiday at the fields, yet think not but that I have made provision for our supper? Dost thou not see this tub that keeps a place here in our house in vain, and does us no service? Behold, I have sold it to a good fellow (that is here present) for fivepence. Wherefore I pray thee lend me thy hand that I may deliver him the tub."

His wife (having invented a present shift) laughed on her husband, saying, "What merchant, I pray you, have you brought home hither, to fetch away my tub for fivepence, for which I, poor woman that sit all day alone in my house, have been proffered so often seven?"

Her husband, being surprised at her words, demanded who he was that had bought the tub.

"Look" (quoth she), "he is gone under to see whether it be sound or no." Then her lover, under the tub, began to stir and rustle himself, and to the end that his words might agree to the words of the woman, he said, "Dame, will you have me tell the truth? This tub is rotten and cracked, as to me seemeth, on every side." And then he turned himself to her husband, saying, "I pray you, honest man, light a candle that I may make the tub clean within, to see if it be for my purpose or no, for I do not mind to cast away my money willfully."

He immediately (being a very ox) lighted a candle, saying, "I pray you, good brother, put not yourself to so much pain. Let me make the tub clean and ready for you." Whereupon he put off his coat and crept under the tub to rub away the filth from the sides. In the mean season this minion lover had his pleasure with the wife, and as he was in the midst of his pastime he turned his head on this side and that side, finding fault with this and with that, till they had both ended their business, when he delivered sevenpence for the tub, and caused the good man himself to carry it on his back to his inn.

THE STORIES OF BARBARUS AND THE BAKER'S WIFE

The baker who bought me was an honest and sober man, but his wife was the most pestilential woman in all the world, insomuch that he endured many miseries and afflictions with her, and I myself did secretly pity his estate and bewail his evil fortune. She had not merely one grievous fault, but all the mischiefs that could be devised. She was crabbed, cruel, lascivious, drunken, obstinate, niggard, naggish, covetous, riotous in filthiness, an enemy to faith and chastity, a despiser of all the gods whom others did worship, one who affirmed she had a god by herself (whereby she deceived all men, especially her husband), one who abandoned her body with continual whoredom.

This mischievous harlot hated me in such sort that she commanded every day, before she was up, that I should be put in the mill to grind; and the first thing she would do in the morning was to see me cruelly beaten, and that I should grind when the other beasts did feed and take rest. When I saw that I was so cruelly handled, she gave me occasion to learn her conversation and life, for I saw oftentime a young man who would privily go into her chamber, whose face I did greatly desire to see, but I could not, by reason that my eyes were covered every day.

And verily if I had been free and at liberty I would have discovered all her abomination. She had an old woman, a messenger of mischief, that daily haunted her house, and made good cheer with her, to the utter undoing and impoverishment of her husband. But I, who was greatly offended with the negligence of Fotis, who made me an ass instead of a bird, did yet comfort myself by this only means, in that, to the miserable deformity of my shape, I had long ears, whereby I might hear all things that were done.

On a day I heard the old woman say to the baker's wife, "Dame, you have chosen (without my counsel) a young man to be your lover, who, as me seemeth, is dull, fearful, without any grace, and dastardly coucheth at the frowning looks of your odious husband, whereby you have no delight nor pleasure with him. How far better is the young man Philesiterus, who is comely, beautiful, in the flower of his youth, liberal, courteous, valiant and stout against the diligent pries and watches of your husband, worthy to embrace the worthiest dames of this country, and worthy to wear a crown of gold for one part that he played to one that was jealous over his wife. Hearken how it was, and then judge the diversity of these two lovers. Know you one Barbarus, a senator of our town, whom the vulgar people call likewise Scorpion for his severity of manners? This Barbarus had a gentlewoman to his wife, whom he caused daily to be enclosed within his house with diligent custody."

Then the baker's wife said, "I know her very well, for we two dwelt together in one house."

"Then you know" (quoth the old woman) "the whole tale of Philesiterus?"

"No, verily" (said she), "but I greatly desire to know it: therefore I pray you, mother, tell me the whole story."

At once the old woman, who knew well how to babble, began to tell as follows:—

"You shall understand that on a day this Barbarus, preparing himself to ride abroad, and willing to keep the chastity of his wife (whom he so well loved) alone to himself, called his man Myrmex (whose faith he had tried and proved in many things), and secretly committed to him the custody of his wife, willing him that he should threaten that if any man did but touch her with his finger as he passed by, he would not only put him in prison, and bind him hand and foot, but also cause him to be put to death, or else to be famished for lack of sustenance; which words he confirmed by oath of all the gods in heaven; and so he departed away.

"When Barbarus was gone, Myrmex, being greatly astonished at his master's threatenings, would not suffer his mistress to go abroad, but as she sat all day a-spinning he was so careful that he sat by her. When night came he went with her to the baths, holding her by the garment, so faithful he was to fulfill the commandment of his master. Howbeit, the beauty of this noble matron could not be hidden from the burning eyes of Philesiterus, who, considering her great chastity, and how she was diligently kept by Myrmex, thought it impossible to have his purpose. Yet (endeavoring by all kinds of means to enterprise the matter, and remembering the fragility of man, which might be enticed and corrupted with money, since by gold the adamant gates may be opened) on a day when he found Myrmex alone, he discovered his love, desiring him to show his favor (otherwise he should certainly die), with assurance that he need not fear, since he might privily be let in and out in the night without knowledge of any person.

"When he thought with these and other gentle words to allure and prick forward the obstinate mind of Myrmex, he showed him glittering gold in his hand, saying that he would give his mistress twenty crowns and him ten. But Myrmex, hearing these words, was greatly troubled, abhorring in his mind to commit so wicked a mischief; wherefore he stopped his ears, and, turning his head, departed away. Howbeit, the glittering hue of these crowns he could never get out of his mind, but, being at home, he seemed to see the money before his eyes, which was so worthy a prey that poor Myrmex, being in divers opinions, could not tell what to do. On the one side he considered the promise which he made to his master, and the punishment which should ensue if he did contrary. On the other side he thought of the gain and the passing pleasure of the crowns of gold. In the end the desire of the money did more prevail than the fear of death, for the beauty of the flourishing crowns did so stick in his mind that where the menaces of his master compelled him to tarry at home, the pestilent avarice of the gold egged him out of doors. Wherefore, putting all shame aside without further delay, he declared the whole matter to his mistress, who, according to the nature of women, when she heard him speak of so great a sum, bound chastity in a string, and gave authority to Myrmex to rule her in that case. Myrmex, seeing the intent of his mistress, was very glad, and for great desire of the gold he ran hastily to Philesiterus, declaring that his mistress was consented to his mind, wherefore he demanded the gold which he promised. Then incontinently Philesiterus delivered him ten crowns, and when night came Myrmex brought him disguised into his mistress's chamber.

"About midnight, when he and she were making sacrifice to the goddess Venus, behold, her husband (contrary to their expectation) came and knocked at the door, calling with a loud voice his servant Myrmex, whose long tarrying increased the suspicion of his master in such sort that he threatened to beat Myrmex cruelly. But he, being troubled with fear, and driven to his latter shifts, excused the matter, saying that he could not find the key, by reason it was so dark. In the mean season Philesiterus, hearing the noise at the door, slipped on his coat and privily ran out of the chamber. When Myrmex had opened the door to his master, who threatened terribly, and had let him in, he went into the chamber to his wife. In the meanwhile Myrmex let out Philesiterus and barred the doors fast, and went again to bed.

"The next morning, when Barbarus awoke, he perceived two unknown slippers lying under his bed which Philesiterus had forgotten when he went away. Then he conceived a great suspicion and jealousy in his mind. Howbeit, he would not discover it to his wife, neither to any other person, but, putting secretly the slippers in his bosom, commanded his other servants to bind Myrmex incontinently, and to bring him bound to the Justice after him, thinking verily that by the means of the slippers he might bolt out the matter. It fortuned that while Barbarus went toward the Justice in a fury and rage, and Myrmex, fast bound, followed him weeping, not because he was accused before his master, but by reason he knew his own conscience guilty, behold, by adventure Philesiterus (going about earnest business) fortuned to meet with them by the way, who, fearing the matter he committed the night before, and doubting lest it should be known, did suddenly invent a means to excuse Myrmex, for he ran upon him and beat him about the head with his fists cruelly, saying, 'Ah, mischievous varlet that thou art, and perjured knave! It were a good deed if the goddess and thy master here would put thee to death, for thou art worthy to be imprisoned, and to wear out these irons, who stole my slippers away when thou wert at the baths yesternight.'

"Barbarus, hearing these words, returned incontinently home, and called his servant Myrmex, commanding him to deliver the slippers again to the right owner."

The old woman had scarce finished her tale when the baker's wife said, "Verily, she is blessed and most blessed that hath the fruition of so worthy a lover; but as for me, poor wretch, I am fallen into the hands of a coward, who is not only afraid of my husband, but also of every clap of the mill, and dares do nothing before the blind face of yonder scabbed ass."

Then the old woman answered, "I promise you certainly, if you will, you shall have this young man at your pleasure." And therewithal, when night came, she departed out of her chamber.

In the mean season the baker's wife made ready a supper, with abundance of wine and exquisite fare, so that there lacked nothing but the coming of the young man, for her husband supped at the house of one of her neighbors. When time came that my harness should be taken off and that I should rest myself, I was not so joyful of my liberty, as that when the veil was taken from my eyes I should see all the abomination of this mischievous quean.

When night was come and the sun gone down, behold, the old woman and the young man, who seemed to me but a child, by reason he had no beard, came to the door. Then the baker's wife kissed him a thousand times, and, receiving him courteously, placed him down at the table. But he had scarce eaten the first morsel when the good man returned home, contrary to his wife's expectation, for she thought he would not have come so soon. But, Lord, how she cursed him, praying God that he might break his neck at the first entry in.

In the mean season she caught her lover and thrust him into the bin where she bolted her flour, and, dissimulating the matter, finally came to her husband, demanding why he came home so soon. "I could not abide" (quoth he) "to see so great a mischief and wicked act which my neighbor's wife committed, but I must run away. Oh, harlot as she is, how she hath dishonored her husband! I swear by this goddess Ceres that if I had not seen it with my eyes, I would never have believed it." His wife, desirous to know the matter, desired him to tell what she had done. Then he accorded to the request of his wife, and, ignorant of the state of his own house, declared the mischance of another.

"You shall understand" (quoth he) "that the wife of the fuller, my companion, who seemed to be a wise and chaste woman regarding her own honesty and the profit of her house, was found this night with her knave. For while we went to wash our hands, he and she were together; who, being troubled by our presence, ran into a corner, where she thrust him into a large cage made with twigs, appointed to lay clothes on to make them white with the smoke and fume of brimstone. Then she sat down with us at the table to color the matter.

"In the mean season the young man, covered in the cage, could not forbear sneezing, by reason of the smoke of the brimstone. The good man, thinking it had been his wife who sneezed, cried, 'Christ help.' But when he sneezed more and more, he suspected the matter, and, willing to know who it was, rose from the table and went to the cage, where he found the young man well-nigh dead with smoke. When he understood the whole matter, he was so inflamed with anger that he called for a sword to kill him; and undoubtedly he had killed him had not I restrained his violent hands from his purpose, assuring him that his enemy would die with the force of the brimstone without the harm he should do. Howbeit, my words would not appease his fury, but as necessity required, we took the young man, well-nigh choked, and carried him out at the doors. In the mean season I counseled his wife to absent herself at her neighbors' houses, till the choler of her husband was pacified, lest he should be moved against her, as he was against the young man. And so, being weary of their supper, I forthwith returned home."

When the baker had told this tale, his impudent wife began to curse and abhor the wife of the fuller, and generally all other wives who abandon their bodies with any other than with their own husbands, breaking the faith and bond of marriage, whereby, she said, they were worthy to be burned alive. But, knowing her own guilty conscience, lest her lover, lying in the bin, should be hurt, she willed her husband to go to bed; but he, having eaten nothing, said that he would sup before he went to rest; wherefore she was compelled, maugre her eyes, to set such things on the table as she had prepared for her lover.

But I, considering the great mischief of this wicked quean, devised with myself how I might reveal the matter to my master, and by kicking away the cover of the bin (where like a snail the young man was couched) make her whoredom apparent and known. At length I was aided by the providence of God, for there was an old man to whom the custody of us was committed, that drove me, poor ass, and the other horses at the same time, to the water to drink. Then had I good occasion ministered to revenge the injury of my master, for as I passed by I perceived the fingers of the young man upon the side of the bin, and, lifting up my heels, I spurned off the flesh with the force of my hoofs, whereby he was compelled to cry out, and to throw down the bin on the ground, and so the whoredom of the baker's wife was known and revealed.

The baker, seeing this, was little moved at the dishonesty of his wife, but he took the young man (trembling for fear) by the hand, and with cold and courteous words spoke in this sort: "Fear not, my son, nor think that I am so barbarous or cruel a person that I would stifle thee up with the smoke of sulphur, as our neighbor accustometh, nor will I not punish thee according to the rigor of the law Julia. No, no, I will not execute my cruelty against so fair and comely a young man as you be. I have always lived with my wife in such tranquillity that, according to the saying of the wise men, whatsoever I say she holds for law, and indeed equity will not suffer but that the husband should bear more authority than the wife."

With these and like words he led the young man to his bedroom, where, after locking his wife in another chamber, he revenged himself at his pleasure for the wrong done to him. On the next morrow he called two of his sturdiest servants, who held up the young man while he scourged him on his buttocks with rods. When he had well beaten him, he said: "Art thou not ashamed, thou who art so tender and delicate a boy, to desire the violation of honest marriages, and to defame thyself with wicked living, whereby thou hast gotten the name of an adulterer?"

After he had spoken these words, he whipped him again and chased him out of his house.

LUCIAN (A.D. 120–200)

Lucian was not only a man of all trades but a man of many countries. He was a Syrian, born at Samosata, who settled in Greece, lectured in Gaul, roamed through the world of Rome, and died in Egypt. Since the Roman Empire had become Hellenized, Lucian wrote in Greek. An intellectual entertainer, he delivered lectures and wrote sketches that formed the basis of such satirical pieces as the Dialogues of the Gods, *which not only humanized but made fun of the deities;* Dialogues of the Dead, *which pilloried the weaknesses of mankind; and* Dialogues of the Hetaerae, *which, unlike the portraits of glamorized courtesans of antiquity, depicted the ordinary prostitutes of the lower class. A great mocker, Lucian has been called a Greek Rabelais by one critic and, by another, "the Anatole France of the ancient world." Although he exposed his victims, he never burdened them with a general philosophy or his own misanthropy.*

The selections from Dialogues of a Hetaerae *are founded on a French version translated by M. S. Buck.*

THE LESBIAN

(DIALOGUE V)

CLONARION: They are saying strange things of thee, Lenia: that Megilla, the rich woman of Lesbos, loves thee as though she were a man; that you unite, although I cannot understand how. Is it so? . . . Thou art blushing! Then it is true?

LENIA: It is true, Clonarion, but I am ashamed to speak of it. It is all so very strange!

CLONARION: But, by the goddess, how can it be? What can she give thee? What do you do, together upon the couch? Ah, well! Thou lovest me no longer, else thou wouldst hide nothing.

LENIA: I love thee more than any other woman. But that woman is strangely like a man.

CLONARION: I do not understand. Is thy love like so many of the Lesbian women—those who refuse to suffer anything from men, but who take their pleasure with women as though they themselves were men?

LENIA: She is something like that.

CLONARION: Tell me, little one, how she revealed her passion, how thou wert persuaded, and all the rest.

LENIA: She had prepared a dinner with Demonassa of Corinth, who is also rich and who amuses herself as Megilla does. They had sent for me to sing and play the cithara during the repast. After I had sung, because it was very late and time to sleep, and they had finished drinking, Megilla said to me: Come, my dear Lenia, it is quite time for bed and thou canst sleep here between us two.

CLONARION: And you went to bed. . . . Then what happened?

LENIA: At first they kissed me as though they were men, not only pressing their lips to mine, but half parting them also. They entangled their limbs with mine, crushing my breasts. Demonassa even bit me in her embrace. As for me, I had no idea what they wished to do by all this. At last Megilla, who was already much inflamed, lifted from her head very perfect and well-fitting false hair and showed herself cropped like a male athlete. Seeing this, I was stupefied. But she said: My little Lenia, hast thou not already seen young men who were fair? —But I see no young man here, Megilla. —Think not of me as a woman. I call myself Megillus and, long ago, I espoused Demonassa, who is my wife. . . . I began to laugh, Clonarion. —Therefore, I said, thou art a man, Megillus, and we are not aware of it? Thus, they say, Achilles was hidden in the midst of young women. But hast thou that which distinguishes men? Dost thou for Demonassa, as a man would do? —It is true, Lenia, she replied, I have not everything, but I am not entirely unprovided for. Thou wilt see I can unite in my own way, which will be no less agreeable than the other. —But surely thou art not one of the hermaphrodites who, they say, exist and have both sexes? Of a truth, my dear Clonarion, I hardly under-

stood, yet. —No she responded I am entirely a man. —I have heard, I said,
from Ismenodora of Boetia, that at Thebes there was a woman who grew up
into a man and who was much esteemed as a conjurer. Her name was Tiresias,
I think. Art thou something like her? —Not at all, my dear Lenia. To the
world, I am like all of you; but my tastes, my passions, are those of a man.
—Do these passions suffice thee? I asked. —Give thyself to me, Lenia, since
thou canst not believe what I have told thee, and thou wilt see that I give
precedence to men in nothing. In fact, I have the equal of anything a man
might have. But come; thou wilt see. . . . I gave myself, Clonarion; she implored me so! Afterward, she gave me a splendid necklace and some fine
tunics. . . . But I was embraced as though by a man; she caressed me and
kissed me to suffocation, seeming to enjoy it greatly.

CLONARION: But what did she do? And how? Is this all I am to hear?

LENIA: Ask me no indiscreet questions, for these things are shameful. No,
by celestial Aphrodite, I will tell no more.

A CURIOUS DECEPTION

(DIALOGUE XII)

IOESSA: Thou scornest me, Lysias, and no doubt I deserve it, for I have
never demanded money of thee nor have I ever closed my door to thee because of someone else. I have never induced thee to cheat thy father or steal
jewels for me from thy mother, as the other courtesans do. Rather, from the
moment I first knew thee, I have received thee without demanding anything,
without making thee pay any expense. . . . As for thee, since thou hast seen
how completely I submit to thee and how I desire thy love, thou has played
with Lycaena under my very eyes in order to hurt me and thou hast praised
Magidion, the harp player, even when thou wert lying with me. I feel these
outrages keenly; I am saddened and I weep. . . . Perhaps, someday, thou
wilt weep when they tell thee Ioessa is dead—that she has strangled herself
or cast herself headfirst into some deep well, quitting her life to rid thee of
the annoyance of her presence. Then thou couldst triumph and vaunt thyself
as the cause of so fair a deed. . . . But why pierce me with angry glances?
Why shake with choler? If thou wouldst reproach me, speak; and Pythias
shall be our judge. . . . Well, thou wouldst go without a word? Thou seest,
Pythias, how I suffer from this ingrate.

PYTHIAS: What cruelty! Thou art a stone, not a man, if thou art not moved
by such tears! But if all this is true, it is thou, Ioessa, who hast spoiled him in
loving him too much and in letting him see it. That is no way to hold him;
all the men become disdainful when they see they are loved. Stop thy weeping, little one; and if thou wilt do as I say, close thy door two or three times
to this ingrate. He will soon be inflamed and ready to lose his mind on thy
account.

IOESSA: Ah! Don't talk like that. What? Close my door to Lysias? Rather, I pray the gods he will not send me away first!

PYTHIAS: He would soon return.

IOESSA: Thou wouldst ruin me, Pythias; perhaps he has heard this advice of thine.

LYSIAS: If I return here, Pythias, it will not be for this woman whom I have no desire to see again, but for thyself, lest thou blame my conduct and say that Lysias is inflexible.

PYTHIAS: I will most certainly say that, Lysias.

LYSIAS: Thou wouldst have me love this Ioessa, then, because she happens to be weeping, although I know that she has deceived me. Only the other night, I surprised her in bed with a young man.

PYTHIAS: Ah well, Lysias, is she not a courtesan? But when didst thou find them together?

LYSIAS: About five days ago. . . . Yes, just five days, for it was the second of the month, and this is the seventh. My father, informed of my passion for this honest girl, had shut me in the house and stationed a porter at the door. Impatient to see her, I resorted to a trick. I persuaded Dromon to lean against the wall, at a place where it was low, and let me stand upon his back so I could easily climb over. In this way, I managed it. But, to shorten the story, when I came here, I found the door of the courtyard carefully fastened. The night was well advanced, so I didn't knock on the door, but gently lifted it from its hinges as I had done many times before, and entered without making a noise. Everyone was asleep. I groped my way along the wall and soon arrived at the bed of infidelity.

IOESSA: What is this? O blessed Demeter! What torments I suffer!

LYSIAS: As I heard two people breathing, I thought at first that Lydia slept with her. But, feeling, I touched a delicate, beardless chin and a cropped head, reeking with perfumes. At that moment, if I had carried a sword, most certainly, without hesitation, I would have—— What are you laughing at, Pythias, is there anything laughable in this?

IOESSA: Knowest thou, Lysias, the cause of thy troubles? It was Pythias herself who was with me.

PYTHIAS: Don't tell him, Ioessa.

IOESSA: And why not? Yes, my dear, it was Pythias. I had persuaded her to pass the night with me, because I was lonesome at thine absence.

LYSIAS: Pythias with a shaven head? And in six days she has grown hair like this?

IOESSA: She was obliged to shave her head after a sickness which made the hair fall out. But show him, Pythias; show him so he will be convinced. There! See the young adulterer thou wert so jealous of!

LYSIAS: How was I to know, being in love, and after having touched . . . ?

IOESSA: Thou art convinced. And now wouldst thou have me repay thee all the sorrows thou hast caused me, by being most justly angry in my turn?

LYSIAS: No, my dear. Rather, let us go to dinner. Pythias shall join our festival, for I would like to have her present at our reconciliation.

IOESSA: She shall stay. What troubles thou hast caused me, Pythias—and thou the most amiable of young people!

PYTHIAS: Yes, but I have repaired them and thou must bear me no ill will. Only, Lysias, don't tell anyone about my wig.

The Renaissance

GESTA ROMANORUM

The Gesta Romanorum *was the most popular storybook of the Middle Ages, but, although many of the tales appeared and reappeared in other versions and later literature, no complete English version was printed until the nineteenth century. As the title indicates, the work was translated from the Latin, but the one hundred and eighty stories that comprise it had Teutonic and also Oriental sources.*

The stories in Gesta Romanorum *are on many levels. Some are heroic; some are innocent; a large number are cynical. The Rev. Charles Swan, who made a two-volume translation of the work in 1824, felt it necessary to apologize for the prevalence of what was frankly bawdy. "The many stories on the subject of adultery seem to indicate a bad moral state of society at the time they were written, and it is to be feared that the lawless feeling which chivalry in its decline exhibited, affords an unhappy confirmation."*

The "bad moral state of society" must have troubled the monks who compiled the stories in the Middle Ages, and they did their best to offset any possible lewd effects by adding what they believed to be pertinent "morals." Since it was not uncommon to find double meanings in everything, they turned every story into an allegory. These added morals, or "applications," were often made relevant by a wide stretch of interpretation, and what was a basic levity acquired a secondary piety. Nevertheless, the pious editors did not lose sight of the fact that these were stories originally told for enjoyment, and even the censorious Rev. Swan referred to them as "Entertaining Moral Stories." They were, according to his subtitle, "Invented by the Monks as a Fireside Recreation, and commonly applied in their Discourses from the Pulpit." In order to preserve the dual spirit of the original work and its later treatment as a series of moral lessons, the theological and sometimes irrelevant "applications" have been retained.

A sly satirical note runs through the Gesta, a humor often unconsciously achieved by understatements and incongruities. For example, in the first of the selections (as pointed out by Edgar Johnson in A Treasury of Satire) *the death-dealing tree is referred to as a "gentle" tree, and the desire of wives to kill themselves is called a "laudable wish." The widely inappropriate "applications" make the lurid stories far more laughable than they were ever intended to be.*

OF HANGING

Valerius tells us that a man named Paletinus one day burst into a flood of tears, and, calling his son and his neighbors around him, said, "Alas! Alas! I have now growing in my garden a fatal tree, on which my first poor wife hanged herself, then my second, and after that my third. Have I not therefore cause for the wretchedness I exhibit?"

"Truly," said one who was called Arrius, "I marvel that you should weep at such an unusual instance of good fortune! Give me, I pray you, two or three sprigs of that gentle tree, which I will divide with my neighbors, and thereby afford every man an opportunity of indulging the laudable wishes of his spouse."

Paletinus complied with his friend's request, and ever after found this remarkable tree the most productive part of his estate.[1]

APPLICATION: My beloved, the tree is the cross of Christ. The man's three wives are pride, lusts of the heart, and lusts of the eyes, which ought to be thus suspended and destroyed. He who solicited a part of the tree is any good Christian.

OF MAINTAINING TRUTH TO THE LAST

In the reign of Gordian, there was a certain noble soldier who had a fair but vicious wife. It happened that her husband having occasion to travel, the lady sent for her gallant. Now, one of her handmaids, it seems, was skillful in interpreting the song of birds; and in the court of the castle there were three cocks.

During the night, while the gallant was with his mistress, the first cock began to crow. The lady heard it, and said to her servant, "Dear friend, what says yonder cock?" She replied, "That you are grossly injuring your husband." "Then," said the lady, "kill that cock without delay."

They did so; but soon after the second cock crew, and the lady repeated her question. "Madam," said the handmaid, "he says, 'My companion died for revealing the truth, and for the same cause, I am prepared to die.'" "Kill him," cried the lady, which they did.

After this the third cock crew. "What says he?" asked she again. "Hear, see, and say nothing, if you would live in peace." "Oh, oh!" said the lady. "He is a wise bird. Don't kill him." And her order was obeyed.[2]

APPLICATION: My beloved, the soldier is Christ; the wife is the soul. The gallant is the devil. The handmaid is conscience. The first cock is our Saviour, who was put to death; the second is the martyrs; and the third is a preacher

[1] This story is credited to Valerius Maximus, but it is actually much older. It appears as an anecdote recorded by Cicero in his second book, *De Oratore...*

[2] This tale, of ancient Oriental origin, is still current in European folklore. In the Italian version the three cocks become, somewhat more logically, three parrots.

who ought to be earnest in declaring the truth but, being deterred by menaces, is afraid to utter it.

OF WOMEN, WHO NOT ONLY BETRAY SECRETS BUT LIE FEARFULLY

There were two brothers, of whom one was a layman and the other a parson. The former had often heard his brother declare that there never was a woman who could keep a secret. He had a mind to put this maxim to the test in the person of his own wife, and one night he addressed her in the following manner: "My dear wife, I have a secret to communicate to you, if I were certain that you would reveal it to nobody. Should you divulge it, it would cause me the greatest uneasiness and vexation."

"My lord," answered his wife, "fear not; we are one body, and your advantage is mine. In like manner, your injury must deeply affect me." "Well, then," said he, "know that, my bowels being oppressed to an extraordinary degree, I fell very sick. My dear wife, what will you think? I actually voided a huge black crow, which instantly took wing, and left me in the greatest trepidation and confusion of mind." "Is it possible?" asked the innocent lady. "But, husband, why should this trouble you? You ought rather to rejoice that you are freed from such a pestilent tenant."

Here the conversation closed. In the morning, the wife hurried off to the house of a neighbor. "My best friend," said she, "may I tell you a secret?" "As safely as to your own soul," answered the fair auditor. "Why," replied the other, "a marvelous thing has happened to my poor husband. Being last night extremely sick, he voided two prodigious black crows, feathers and all, which immediately flew away. I am much concerned." The other promised very faithfully—and immediately told her neighbor that *three* black crows had taken this most alarming flight.

The next edition of the story made it *four*; and in this way it spread, until it was very credibly reported that *sixty* black crows had been evacuated by one unfortunate varlet! But the joke had gone further than he dreamed of; he became much disturbed, and, assembling his busy neighbors, explained to them that, having wished to prove whether or not his wife could keep a secret, he had made such a communication.

APPLICATION: My beloved, the layman is any worldly-minded man who, thinking to do one foolish thing without offense, falls into a thousand errors. But he assembles the people—that is, past and present sins—and by confession expurgates his conscience.

OF WOMEN, WHO ARE NOT TO BE TRUSTED

Macrobius states that a Roman youth, named Papirius, was once present with his father in the Senate at a time when a very important matter was debated, which, on pain of death, was to be kept secret. When the lad returned home, his mother asked him what it was that was guarded under so heavy a penalty. He replied that it was unlawful to reveal it. The mother, little satisfied with the boy's reply, entreated, promised, threatened, and even scourged him, in the hope of extorting a communication. But he remained inflexible; and at last, willing to satisfy her, and yet retain his secret, said, "The council met upon this matter: whether it were more beneficial to the state that one man should have many wives, or one woman many husbands."

The mother no sooner heard this than away she posted to divide the important secret with other Roman dames. And on the following day, assembling in a large body, they went without hesitation to the senators, earnestly requesting that one woman might be married to two men, rather than two women to one man. The senators, astonished at the shameless frenzy of a sex naturally modest, deliberated upon the best remedy. The boy Papirius, finding this, related to them the circumstance which had occasioned the uproar; and they, bestowing great commendation on his ingenuity, passed a decree that he should be present at their consultations whenever he would.

APPLICATION: My beloved, the boy is anyone whose life is pure: the father is a prelate; and the mother is the world.

OF THE EXECRABLE DEVICES OF OLD WOMEN

In the kingdom of a certain empress there lived a knight, who was happily espoused to a noble, chaste, and beautiful wife. It happened that he was called upon to take a long journey, and previous to his departure he said to the lady, "I leave you no guard but your own discretion; I believe it to be wholly sufficient." He then embarked with his attendants. She meanwhile continued at her own mansion, in the daily practice of every virtue. A short period had elapsed, when the urgent entreaties of a neighbor prevailed with her to appear at a festival; where, among other guests, was a youth, upon whom the excellence and beauty of the lady made a deep impression. He became violently enamored of her, and dispatched various emissaries to declare his passion, and win her to approve his suit. But the virtuous lady received his advances with the utmost scorn.

This untoward repulse greatly disconcerted the youth, and his health daily declined. Nevertheless he visited the lady oft, which availed him nothing; he was still despised.

It chanced that on one occasion he went sorrowfully toward the church; and upon the way, an old woman accosted him, who by pretended sanctity had long obtained an undue share of reverence and regard. She demanded the cause of the youth's apparent uneasiness. "It will nothing profit me to tell thee," said he. "But," replied the old woman, "as long as the sick man hides his malady from the physician he cannot be cured: discover the wound, and it is not impossible but a remedy may be found. With the aid of heaven I will restore you to health." Thus urged, the youth made known to her his love for the lady. "Is that all?" said the beldam. "Return to your home; I will find a medicine that shall presently relieve you." Confiding in her assurances, he went his way and the other hers.

It seems she possessed a little dog, which she obliged to fast for two successive days; on the third, she made bread of the flour of mustard, and placed it before the pining animal. As soon as it had tasted the bread, the pungent bitterness caused the water to spring into its eyes, and the whole of that day tears flowed copiously from them. The old woman, accompanied by her dog, posted to the house of the lady whom the young man loved; and the opinion entertained of her sanctity secured her an honorable and gracious reception.

As they sat together, the lady noticed the weeping dog, and was curious to ascertain the cause. The crone told her not to inquire, for that it involved a calamity too dreadful to communicate. Such a remark, naturally enough, excited still more the curiosity of the fair questioner, and she earnestly pressed her to detail the story. This was what the old hag wanted; she said, "That little dog was my daughter—too good and excellent for this world. She was beloved by a young man, who, thrown into despair by her cruelty, perished for her love. My daughter, as a punishment for her hardhearted conduct, was suddenly changed into the little dog respecting which you inquire." Saying these words, a few crocodile tears started into her eyes; and she continued, "Alas! how often does this mute memorial recall my lost daughter, once so beautiful and virtuous: now—oh, what is she now? Degraded from the state of humanity, she exists only to pine away in wretchedness, and waste her life in tears. She can receive no comfort; and they who would administer it can but weep for her distresses, which surely are without a parallel."

The lady, astonished and terrified at what she heard, secretly exclaimed, "Alas! I too am beloved; and he who loves me is in like manner at the point of death," and then, instigated by her fears, discovered the whole circumstance to the old woman, who immediately answered, "Beautiful lady, do not disregard the anguish of this young man: look upon my unhappy daughter, and be warned in time. As she is, you may be."

"Oh!" returned the credulous lady. "My good mother, counsel me; what would you have me do? Not for worlds would I become as she is." "Why, then," answered the treacherous old woman, "send directly for the youth, and give him the love he covets." The lady said, "May I entreat your holiness to fetch him: there might be some scandal circulated if another went." "My dear daughter," said she, "I suffer with you, and will presently bring him hither." She arose and returned with him; and thus the youth obtained his mistress. And so, through the old woman's means, the lady was led to adultery.

APPLICATION: My beloved, the knight is Christ; the wife is the soul, to which God gave free will. It is invited to the feast of carnal pleasures, where a youth—that is, the vanity of the world—becomes enamored of it. The old woman is the devil; the dog, the hope of a long life, and the presumptuous belief of God's clemency, which lead us to deceive and soothe the soul.

OF ABSENCE OF PARENTAL RESTRAINT

A soldier, going into a far country, entrusted his wife to the care of her mother. But some time after her husband's departure the wife fell in love with a young man, and communicated her wishes to the mother. She approved of the connection, and without delay sent for the object of her daughter's criminal attachment.

But while they feasted, the soldier unexpectedly returned and beat at his gate. The wife, in great tremor, concealed the lover in her bed, and then opened the door for her husband. Being weary with travel, he commanded his bed to be got ready; and the wife, more and more disturbed, knew not what she should do.

The mother observing her daughter's perplexity, said, "Before you go, my child, let us show your husband the fair sheet which we have made." Then standing up, she gave one corner of the sheet to her daughter and held the other herself, extending it before him so as to favor the departure of the lover, who took the hint and escaped. When he had got clearly off, "Now," said the mother, "spread the sheet upon the bed with your own hands—we have done our parts in *weaving* it."

APPLICATION: My beloved, the soldier is any man who is a wanderer in this world. The wife is the flesh; the mother is the world; and the sheet, worldly vanities.

FROM: THE ARABIAN NIGHTS

The group of stories known as The Arabian Nights *is actually Persian in origin; the beautiful teller of tales, Scheherazade, was originally a Persian girl "endowed with wit and knowledge, by name Shehrzad." The Arabs expanded the collection to 264 romances and called it* A Thousand Nights and One Night, *since some of the stories took more than one night to tell. Curiously enough, some of the best-liked tales, such as "Aladdin" and "Ali Baba," were not part of the compilation but were added by a French editor in the early eighteenth century.*

The Persian originals hark back to the sixth century, although many of the incidents were the stock in trade of storytellers long before that. The Arabian enlargement, familiar to us through the translations of John Payne and Richard Burton, dates from the eighth century and continued to grow for almost a thousand years. In the Western world, the stories have been so emasculated that their readers today consist almost entirely of children. However, the audiences that heard them in the Orient were not only mixed but mature. When the professional storyteller addressed his listeners in the crowded bazaars or gathered around isolated campfires, he was talking to people not only about themselves but also about many other kinds of people. "The whole Oriental world of the khalifat lives for us in these enchanted pages," wrote Joseph Campbell in an introduction to The Portable Arabian Nights, "from which nothing is rejected as common or unclean, and where all classes are represented, slave, king, courtier and countryman, pietist and freethinker, ignorant and learned, wise and foolish, moralist and debauchee. In the main, the life is that of the people, those Arabs so essentially brave, sober, hospitable, and kindly, almost hysterically sensitive to emotions of love and piety, yet capable of strange excesses of brutality. . . ."

Much of this brutality is shocking and even shameful to Western minds. The large work covers an incredible range; historical tales with historical personages, supernatural stories, anecdotes of rogues and charlatans, wild fantasies, fables, illicit and lawful romances, as well as monstrous and perverse inventions. The matter of turpitude was considered at some length by Burton in his wise if wordy introduction. He speaks of the "naïve and childlike indecency" which is heard in general conversation throughout the East. "It treats in an unconventionally free and naked manner of subjects and matters which are usually, by common consent, left undescribed . . . For instance the European novelist marries off his hero and heroine and leaves them to consummate marriage in privacy; even Tom Jones has the decency to bolt the door. But the Eastern storyteller, especially this unknown 'prose Shakespeare,' must usher you, with a flourish, into the bridal chamber and narrate to you, with infinite gusto, everything he sees and hears. Again we must remember that grossness and indecency are matters of time and place; what is offensive in England is not so in Egypt. Withal The Nights will not be found in this matter coarser than many passages of Shakespeare, Sterne, and Swift."

The connecting theme of the stories is both simple and ingenious. Embittered by the infidelity of his wife, King Shehriyar determines to revenge himself on womankind. He takes a new bride every day, enjoys her that night, and next morning has the vizier put her to death. The vizier's daughter, Shehrzad, believes that she can deliver the women from their fate and persuades her father to let her marry the king. Being "wise, witty, prudent, and well bred," and having read thousands of chronicles, legends, and folk tales, Shehrzad regales the king with suspenseful narratives and is always in the middle of one when night ends. The king puts off her execution from day to day to hear how each story comes out. After one thousand and one nights, during which time Shehrzad has borne him three sons, King Shehriyar releases her from the doom of death and rejoices because he finds her "chaste, pure, noble, and pious . . . Therewith joy spreads throughout the palace of *the king and the good news was bruited abroad in the city. It was a night not to be counted among lives, and its color was whiter than the face of day."*

STORY OF KING SHEHRIYAR AND HIS BROTHER

It is recorded in the chronicles of the things that have been done of time past that there lived once, in the olden days and in bygone ages and times, a king of the kings of the sons of Sasan, who reigned over the Islands of India and China and was lord of armies and guards and servants and retainers. He had two sons, an elder and a younger, who were both valiant cavaliers, but the elder was a stouter horseman than the younger. When their father died, he left his empire to his elder son, whose name was Shehriyar, and he took the government and ruled his subjects justly, so that the people of the country and of the empire loved him well; whilst his brother Shahzeman became King of Samarkand of Tartary.

The two kings abode each in his own dominions, ruling justly over their subjects and enjoying the utmost prosperity and happiness, for the space of twenty years, at the end of which time the elder king yearned after his brother and commanded his vizier to repair to the latter's court and bring him to his own capital. The vizier replied, "I hear and obey," and set out at once and journeyed till he reached King Shahzeman's court in safety, when he saluted him for his brother and informed him that the latter yearned after him and desired that he would pay him a visit; to which King Shahzeman consented gladly and made ready for the journey and appointed his vizier to rule the country in his stead during his absence. Then he caused his tents and camels and mules to be brought forth and encamped, with his guards and attendants, without the city, in readiness to set out next morning for his brother's kingdom.

In the middle of the night it chanced that he bethought him of somewhat he had forgotten in his palace: so he returned thither privily and entered his apartments, where he found his wife asleep in his own bed in the arms of one of his black slaves. When he saw this, the world grew black in his sight, and he said to himself, "If this is what happens whilst I am yet under the city walls, what will be the condition of this accursed woman during my absence at my brother's court?" Then he drew his sword and smote the twain and slew them and left them in the bed and returned presently to his camp, without telling anyone what had happened.

Then he gave orders for immediate departure and set out at once and traveled till he drew near his brother's capital, when he dispatched vaunt-couriers to announce his approach. His brother came forth to meet him and saluted him and rejoiced exceedingly and caused the city to be decorated in his honor. Then he sat down with him to converse and make merry; but King Shahzeman could not forget the perfidy of his wife and grief grew on him more and more and his color changed and his body became weak.

Shehriyar saw his condition, but attributed it to his separation from his country and his kingdom, so let him alone and asked no questions of him, till one day he said to him, "O my brother, I see that thou art grown weak of body and hast lost thy color." And Shahzeman answered, "O my brother, I have an internal wound," but did not tell him about his wife. Said Shehriyar, "I wish thou wouldst ride forth with me a-hunting; maybe it would lighten thy heart." But Shahzeman refused; so his brother went out to hunt without him.

Now there were in King Shahzeman's apartments lattice windows overlooking his brother's garden, and as the former was sitting looking on the garden, behold, a gate of the palace opened, and out came twenty damsels and twenty black slaves, and among them his brother's wife, who was wonderfully fair and beautiful. They all came up to a fountain, where the girls and slaves took off their clothes and sat down together. Then the queen called out, "O Mesoud!" And there came to her a black slave, who embraced her and she him. Then he lay with her, and so likewise did the other slaves with the girls. And they ceased not from kissing and clipping and clicketing and carousing until the day began to wane. When the King of Tartary saw this, he said to himself, "By Allah, my mischance was lighter than this!" And his grief and chagrin relaxed from him and he said, "This is more grievous than what happened to me!" So he put away his melancholy and ate and drank.

Presently his brother came back from hunting and they saluted each other: and Shehriyar looked at Shahzeman and saw that his color had returned and his face was rosy and he ate heartily, whereas before he ate but little. So he said to him, "O my brother, when I last saw thee, thou wast pale and wan; and now I see that the color has returned to thy face. Tell me how it is with thee." Quoth Shahzeman, "I will tell thee what caused my loss of color, but excuse me from acquainting thee with the cause of its return to me." Said Shehriyar, "Let me hear first what was the cause of thy pallor and weakness." "Know then, O my brother," rejoined Shahzeman, "that when thou sentest thy vizier to bid me to thee, I made ready for the journey and had actually quitted my capital city, when I remembered that I had left behind me a certain jewel, that which I gave thee. So I returned to my palace, where I found my wife asleep in my bed in the arms of a black slave. I slew them both and came to thee: and it was for brooding over this affair that I lost my color and became weak. But forgive me if I tell thee not the cause of my restoration to health."

When his brother heard this, he said to him, "I conjure thee by Allah, tell me the reason of thy recovery!" So he told him all that he had seen, and Shehriyar said, "I must see this with my own eyes." "Then," replied Shahzeman, "feign to go forth to hunt and hide thyself in my lodging and thou shalt see all this and have ocular proof of the truth."

So Shehriyar ordered his attendants to prepare to set out at once; whereupon the troops encamped without the city, and he himself went forth with them and sat in his pavilion, bidding his servants admit no one. Then he disguised himself and returned secretly to King Shahzeman's palace and sat with him at the lattice overlooking the garden, until the damsels and their mistress came out with the slaves and did as his brother had reported, till the call to afternoon prayer. When King Shehriyar saw this, he was as one distraught and said to his brother, "Arise, let us depart hence, for we have no concern with kingship, and wander till we find one to whom the like has happened as to us: else our death were better than our life."

Then they went out by a postern of the palace and journeyed days and nights till they came to a tree standing in the midst of a meadow, by a spring of water, on the shore of the salt sea: and they drank of the stream and sat down by it to rest. When the day was somewhat spent, behold, the sea became troubled and there rose from it a black column that ascended to the sky and made toward the meadow. When the princes saw this they were afraid and climbed up to the top of the tree, which was a high one, that they might see what was the matter; and behold, it was a genie of lofty stature, broad-browed and wide-chested, bearing on his head a coffer of glass with seven locks of steel. He landed and sat down under the tree, where he set down the coffer and, opening it, took out a smaller one. This also he opened, and there came forth a damsel slender of form and dazzlingly beautiful, as she were a shining sun, as says the poet Uteyeh:

> She shines out in the dusk, and lo! the day is here,
> And all the trees flower forth with blossoms bright and clear,
> The sun from out her brows arises, and the moon,
> When she unveils her face, doth hide for shame and fear.
> All living things prostrate themselves before her feet,
> When she unshrouds and all her hidden charms appear;
> And when she flashes forth the lightnings of her glance,
> She maketh eyes to rain, like showers, with many a tear.

When the genie saw her, he said to her, "O queen of noble ladies, thou whom indeed I stole away on thy wedding night, I have a mind to sleep awhile." And he laid his head on her knees and fell asleep.

Presently the lady raised her eyes to the tree and saw the two kings among the branches: so she lifted the genie's head from her lap and laid it on the ground, then rose and stood beneath the tree and signed to them to descend, without heeding the Afrit. They answered her in the same manner, "God on thee! Excuse us from this." But she rejoined by signs, as who should say, "If you do not come down, I will wake the Afrit on you, and he will kill you without mercy." So they were afraid and came down to her, whereupon she came up to them and offered them her favors, saying, "To it, both of you, and lustily; or I will set the Afrit on you." So for fear of him, King Shehriyar said to his brother Shahzeman, "O brother, do as she bids thee." But he replied, "Not I; do thou have at her first." And they made signs to each other to pass first, till she said, "Why do I see you make signs to each other? An you come not forward and fall to, I will rouse the Afrit on you." So, for fear of the genie, they lay with her one after the other; and when they had done, she bade them arise, and took out of her bosom a purse containing a necklace made of five hundred and seventy rings, and said to them, "Know ye what these are?" They answered, "No." And she said, "Every one of the owners of these rings has had to do with me in despite of this Afrit. And now give me your rings, both of you." So each of them took off a ring and gave it to her. And she said to them, "Know that this genie carried me off on my wedding night and laid me in a box and shut the box up in a glass chest, on which he clapped seven strong locks and sank it to the bottom of the roaring stormy sea, knowing not that nothing can hinder a woman, when she desires aught."

When the two kings heard this they marveled and said, "Allah! Allah! There is no power and no virtue save in God the Most High, the Supreme! We seek aid of God against the malice of women, for indeed their craft is great!" Then she said to them, "Go your ways."

So they returned to the road, and Shehriyar said to Shahzeman, "By Allah, O my brother, this Afrit's case is more grievous than ours. For this is a genie and stole away his mistress on her wedding night and clapped her in a chest, which he locked with seven locks and sank in the midst of the sea, thinking to guard her from that which was decreed by fate; yet have we seen that she has lain with five hundred and seventy men in his despite, and now with thee and me to boot. Verily, this is a thing that never yet happened to any, and it should surely console us. Let us therefore return to our kingdoms and resolve never again to take a woman to wife; and as for me, I will show thee what I will do."

So they set out at once and presently came to the camp outside Shehriyar's capital and, entering the royal pavilion, sat down on their bed of estate. Then the chamberlains and amirs and grandees came in to them and Shehriyar commanded them to return to the city. So they returned to the city and Shehriyar went up to his palace, where he summoned his vizier and bade him forthwith put his wife to death. The vizier accordingly took the queen and killed her, whilst Shehriyar, going into the slave girls and concubines, drew his sword and slew them all. Then he let bring others in their stead and took an oath that every night he would go in to a maid and in the morning put her to death, for that there was not one chaste woman on the face of the earth. As for Shahzeman, he sought to return to his kingdom at once; so his brother equipped him for the journey and he set out and fared on till he came to his own dominions.

Meanwhile, King Shehriyar commanded his vizier to bring him the bride of the night, that he might go in to her: so he brought him one of the daughters of the amirs and he went in to her, and on the morrow he bade the vizier cut off her head. The vizier dared not disobey the king's commandment, so he put her to death and brought him another girl, of the daughters of the notables of the land. The king went in to her also, and on the morrow he bade the vizier kill her; and he ceased not to do thus for three years, till the land was stripped of marriageable girls, and all the women and mothers and fathers wept and cried out against the king, cursing him and complaining to the Creator of heaven and earth and calling for succor upon Him who heareth prayer and answereth those that cry to Him; and those that had daughters left fled with them, till at last there remained not a single girl in the city apt for marriage.

One day the king ordered the vizier to bring him a maid as of wont: so the vizier went out and made search for a girl, but found not one and returned home troubled and careful for fear of the king's anger. Now this vizier had two daughters, the elder called Shehrzad and the younger Dunyazad, and the former had read many books and histories and chronicles of ancient kings and stories of people of old time: it is said indeed that she had collected a thousand books of chronicles of past peoples and bygone kings and poets. Moreover, she had read books of science and medicine; her memory was stored with verses and stories and folklore and the sayings of kings and sages, and she was wise, witty, prudent, and well bred. She said to her father, "How comes it that I see thee troubled and oppressed with care and anxiety? Quoth one of the poets:

> "Tell him that is of care oppressed,
> That grief shall not endure alway,
> But even as gladness fleeteth by,
> So sorrow too shall pass away."

When the vizier heard his daughter's words, he told her his case, and she said, "By Allah, O my father, marry me to this king, for either I will be the means of the deliverance of the daughters of the Muslims from slaughter, or I will die and perish as others have perished." "For God's sake," answered the vizier, "do not thus adventure thy life!" But she said, "It must be so."

Translated by JOHN PAYNE

SHERKAN AND THE LADY WRESTLER

(FROM: KING OMAR BEN ENNUMAN AND HIS SONS)

When the king heard the vizier's speech, it pleased him and he approved his counsel: so he bestowed on him a dress of honor and said to him, "It is with such as thee that kings take counsel, and it befits that thou command the van of the army and my son Sherkan the main battle." Then he sent for Sherkan and expounded the matter to him, telling him what the ambassadors and the vizier had said, and enjoined him to take arms and prepare to set out, charging him not to cross the vizier Dendan in aught that he should do. Then he bade him choose from among his troops ten thousand horsemen armed cap-a-pie and inured to war and hardship. Accordingly, Sherkan rose at once and chose out ten thousand horsemen, in obedience to his father's commandment, after which he entered his palace and mustered his troops and distributed money to them, saying, "Ye have three days to make ready." They kissed the earth before him and proceeded at once to make their preparations for the campaign; whilst Sherkan repaired to the armories and provided himself with all the arms and armor that he needed, and thence to the stables, whence he took horses of choice breeds and others.

When the three days were ended, the troops marched out of Baghdad, and King Omar came forth to take leave of his son, who kissed the earth before him, and he gave him seven thousand purses. Then he turned to the vizier Dendan and commended to his care his son Sherkan's army and charged the latter to consult the vizier in all things, to which they both promised obedience. After this, the king returned to Baghdad, and Sherkan commanded the officers to draw out the troops in battle array. So they mustered them and the number of the army was ten thousand horsemen, besides footmen and followers. Then they loaded the beasts and beat the drums and blew the clarions and unfurled the banners and the standards, whilst Sherkan mounted, with the vizier Dendan by his side and the standards waving over them, and the army set out and fared on, with the ambassadors in the van, till the day departed and the night came, when they halted and encamped for the night. On the morrow, as soon as God brought in the day, they took horse and continued their march, nor did they cease to press onward, guided by the ambassadors, for the space of twenty days. On the twenty-first day, at nightfall, they came to a wide and fertile valley, whose sides were thickly wooded and covered with grass, and there Sherkan called a three days' halt. So they dismounted and pitched their tents, dispersing right and left in the valley, whilst the vizier Dendan and the ambassadors alighted in the midst.

As for Sherkan, when he had seen the tents pitched and the troops dispersed on either side and had commanded his officers and attendants to camp beside the vizier Dendan, he gave reins to his horse, being minded to explore the valley and himself mount guard over the army, having regard to his father's injunctions and to the fact that they had reached the frontier of the land of Roum and were now in the enemy's country. So he rode on alone along the valley, till a fourth part of the night was passed, when he grew weary and sleep overcame him, so that he could no longer spur his horse. Now he was used to sleep on horseback; so when drowsiness got the better of him, he fell asleep and the horse paced on with him half the night and entered a forest; but Sherkan awoke not, till the steed smote the earth with his hoof. Then he started from sleep and found himself among trees; and the moon arose and lighted up the two horizons. He was troubled at finding himself alone in this place and spoke the words, which whoso says shall never be confounded; that is to say, "There is no power and no virtue but in God the Most High, the Supreme!" But as he rode on in fear of the wild beasts, behold, the trees thinned and the moon shone out upon a meadow as it were one of the meads of Paradise; and he heard therein a noise of talk and pleasant laughter, such as ravishes the wit of men.

So King Sherkan dismounted and, tying his horse to a tree, fared on a little way, till he espied a stream of running water and heard a woman talking and saying in Arabic, "By the virtue of the Messiah, this is not handsome of you! But whoso speaks a word, I will throw her down and bind her with her girdle." He followed in the direction of the voice and saw gazelles frisking and wild cattle pasturing and birds in their various voices expressing joy and gladness: and the earth was embroidered with all manner of flowers and green herbs . . .

Midmost the meadow stood a monastery, and within the enclosure was a citadel that rose high into the air in the light of the moon. The stream passed through the midst of the monastery and therenigh sat ten damsels like moons, high-bosomed maids, clad in dresses and ornaments that dazzled the eyes . . .

Sherkan looked at the ten girls and saw in their midst a lady like the moon at its full, with ringleted hair and shining forehead, great black eyes and curling brow-locks, perfect in person and attributes . . .

Then Sherkan heard her say to the girls, "Come on, that I may wrestle with you, ere the moon set and the dawn come." So they came up to her, one after another, and she overthrew them, one by one, and bound their hands behind them with their girdles. When she had thrown them all, there turned to her an old woman, who was before her, and said, as if she were wroth with her, "O wanton, dost thou glory in overthrowing these girls? Behold, I am an old woman, yet have I thrown them forty times! So what hast thou to boast of? But if thou have strength to wrestle with me, stand up that I may grip thee and put thy head between thy feet." The young lady smiled at her words, although her heart was full of anger against her, and said, "O my lady Dhat ed Dewahi, wilt indeed wrestle with me, or dost thou jest with me?" "I mean to wrestle with thee in very deed," replied she. "Stand up to me then," said the damsel, "if thou have strength to do so."

When the old woman heard this she was sore enraged and the hair of her body stood on end, like that of a hedgehog. Then she sprang up, whilst the damsel confronted her, and said, "By the virtue of the Messiah, I will not wrestle with thee, except I be naked, O baggage!" So she loosed her trousers and, putting her hand under her clothes, tore them off her body; then, taking a handkerchief of silk, she bound it about her middle and became as she were a bald Afriteh or a pied snake. Then she turned to the young lady and said to her, "Do as I have done." All this time Sherkan was watching them and laughing at the loathly favor of the old woman. So the damsel took a sash of Yemen stuff and doubled it about her waist, then tucked up her trousers and showed legs of alabaster and above them a hummock of crystal, soft and swelling, and a belly that exhaled musk from its dimples, as it were a bed of blood-red anemones, and breasts like double pomegranates. Then the old woman bent to her and they took hold of one another, whilst Sherkan raised his eyes to heaven and prayed to God that the damsel might conquer the old hag.

Presently, the former bored in under the latter, and, gripping her by the breech with the left hand and by the gullet with the right, hoisted her off the ground; whereupon the old woman strove to free herself and in the struggle wriggled out of the girl's hands and fell on her back. Up went her legs and showed her hairy tout in the moonlight, and she let fly two great cracks of wind, one of which smote the earth, whilst the other smoked up to the skies. At this Sherkan laughed till he fell to the ground, and said, "He lied not who dubbed thee Lady of Calamities! Verily, thou sawest her prowess against the others." Then he arose and looked right and left, but saw none save the old woman thrown down on her back. So he drew near to hear what should pass between them; and behold, the young lady came up to the old one and, throwing over her a veil of fine silk, helped her to dress herself, making excuses to her and saying, "O my lady Dhat ed Dewahi, I did not mean to throw thee so roughly, but thou wriggledst out of my hands; so praised be God for safety!" She returned her no answer, but rose in her confusion and walked away out of sight, leaving the young lady standing alone, by the other girls thrown down and bound.

Then said Sherkan to himself, "To every fortune there is a cause. Sleep fell not on me nor did the steed bear me hither but for my good fortune; for of a surety this damsel and what is with her shall be my prize." So he turned back and mounted and drew his scimitar; then he gave his horse the spur and he started off with him, like an arrow from a bow, whilst he brandished his naked blade and cried out, "God is most great!" When the damsel saw him, she sprang to her feet and, running to the bank of the river, which was there six cubits wide, made a spring and landed on the other side, where she turned and, standing, cried out in a loud voice, "Who art thou, sirrah, that breakest in on our pastime, and that with thy whinger bared, as thou wert charging an army? Whence comest thou and whither art thou bound? Speak the truth, and it shall profit thee, and do not lie, for lying is of the losel's fashion. Doubtless thou hast strayed this night from thy road, that thou has happened on this place. So tell me what thou seekest: if thou wouldst have us set thee in the right road, we will do so, or if thou seek help, we will help thee."

When Sherkan heard her words he replied, "I am a stranger of the Muslims, who am come out by myself in quest of booty, and I have found no fairer purchase this moonlit night than these ten damsels; so I will take them and rejoin my comrades with them." Quoth she, "I would have thee to know that thou hast not yet come at the booty: and as for these ten damsels, by Allah, they are no purchase for thee! Indeed, the fairest purchase thou canst look for is to win free of this place; for thou art now in a mead, where, if we gave one cry, there would be with us anon four thousand knights. Did I not tell thee that lying is shameful?" And he said, "The fortunate man is he to whom God sufficeth and who hath no need of other than Him." "By the virtue of the Messiah," replied she, "did I not fear to have thy death at my hand, I would give a cry that would fill the meadow on thee with horse and foot; but I have pity on the stranger: so if thou seek booty, I require of thee that thou dismount from thy horse and swear to me, by thy faith, that thou wilt not approach me with aught of arms, and we will wrestle, I and thou. If thou throw me, lay me on thy horse and take all of us to thy booty; and if I throw thee, thou shalt be at my commandment. Swear this to me, for I fear thy perfidy, since experience has it that, as long as perfidy is in men's natures, to trust in everyone is weakness. But if thou wilt swear, I will come over to thee."

Quoth Sherkan (and indeed he lusted after her and said to himself, "She does not know that I am a champion of the champions"), "Impose on me whatever oath thou deemest binding, and I will swear not to draw near thee till thou hast made thy preparations and sayest, 'Come and wrestle with me.' If thou throw me, I have wealth wherewith to ransom myself, and if I throw thee, I shall get fine purchase." Then said she, "Swear to me by Him who hath lodged the soul in the body and given laws to mankind that thou wilt not beset me with aught of violence, but by way of wrestling; else mayst thou die out of the pale of Islam." "By Allah," exclaimed Sherkan, "if a cadi should swear me, though he were cadi of the cadis, he would not impose on me the like of this oath!" Then he took the oath she required and tied his horse to a tree, sunken in the sea of reverie and saying in himself, "Glory to Him who fashioned her of vile water!"

Then he girt himself and made ready for wrestling and said to her, "Cross the stream to me." Quoth she, "It is not for me to come to thee: if thou wilt, do thou cross over to me." "I cannot do that," replied he, and she said, "O boy, I will come to thee." So she gathered her skirts and, making a spring, landed on the other side of the river by him; whereupon he drew near to her, wondering at her beauty and grace, and saw a form that the hand of Omnipotence had tanned with the leaves of the Jinn and which had been fostered by divine solicitude, a form on which the zephyrs of fair fortune had blown and over whose creation favorable planets had presided. Then she called out to him, saying, "O Muslim, come and wrestle before the day break!" and tucked up her sleeves, showing a forearm like fresh curd; the whole place was lighted up by its whiteness and Sherkan was dazzled by it. Then he bent forward and clapped his hands and she did the like, and they took hold and gripped each other.

He laid his hands on her slender waist, so that the tips of his fingers sank into the folds of her belly, and his limbs relaxed and he stood in the stead of desire, for there was displayed to him a body in which was languishment of hearts, and he fell a-trembling like the Persian reed in the hurricane. So she lifted him up and, throwing him to the ground, sat down on his breast with buttocks like a hill of sand, for he was not master of his reason. Then she said to him, "O Muslim, it is lawful among you to kill Christians; what sayest thou to my killing thee?" "O my lady," replied he, "as for killing me, it is unlawful; for our Prophet (whom God bless and preserve!) hath forbidden the slaying of women and children and old men and monks." "Since this was revealed unto your Prophet," rejoined she, "it behooves us to be even with him therein; so rise: I give thee thy life, for beneficence is not lost upon men." Then she got off his breast, and he rose and brushed the earth from his head, and she said to him, "Be not abashed; but, indeed, one who enters the land of the Greeks in quest of booty and to succor kings against kings, how comes it that there is no strength in him to defend himself against a woman?" "It was not lack of strength in me," replied he; "nor was it thy strength that overthrew me, but thy beauty: so if thou wilt grant me another bout, it will be of thy favor." She laughed and said, "I grant thee this: but these damsels have been long bound and their arms and shoulders are weary, and it were fitting I should loose them, since this next bout may peradventure be a long one." Then she went up to the girls and, unbinding them, said to them in the Greek tongue, "Go and put yourselves in safety, till I have brought to nought this Muslim's craving for you." So they went away, whilst Sherkan looked at them and they gazed at him and the young lady.

Then she and he drew near again and set breast against breast; but, when he felt her belly against his, his strength failed him, and she, feeling this, lifted him in her hands, swiftlier than the blinding lightning, and threw him to the ground. He fell on his back, and she said to him, "Rise: I give thee thy life a second time. I spared thee before for the sake of thy Prophet, for that he forbade the killing of women, and I do so this second time because of thy weakness and tender age and strangerhood; but I charge thee, if there be, in the army sent by King Omar ben Ennuman to the succor of the King of Constantinople, a stronger than thou, send him hither and tell him of me, for in wrestling there are divers kinds of strokes and tricks, such as feinting and the fore-hipe and the back-hipe and the leg-crick and the thigh-twist and the jostle and the cross-buttock." "By Allah, O my lady," replied Sherkan (and indeed he was greatly incensed against her), "were I the Chief Es Sefedi or Mohammed Caïmal or Ibn es Seddi, I had not observed the fashions thou namest; for, by Allah, it was not by thy strength that thou overthrewest me, but by filling me with the desire of thy buttocks; because we people of Chaldaea love great thighs, so that nor wit nor foresight was left in me. But now if thou have a mind to try another fall with me, with my wits about me, I have a right to this one bout more, by the rules of the game, for my presence of mind has now returned to me." "Hast thou not had enough of wrestling, O conquered one?" rejoined she. "However, come if thou wilt; but know that this bout must be the last."

Then they took hold of each other and he set to in earnest and warded himself against being thrown down: so they strained awhile, and the damsel found in him strength such as she had not before observed and said to him, "O Muslim, thou art on thy guard!" "Yes," replied he; "thou knowest that there remaineth but this bout, and after each of us will go his own way." She laughed and he laughed too: then she seized the opportunity to bore in upon him unawares and, gripping him by the thigh, threw him to the ground, so that he fell on his back. She laughed at him and said, "Thou art surely an eater of bran; for thou art like a Bedouin bonnet that falls at a touch, or a child's toy that a puff of air overturns. Out on thee, thou poor creature! Go back to the army of the Muslims and send us other than thyself, for thou lackest thews, and cry us among the Arabs and Persians and Turks and Medes, 'Whoso has might in him, let him come to us.'" Then she made a spring and landed on the other side of the stream and said to Sherkan, laughing, "It goes to my heart to part with thee; get thee to thy friends, O my lord, before the morning, lest the knights come upon thee and take thee on the points of their lances. Thou hast not strength enough to defend thee against women; so how couldst thou make head against men and cavaliers?"

Translated by JOHN PAYNE

THE SCAVENGER AND THE NOBLE LADY OF BAGHDAD

At Mecca, one day, in the season of pilgrimage, whilst the people were making the enjoined circuits about the Holy House and the place of compassing was crowded, a man laid hold of the covering of the Kaabeh and cried out, from the bottom of his heart, saying, "I beseech Thee, O God, that she may once again be wroth with her husband and that I may lie with her!" A company of the pilgrims heard him and, falling on him, loaded him with blows and carried him to the governor of the pilgrims, to whom said they, "O Amir, we found this man in the Holy Places, saying thus and thus." The governor commanded to hang him; but he said, "O Amir, I conjure thee, by the virtue of the Prophet (whom God bless and preserve), hear my story and after do with me as thou wilt." "Say on," quoth the amir.

Know then, O Amir, said the man, that I am a scavenger, who works in the sheep slaughterhouses and carries off the blood and the offal to the rubbish heaps. One day, as I went along with my ass loaded, I saw the people running away, and one of them said to me, "Enter this alley, lest they kill thee." Quoth I, "What ails the folk to run away?" And he answered, "It is the eunuchs in attendance on the wife of one of the notables, who drive the people out of her way and beat them all, without distinction." So I turned aside with the ass and stood, awaiting the dispersal of the crowd. Presently up came a number of eunuchs with staves in their hands, followed by nigh thirty women, and amongst them a lady as she were a willow wand or a thirsty gazelle, perfect in beauty and elegance and amorous grace. When she came to the mouth of the passage where I stood, she turned right and left and, calling one of the eunuchs, whispered in his ear; whereupon he came up to me and, laying hold of me, bound me with a rope and haled me along after him, whilst another eunuch took my ass and made off with it. I knew not what was to be done, and the people followed us, crying out, "This is not allowed of God! What has this poor scavenger done that he should be bound with ropes?" and saying to the eunuchs, "Have pity on him and let him go, so God have pity on you!" And I the while said in myself, "Doubtless the eunuch seized me because his mistress smelled the offal and it sickened her. Belike she is with child or ailing; but there is no power and no virtue save in God the Most High, the Supreme!"

So I walked on behind them, till they stopped at the door of a great house and, entering, brought me into a great hall. I know not how I shall describe its goodliness, furnished with magnificent furniture. The women withdrew to the harem, leaving me bound with the eunuch and saying in myself, "Doubtless they will torture me here till I die, and none know of my death." However, after a while, they carried me into an elegant bathroom, adjoining the hall; and as I sat there, in came three damsels, who seated themselves round me and said to me, "Strip off thy rags." So I pulled off my threadbare clothes, and one of them fell a-rubbing my feet, whilst another washed my head and the third scrubbed my body. When they had made an end of washing me, they brought me a parcel of clothes and said to me, "Put these on." "By Allah," answered I, "I know not how!" So they came up to me and dressed me, laughing at me the while; after which they brought casting bottles, full of rose water, and sprinkled me therewith. Then I went out with them into another saloon—by Allah, I know not how to set out its goodliness, for the much paintings and furniture therein; and here I found the lady seated on a couch of Indian cane with ivory feet and before her a number of damsels.

When she saw me she rose and called to me; so I went up to her and she made me sit by her side. Then she called for food, and the damsels brought all manner of rich meats, such as I never saw in all my life; I do not even know the names of the dishes. So I ate my fill, and when the dishes had been taken away and we had washed our hands, she called for fruits and bade me eat of them; after which she bade one of the waiting women bring the wine service. So they set on flagons of divers kinds of wine and burned perfumes in all the censers, while a damsel like the moon rose and served us with wine to the sound of the smitten strings. We sat and drank, the lady and I, till we were warm with wine, whilst I doubted not but that all this was an illusion of sleep. Presently she signed to one of the damsels to spread us a bed in such a place, which being done, she took me by the hand and led me thither. So I lay with her till the morning, and as often as I pressed her in my arms, I smelled the delicious fragrance of musk and other perfumes that exhaled from her, and could think no otherwise but that I was in paradise or in the mazes of a dream. When it was day she asked me where I lodged, and I told her, "In such a place"; whereupon she gave me a handkerchief gold and silver wrought, with somewhat tied in it, and bade me depart, saying, "Go to the bath with this." So I rejoiced and said to myself, "If there be but five farthings here, it will buy me the morning meal." Then I left her, as I were leaving paradise, and returned to my lodging, where I opened the handkerchief and found in it fifty dinars of gold. I buried them in the ground and, buying two farthings' worth of bread and meat, sat down at the door and breakfasted; after which I sat pondering my case till the time of afternoon prayer, when a slave girl accosted me, saying, "My mistress calls for thee." So I followed her to the house aforesaid and she carried me in to the lady, before whom I kissed the earth, and she bade me sit and called for meat and wine as on the previous day; after which I again lay with her all night. On the morrow she gave me a second handkerchief, with other fifty dinars therein, and I took it and, going home, buried this also.

Thus did I eight days running, going in to her at the hour of afternoon prayer and leaving her at daybreak; but, on the eighth night, as I lay with her, one of her maids came running in and said to me, "Arise, go up into yonder closet." So I rose and went into the closet, which was over the gate and had a window giving upon the street in front of the house. Presently I heard a great clamor and tramp of horse and, looking out of the window, saw a young man, as he were the rising moon on the night of her full, come riding up, attended by a number of servants and soldiers. He alighted at the door and, entering, found the lady seated on the couch in the saloon. So he kissed the earth before her, then came up to her and kissed her hands; but she would not speak to him. However, he ceased not to soothe her and speak her fair, till he made his peace with her, and they lay together that night. Next morning the soldiers came for him, and he mounted and rode away; whereupon she came in to me and said, "Sawest thou yonder man?" "Yes," answered I; and she said, "He is my husband, and I will tell thee what befell me with him.

"It chanced one day that we were sitting, he and I, in the garden within the house, when he rose from my side and was absent a long while, till I grew tired of waiting and said to myself, 'Most like, he is in the wardrobe.' So I went thither, but not finding him there, went down to the kitchen, where I saw a slave girl, of whom I inquired for him, and she showed him to me lying with one of the cookmaids. When I saw this I swore a great oath that I would do adultery with the foulest and filthiest man in Baghdad; and the day the eunuch laid hands on thee, I had been four days going round about the town in quest of one who should answer this description, but found none fouler nor more filthy than thee. So I took thee, and there passed between us that which God foreordained to us; and now I am quit of my oath. But," added she, "if my husband return yet again to the cookmaid and lie with her, I will restore thee to thy late place in my favors."

When (continued the scavenger) I heard these words from her lips, what while she transfixed my heart with the arrows of her glances, my tears streamed forth, till my eyelids were sore with weeping, and I repeated the saying of the poet:

> "Vouchsafe me the kiss of thy left hand, I prithee,
> And know that it's worthier far than thy right;
> For 'tis but a little while since it was washing
> Sir reverence away from the stead of delight."

Then she gave me other fifty dinars (making in all four hundred dinars I had of her) and bade me depart. So I went out from her and came hither, that I might pray God (blessed and exalted be He!) to make her husband return to the cookmaid, so haply I might be again admitted to her favors.

When the governor of the pilgrims heard the man's story, he set him free and said to the bystanders, "God on you, pray for him, for indeed he is excusable."

Translated by JOHN PAYNE

THE CONFECTIONER, HIS WIFE, AND THE PARROT

Once upon a time there dwelt in Egypt a confectioner who had a wife famed for beauty and loveliness; and a parrot which, as occasion required, did the office of watchman and guard, bell and spy, and flapped her wings did she but hear a fly buzzing about the sugar. This parrot caused abundant trouble to the wife, always telling her husband what took place in his absence.

Now one evening, before going out to visit certain friends, the confectioner gave the bird strict injunctions to watch all night and bade his wife make all fast, as he should not return until morning. Hardly had he left the door than the woman went for her old lover, who returned with her, and they passed the night together in mirth and merriment, while the parrot observed all. Betimes in the morning the lover fared forth and the husband, returning, was informed by the parrot of what had taken place; whereupon he hastened to his wife's room and beat her with a painful beating. She thought in herself, "Who could have informed against me?" and she asked a woman that was in her confidence whether it was she. The woman protested by the worlds visible and invisible that she had not betrayed her mistress; but informed her that on the morning of his return home, the husband had stood some time before the cage listening to the parrot's talk.

When the wife heard this, she resolved to contrive the destruction of the bird. Some days after, the husband was again invited to the house of a friend where he was to pass the night; and, before departing, he enjoined the parrot with the same injunctions as before; wherefore his heart was free from care, for he had his spy at home. The wife and her confidante then planned how they might destroy the credit of the parrot with the master. For this purpose they resolved to counterfeit a storm; and this they did by placing over the parrot's head a hand mill (which the lover worked by pouring water upon a piece of hide), by waving a fan, and by suddenly uncovering a candle hid under a dish. Thus did they raise such a tempest of rain and lightning that the parrot was drenched and half drowned in a deluge. Now rolled the thunder, then flashed the lightning; that from the noise of the hand mill, this from the reflection of the candle; when thought the parrot to herself, "In very sooth and flood hath come on, such an one as belike Noah himself never witnessed." So saying she buried her head under her wing, a prey to terror.

The husband, on his return, hastened to the parrot to ask what had happened during his absence; and the bird answered that she found it impossible to describe the deluge and tempest of the last night, and that years would be required to explain the uproar of the hurricane and storm. When the shopkeeper heard the parrot talk of last night's deluge, he said: "Surely, O bird, thou art gone clean daft! Where was there, even in a dream, rain or lightning last night? Thou hast utterly ruined my house and ancient family. My wife is the most virtuous woman of the age and all thine accusations of her are lies." So in his wrath he dashed the cage upon the ground, tore off the parrot's head, and threw it from the window.

Translated by RICHARD BURTON

GIOVANNI BOCCACCIO (1313–1375)

Eight years before the death of a half-forgotten Florentine, Dante Alighieri, there was born another Florentine, Giovanni Boccaccio, who was to restore Dante's repute as an epic poet. Although the year of his birth has been established as 1313, the exact date and place of the event are uncertain. Boccaccio's father was a banker, but nothing is known about his mother, for the good reason that she was barely acquainted with his father. An entertaining young Parisienne (name undisclosed), Giovanni was her illegitimate son. When the boy was seven years old, his father married another woman, and his stepmother, who had her own son to think of, did not waste much love on her husband's by-blow. His father tried to make him "a man of commerce"—he was first apprenticed to a merchant and, when he showed no talent for trade, was made to study law—but he revolted against any business or profession except that of literature. He says that he had a leaning toward poetry from the beginning: "I remember that, when I was seven, long before I read any stories or was taught anything at all, I was already composing little poems." As he matured he never doubted that it was his destiny to write.

Write he did, and to such purpose that, by the time he was forty, he was the acknowledged "Father of Italian Prose." Before that time, however, he had various light affairs with the ladies—he rather boasted of his amorous gallantry—and one serious entanglement. He was twenty-three when, attending church services, he met Maria d'Aquino. A patrician, the illegitimate daughter of King Robert of Sicily, she was married; Boccaccio called her Fiammetta, "the Little Flame," and it is indicated that his fierce desire was reciprocated. She appears and reappears throughout his prose and poetry, an idealized woman, everything that Beatrice was to Dante except that Fiammetta was the fulfillment of the flesh rather than the incarnation of the spirit.

Boccaccio was forty when the first stories of the Decameron *began to ap-*

pear. They were immediately lauded as works of the highest imagination and attacked as indecent fictions celebrating sexual irregularities, especially on the part of corrupt idlers, debased wives, and depraved monks. Boccaccio used a simple device: Seven young women and three young men flee from effete and haunted Florence, afflicted by the plague, to the pure air of the quiet countryside. There they while away the time bathing, sunning themselves, singing, playing games, and, chiefly, telling tales to one another. The hundred stories which result cover a vast field; they include contemporary anecdotes and gossip, classical legends, elaborately ornamented jokes, modern fables, restored myths, reanimated folklore, spiritual discourses, courtly romances—either original or adapted from the world's fund of storytelling. The language is free as talk, outspoken, candid, and, on occasion, appropriately coarse; the attitude is both simple and sophisticated; the picture evoked is a pageant of medieval life. An inexhaustible source of plots for poets, novelists, and dramatists, the Decameron has been ransacked for centuries, notably by Chaucer, Shakespeare, Jonson, La Fontaine, Margaret of Navarre, Molière, Dryden, Keats, and the ever so Victorian laureate, Tennyson.

Biographers mention certain putative children. At least one daughter and a son have been identified. But there is no word that Boccaccio ever married. As he grew older he grew worried about the state of his soul. Becoming the intimate friend of Petrarch, he turned to serious poetry and spiritual meditations. He wrote a treatise on Dante, lectured on The Divine Comedy, and was responsible for the rediscovery of the poet's magnificence. It was inevitable that Boccaccio should recant his youthful indulgences; entering the Church, he repudiated his greatest work, the Decameron, because of its licentious amorality. An uneasy sinner, he died at the age of sixty-two.

The following stories from the Decameron are the work of John Payne and other translators, revisers, and editors.

FROM: THE DECAMERON

THE MONK, THE ABBOT, AND THE GIRL
(*The first day: the fourth story*)

There was in Lunigiana, a country not far from here, a monastery far more noted for sanctity than it is today. And in it there was a young monk whose liveliness and lustiness neither fasts nor vigils could discourage. One day near noon, when all the other monks slept, as he went all alone round about the convent, which stood in a solitary place, he espied a very well-favored lass, belike some husbandman's daughter of the country, who went about the fields culling certain herbs. No sooner had he set eyes on her than he was violently assailed by carnal appetite. Wherefore, accosting her, he entered into parley with her and so led on from one thing to another that he came to an accord with her and brought her to his cell, unperceived of any. But whilst, carried away by overmuch ardor, he disported himself with her less cautiously than was prudent, it chanced that the abbot arose from sleep and, softly passing by the monk's cell, heard the racket that the twain made together. Whereupon he came stealthily up to the door to listen, that he might the better recognize the voices, and manifestly perceiving that there was a woman in the cell, was at first minded to cause open to him, but after bethought himself to hold another course in the matter and, returning to his chamber, awaited the monk's coming forth.

The latter, all taken up as he was with the wench and his exceeding pleasure and delight in her company, was none the less on his guard and himseeming he heard some scuffling of feet in the dormitory, he set his eye to a crevice and plainly saw the abbot stand hearkening unto him. Whereby he understood but too well that the latter must have gotten wind of the wench's presence in his cell and knowing that sore punishment would ensue to him thereof, he was beyond measure chagrined. However, without discovering aught of his concern to the girl, he hastily revolved many things in himself, seeking to find some means of escape, and presently hit upon a rare device, which went straight to the mark he aimed at. Accordingly, making a show of thinking he had abidden long enough with the damsel, he said to her, "I must go cast about for a means how thou mayest win forth hence, without being seen; wherefore do thou abide quietly until my return."

Then, going forth and locking the cell door on her, he betook himself straight to the abbot's chamber and presenting him with the key, according as each monk did, whenas he went abroad, said to him, with a good countenance, "Sir, I was unable to make an end this morning of bringing off all the fagots I had cut; wherefore with your leave I will presently go to the wood and fetch them away." The abbot, deeming the monk unaware that he had been seen of him, was glad of such an opportunity to inform himself more fully of the offense committed by him and accordingly took the key and gave him the leave he sought. Then, as soon as he saw him gone, he fell to considering which he should rather do: whether open his cell in the presence of all the other monks and cause them to see his default, so that they might have no occasion to murmur against him when he should punish the offender, or seek first to learn from the girl herself how the thing had passed. And, thinking that she might be the wife or daughter of such a man that he would be loath to have done her the shame of showing her to all the monks, he determined first to see her and after come to a conclusion; wherefore, betaking himself to the cell, he opened it and entering, shut the door after him.

The girl, seeing the abbot enter, was all aghast and fell a-weeping for fear of shame; but my lord abbot, casting his eyes upon her and seeing her young and handsome, old as he was, suddenly felt the pricks of the flesh no less importunate than his young monk had done and fell a-saying in himself, "Marry, why should I not take somewhat of pleasure, whenas I may, more by token that displeasure and annoy are still at hand, whenever I have a mind to them? This is a handsome wench and is here unknown of any in the world.

If I can bring her to do my pleasure, I know not why I should not do it. Who will know it? No one will ever know it and a sin that's hidden is half forgiven. Maybe this chance will never occur again. I hold it great sense to avail ourselves of a good, whenas God the Lord sendeth us thereof."

So saying and having altogether changed purpose from that wherewith he came, he drew near to the girl and began gently to comfort her, praying her not to weep, and passing from one word to another, he ended by discovering to her his desire. The girl, who was neither iron nor adamant, readily enough lent herself to the pleasure of the abbot, who, after he had clipped and kissed her again and again, mounted upon the monk's pallet and having belike regard to the grave burden of his dignity and the girl's tender age and fearful of irking her for overmuch heaviness, bestrode not her breast, but set her upon his own and so a great while desported himself with her.

Meanwhile, the monk, who had only made believe to go to the wood and had hidden himself in the dormitory, was altogether reassured, whenas he saw the abbot enter his cell alone, doubting not but his device should have effect, and when he saw him lock the door from within, he held it for certain. Accordingly, coming forth of his hiding place, he stealthily betook himself to a crevice, through which he both heard and saw all that the abbot did and said. When it seemed to the latter that he had tarried long enough with the damsel, he locked her in the cell and returned to his own chamber, whence, after a while, he heard the monk stirring and, deeming him returned from the wood, thought to rebuke him severely and cast him into prison, so himself might alone possess the prey he had gotten; wherefore, sending for him, he very grievously rebuked him, and with a stern countenance, and commanded that he should be put in prison.

The monk very readily answered, "Sir, I have not yet pertained long enough to the order of St. Benedict to have been able to learn every particular thereof, and you had not yet shown me that monks should make of women a means of mortification, as of fasts and vigils; but, now that you have shown it me, I promise you, so you will pardon me this default, never again to offend therein, but still to do as I have seen you do." The abbot, who was a quick-witted man, readily understood that the monk not only knew more than himself, but had seen what he did; wherefore, his conscience pricking him for his own default, he was ashamed to inflict on the monk a punishment which he himself had merited even as he. Accordingly, pardoning him and charging him keep silence of that which he had seen, they privily put the girl out of doors, and it is to be believed that they caused her return thither more than once thereafterward.

ADVENTURES OF THE SULTAN OF BABYLON'S DAUGHTER
(*The second day: the seventh story*)

A long time ago there lived a sultan of Babylon, who was a fortunate monarch indeed. Among his other children, he had a daughter named Alatiel, who, in the opinion of all that saw her, was the fairest lady in the whole world. And because the King of Algarve had afforded him great assistance in defeating a most numerous army of Arabians that had assailed him, and had demanded her afterwards in marriage, he very willingly consented thereto; and providing a ship, well equipped for the purpose, with all necessary provisions, and sending an honorable train both of lords and ladies to bear her company, he commended her at parting to the protection of heaven. The sailors, as soon as a fit opportunity offered, hoisted their sails and, leaving the port of Alexandria, sailed prosperously many days; when, having passed the island of Sardinia, and now seeming to be near the end of their voyage, on a sudden contrary winds arose, which were so boisterous and bore so hard upon the ship that they often gave themselves over for lost. Nevertheless, for two days together, they tried all the means they could devise, amidst an infinite number of tempests, to weather it out; but all to no purpose, for every blast was worse than the former. And not being able to comprehend by marinal judgment where they were, or to see to any distance on account of the clouds and dark night, being now not far from Majorca, they felt the ship split; and perceiving no hopes of escaping, everyone caring for himself only, they threw a little boat into the sea, reposing more confidence of safety that way than by abiding any longer in the broken ship. The men therefore that were in the ship went into the boat, one after another, although those who were first down made strong resistance with their drawn weapons against other followers; and, thinking to avoid death by this means, they ran directly into it; for the boat, not being able to bear them all, sunk straight to the bottom, and the people therein all perished.

The ship being driven furiously by the winds, though it was burst and half full of water, was at last stranded on the island of Majorca, no other person remaining on board but the lady and her women, all lying as it were lifeless, through the terror occasioned by the tempest. It struck with such violence that it was fixed in the sand about a stone's throw from the shore; where it continued all that night, the winds not being able to move it. When daylight appeared, and the storm was something abated, the lady, almost dead, lifted up her head and began, weak as she was, to call first one and then another of her servants; but all to no purpose, for such as she called for were far enough from her. Wherefore, receiving no answer and seeing no one, she was greatly astonished; and raising herself up as well as she could, she beheld the ladies that were of her company, and some other of her women, lying all about her; and trying first to rouse one and then another of them, she scarcely found any that had the least understanding left, so much had sickness and fear together affected them, which added greatly to her consternation. Nevertheless, necessity constraining her, seeing that she was alone she knew not where, she shook those that were living till she made them get up, and perceiving that they were utterly ignorant of what was become of all the men, and seeing the ship driven upon the sands and full of water, she began with them to lament most grievously.

It was noonday before they could descry any person on the shore or else-where to afford them the least assistance. At length, about that time, a gen-tleman, whose name was Pericon da Visalgo, passing that way on his return from a country house, with many of his servants, on horseback, upon seeing the ship, imagined what had happened and immediately sent one of them on board to see what was remaining in her. The servant got into the ship with some difficulty and found the lady with the little company that was left her, who had all hidden themselves, through fear, under the forecastle. As soon as they saw him, they begged for mercy; but, not understanding each other's language, they then strove by signs to inform him of their misfortune. The servant carried the best account he could to his master of what he had seen; who ordered the ladies, and everything that was in the ship of any value, to be brought on shore, conducting them to one of his castles, where he endeavored to comfort them under their misfortunes by this generous en-tertainment. By the richness of her dress, he supposed the chief lady to be some person of great consequence, which appeared more plainly by the great respect that was paid to her by all the women; and although she was pale and in disorder through the great fatigue she had sustained, yet was he much taken with her beauty; and he resolved, if she had no husband, to make her his wife; or, if he could not have her as such, still not to lose her entirely. Pericon was a man of stern looks, and rough in his person; and having treated the lady well for some time, by which means she had recovered her beauty, he was grieved that they could not understand each other and that he was unable to learn who she was; yet, being passionately in love, he used all the engaging arts he could devise to bring her to a compliance, but all to no purpose; she refused all familiarities with him, which inflamed him the more. This the lady perceived, and finding, after some stay there, by the customs of the place, that she was among Christians, and where, if she came to be known, it would be of no great service to her; supposing also that at last Pericon would gain his will, if not by fair means, yet by force, she resolved, with a true greatness of spirit, to tread all misfortune underfoot. She com-manded her women, of whom she had but three now alive, never to disclose her quality, unless there should be hopes of regaining their liberty. She rec-ommended farther to them to maintain their chastity, and declaring her fixed resolution never to comply with anyone besides her husband; for which they all commended her, promising to preserve their honor as she had com-manded them.

Every day did Pericon's passion increase, so much the more as the thing desired was near and yet so difficult to be obtained: wherefore, perceiving that entreaty was to no purpose, he resolved to try what art and contrivance could do, reserving force to the last. And having once observed that wine was pleasing to her, not having been accustomed to it, as being forbidden by her country's laws, he determined to surprise her by means of this minister of Venus. And seeming now to have given over his amorous pursuit, which she had used her best endeavors to withstand, he provided one night an elegant entertainment, at which she was present, when he gave it in charge to the servant that waited upon her to serve her with several wines mingled together, which he accordingly did; whilst she, suspecting no such treachery and pleased with the rich flavor, drank more than suited with her modesty and, forgetting all her past troubles, became gay and merry; so that, seeing some of the women dance after the custom of Majorca, she also began to dance after the manner of the Alexandrians; which when Pericon observed, he supposed himself in a fair way of success, and plying her still with more meat and drink, continued this reveling the greatest part of the night. At length, when the guests departed, he went into her chamber with the lady, who, having at that time more exhilaration than modesty, undressed herself before him, as if he had been one of her women, and got into bed. He made no delay in following her, and having quenched the light, lay down by her side; she, nothing loath, suffered him to accomplish his purpose. After this experience of affairs whereof she had heretofore been ignorant, she repented her lost time, being sorry that she had not sooner yielded to his solicitations; and, without waiting for a request, often thereafter invited him to a repetition—not, indeed, by words, but by gestures fully as expressive. At length fortune, unwilling that she who was to have been the wife of a king should become the mistress of a nobleman, prepared for her a more barbarous and cruel alliance.

Pericon had a brother, twenty-five years of age, of a most complete person, called Marato; who, having seen her and flattering himself, from her behavior toward him, that he was not displeasing to her, supposing also that nothing obstructed his happiness except the guard which his brother had over her, consequently contrived a most cruel design, which was not long without its wicked effect. There was by chance a ship in the haven at that time, laden with merchandise bound for Chiarenza in Romania, of which two young Genoese were the masters, who only waited for the first fair wind to go out; with them Marato made a contract to receive him with the lady the following night. When night came, having ordered how the thing should be managed, he went openly to the house, nobody having the least mistrust of him, taking with him some trusty friends, whom he had secured for that service, and concealed them near the house; in the middle of the night, therefore, he opened the door to them, and they slew Pericon as he was asleep in bed with the lady; seizing upon her, whom they found awake and in tears, and threatening to kill her if she made the least noise. They took also everything of value that belonged to Pericon, with which Marato and the lady went instantly on board, whilst his companions returned about their business. The wind proving fair, they soon set sail, whilst the lady, reflecting on both her misfortunes, seemed to lay them much to heart for a time; till Marato, having wrought upon her senses by a powerful charm, known as Saint Cresci, consoled her so agreeably that she began to have the same affection for him that she had entertained for his brother; when fortune, as if not content with what she had already suffered, prepared another change of life for her.

Her person and behavior were such as to enamor the two masters of the ship, who neglected all other business to serve and please her, taking care all the while that Marato should have no cause to suspect it. And, being apprised of each other's love, they had a consultation together about it, when it was agreed to have her in common between them, as if love, like merchandise, admitted of partnership; and observing that she was narrowly watched by Marato, and their design thereby frustrated, they took the opportunity one day, as the ship was under full sail, and he standing upon the poop looking toward the sea, to go behind and throw him overboard; whilst the ship had sailed on a full mile before it was known that he had fallen in. As soon as the lady heard of it, and saw no likely means of recovering him again, she fell into fresh troubles when the two lovers came quickly to comfort her, using many kind and tender expressions which she did not understand; though, indeed, she did not then so much lament Marato as her own private misfortunes. After some little time, imagining that she was sufficiently comforted, they fell into a dispute concerning which should have the first enjoyment of her; and from words they drew their swords and came to blows, the ship's crew not being able to part them, when one soon fell down dead, the other being desperately wounded; which occasioned fresh uneasiness to the lady, who now saw herself left alone, without anyone to advise and help her; she was fearful also that the masters' relations and friends would turn their resentment against her; but the entreaties of the wounded survivor and their speedy arrival at Chiarenza, saved her from the danger of death.

She went on shore with him there, and they dwelt together at an inn; whilst the fame of her beauty was spread all over the city, till it reached the ears of the Prince of Morea, who was then by chance at Chiarenza. He was impatient to get a sight of her, and after he had seen her was so charmed that he could think of nothing else; and being told in what manner she came hither, he began to contrive means how to obtain her, which when the wounded man's relations understood, they immediately sent her to him, to her great joy, no less than the prince's, she now thinking herself freed from all danger. The prince, perceiving her rare accomplishments, joined to a matchless person, though he could have no information concerning her, yet concluded that she must be nobly descended; and such was his fondness for her that he treated her not as a mistress but a wife. She now recollecting what she had already suffered, and being well satisfied with her present situation, began to be easy and cheerful, whilst her charms increased to that degree that she was the chief subject of discourse throughout Romania.

Hereupon the Duke of Athens, a young and gay person, a relation also to the prince, had a mind to see her; and came one day thither under pretense of a visit to him, as usual, with a noble retinue, when he was handsomely entertained. Talking together, after some time, concerning the lady's great beauty, the duke asked whether she was such as fame had reported; to which the prince replied, "She far exceeds it; but let your own eyes convince you, and not my bare assertion." The duke soliciting the prince very earnestly to gratify his curiosity, they went into her apartment together, when she received them with great good manners and cheerfulness, being apprised of their coming; and though they could not have the pleasure of conversing together, as she understood little or nothing of their language, yet they looked upon her, the duke more especially, as a prodigy of nature, scarcely believing her to be a mortal creature; and, without perceiving how much of the amorous poison he had taken in by intently gazing upon her, and meaning only to gratify himself with the sight of her, he soon became over head and ears in love.

After they had parted from her and he had had time to reflect, he began to think the prince the happiest person in the universe, in being possessed of such a beauty; and, after much musing upon it, having more regard to his lust than to his honor, he resolved at all adventures to deprive him of that bliss and to secure it for himself; and having a heart to put what he had resolved into execution, setting all reason and justice aside, his mind was wholly taken up in devising a fit stratagem for his purpose.

One day, therefore, according to a most wicked agreement which he had made with a *valet de chambre* belonging to the prince, whose name was Ciuriaci, he gave secret orders to have his horses and baggage got ready for a sudden departure; and the following night, taking a friend with him, and being both completely armed, they were introduced by that servant into the prince's chamber, whom they found in his shirt, looking out of a window towards the sea, to take the cool air, the weather being very hot, whilst the lady was fast asleep. Having already instructed his friend what he would have done, he went softly up to the window and stabbed the prince with a dagger through the small of his back and threw him out. Now the palace was seated upon the seashore and very lofty; and the window whence the prince stood looking was directly over some houses which the force of the waves had beaten down and which were but little frequented; on which account, as the duke had before contrived it, there was no great likelihood of the affair being discovered. The duke's companion, when he saw that the work was done, took a cord which he carried with him for that purpose, and seeming as if he were going to caress Ciuriaci, threw it about his neck and drew it so tightly that he prevented his crying out, whilst the duke coming to his assistance, they soon dispatched and threw him down after the prince. This being done, and plainly perceiving that they were not heard or seen by the lady or anyone else, the duke took a light in his hand and went softly to the bed, where she lay in a sound sleep, and having gently removed the coverlet, stood beholding her some time with the utmost admiration. If she appeared so charming before in her garments, what was she not without them! Not at all dismayed with his late-committed sin, his hands yet reeking with blood, he crept into bed to her, she taking him all the while for the prince. After he had been with her for some time, he arose and ordered his people to seize her in such a manner that she could make no outcry; and, going through the same back door at which he had been introduced, he set her on horseback and carried her away towards Athens. But as he was married he did not choose to bring her thither, but left her at one of his country seats, a little way out of town, where he secretly kept her, to her great grief, but allowing her everything that was necessary to a person of her rank.

The prince's servants waited that day till noon expecting his rising; but hearing nothing of him, and thrusting open the chamber doors, which were only closed, and finding nobody within, they concluded that he and the lady were gone privately to some other place to divert themselves for a few days, and therefore thought no more about the matter. The next day it happened, by great chance, that a fool going amongst those ruinous houses where the dead bodies were lying, took hold of the cord that was about Ciuriaci's neck, and dragged him along after him, which surprised many people to whom he was known, who, by fair words and much persuasion, prevailed upon the fellow to show them where he had found him; and there, to the great grief of the whole city, they saw the prince's body also, which they caused to be interred with all due pomp and reverence. Inquiring afterward who should commit so horrid a deed, and perceiving that the Duke of Athens was not to be found but was gone privately away, they judged (as it really was) that he had done it, and taken the lady with him. Immediately they elected the prince's brother to be their sovereign, inciting him to revenge so horrid a fact and promising to assist him to the utmost of their power. He being afterward fully assured of the truth of what they had before but surmised, collected together all his relations, friends, and vassals, and mustering a powerful army, directed his course against the duke, who had no sooner heard of these preparations but he also levied a great army, and many princes came to his relief. Amongst the rest, the Emperor of Constantinople sent his son Constantine and his nephew Emanuel, attended by a goodly body of troops, who were kindly received by the duke, and the duchess more especially.

Things tending every day more and more to a war, the duchess had them both one day into her chamber, when, with abundance of tears, she recounted to them the whole history and occasion of the war, and the ill-usage she had received from the duke on account of this woman, whom she imagined he kept privately; and complaining very earnestly to them, she conjured them, for his honor and her own ease and comfort, to give her their best assistance. The two young lords knew all this matter before, and therefore, without asking many questions, they comforted her as well as they could, and informing themselves where the lady was kept, they took their leave. Hearing much talk of her marvelous beauty, they became very desirous of seeing her and entreated the duke to show her to them, who, never remembering what had happened to the prince on a like occasion, promised to do so; and, ordering a magnificent entertainment to be prepared in a pleasant garden belonging to the palace where the lady was kept, the next day he took them, and a few friends, to dine with her. Constantine, being seated at the table, began, full of admiration, to gaze upon her, declaring to himself that he had never seen anything like her, and that the duke, or any other person, was excusable, who, to possess so rare a beauty, should commit any act of baseness or treason; and looking still more and more upon her, and evermore commending her, it happened to him just as it had to the duke; for, going away quite enamored of her, he had given over all thoughts of the war, contriving only how to steal her away from the duke at the same time that he carefully concealed his love from everyone.

Whilst he was in this agitation, the time came when they were to march against the prince, who was now advancing near the duke's territories; upon which the duke, with Constantine and the rest, according to the resolution that was taken, marched out of Athens to secure the frontiers and to prevent the prince's passing any further. Continuing there for some days, and Constantine having still the lady at heart, and concluding, now the duke was absent, that he might more easily compass his intent, he, that there might be a pretense for his return, feigned himself extremely sick; and, with the duke's consent, leaving the command of his troops to Emanuel, he returned to Athens to his sister's, where, after some days, having encouraged her to talk of her husband's baseness in keeping a mistress, he at last said that, if she would give her consent, he would rid her of that trouble by removing the lady out of the way. The duchess, supposing that this was spoken out of pure regard to her and not to the lady, replied that she should be very glad if it could be done in such a manner as the duke should never know that she was in any way accessory, which Constantine fully promised; and she accordingly agreed that he should do it as he thought most advisable. He provided, therefore, with all secrecy, a light vessel, and sent it one evening near to the garden where the lady was kept, having first informed some of his people that were in it what he would have them do; and taking others with him to the house, he was kindly received by the servants in waiting there, and by the lady herself, who took a walk with him at his request, attended by the servants belonging to them both, into the garden; when, drawing her aside toward a door which opened to the sea, as if he had business to communicate from the duke, on a signal given the bark was brought close to the shore and she seized upon and carried into it, whilst he, turning back to the people that were with her, said, "Let no one stir or speak a word at the peril of his life; for my design is not to rob the duke of his lady, but to take away the reproach of my sister." To this, none being hardy enough to return an answer, Constantine, boarding the vessel and seating himself by the lady, who shed abundant tears, bid the men ply their oars and make the best of their way, which they accordingly did, so that they reached Aegina by the next morning. There they landed and reposed awhile; and during their stay Constantine found means to console his captive, who had great reason to curse her beauty. From thence they went to Chios, where, for fear of his father and to prevent her being taken away from him, he chose to abide as a place of security; and, though she seemed uneasy for a time, yet she soon recovered as she had done before and became reconciled to the state of life wherein bad fortune had thrown her.

In the meantime Osbech, King of the Turks, who was constantly at war with the Emperor, came by chance to Smyrna, and hearing how Constantine lived a lascivious life at Chios with a mistress that he had stolen, and no provision made for his safety, he went privately one night with some armed vessels and made a descent upon the town, surprising many people in their beds before they knew of his coming upon them and killing all that stood upon their defense; and after he had burnt and destroyed the whole country, he put the prisoners and booty which he had taken on board and returned to Smyrna. Upon taking a view of the prisoners, Osbech, who was a young man, saw this lady, and knowing that she was Constantine's mistress because she was found asleep in his bed, he was much pleased at it and took her for his own wife, and having celebrated their nuptials, they lived together very happily for several months.

Before this event happened, the Emperor had been making a treaty with Bassano, King of Cappadocia, who was to fall on Osbech on one side, whilst he attacked him on the other; but they could not come to a full agreement, because Bassano made a demand of some things which the other was unwilling to grant; yet now, hearing of what had befallen his son and being in the utmost concern, he immediately closed with the King of Cappadocia, requesting him to march with all expedition against Osbech, whilst he was preparing to invade him on his part. When Osbech heard of this, he assembled his army before he should be surrounded by two such mighty princes, and marched on to meet the King of Cappadocia, leaving his lady behind, with a faithful servant of his, at Smyrna; they soon came to a battle, wherein Osbech's army was entirely routed and himself slain.

Bassano remaining victorious, he proceeded on to Smyrna, the people making their submission to him all the way as he went. Meanwhile Osbech's servant, whose name was Antiochus, who had the lady in charge, although he was in years, yet seeing her so beautiful, and forgetting the regard which was due to his lord, soon became in love with her himself; and, as he understood her language, it was a great comfort to her, because she had been forced to live for some years like a deaf and dumb person for want of understanding other people or being understood by them. This gave him great advantages, and whilst his master was warring abroad, he spared no pains to gain her consent, in which he succeeded so well that she conceived a strong affection for him and became his mistress. But when they understood that Osbech was slain and that Bassano carried all before him, without waiting for his coming upon them, they fled away privately, taking with them what belonged to Osbech of any value, and came to Rhodes. They had not been there long before Antiochus was taken extremely ill; and having a merchant of Cyprus along with him, who was his great friend, and finding himself at the point of death, he resolved to bequeath to him the care of his lady and wealth also; and calling them both to him, he spoke as follows: "I find myself declining apace, which grieves me much, because I had never more pleasure in living than at present; yet one thing is a great comfort to me; namely, that I shall die in the arms of those two persons whom I love and value beyond all the rest of the world, that is to say, in yours, my dearest friend, and in that lady's whom I have loved ever since I have known her, more than my own life. I am uneasy, indeed, when I consider that I leave her here a stranger and destitute both of help and advice, and should be infinitely more so if you were not with us, who, I know, will take the same care of her, on my account, as you would of myself; therefore I entreat you, in case I should die, to take my affairs and her together under your protection and to act, with regard to both, as you think will be most for the comfort of my departed soul. And you, my dearest love, let me beg of you never to forget me, that I may boast, in the next world, that I have been loved by the fairest lady that ever nature formed. Assure me of these two things, and I shall die satisfied."

The merchant and lady were both much concerned, and promised to fulfill his desires, if he should chance to die; and soon afterward he departed this life, when they took care to have him decently interred; which being done, and the merchant having dispatched all his affairs and wanting to return home in a Catalan ship that was there, questioned the lady, to know what she intended to do, because it became necessary for him to go back to Cyprus; she made answer that she was willing to go with him, hoping that for the love he bore toward his friend he would regard her as his own sister. He replied that he was ready to oblige her in everything; and, that he might the better defend her from all injuries whatever, till they came to Cyprus, he should call her his wife. Being on board the ship, they had a cabin with one little bed allotted them, agreeably to the account they had given of themselves, by which means that thing was brought about which neither of them intended when they came from Rhodes; that is to say, thrown thus closely together, they were unable to resist the amorous incitements of their situation and forgot all the fine promises they had made to Antiochus. Before they reached Baffa, where the Cyprian merchant dwelt, they began to consider themselves as man and wife, and as such took up their abode there.

Now a certain gentleman happened to arrive at Baffa about that time, on his own private affairs, whose name was Antigonus, one advanced in years, and of more understanding than wealth; for in meddling much in the affairs of the King of Cyprus he had found fortune very unkind to him. Passing one day by the house where the lady lodged, the merchant being gone about his business to Armenia, and seeing her by chance at the window, he took more than ordinary notice of her, on account of her beauty; till at length he began to recollect he had seen her somewhere before but could by no means remember where. She, also, who had long been the sport of fortune, the time now drawing near when her troubles were to have an end, as soon as she saw Antigonus, remembered that she had seen him in no mean station in her father's service at Alexandria. And having now great hopes of regaining her former dignity by his advice and assistance, she took the opportunity of the merchant's absence to send for him. Being come to her, she modestly asked him whether he were not Antigonus of Famagosta, as she really believed.

He answered that he was, and added, "Madam, I am convinced that I know you, but I cannot call to mind where it is that I have seen you; therefore, if it be no offense, let me entreat you to tell me who you are."

The lady, perceiving him to be the same person, wept very much, and throwing her arms about his neck, asked him, at last, as one confounded with surprise, if he had never seen her at Alexandria. Then he immediately knew her to be Alatiel, the Sultan's daughter, whom they supposed to have been drowned; and being about to pay homage to her, she would not suffer him to do it, but made him sit down. He then, in a most humble manner, asked her where she had been, and whence she now came; because for some years it was believed, through all Egypt, that she was drowned. She replied, "I had much rather it had so happened than to have led such a life as I have done; and I believe my father, if he knew it, would wish the same." With these words the tears ran down her cheeks in great abundance; and he replied, "Madam, do not afflict yourself before it is necessary to do so; tell me only what has happened to you; perhaps it may be of such a nature that, by the help of God, we may find a remedy." "Antigonus," replied the fair lady, "I think when I see you that I behold my father: moved therefore with the like duty and tenderness that I owe to him, I shall reveal to you what I might have kept secret. There are few persons that I should desire to meet with sooner than yourself to advise me; if, therefore, when you have heard my whole story, you think there is any probability of restoring me to my former dignity, I must beg your assistance; if you think there is none, then I conjure you to tell no person living that you have either seen or heard anything about me."

After which, shedding an abundance of tears during the whole relation, she gave a full account of what had befallen her, from the time of her shipwreck at Majorca to that very hour. Antigonus showed himself truly concerned at what he had heard, and, thinking some little time about it, he said to her, "Madam, since it has never been known, in all your misfortunes, who you were, I will assuredly restore you to your father, to whom you shall be more dear than ever, and afterwards you shall be married to the King of Algarve." She inquiring how that could be brought about, he let her know in what manner he intended to do it. Therefore, that no delay might intervene to prevent it, he returned directly to Famagosta, and waiting upon the King, he thus addressed him: "My liege, you may, if you please, do at once great honor to yourself and service to me who am impoverished on your account, and that without any expense." The King desiring to know by what means, Antigonus thus answered: "A young lady is just come to Baffa—daughter to the Sultan—who was generally thought to have been drowned and who, to preserve her honor, hath undergone great calamities; she is now without means, and desirous of returning to her father; if, therefore, you will be so good as to send her home under my conduct, it will redound greatly to your honor and prove much to my advantage, nor can the Sultan ever forget the favor." The King, moved by a truly royal spirit, replied that he was well pleased with the proposal and caused her to be brought in great state to Famagosta, where she was received with all honor and respect, both by him and the Queen; and, being questioned by them concerning her misfortunes, she made such answers as she had been before taught by Antigonus.

In a few days afterward, at her own request, she was sent with a great retinue both of lords and ladies, and conducted all the way by Antigonus, to the Sultan's court; where, with what joy they were all received, it is needless here to mention. When they had rested awhile after their journey, the Sultan became desirous of knowing how it happened that she was now living, and where she had been all this time, without his being ever able to hear a word concerning her. Then she, who had all Antigonus' lectures perfectly by heart, spoke to her father thus:

"My father, about twenty days after my departure from you, our ship was split in the night by a violent tempest and driven on the western coasts, near to a place called Aguamorta; nor did I ever learn what befell the men that were in it. I only remember this, that when daylight appeared and I seemed recovered, as it were, from death to life, certain peasants of the country, spying the ship's wreck, came to plunder it; whilst I was carried first on shore, with two of my women, who were immediately borne away by some young fellows and taken different ways, so that I could never learn what became of either of them. I also was seized by two of them, making the best defense I could; and as they were dragging me toward the wood by the hair of my head, four persons on horseback came riding by, when they immediately left me and fled. The gentlemen on horseback, who appeared to possess some authority, came to me, and we spoke to each other, without knowing what either of us said. At last, after conferring together, they set me upon one of their horses, and carried me to a monastery of religious women, according to their laws, where I was received with great honor and respect; and in their company I served with much devotion Saint Waxeth-in-Deepdene, a miraculous saint, whom the women of that country hold in great esteem. And after I had been there for some time and learnt a little of their language, they began to inquire of me who I was and from whence I came; whilst I, fearful of telling the truth, lest they should have expelled me as an enemy to their religion, made them believe that I was daughter to a gentleman of Cyprus, who, sending me to be married to one of Crete, we happened to be driven thither by ill weather and shipwrecked. Conforming to their customs in many things, lest I should give offense, I was asked, at length, by the chief among them, whom they call Lady Abbess, whether I desired to return to Cyprus; and I answered that I desired nothing more. But she, tender of my honor, would never trust me with any persons that were going to Cyprus till, about two months ago, certain French gentlemen with their ladies came this way, one of whom was related to the abbess; who, understanding that they were going to visit the Holy Sepulcher at Jerusalem, where He whom they believe to be God was buried, after He had been put to death by the Jews, recommended me to them, and desired that they would deliver me to my father at Cyprus. What respect and civilities I received both from the gentlemen and their ladies, it would be needless to mention. Accordingly we went on shipboard, and came in a few days to Baffa where, when I saw myself arrived, a stranger to every person, nor knowing what to say to these gentlemen who were to present me to my father, behold, by the great providence of God, whom should I meet with upon the shore but Antigonus—the very moment we were landed? I called to him in our language, that none of them might understand us, and desired him to own me as his daughter. He easily understood my meaning, and showing great tokens of joy, entertained the company as well as his narrow circumstances would allow and brought me to the King of Cyprus, who received and sent me hither, with such marks of respect as I am no way able to relate. If there be anything omitted in this relation, Antigonus, who has often heard the whole from me, will report it."

Antigonus then, turning to the Sultan, said, "My lord, according both to her own account and the information of the gentlemen and their wives, she has said nothing but truth. One part only she has omitted, as not suiting with her great modesty to report; namely, what the gentlemen and their ladies told me of the most chaste and virtuous life that she had led amongst those religious women, and of their great sorrow at parting, which, if I were fully to recount to you, would take up all this day and night too. Let it suffice then that I have said enough, according to what I could both hear and see, to convince you that you have the fairest as well as the most virtuous daughter of any prince in the world."

The Sultan was overjoyed with this relation, begging over and over that God would pour down His blessings on all who had showed favor to his daughter, and particularly the King of Cyprus, who had sent her home so respectfully; and, having bestowed great gifts upon Antigonus, he gave him leave to return to Cyprus, sending letters, as also a special ambassador, to the King, to thank him on her account. And now, desiring that what he had formerly proposed should take effect—namely, that she should be married to the King of Algarve—he wrote to give him a full relation of the whole matter, adding that he should send for her, if he desired the match to proceed. The King was much pleased with the news, and sent for her in great state; and she, who had lain with eight men belike a thousand times, was put to bed to him as a pure virgin. As such he received her in full confidence, and she, as his queen, lived happily with him for the rest of their lives. Hence comes the saying: "A kissed mouth suffers no harm, but renews itself like the moon."

THE NOT-SO-DUMB GARDENER AND THE CONVENT OF WOMEN
(*The third day: the first story*)

In these parts there was—and still is—a convent of women, famous for its sanctity which, since I do not wish to injure its repute, I will not name. It consisted of only eight nuns and an abbess, all young, as well as an old fool of a gardener. The latter, being discontented with his wages, settled his account with the convent's bailiff and returned to his home. There, among others, who welcomed him, was a young laborer, hale and hearty, and (for a countryman) well favored. His name was Masetto, who asked him where he had been so long. The good man, whose name was Nuto, told him, whereupon Masetto asked him in what he had served the convent, and he, "I tended a great and goodly garden of theirs, and moreover I went whiles to the coppice for faggots and drew water and did other such small matters of service; but the nuns gave me so little wage that I could scarce find me in shoon withal. Besides, they are all young and methinketh they are possessed of the devil, for there was no doing anything to their liking. Nay, when I was at work whiles in the garden-orchard, quoth one, 'Set this here,' and another, 'Set that here,' and a third snatched the spade from my hand, saying, 'That is naught;' brief, they gave me so much vexation that I would leave work be and begone out of the garden; insomuch that, what with one thing and what with another, I would abide there no longer and took myself off. When I came away, their bailiff besought me, an I could lay my hand on anyone apt unto that service, to send the man to him, and I promised it him; but may God make him sound of the loins as he whom I shall get him, else will I send him none at all!" Masetto, hearing this, was taken with so great a desire to be with these nuns that he was all consumed therewith, judging from Nuto's words that he might avail to compass somewhat of that which he desired. However, foreseeing that he would fail of his purpose, if he discovered aught thereof to Nuto, he said to the latter, "Egad, thou didst well to come away. How is a man to live with women? He were better abide with devils. Six times out of seven they know not what they would have themselves."

After they had made an end of their talk, Masetto began to cast about what means he should take to be with them, and, feeling himself well able to do the offices of which Nuto had spoken, he had no fear of being refused on that head, but misdoubted him he might not be received, for that he was young and well looked. Wherefore, after pondering many things in himself, he bethought himself thus: "The place is far hence and none knoweth me there, an I can but make a show of being dumb, I shall for certain be received there." Having fixed upon this device, he set out with an ax he had about his neck, without telling any whither he was bound, and betook himself, in the guise of a beggarman, to the convent, where being come, he entered in and, as luck would have it, found the bailiff in the courtyard. Him he accosted with signs such as dumb folk use and made a show of asking food of him for the love of God and that in return he would, an it were needed, cleave wood for him. The bailiff willingly gave him to eat and after set before him divers logs that Nuto had not availed to cleave, but of all which Masetto, who was very strong, made a speedy dispatch. By and by, the bailiff, having occasion to go to the coppice, carried him thither and put him to cutting faggots; after which, setting the ass before him, he gave him to understand by signs that he was to bring them home. This he did very well; wherefore the bailiff kept him there some days, so he might have him do certain things for which he had occasion.

One day it chanced that the abbess saw him and asked the bailiff who he was. "Madam," answered he, "this is a poor deaf and dumb man, who came hither the other day to ask an alms; so I took him in out of charity and have made him do sundry things of which we had need. If he knew how to till the garden and chose to abide with us, I believe we should get good service of him; for that we lack such an one and he is strong and we could make what we would of him; more by token that you would have no occasion to fear his playing the fool with yonder lasses of yours." "I' faith," rejoined the abbess, "thou sayest sooth. Learn if he knoweth how to till and study to keep him here; give him a pair of shoes and some old hood or other and make much of him, caress him, give him plenty to eat." Which the bailiff promised to do. Masetto was not so far distant but he heard all this, making a show the while of sweeping the courtyard, and said merrily in himself, "An you put me therein, I will till you your garden as it was never tilled yet." Accordingly, the bailiff, seeing that he knew right well how to work, asked him by signs if he had a mind to abide there, and he replied on like wise that he would do whatsoever he wished; whereupon the bailiff engaged him and charged him till the garden, showing him what he was to do; after which he went about other business of the convent and left him.

Presently, as Masetto went working one day after another, the nuns fell to plaguing him and making mock of him, as ofttimes it betideth that folk do with mutes, and bespoke him the naughtiest words in the world, thinking he understood them not; whereof the abbess, mayhap supposing him to be tailless as well as tongueless, recked little or nothing. It chanced one day, however, that, as he rested himself after a hard morning's work, two young nuns, who went about the garden, drew near the place where he lay and fell to looking upon him, whilst he made a show of sleeping. Presently quoth one, who was somewhat the bolder of the twain, to the other, "If I thought thou wouldst keep my counsel, I would tell thee a thought which I have once and again had and which might perchance profit thee also." "Speak in all assurance," answered the other, "for certes I will never tell it to any." Then said the forward wench, "I know not if thou have ever considered how straitly we are kept and how no man dare ever enter here, save the bailiff, who is old, and yonder dumb fellow; and I have again and again heard ladies who come to visit us say that all other delights in the world are but toys in comparison with that which a woman enjoyeth whenas she hath to do with a man. Wherefore I have often had it in mind to make trial with this mute, since with others I may not, if it be so. And indeed he is the best in the world to that end, for that, e'en if he would, he could not nor might tell it again. Thou seest he is a poor silly lout of a lad, who hath overgrown his wit, and I would fain hear how thou deemest of the thing."

"Alack!" rejoined the other, "what is this thou sayest? Knowest thou not that we have promised our virginity to God?" "Oh, as for that," answered the first, "how many things are promised Him all day long, whereof not one is fulfilled unto Him! An we have promised it Him, let Him find Himself another or others to perform it to Him." "Or if," went on her fellow, "we should prove with child, how would it go then?"

Quoth the other, "Thou beginnest to take thought about ill before it cometh. When that betideth, then we will look to it. There will be a thousand ways to take care that it shall never be known, provided we ourselves tell it not."

The other, hearing this, and now having a greater itch than her companion to prove what kind of a beast a man was, said, "Well, then, how shall we do?" Quoth the first, "Thou seest it is nigh upon noon and methinketh the sisters are all asleep, save only ourselves; let us look about the garden if there be any there, and if there be none, what have we to do but to take him by the hand and carry him into yonder hut, whereas he harboureth against the rain, and there let one of us abide with him, whilst the other keepeth watch? He is so simple that he will do whatever we will."

Masetto heard all this talk and, disposed to compliance, waited but to be taken by one of the nuns. The latter having looked well all about and satisfied themselves that they could be seen from nowhere, she who had broached the matter came up to Masetto and aroused him, whereupon he rose incontinent to his feet. The nun took him coaxingly by the hand and led him, grinning like an idiot, to the hut, where, without overmuch pressing, he did what she would. Then, like a loyal comrade, having had her will, she gave place to her fellow, and Masetto, still feigning himself a simpleton, did their pleasure. Before they departed thence, each of the girls must needs once more prove how the mute could horse it, and after devising with each other, they agreed that the thing was as delectable as they had heard—nay, more so.

Accordingly, watching their opportunity, they went oftentimes at fitting seasons to divert themselves with the mute, till one day it chanced that one of their sisters, espying them in the act from the lattice of her cell, showed it to other twain. At first they talked of denouncing the culprits to the abbess, but, after, changing counsel and coming to an accord with the first two, they became sharers with them in Masetto's services, and to them the other three nuns were at divers times and by divers chances added as associates.

Ultimately, the abbess, who had not yet got wind of these doings, walking one day alone in the garden, the heat being great, found Masetto (who had enough of a little fatigue by day, because of overmuch posting it by night) stretched out asleep under the shade of an almond tree, and the wind lifting the fore part of his clothes, all abode discovered. The lady, beholding this and seeing herself alone, fell into that same appetite which had gotten hold of her nuns, and, arousing Masetto, carried him to her chamber, where, to the no small miscontent of the others, who complained loudly that the gardener came not to till the garden, she kept him several days, proving and reproving that delight which she had erst been wont to blame in others. At last she sent him back to his own lodging, but was fain to have him often again, and as, moreover, she required of him more than his share, Masetto was troubled. Unable to satisfy so many, he bethought himself that his playing the mute might, if it endured longer, result in his exceeding great hurt.

Therefore, being one night with the abbess, he gave loose to his tongue and bespoke her thus: "Madam, I have heard say that one cock sufficeth unto half a score hens, but that half a score men can ill or hardly satisfy one woman. Whereas needs must I serve nine, and to this I can no wise endure. Nay, for that which I have done up to now, I am come to such a pass that I can do neither little nor much; wherefore do ye either let me go in God's name or find a remedy for the matter."

The abbess, hearing him speak whom she held dumb, was all amazed and said, "What is this? Methought thou wast dumb." "Madam," answered Masetto, "I was indeed dumb, not by nature, but by reason of a malady which bereft me of speech, and only this very night for the first time do I feel it restored to me, wherefore I praise God as most I may." The lady believed this and asked him what he meant by saying that he had to serve nine.

Masetto told her how the case stood, whereby she perceived that she had no nun but was far wiser than herself; but, like a discreet woman as she was, she resolved to take counsel with her nuns to find some means of arranging the matter, without letting Masetto go, so the convent might not be defamed by him. Accordingly, having openly confessed to one another that which had been secretly done of each, they all of one accord, with Masetto's consent, so ordered it that the people round about believed speech to have been restored to him, after he had long been mute, through their prayers and by the merits of the saint in whose name the convent was intituled, and their bailiff being lately dead, they made Masetto bailiff in his stead and apportioned his toils on such wise that he could endure them.

Thereafter, albeit he begat upon them monikins galore, the thing was so discreetly ordered that nothing took vent thereof till after the death of the abbess, when Masetto began to grow old and had a mind to return home rich. The thing becoming known enabled him lightly to accomplish his desire, and thus Masetto, having by his foresight contrived to employ his youth to good purpose, returned in his old age, rich and a father, without being at the pains or expense of rearing children, to the place whence he had set out with an ax about his neck, avouching that thus did Christ entreat whoso set horns to his cap.

PUTTING THE DEVIL IN HELL
(*The third day: the tenth story*)

In the city of Capsa in Barbary, there lived a very rich man who, among his other children, had a fair and winsome young daughter, by name Alibech. She, not being a Christian and hearing many Christians who abode in the town mightily extol the Christian faith and the service of God, one day questioned one of them in what manner one might avail to serve God with the least hindrance. The other answered that they best served God who most strictly eschewed the things of the world, as those did who had betaken them into the solitudes of the deserts of Thebaïs. The girl, who was maybe fourteen years old and very simple, moved by no ordered desire, but by some childish fancy, set off next morning by stealth and all alone to go to the desert of Thebaïs, without letting any know her intent. After some days, her desire persisting, she won, with no little toil, to the deserts in question and, seeing a hut afar off, went thither and found at the door a holy man, who marveled to see her there and asked her what she sought. She replied that, being inspired of God, she went seeking to enter into His service and was now in quest of one who should teach her how it behooved to serve Him.

The worthy man, seeing her young and very fair and fearing lest, an he entertained her, the devil should beguile him, commended her pious intent and, giving her somewhat to eat of roots of herbs and wild apples and dates and to drink of water, said to her, "Daughter mine, not far hence is a holy man, who is a much better master than I of that which thou goest seeking; do thou betake thyself to him;" and put her in the way. However, when she reached the man in question, she had of him the same answer and, faring farther, came to the cell of a young hermit, a very devout and good man, whose name was Rustico and to whom she made the same request as she had done to the others. He, having a mind to make a trial of his own constancy, sent her not away, as the others had done, but received her into his cell, and the night being come, he made her a little bed of palm fronds and bade her lie down to rest thereon. This done, temptations tarried not to give battle to his powers of resistance, and he, finding himself grossly deceived by these latter, turned tail, without awaiting many assaults, and confessed himself beaten; then, laying aside devout thoughts and orisons and mortifications, he fell to revolving in his memory the youth and beauty of the damsel and bethinking himself what course he should take with her, so as to win to that which he desired of her, without her taking him for a debauched fellow.

Accordingly, having sounded her with sundry questions, he found that she had never known man and was in truth as simple as she seemed. Wherefore he bethought him how, under color of the service of God, he might bring her to his pleasure. In the first place he showed her with many words how great an enemy the devil was of God, and afterwards gave her to understand that the most acceptable service that could be rendered to God was to put the devil into hell, whereto He had condemned him. The girl asked him how this might be done; and he, "Thou shalt soon know that; do thou but as thou shalt see me do." So saying, he proceeded to put off the few garments he had and abode stark naked, as likewise did the girl, whereupon he fell on his knees, as he would pray, and caused her abide over against himself.

Matters standing thus and Rustico being more than ever inflamed in his desires to see her so fair, there came the resurrection of the flesh, which Alibech observing and marveling, "Rustico," quoth she, "what is that I see on thee which thrusteth forth thus and which I have not?" "Faith, daughter mine," answered he, "this is the devil thereof I bespoke thee; and see now, he giveth me such sore annoy that I can scarce put up with it." Then said the girl, "Now praised be God! I see I fare better than thou, in that I have none of yonder devil." "True," rejoined Rustico, "but thou hast otherwhat that I have not, and thou hast it instead of this." "What is that?" asked Alibech; and he, "Thou hast hell, and I tell thee methinketh God hath sent thee hither for my soul's health, for that, whenas this devil doth me this annoy, an it please thee have so much compassion on me as to suffer me put him back into hell, thou wilt give me the utmost solacement and wilt do God a very great pleasure and service, so indeed thou be come into these parts to do as thou sayst."

The girl answered in good faith, "Marry, father mine, since I have hell, be it whensoever it pleaseth thee;" whereupon quoth Rustico, "Daughter, blessed be thou; let us go then and put him back there, so he may after leave me in peace." So saying, he laid her on one of their little beds and taught her how she should do to imprison that accursed one of God. The girl, who had never yet put any devil in hell, for the first time felt some little pain; wherefore she said to Rustico, "Certes, father mine, this same devil must be an ill thing and an enemy in very deed of God, for that it irketh hell itself, let be otherwhat, when he is put back therein." "Daughter," answered Rustico, "it will not always happen thus;" and to the end that this should not happen, six times, or ever they stirred from the bed, they put him in hell again, insomuch that for the nonce they so took the conceit out of his head that he willingly abode at peace. But, it returning to him again and again the ensuing days and the obedient girl still lending herself to take it out of him, it befell that the sport began to please her and she said to Rustico, "I see now that those good people in Capsa spoke sooth, when they avouched that it was so sweet a thing to serve God; for, certes, I remember me not to have ever done aught that afforded me such pleasance and delight as putting the devil in hell; wherefore methinketh that whoso applieth himself unto aught other than God His service is a fool."

Accordingly, she came ofttimes to Rustico and said to him, "Father mine, I came here to serve God and not to abide idle; let us go put the devil in hell." Which doing, she said whiles, "Rustico, I know not why the devil fleeth away from hell; for, an he abode there as willingly as hell receiveth him and holdeth him, he would never come forth therefrom." The girl,

then, on this wise often inviting Rustico and exhorting him to the service
of God, so took the bombast out of his doublet that he felt cold what time
another had sweated. Wherefore he fell to telling her that the devil was
not to be chastised nor put into hell, save whenas he should lift up his
head for pride. "And we," added he, "by God's grace, have so baffled him
that he prayeth our Lord to suffer him abide in peace;" and on this wise
he for a while imposed silence on her. However, when she saw that he
required her not of putting the devil into hell, she said to him one day,
"Rustico, even if thy devil be chastened and give thee no more annoy, my
hell letteth me not be. Wherefore thou wilt do well to aid me with thy
devil in abating the raging of my hell, even as with my hell I have helped
thee take the conceit out of thy devil."

Rustico, who lived on roots and water, could ill avail to answer her calls
and told her that it would need overmany devils to appease hell, but he
would do what he might thereof. Accordingly, he satisfied her bytimes, but
so seldom it was but casting a bean into the lion's mouth. Whereat the girl,
believing she served not God as diligently as she would fain have done,
murmured somewhat. Whilst this debate was going on between Rustico, his
devil, and Alibech, her hell, for overmuch desire on the one part and lack of
power on the other, it befell that a fire broke out in Capsa and burnt
Alibech's father in his own house, with as many children and other family as
he had. By reason of this, she became heir to all his estate. Thereupon a
young man called Neerbale, who had spent all his substance in gallantry,
hearing that she was alive, set out in search of her. Finding her, before the
court had laid hands upon her father's estate, to Rustico's great satisfaction
but against her own will, he brought her back to Capsa, where he took her
to wife and succeeded, in her right, to the ample inheritance of her father.

There, being asked by the women at what she served God in the desert,
she answered (Neerbale having not yet lain with her) that she served Him
at putting the devil in hell and that Neerbale had done a grievous sin in
that he had taken her from such service. The ladies asked, "How putteth
one the devil in hell?" And the girl, what with words and what with gestures,
expounded it to them; whereat they set up so great a laughing that they
laugh yet and said, "Give yourself no concern, my child; nay, for that is
done here also and Neerbale will serve our Lord full well with thee at this."
Therefore, telling it from one to another throughout the city, they brought
it to a common saying there that the most acceptable service one could
render to God was to put the devil in hell, which byword, having passed
the sea hither, is yet current here. Wherefore do all you young ladies, who
have need of God's grace, learn to put the devil in hell, for that this is
highly acceptable to Him and pleasing to both parties and much good may
grow and ensue therefrom.

THE NIGHTINGALE
(*The fifth day: the fourth story*)

Not long ago there lived in Romagna a gentleman of great worth and good breeding named Lizio da Valbona, who had in his old age, by his wife, Giacomina, a daughter, Caterina. She was the most beautiful girl in the country and, since she was their only child, was loved and tended with the most scrupulous care, for they hoped to make a grand alliance by her.

Now there was a young gentleman named Ricciardo, who often came to the house and conversed with Messer Lizio and his wife, who treated him as though he were their own son. Ricciardo, however, did not look upon Caterina as his sister. The more he looked, the fairer he found her, and so fell deeply but secretly in love.

When Caterina perceived this, she soon showed a reciprocal affection. This delighted the young man exceedingly, and he was often desirous of expressing his passion to her, yet could never dare to do it. At length he had the opportunity and courage one day to say, "Pray, Caterina, let me not die for love." She replied, "Would to heaven you would show me the like mercy!" This greatly pleased him, and he added, "I shall study your will and pleasure in everything; do you find a way to make us happy together." She then returned, "Ricciardo, you see how I am watched, and therefore am unable to contrive the means for your coming to me; but if you can think of any method to do it, without my being censured, tell me, and I shall be very glad." He, after some consideration, said, "My dear Caterina, I can think of no other way but that you should get leave to lie in the gallery adjoining your father's garden; if I knew you were there at night, I should not fail to get there, however high it may be from the ground." She replied, "If you are resolved, I think I can manage to lie there." Ricciardo having given his promise, they hastily embraced, fearful of being observed, and he departed.

Next day, it being then toward the end of May, the girl complained to her mother that she had been unable to sleep the night before, the weather being so hot. "What do you mean, child?" answered she. "Hot weather, indeed! it is quite the contrary." "Mother," said Caterina, "you ought to speak to my father of the matter; but, however it be, you should remember that young folk are more affected in this way than their elders." "True enough," replied her mother, "but I cannot make cold or hot weather prevail, as you seem to desire; we must take these things as they are, according to the season. Perhaps the next night will be cooler, and you will sleep better." "Heaven grant it!" said Caterina; "but it is not usually seen that as summer comes on the heat decreases." "What would you have, then?" she asked. "If it be agreeable to my father and you," replied the girl, "I would have a little bed made up in the gallery near his chamber, over the garden, where I could lie and listen to the nightingale, and breathe the fresh air, and be more at ease than in our room." "Ah well," said her mother, "say no more; I shall speak to your father, and he must decide."

When Lizio's wife informed him of this affair, he, being old and rather testy, exclaimed, "What nightingale is this that she wants to put her to sleep? I'll make her sleep to the song of the cricket." Caterina, being told of this, not only lay awake all the next night, more from chagrin than heat, but kept her mother awake likewise, by her continual complaining; so that early in the morning the wife went to Messer Lizio, saying: "You have little care, truly, for your daughter. Why can you not let her lie in the gallery? The heat has troubled her so much that she has not slept all night long. And why should you wonder at her desire to hear the nightingale? She is but a child, and children are pleased with childish things." "Very well," he answered; "let a bed be made for her there, if you like to have it so, and let it be hung round with serge curtains; so that she may sleep, or listen to the nightingale as much as she pleases."

Caterina, being informed of this, immediately set about having a bed placed in the gallery on the coming night, and by a prearranged signal conveyed the news to Ricciardo, who knew what was then to be done. Messer Lizio, when his daughter had lain down to rest, locked the door leading to the gallery and went to bed also. So soon as he was assured that all was quiet, Ricciardo, with the aid of a ladder, climbed upon a wall, and from thence grasping some points of vantage on another wall (not without great trouble and danger), reached the gallery, where he was noiselessly but very joyfully received by the young lady; and after many fond kisses they retired to the couch, passing the night in a very agreeable manner—the nightingale singing several times.

The darkness at this season being of short duration, daybreak was approaching when the need for repose overcame them, and they fell asleep. Owing to the warmth of the air, they had cast off all their covering, and the girl lay with her right arm round her lover's neck, her left hand having wandered and held—it would scarcely be modest to say what—and in this fashion they were lying when Messer Lizio arose, who, calling to mind his daughter's anxiety to lie in the gallery, opened the door, saying to himself, "Let us see how the nightingale has made Caterina sleep." Then he advanced and drew the bed curtains, and beheld her and Ricciardo in the above-mentioned posture, and, recognizing the young man, he went to his wife's bedchamber, and called her up, saying: "Wife, get up; come and see how it was your daughter had so great a longing for the nightingale, which you will see she has now caught and holds fast." "Indeed! Is it possible?" she replied. "You shall see," said he, "if you make haste." Whereupon she clothed herself speedily and followed her husband, and when the curtains where drawn Madonna Giacomina saw plainly that her daughter had caught the nightingale, whose song she had admired, and would not let it escape. Then the old lady, resenting Ricciardo's deceit, would have exclaimed against him, but Lizio addressed her thus: "Wife, if you love me, take care you speak no word of this; for be sure that, if she has caught it, hers it shall be. Ricciardo comes of a good and wealthy family, with whom we might well be allied; and if he would escape without damage, he must first espouse her; then he will find that he has put his nightingale in his own cage, and not into another's." Whereupon the mother was satisfied, seeing that her husband was appeased; and considering that her daughter had passed the night well, and was then peacefully at rest, having secured the nightingale, she said no more.

Shortly afterwards Ricciardo awoke, and, seeing that already it was broad day, he gave himself up for lost and, turning to Caterina, said, "Alas, my dear, daylight has surprised us! What shall we do?" Whereupon Messer Lizio, who stood by, advanced and drew the curtains, saying, "We shall do very well." When the young man saw him, he was marvelously astonished and, sitting up in the bed, cried, "Sir, I ask your pardon in God's name; I acknowledge that I have wronged you and played the traitor and deserve death in return; do with me as you please, but I pray you to spare my life."

To which Lizio responded: "Ricciardo, the love I bore you and the trust I reposed in you, did not deserve this return; nevertheless, since it is so, and since the passions of youth have carried you so far, that you may avoid death, and I dishonor, I require that before you quit this place you take Caterina as your lawful wife; that, as she has been yours this last night, so shall she be as long as life shall last; thus shall you gain my love and your own life. If you consent not to this, commend your soul to God."

While these speeches were being uttered, poor Caterina relaxed her hold upon the nightingale, and, having recovered herself, began to weep plenteously and to beseech her father to forgive her lover, whom, on the other hand, she besought to submit himself to her father's will; though much solicitation was not needed in this matter, there being on one side shame for a fault committed and the resolve to amend; on the other, the desire to escape a sudden death; and, besides, fervent affection and a wish to remain in continued possession of the beloved object—all which made him say, frankly and without reservation, that he would satisfy her father in every way.

Messer Lizio thereupon borrowed from his wife one of her rings, and, without quitting the spot, made Ricciardo formally espouse Caterina. Which being accomplished, the old folk went away, saying: "Now rest yourselves, for perchance repose is what you most need." And being left alone, the lovers embraced and added a couple more to the nightingale's songs before getting up; and thus ended the first day. Afterward, when Ricciardo had conferred more fully with Lizio, a new espousal was arranged in the presence of relations and friends, as was becoming, and with much state and ceremony the bride was led home on the wedding day. Long after did the nightingale sing both by day and night, to the full satisfaction of both husband and wife.

THE FALSE PHANTOM
(*The seventh day: the first story*)

In Florence there lived a wool comber named Gianni Lotteringhi, a man who was better at his craft than in many other things. Something of a simpleton, he was often made leader of the Laudsingers, and he had other little offices of a similar sort, of which he was very proud. Since he was a man of some wealth, he gave many a good contribution to the clergy who, in return for a pair of hose, a robe, and other gifts, taught him many goodly orisons and gave him the paternoster in the common tongue—all of which he learned diligently.

Now he had a very fair and loveworthy wife, Mistress Tessa, who was extremely discreet. Knowing her husband's simplicity, and being enamored of Federigo di Neri Pegolotti, a brisk and handsome youth, and he of her, took order with a serving maid of hers that he should come speak with her at a very goodly country house which her husband had at Camerata, where she sojourned all the summer and whither Gianni came whiles to sup and sleep, returning in the morning to shop and bytimes to his Laudsingers.

Federigo, who desired this beyond measure, taking his opportunity, repaired thither on the day appointed him toward vespers and, Gianni not coming thither that evening, supped and lay the night in all ease and delight with the lady, who, being in his arms, taught him that night a good half dozen of her husband's lauds. Then, neither she nor Federigo purposing that this should be the last, as it had been the first, time, they took order together on this wise: So it should not be needful to send the maid for him each time, every day, as he came and went to and from a place he had a little farther on, he should keep his eye on a vineyard that adjoined the house, where he would see an ass's skull set up on one of the vine poles. When as he saw with the muzzle turned towards Florence, he should without fail and in all assurance betake himself to her that evening after dark; and if he found the door shut, he should knock softly thrice and she would open to him. But whenas he saw the ass's muzzle turned towards Fiesole, he should not come, for that Gianni would be there. And doing on this wise, they foregathered many a time.

But once, amongst other times, it chanced that, Federigo being one night to sup with Mistress Tessa and she having let cook two fat capons, Gianni, who was not expected there that night, came thither very late, whereat the lady was much chagrined, and having supped with her husband on a piece of salt pork, which she had let boil apart, caused the maid wrap the two boiled capons in a white napkin and carry them, together with good store of new-laid eggs and a flask of good wine, into a garden she had, whither she could go without passing through the house, and where she was wont to sup whiles with her lover, bidding her lay them at the foot of a peach tree that grew beside a lawn there.

But such was her trouble and annoy that she remembered not to bid the maid wait till Federigo should come and tell him that Gianni was there and that he should take the viands from the garden. Wherefore, she and Gianni betaking themselves to bed and the maid likewise, it was not long before Federigo came to the door and knocked softly once. The door was so near to the bedchamber that Gianni heard it plainly. His lady did also, but she pretended to be asleep, so that her husband might not be suspicious. After waiting a little, Federigo knocked again. Whereupon Gianni, wondering, nudged his wife and said, "Tessa, hearest thou what I hear? Meseemeth there is a knocking at our door."

The lady, who had heard it much better than he, made a show of awaking and said, "Eh? How sayst thou?" "I say," answered Gianni, "that meseemeth there is a knocking at our door." "Knocking!" cried she. "Alack, Gianni mine, knowst thou not what it is? It is a phantom, that hath these last few nights given me the greatest fright that ever was, insomuch that, whenas I hear it, I put my head under the clothes and dare not bring it out again until it is broad day." Quoth Gianni, "Go to, wife; have no fear, if it be so; for I said the *Te Lucis* and the *Intemerata* and such and such other pious orisons before we lay down, and crossed the bed from side to side in the name of the Father, the Son, and the Holy Ghost, so that we have no need to fear, for that, what power soever it have, it cannot avail to harm us."

The lady, fearing lest Federigo should perchance suspect otherwhat and be angered with her, determined at all hazards to arise and let him know that Gianni was there; wherefore quoth she to her husband, "That is all very well; thou sayst thy words, thou; but, for my part, I shall never hold myself safe nor secure, except we exorcise it, since thou art here." "And how is it to be exorcised?" asked he; and she, "I know full well how to exorcise it; for, the other day, when I went to the Pardon at Fiesole, a certain anchoress (the very holiest of creatures, Gianni mine, God only can say how holy she is), seeing me thus fearful, taught me a pious and effectual orison and told me that she had made trial of it several times, ere she became a recluse, and that it had always availed her. God knoweth I should never have dared go alone to make proof of it; but, now that thou art here, I would have us go exorcise the phantom."

Gianni answered that he would well, and accordingly they both arose and went softly to the door, without which Federigo, who now began to misdoubt him of somewhat, was yet in waiting. When they came thither, the lady said to Gianni, "Do thou spit, whenas I shall bid thee." And he answered, "Good." Then she began the conjuration and said, "Phantom, phantom, that goest by night, with tail upright thou camest to us; now get thee gone with tail upright. Begone into the garden to the foot of the great peach tree; there shalt thou find an anointed twice-anointed one and an hundred turds of my sitting hen; set thy mouth to the flagon and get thee gone again and do thou no hurt to my Gianni nor to me." Then to her husband, "Spit, Gianni," quoth she, and he spat. Federigo, who heard all this from without and was now quit of jealousy, had, for all his vexation, so great a mind to laugh that he was like to burst, and when Gianni spat, he said under his breath, "Would it were thy teeth!"

The lady, having thrice conjured the phantom on this wise, returned to bed with her husband, whilst Federigo, who had not supped, looking to sup with her, and had right well apprehended the words of the conjuration, betook himself to the garden and, finding the capons and wine and eggs at the foot of the great peach tree, carried them off to his house and there supped at his ease; and after, when he next foregathered with the lady, he had a hearty laugh with her anent the conjuration aforesaid.

THE WIFE WHO DID THE IMPOSSIBLE THREE TIMES
(The seventh day: the ninth story)

In Argos, an ancient city far more famous for its kings than anything else, there lived a nobleman called Nicostratus who, in the latter years of his life, married a young girl, Lydia, who was as lively as she was lovely. Being a nobleman, he kept many hounds, hawks, and servants, among whom was a young man by the name of Pyrrhus. Pyrrhus, whom his master trusted above all the rest, was well read and courteous; but he was also young and sprightly, and Lydia fell in love with him. She was so sore enamored that neither by day nor by night could she think of anything else but him. He, on the other hand—either because he did not or would not perceive her fondness for him—seemed unaffected by her. This caused her great grief and, in the hope of making him understand her passion, she summoned one of her favorite maids. "Lusca," said Lydia, "the things I have done for you should make you faithful as well as obedient; therefore, take care that you say nothing of what I am going to tell you except to the one person concerned. You see that I am young, disposed to mirth, in good health, and rich enough to procure whatever a woman may need—in short, only one thing afflicts me: that my husband is too old, wherefore I am deprived of those pleasures that are my due. This being so, it has long been my opinion that I ought not to be my own enemy, though fortune may have been so unkind as to bestow on me an elderly husband, but should seek to find some consolation. And, that I may be as prosperous in this as in other matters, I have fixed my affection on Pyrrhus as the most worthy; and truly I am never at ease save when he is present, nor can I live much longer if my desire to enjoy his company be not satisfied. If you have any regard for me, then, let him know my love for him in the best manner you are able; and entreat him, on my part, that he would please to come hither to me."

The girl promised to do so; and, on the very first opportunity, she took Pyrrhus aside and delivered her message. This surprised him very much, as not having the least notion of such a thing; and being apprehensive that it might be done to try him, he answered roughly, "Lusca, I can never think this comes from my lady, so take care what you say; or, if she did say so, you could never have her orders to disclose it; or, even admitting that, still I have that regard for my lord that I could never offer to do him such an injury; I charge you, then, let me hear no more about it." Lusca, not at all abashed at his stern way of speaking, replied, "Pyrrhus, I shall speak at all times what I am ordered by my lady to say, whether it offend you or not; but, for your part, you are no better than a brute." And she returned full of wrath to her mistress, who was fit to die on hearing it; and in a few days she said again, "You know, Lusca, that one stroke never fells an oak; then go once more to him who would fain be loyal at my expense, and represent my passion for him in such a manner that he may be affected with it; for, if he continues so indifferent, it will go near to cost me my life, and he, supposing himself the object of a trick or jest, may take some malicious mode of revenging himself."

The girl desired her to take courage; and, going again to Pyrrhus and finding him in good humor, she said, "I told you a few days ago, of the great regard my lady had for you; and I now assure you that, if you continue in the same resolution, she will never survive it; then be persuaded, or I shall think you the greatest fool in the world. What an honor will it be to have the love of such a lady! Consider how greatly you are obliged to Fortune; she offers you a most beautiful woman, and a refuge from your necessities. Who will be happier than yourself, if you be wise? Do but represent to yourself whatever an ambitious heart can desire; all will be yours. Open then your understanding to my words, and remember, that Fortune is wont to come once in our lives to us with cheerful looks and her lap full of favors; if we turn our backs on her at that time, we may thank ourselves should we be poor and miserable all the rest of our days. You talk of honor and fidelity; there is something indeed in that plea among friends; but, with regard to servants, in such a case they may do just as their masters would behave to them. Can you imagine, had you a wife, daughter, or sister that our master fancied, that he would stand on such nice terms of duty and loyalty as you now do to his wife? You can never be so foolish, but must believe that, if persuasion was ineffectual, he would make use of force. Let us serve them, therefore, as they would serve us: make use of Fortune's kind offer in your favor; for, depend upon it, if you refuse, setting aside the death of the lady, which will surely follow, you will repent the longest day you have to live."

Pyrrhus, who had made several reflections on what she had said before to him and had resolved to make a different reply if ever she came again, being now not averse to the thing, provided he could be assured she was in earnest, made answer. "Lusca, this is all true, I confess; but yet, as my lord is a very wise and provident person, and as I am entrusted with the management of all his affairs, I am afraid that my lady only does this to try me. Three things then I require that she shall do to clear all doubt from my mind; these being done, I shall be wholly at her service. The first is that she kill my lord's favorite hawk before his face; the second, that she send me a lock of his beard; and the third, one of his soundest and best teeth." These seemed to the maid very hard conditions, and more so to the mistress; but love, who is a good comforter as well as counselor, soon made her resolve. Accordingly, she sent him word, by the same person, that all three should be done; and, farther, that as he had such an opinion of his lord's wisdom, she would also undertake that they should prove their mutual affection in the most convincing manner, in his very presence, making him disbelieve the evidence of his own senses.

Pyrrhus then waited to see what course she meant to take. In a few days, therefore, Nicostratus having prepared a great entertainment for his friends, as he used frequently to do, just as the cloth was taken away she came into the hall, richly dressed, wearing a green samite, and there, in the presence of Pyrrhus and the whole company, went to the perch where this hawk was and unloosed him, as if she had a mind to take him upon her hand, when, taking him by the jesses, she dashed his brains out against the wall. And while Nicostratus was crying out, "Alas! my dear, what have you done?" she took no notice, but turned to the gentlemen present and said, "I should scarcely revenge myself of a king that was to do me an injury, if I wanted courage to wreak myself on a paltry hawk. You must know that this bird has deprived me of all the pleasure that wives expect from their husbands; for by break of day mine is up and on horseback, after his favorite diversion, whilst I lie in bed alone and neglected; for which reason I have long taken a resolution to do this thing, and only waited for an opportunity to have so many equitable judges present as I take you to be." The gentlemen, who supposed that Nicostratus had no other cause of quarrel with his wife, laughed heartily; and, turning to the husband, who seemed a good deal disturbed, they said, "She has done very well in taking her revenge upon this hawk," and, after a little raillery, she having retired, changed his resentment into a fit of laughter. Pyrrhus, upon seeing this, said to himself, "She has made a good beginning; Heaven grant that she may persevere!"

The hawk being thus dispatched, it was not long before she happened to be toying with her husband in the chamber, whilst he, pulling her gently by the hair, gave occasion for her to put Pyrrhus' second command in execution, wherefore, taking hold of a little lock of his beard, and laughing heartily at the same time, she pulled so hard that it was quite severed from his chin. He grew very peevish at this and was going to quarrel with her, when she said, "You make an angry face, truly, because I plucked half a dozen hairs off your beard; you were not sensible what I suffered when you pulled me by the hair just now." So, continuing their play from one word to another, she took care of the tuft of his beard, and sent it that very day to her lover.

She was more perplexed about the last thing; but, having an enterprising genius, which was rendered more so by love, she soon resolved on what means to use to bring that about. And, as Nicostratus had two pages in his house, given him by their fathers, who were gentlemen, in order to learn good breeding, one of whom carved his victuals, whilst the other filled out the wine, she made them both believe one day that their breath was very offensive; and she taught them, when they waited upon Nicostratus, to turn their heads on one side always, but never to speak of it to any person. This they believed, and did as they were directed. One day she said to him, "Did you ever take notice of your pages' behavior when they wait upon you?" "Yes," said he, "I have, and have been often going to ask them the reason." "Then," she replied, "you may spare yourself that trouble, for I can tell you. I have kept it some time from you, for fear of disobliging you; but, now I see other people take notice of it, I can conceal it no longer. It is then because you have a stinking breath; I know not what the cause may be, for it did not use to be so; but it is a most grievous thing, as you associate much with gentlefolk; therefore I would have you take some method or other to get rid of it." "What," said Nicostratus, "can it be owing to? Have I a foul tooth in my head?" She replied, "Perhaps you have;" and, taking him to the window, she made him open his mouth, and after looking carefully in every part, she said, "Oh, my dear! how could you bear with it so long? Here is a tooth which seems not only rotten, but entirely consumed, and if you keep it any longer in your mouth, will certainly decay all on the same side: I advise you then to have it out before it goes any farther." "As you think so," quoth he, "and I approve of it too, send instantly for a surgeon to draw it out." "Tell me of no surgeons," said she. "I will never agree to that; it seems to stand in such a manner that I think I could do it myself; besides, those fellows are so barbarous upon those occasions that my heart could never bear to have you under their hands. Therefore I will try to do it myself; and, if it gives you too much pain, I will let you go again, which those people will never do." Getting now an instrument for that purpose, and sending everyone out of the room, excepting Lusca, she shut the door and made him lie upon a bench; and laying hold of a tooth, whilst the maid kept him fast down, she put him to most intolerable pain and at length drew it out by main force; then, concealing the tooth and producing a rotten one, which she had ready in her hand, she said to the poor man, who was almost dead, "See here, what it was you had in your mouth so long!" and he, believing it to be so, though he had felt the most exquisite torture and complained much, yet as it was out, thought himself cured; and, having taken some good comforting things, the pain abated, and he went out of the chamber.

The tooth she immediately sent to her lover, who, being now convinced of her love, said he would hold himself in readiness to obey all her commands. But she, willing to give him some farther assurance, and thinking every hour an age till she could be with him, feigned herself to be very ill; and her husband coming one day after dinner to see her, and nobody with him but Pyrrhus, she desired that, by way of ease to her malady, they would take her into the garden. Accordingly, Nicostratus took hold of one arm, and Pyrrhus the other, and leading her thither, laid her on a grass plat under a fine pear tree; and sitting down by her, she, who had before instructed him what to do, said to Pyrrhus, "I have a great desire to have some of those pears; do you climb up into the tree and get me a few." Pyrrhus immediately went up, and, as he was throwing down some of the pears, he began to call out, "Ah, sir, what are you about? And you, madam, are you not ashamed to permit it? Think you that I am blind? Just now you were very sick; you must be quickly cured if you can act thus. But if you are so disposed, you have many private chambers where you might more fitly take your pleasure than in my presence." The lady turned to her husband and said, "What is Pyrrhus talking of? He is in a dream, surely." "No, madam," quoth he, "I am in no dream. What! Did you think I could not see you?" Nicostratus wondered, and said, "Surely, Pyrrhus, you are raving." "No, sir," he replied, "nor are you; had the pear tree been as much agitated as you were, every branch would now be bare." Quoth the lady, "What can be the meaning of this? Were I well enough I would actually go into the tree myself to behold the marvels that he talks of seeing from thence." Pyrrhus still continued in the same story, when Nicostratus desired him to come down and asked him what he had really seen. Pyrrhus replied, "I presume you think me a silly fellow and a dreamer: I assure you I saw you and my lady straitly conjoined, since you will force me to say so, and in descending I saw you arise and sit down in the place where you now are." "The man is out of his wits," quoth Nicostratus; "we neither of us so much as stirred from the place where we were sitting." "Then," said Pyrrhus, "I tell you I saw it."

Nicostratus was now more and more surprised, and said, "I will see whether this tree be enchanted or not, and whether such wonders can be seen by him who climbs it;" and therewith he ascended, when Pyrrhus and the lady without loss of time began their diversion. Nicostratus, on seeing this, cried out, "Thou wicked woman, what dost thou? And Pyrrhus too, in whom I have put such trust!" So saying, he prepared to come down, the lady and her lover answering, "We are sitting here," and while he descended, they resumed their seats in the spot where he had left them; nevertheless, though he found them thus, he violently reproached them, whilst Pyrrhus said to him, "Now, sir, I am convinced that I saw falsely myself, when I was in the tree, as yours is the same case; for I can be positive that you were mistaken. Do but reason with yourself; can it be supposed that your lady, who is the most virtuous and prudent of all others, should ever attempt to do such a thing before your very face? And, for my own part, I would be torn limb from limb before I would ever entertain such a thought, much less do so in your presence. The fault, then, in this mistaken appearance must proceed from the tree; for all the world could never have convinced me but that I saw you and my lady together in the same manner, if I had not heard from yourself that we appeared so to you." On this, she said, with a good deal of warmth, "Do you think, were I so loosely given, that I should be such a fool as to do these things before your eyes? No, if I had a mind to act in that way, it would be in some secret chamber, without letting you know anything of the matter."

Nicostratus, believing at last what they both said, came into a little better temper and began to talk of the novelty and wonder of the occurrence; whilst the lady, who seemed concerned for the ill opinion he had received concerning her, added, "Most certainly this tree shall never occasion any more scandal either to me or any other woman if I can help it: run, therefore, Pyrrhus, for an ax and cut it down, so avenging us both; though the ax might be well employed upon my husband's weak noddle for believing his own eyes in a case so repugnant both to common sense and reason."

Pyrrhus soon brought an ax and cut down the tree, upon which she said to Nicostratus, "My wrath is over, now I see my honor's adversary thus demolished." And he having begged her pardon, she freely forgave him, charging him, for the future, never to presume such a thing of her, who loved him more dearly than her own life. Thus the poor deluded husband returned into the house with his wife and Pyrrhus, where they often enjoyed one another's company with less inconvenience than when under the pear tree. Heaven grant us the like good fortune!

THE WIFE WHO SOLD HERSELF CHEAPLY
(*The eighth day: the first story*)

In Milan there lived a German by the name of Gulfardo, a stout fellow and very loyal to those he served. Moreover he was extremely punctual in the repayment of all loans which were made to him, and consequently many merchants were always ready to lend him any quantity of money he desired.

During his stay in Milan, he set his heart upon a fair lady named Madam Ambruogia, wife of a rich merchant, Guasparruolo Cagastraccio, his close friend. Loving her very discreetly, so that neither her husband nor any other suspected it, he sent one day to speak with her, praying her that it would please her vouchsafe him her favors and protesting that he, on his part, was ready to do whatsoever she should command him. The lady, after many parleys, came to this conclusion: that she was ready to do that which Gulfardo wished, provided two things should ensue thereof; one, that this should never be by him discovered to any and the other, that, as she had need of two hundred gold florins for some occasion of hers, he, who was a rich man, should give them to her; after which she would still be at his service.

Gulfardo, hearing this, and indignant at the sordidness of her whom he had accounted a lady of worth, was like to exchange his fervent love for hatred and, thinking to cheat her, sent back to her, saying that he would very willingly do this and all else in his power that might please her and that therefore she should e'en send him word when she would have him go to her, for that he would carry her the money, nor should any ever hear aught of the matter, save a comrade of his in whom he trusted greatly and who still bore him company in whatsoever he did. The lady, or rather, I should say, the vile woman, hearing this, was well pleased and sent to him, saying that Guasparruolo her husband was to go to Genoa for his occasions a few days thence and that she would presently let him know of this and send for him. Meanwhile, Gulfardo, taking his opportunity, repaired to Guasparruolo and said to him, "I have present occasion for two hundred gold florins, the which

I would have thee lend me at that same usance whereat thou art wont to lend me other monies." The other replied that he would well and straightway counted out to him the money.

A few days thereafterward Guasparruolo went to Genoa, even as the lady had said, whereupon she sent to Gulfardo to come to her and bring the two hundred gold florins. Accordingly, he took his comrade and repaired to the lady's house, where finding her expecting him, the first thing he did was to put into her hands the two hundred gold florins, in his friend's presence, saying to her, "Madam, take these monies and give them to your husband, whenas he shall be returned." The lady took them, never guessing why he said thus, but supposing that he did it so his comrade should not perceive that he gave them to her by way of price, and answered, "With all my heart; but I would fain see how many they are." Accordingly, she turned them out upon the table and, finding them full two hundred, laid them up, mighty content in herself. Then, returning to Gulfardo and carrying him into her chamber, she satisfied him of her person not that night only, but many others before her husband returned from Genoa.

As soon as the latter came back, Gulfardo, having spied out a time when Guasparruolo was in company with his wife, betook himself to him, together with his comrade aforesaid, and said to him, in the lady's presence. "Guasparruolo, I had no occasion for the monies, to wit, the two hundred gold florins, thou lentest me the other day, for that I could not compass the business for which I borrowed them. Accordingly, I brought them presently back to thy lady here and gave them to her; wherefore look thou cancel my account."

Guasparruolo, turning to his wife, asked her if she had had the monies, and she, seeing the witness present, knew not how to deny, but said, "Ay, I had them and had not yet remembered me to tell thee." Whereupon quoth Guasparruolo, "Gulfardo, I am satisfied; get you gone and God go with you; I will settle your account aright."

Gulfardo gone, the lady, finding herself cozened, gave her husband the dishonorable price of her baseness; and on this wise the crafty lover enjoyed his sordid mistress without cost.

THE REASONABLE VENGEANCE
(The eighth day: the eighth story)

There lived in Siena two well-to-do young citizens. One was named Zeppa and the other Spinelloccio. They were next-door neighbors, as intimate with each other as if they had been brothers, and each of them had a handsome wife.

It happened that Spinelloccio often went to Zeppa's house, whether his neighbor was at home or not. In due time he became not only familiar but too intimate with his friend's wife, although no one knew of it. However, one day while, unknown to his wife, Zeppa was at home, Spinelloccio came calling and was informed that his friend was not there. Whereupon Spinelloccio came into the house and, seeing no one else, took her in his arms. Although he saw them fondle one another, Zeppa said not a word. He waited to see how the affair would end, which was that the pair went very lovingly into the chamber and locked the door. This grieved him sorely; yet knowing that making a clamor would no way lessen the injury, but rather add to his shame, he began to think of some revenge, which should make no noise abroad, and with which he should yet be content. Resolving at length what to do, he went into the room after the friend was gone away, when he found her setting her headdress a little to rights, and said, "What are you doing, madam?" She replied, "Do not you see?" "Yes, truly," quoth he, "and I have seen a great deal more than I could have wished." So he charged her with the thing, and she came to an open confession, as it was in vain to deny it, and began to weep and beg his pardon.

He then said to her, "You see you have been guilty of a very great crime; if you expect forgiveness from me, you must resolve to do what I shall enjoin you, which is to tell Spinelloccio that about nine tomorrow morning he must find some pretense of leaving me to go to you, when I will return home; and as soon as you hear me coming in, do you make him go into that chest and lock him up, and after you have done this, I will tell you the rest. Have no doubt, however, about it, for I promise you I will do him no harm."

She agreed to do so; and the next day, the two friends being together at that time, Spinelloccio, who had promised the lady to be with her then, said to Zeppa, "I am engaged to go and dine with a friend, whom I would not have wait for me; so fare you well." Quoth Zeppa, "It is a long while till dinner yet." "Yes," replied the other, "but we have business to confer about, which requires me to be there in good time." So he left him, and took a little circuit, and went to the lady, and they had no sooner shut themselves in the chamber but Zeppa returned; when she, seeming to be very much frightened, made him go into the chest, as the husband had directed, and locked him up. Then came out to her husband, who asked her whether dinner was ready. She replied, "It will be soon." "Then," quoth he, "as Spinelloccio is gone to dine with a friend and left his wife at home by herself, do you call to her out of the window to come and dine with us." She readily obeyed out of fear for herself, and Spinelloccio's wife came, after much entreaty, hearing that her husband was not to dine at home; when Zeppa showed the greatest fondness towards her imaginable, and, making a sign for his wife to go into the kitchen, took his friend's wife by the hand, and led her into the chamber, when he made fast the door. Upon this she began to say, "Alas, sir, what mean you to do? Is this what you invite me for? This the loyalty you bear towards your friend?" Zeppa then drawing near to the chest where her husband was shut up, and holding her fast, said, "Madam, before you utter any complaints, hear what I am going to tell you. I have loved your husband as if he had been my brother; and yesterday, though he knows nothing of it, I found out that he has stretched this intimacy so far as to treat my wife as if she were yourself. Now I respect him so much that I intend to take no other revenge but what is agreeable to the quality of the offense: he has taken his pleasure with my wife, as I intend to do with you. If you will not consent to this, be assured I shall revenge myself in such a manner that both he and you shall have cause to repent it."

"Well, then," quoth she, "since your revenge is to fall upon me, I must be content. Do you only make my peace with your wife for what I shall do, in like manner as I am ready to forgive her." He promised to do that, and to make her a present also of a rich jewel. So saying, he made her recline upon the chest and took his revenge. Spinelloccio, hearing what passed above his head, was fit to burst with vexation; and, had it not been that he was prevented by the fear of Zeppa, he would have clamored against her and abused her, even shut up as he was. But considering again that he had given the provocation and that Zeppa had reason for what he had done and had behaved courteously and like a friend, he resolved to respect him more than ever.

Their pastime being ended, Zeppa and the lady arose, and she demanding the jewel which he had promised, he called up his wife, who said only this, "Now, my dear, we may cry quits," and withal she smiled. Quoth Zeppa then, "Here, open this chest," which she did; and he showed Spinelloccio to his wife. Now it would be difficult to say which of the two was most confounded, whether the man at seeing his friend and knowing that he was privy to what he had done, or the woman at seeing her husband and being conscious that he must have heard what had passed over his head. "Behold," added Zeppa, "this is the jewel; I now give it you." Spinelloccio hereupon came out of the chest, and said, "Zeppa, now we are even; and, as you said before to my wife, it is best for us to continue friends; and, there being nought divisible betwixt us except our wives, I hold it but just that we have them henceforth in common." To this his friend agreed, and all four then dined very amicably together; while from that time forth each of the wives had two husbands, and each of the husbands two wives, without jealousies or quarrels of any kind.

GEOFFREY CHAUCER (1340?-1400)

Geoffrey Chaucer, born in London about 1340, was in his forties when he wrote The Canterbury Tales. *Son of a wine merchant, Chaucer had been a soldier, traveler, diplomat, secret agent, attendant at the court, comptroller of customs, Member of Parliament, and clerk of the king's works: a doer as well as a dreamer. Living continually in action, his multiple activities brought him into contact with people of every kind and on every cultural level.*

All these sorts and strata are recorded in The Canterbury Tales, *a work of immense range, unflagging invention, and infinite gusto. Like Boccaccio, who accomplished in prose what Chaucer achieved in verse, Chaucer used a simple and convenient mechanism: a pilgrimage of many personalities on their way to the shrine of the martyred Thomas à Becket in Canterbury Cathedral, during which each of the travelers told a story. Since the company was extraordinarily mixed—it included a knight, a cook, a monk, a merchant, a friar, a steward, a prioress, and a much-married woman—the stories were equally varied. Consistent with the characters who related them, the tales were moral, bawdy, sentimental, satirical, classical, contemporary, didactic, disputatious, saintly, hilarious, philosophic, and unreservedly rough—they ranged the gamut from poignant tragedy to pure (or impure) farce. Most of the plots were not new; an avid reader, Chaucer found them in Ovid, Livy, Boccaccio, Masuccio, and other authors who collected legends, myths, anecdotes, and rude tales of ordinary life. Chaucer made the borrowed material his own. With a startling gift for comedy—he had begun as a traditionally romantic poet—and a genius for reality hitherto unknown in English literature, Chaucer so personalized his pilgrims that, in their very differences of occupation and attitude, they form a living cavalcade of medieval England.*

Chaucer did not live to complete his masterpiece. But among the seventeen hundred lines of The Canterbury Tales *are some of the most glorious as well as some of the rowdiest pages ever penned. Perhaps the liveliest, although certainly not the most refined, are those devoted to the red-bearded, heavy-set Miller, the "slender choleric" scurrilous Reeve (a kind of overseer), and the ever-so-earthy, inexhaustibly garrulous Wife of Bath, who had had five "church-door" husbands, not including "other company in youth." Each one is described in photographic detail, and the tone of each—hearty, broad, sly, sneering, corrupt, confidential, and sensually serene—is individual and convincing to the least inflection.*

The modern English translations which follow are by Theodore Morrison and are from The Portable Chaucer.

FROM: THE CANTERBURY TALES

THE MILLER'S TALE

> There used to be a rich old oaf who made
> His home at Oxford, a carpenter by trade,
> And took in boarders. With him used to dwell
> A student who had done his studies well,
> But he was poor; for all that he had learned,
> It was toward astrology his fancy turned.
> He knew a number of figures and constructions
> By which he could supply men with deductions
> If they should ask him at a given hour

Whether to look for sunshine or for shower,
Or want to know whatever might befall,
Events of all sorts, I can't count them all.
  He was known as handy Nicholas, this student.
Well versed in love, he knew how to be prudent,
Going about unnoticed, sly, and sure.
In looks no girl was ever more demure.
Lodged at this carpenter's, he lived alone;
He had a room there that he made his own,
Festooned with herbs, and he was sweet himself
As licorice or ginger. On a shelf
Above his bed's head, neatly stowed apart,
He kept the trappings that went with his art,
His astrolabe, his books—among the rest,
Thick ones and thin ones, lay his *Almagest*—
And the counters for his abacus as well.
Over his cupboard a red curtain fell
And up above a pretty zither lay
On which at night so sweetly would he play
That with the music the whole room would ring.
"Angelus to the Virgin" he would sing
And then the song that's known as "The King's Note."
Blessings were called down on his merry throat!
So this sweet scholar passed his time, his end
Being to eat and live upon his friend.
  This carpenter had newly wed a wife
And loved her better than he loved his life.
He was jealous, for she was eighteen in age;
He tried to keep her close as in a cage,
For she was wild and young, and old was he
And guessed that he might smack of cuckoldry.
His ignorant wits had never chanced to strike
On Cato's word, that man should wed his like;
Men ought to wed where their conditions point,
For youth and age are often out of joint.
But now, since he had fallen in the snare,
He must, like other men, endure his care.
  Fair this young woman was, her body trim
As any mink, so graceful and so slim.
She wore a striped belt that was all of silk;
A piecework apron, white as morning milk,
About her loins and down her lap she wore.
White was her smock, her collar both before
And on the back embroidered all about
In coal-black silk, inside as well as out.

And like her collar, her white-laundered bonnet
Had ribbons of the same embroidery on it.
Wide was her silken fillet, worn up high,
And for a fact she had a willing eye.
She plucked each brow into a little bow,
And each one was as black as any sloe.
She was a prettier sight to see by far
Than the blossoms of the early pear tree are,
And softer than the wool of an old wether.
Down from her belt there hung a purse of leather
With silken tassels and with studs of brass.
No man so wise, wherever people pass,
Who could imagine in this world at all
A wench like her, the pretty little doll!
Far brighter was the dazzle of her hue
Than a coin struck in the Tower, fresh and new.
As for her song, it twittered from her head
Sharp as a swallow perching on a shed.
And she could skip and sport as a young ram
Or calf will gambol, following his dam.
Her mouth was sweet as honey ale or mead
Or apples in the hay, stored up for need.
She was as skittish as an untrained colt,
Slim as a mast and straighter than a bolt.
On her simple collar she wore a big brooch pin
Wide as a shield's boss underneath her chin.
High up along her legs she laced her shoes.
She was a pigsney, she was a primrose
For any lord to tumble in his bed
Or a good yeoman honestly to wed.

Now sir, and again sir, this is how it was:
A day came round when handy Nicholas,
While her husband was at Oseney, well away,
Began to fool with this young wife, and play.
These students always have a wily head.
He caught her in between the legs, and said,
"Sweetheart, unless I have my will with you
I'll die for stifled love, by all that's true,"
And held her by the haunches, hard. "I vow
I'll die unless you love me here and now,
Sure as my soul," he said, "is God's to save."
She shied just as a colt does in the trave,
And turned her head hard from him, this young wife,
And said, "I will not kiss you, on my life!
Why, stop it now!" she said. "Stop, Nicholas!

Or I will cry out 'Help, help!' and 'Alas!'
Be good enough to take your hands away."
    "Mercy," this Nicholas began to pray,
And spoke so well and poured it on so fast
She promised she would be his love at last,
And swore by Thomas à Becket, saint of Kent,
That she would serve him when she could invent
Or spy out some good opportunity.
"My husband is so full of jealousy
You must be watchful and take care," she said,
"Or well I know I'll be as good as dead.
You must go secretly about this business."
    "Don't give a thought to that," said Nicholas.
"A student has been wasting time at school
If he can't make a carpenter a fool."
And so they were agreed, these two, and swore
To watch their chance, as I have said before.
When Nicholas had spanked her haunches neatly
And done all I have spoken of, he sweetly
Gave her a kiss, and then he took his zither
And loudly played, and sang his music with her.
    Now in her Christian duty, one saint's day,
To the parish church this good wife made her way,
And as she went her forehead cast a glow
As bright as noon, for she had washed it so
It glistened when she finished with her work.
    Serving this church there was a parish clerk
Whose name was Absolom, a ruddy man
With goose-gray eyes and curls like a great fan
That shone like gold on his neatly parted head.
His tunic was light blue and his nose red,
And he had patterns that had been cut through
Like the windows of St. Paul's in either shoe.
He wore above his tunic, fresh and gay,
A surplice white as a blossom on a spray.
A merry devil, as true as God can save,
He knew how to let blood, trim hair, and shave,
Or write a deed of land in proper phrase,
And he could dance in twenty different ways
In the Oxford fashion, and sometimes he would sing
A loud falsetto to his fiddle string
Or his guitar. No tavern anywhere
But he had furnished entertainment there.
Yet his speech was delicate, and for his part
He was a little squeamish toward a fart.

· This Absolom, so jolly and so gay,
With a censer went about on the saint's day
Censing the parish women one and all.
Many the doting look that he let fall,
And specially on this carpenter's young wife.
To look at her, he thought, was a good life,
She was so trim, so sweetly lecherous.
I dare say that if she had been a mouse
And he a cat, he would have made short work
Of catching her. This jolly parish clerk
Had such a heartful of love hankerings
He would not take the women's offerings;
No, no, he said, it would not be polite.

The moon, when darkness fell, shone full and bright,
And Absolom was ready for love's sake
With his guitar to be up and awake,
And toward the carpenter's, brisk and amorous,
He made his way until he reached the house
A little after the cocks began to crow.
Under a casement he sang sweet and low,
"Dear lady, by your will, be kind to me,"
And strummed on his guitar in harmony.
This lovelorn singing woke the carpenter
Who said to his wife, "What, Alison, don't you hear
Absolom singing under our bedroom wall?"

"Yes, God knows, John," she answered, "I hear it all."
What would you like? In this way things went on
Till jolly Absolom was woebegone
For wooing her, awake all night and day.
He combed his curls and made himself look gay.
He swore to be her slave and used all means
To court her with his gifts and go-betweens.
He sang and quavered like a nightingale.
He sent her sweet spiced wine and seasoned ale,
Cakes that were piping hot, mead sweet with honey,
And since she was town-bred, he proffered money.
For some are won by wealth, and some no less
By blows, and others yet by gentleness.

Sometimes, to keep his talents in her gaze,
He acted Herod in the mystery plays
High on the stage. But what can help his case?
For she so loves this handy Nicholas
That Absolom is living in a bubble.
He has nothing but a laugh for all his trouble.
She leaves his earnestness for scorn to cool

And makes this Absolom her proper fool.
For this is a true proverb, and no lie:
"It always happens that the nigh and sly
Will let the absent suffer." So 'tis said,
And Absolom may rage or lose his head
But just because he was farther from her sight
This nearby Nicholas got in his light.

Now hold your chin up, handy Nicholas,
For Absolom may wail and sing "Alas!"
One Saturday when the carpenter had gone
To Oseney, Nicholas and Alison
Agreed that he should use his wit and guile
This simple jealous husband to beguile.
And if it happened that the game went right
She would sleep in his arms the livelong night,
For this was his desire and hers as well.
At once, with no more words, this Nicholas fell
To working out his plan. He would not tarry,
But quietly to his room began to carry
Both food and drink to last him out a day,
Or more than one, and told her what to say
If her husband asked her about Nicholas.
She must say she had no notion where he was;
She hadn't laid eyes on him all day long;
He must be sick, or something must be wrong;
No matter how her maid had called and cried
He wouldn't answer, whatever might betide.

This was the plan, and Nicholas kept away,
Shut in his room, for that whole Saturday.
He ate and slept or did as he thought best
Till Sunday, when the sun was going to rest,
This carpenter began to wonder greatly
Where Nicholas was and what might ail him lately.
"Now, by St. Thomas, I begin to dread
All isn't right with Nicholas," he said.
"He hasn't, God forbid, died suddenly!
The world is ticklish these days, certainly.
Today I saw a corpse to church go past,
A man that I saw working Monday last!
Go up," he told his chore boy, "call and shout,
Knock with a stone, find what it's all about
And let me know."

     The boy went up and pounded
And yelled as if his wits had been confounded.
"What, how, what's doing, Master Nicholas?

How can you sleep all day?" But all his fuss
Was wasted, for he could not hear a word.
He noticed at the bottom of a board
A hole the cat used when she wished to creep
Into the room, and through it looked in deep
And finally of Nicholas caught sight.
This Nicholas sat gaping there upright
As though his wits were addled by the moon
When it was new. The boy went down, and soon
Had told his master how he had seen the man.

    The carpenter, when he heard this news, began
To cross himself. "Help us, St. Frideswide!
Little can we foresee what may betide!
The man's astronomy has turned his wit,
Or else he's in some agonizing fit.
I always knew that it would turn out so.
What God has hidden is not for men to know.
Aye, blessed is the ignorant man indeed,
Blessed is he that only knows his creed!
So fared another scholar of the sky,
For walking in the meadows once to spy
Upon the stars and what they might foretell,
Down in a clay pit suddenly he fell!
He overlooked that! By St. Thomas, though,
I'm sorry for handy Nicholas. I'll go
And scold him roundly for his studying
If so I may, by Jesus, heaven's King!
Give me a staff, I'll pry up from the floor
While you, Robin, are heaving at the door.
He'll quit his books, I think."
                           He took his stand
Outside the room. The boy had a strong hand
And by the hasp he heaved it off at once.
The door fell flat. With gaping countenance
This Nicholas sat studying the air
As still as stone. He was in black despair,
The carpenter believed, and hard about
The shoulders caught and shook him, and cried out
Rudely, "What, how! What is it? Look down at us!
Wake up, think of Christ's passion, Nicholas!
I'll sign you with the cross to keep away
These elves and things!" And he began to say,
Facing the quarters of the house, each side,
And on the threshold of the door outside,
The night spell: "Jesu and St. Benedict

From every wicked thing this house protect . . . "
   Choosing his time, this handy Nicholas
Produced a dreadful sigh, and said, "Alas,
This world, must it be all destroyed straightway?"
   "What," asked the carpenter, "what's that you say?
Do as we do, we working men, and think
Of God."
          Nicholas answered, "Get me a drink,
And afterwards I'll tell you privately
Of something that concerns us, you and me.
I'll tell you only, you among all men."
   This carpenter went down and came again
With a draught of mighty ale, a generous quart.
As soon as each of them had drunk his part
Nicholas shut the door and made it fast
And sat down by the carpenter at last
And spoke to him. "My host," he said, "John dear,
You must swear by all that you hold sacred here
That not to any man will you betray
My confidence. What I'm about to say
Is Christ's own secret. If you tell a soul
You are undone, and this will be the toll:
If you betray me, you shall go stark mad."
   "Now Christ forbid it, by His holy blood,"
Answered this simple man. "I don't go blabbing.
If I say it myself, I have no taste for gabbing.
Speak up just as you like, I'll never tell,
Not wife nor child, by Him that harrowed hell."
   "Now, John," said Nicholas, "this is no lie.
I have discovered through astrology
And studying the moon that shines so bright
That Monday next, a quarter through the night,
A rain will fall, and such a mad, wild spate
That Noah's flood was never half so great.
This world," he said, "in less time than an hour
Shall drown entirely in that hideous shower.
Yes, every man shall drown and lose his life."
   "Alas," the carpenter answered, "for my wife!
Alas, my Alison! And shall she drown?"
For grief at this he nearly tumbled down,
And said, "But is there nothing to be done?"
   "Why, happily there is, for anyone
Who will take advice," this handy Nicholas said.
"You mustn't expect to follow your own head.
For what said Solomon, whose words were true?

'Proceed by counsel, and you'll never rue.'
If you will act on good advice, no fail,
I'll promise, and without a mast or sail,
To see that she's preserved, and you and I.
Haven't you heard how Noah was kept dry
When, warned by Christ beforehand, he discovered
That the whole earth with water should be covered?"

   "Yes," said the carpenter, "long, long ago."
"And then again," said Nicholas, "don't you know
The grief they all had trying to embark
Till Noah could get his wife into the Ark?[1]
That was a time when Noah, I dare say,
Would gladly have given his best black wethers away
If she could have had a ship herself alone.
And therefore do you know what must be done?
This demands haste, and with a hasty thing
People can't stop for talk and tarrying.

   "Start out and get into the house right off
For each of us a tub or kneading trough,
Above all making sure that they are large,
In which we'll float away as in a barge.
And put in food enough to last a day.
Beyond won't matter; the flood will fall away
Early next morning. Take care not to spill
A word to your boy Robin, nor to Jill
Your maid. I cannot save her, don't ask why.
I will not tell God's secrets, no, not I.
Let it be enough, unless your wits are mad,
To have as good a grace as Noah had.
I'll save your wife for certain, never doubt it.
Now go along, and make good time about it.

   "But when you have, for her and you and me,
Brought to the house these kneading tubs, all three,
Then you must hang them under the roof, up high,
To keep our plans from any watchful eye.
When you have done exactly as I've said,
And put in snug our victuals and our bread,
Also an ax to cut the ropes apart
So when the rain comes we can make our start,
And when you've broken a hole high in the gable
Facing the garden plot, above the stable,
To give us a free passage out, each one,

[1] A stock comic scene in the mystery plays, of which the carpenter would have been an avid spectator.

Then, soon as the great fall of rain is done,
You'll swim as merrily, I undertake,
As the white duck paddles along behind her drake.
Then I shall call, 'How, Alison! How, John!
Be cheerful, for the flood will soon be gone.'
And 'Master Nicholas, what ho!' you'll say.
'Good morning, I see you clearly, for it's day.'
Then we shall lord it for the rest of life
Over the world, like Noah and his wife.
 "But one thing I must warn you of downright.
Use every care that on that selfsame night
When we have taken ship and climbed aboard,
No one of us must speak a single word,
Nor call, nor cry, but pray with all his heart.
It is God's will. You must hang far apart,
You and your wife, for there must be no sin
Between you, no more in a look than in
The very deed. Go now, the plans are drawn.
Go, set to work, and may God spur you on!
Tomorrow night when all men are asleep
Into our kneading troughs we three shall creep
And sit there waiting, and abide God's grace.
Go along now, this isn't the time or place
For me to talk at length or sermonize.
The proverb says, 'Don't waste words on the wise.'
You are so wise there is no need to teach you.
Go, save our lives—that's all that I beseech you!"
 This simple carpenter went on his way.
Many a time he said, "Alack the day,"
And to his wife he laid the secret bare.
She knew it better than he; she was aware
What this quaint bargain was designed to buy.
She carried on as if about to die,
And said, "Alas, go get this business done.
Help us escape, or we are dead, each one.
I am your true, your faithful wedded wife.
Go, my dear husband, save us, limb and life!"
 Great things, in all truth, can the emotions be!
A man can perish through credulity
So deep the print imagination makes.
This simple carpenter, he quails and quakes.
He really sees, according to his notion,
Noah's flood come wallowing like an ocean
To drown his Alison, his pet, his dear.
He weeps and wails, and gone is his good cheer,

And wretchedly he sighs. But he goes off
And gets himself a tub, a kneading trough,
Another tub, and has them on the sly
Sent home, and there in secret hangs them high
Beneath the roof. He made three ladders, these
With his own hands, and stowed in bread and cheese
And a jug of good ale, plenty for a day.
Before all this was done, he sent away
His chore boy Robin and his wench likewise
To London on some trumped-up enterprise,
And so on Monday, when it drew toward night,
He shut the door without a candlelight
And saw that all was just as it should be,
And shortly they went clambering up, all three.
They sat there still, and let a moment pass.
    "Now then, 'Our Father,' mum!" said Nicholas,
And "Mum!" said John, and "Mum!" said Alison,
And piously this carpenter went on
Saying his prayers. He sat there still and straining,
Trying to make out whether he heard it raining.
    The dead of sleep, for very weariness,
Fell on this carpenter, as I should guess,
At about curfew time, or little more.
His head was twisted, and that made him snore.
His spirit groaned in its uneasiness.
Down from his ladder slipped this Nicholas,
And Alison too, downward she softly sped
And without further word they went to bed
Where the carpenter himself slept other nights.
There were the revels, there were the delights!
And so this Alison and Nicholas lay
Busy about their solace and their play
Until the bell for lauds began to ring
And in the chancel friars began to sing.
    Now on this Monday, woebegone and glum
For love, this parish clerk, this Absolom
Was with some friends at Oseney, and while there
Inquired after John the carpenter.
A member of the cloister drew him away
Out of the church, and told him, "I can't say.
I haven't seen him working hereabout
Since Saturday. The abbot sent him out
For timber, I suppose. He'll often go
And stay at the granary a day or so.
Or else he's at his own house, possibly.

I can't for certain say where he may be."
    Absolom at once felt jolly and light,
And thought, "Time now to be awake all night,
For certainly I haven't seen him making
A stir about his door since day was breaking.
Don't call me a man if when I hear the cock
Begin to crow I don't slip up and knock
On the low window by his bedroom wall.
To Alison at last I'll pour out all
My love pangs, for at this point I can't miss,
Whatever happens, at the least a kiss.
Some comfort, by my word, will come my way.
I've felt my mouth itch the whole livelong day,
And that's a sign of kissing at the least.
I dreamed all night that I was at a feast.
So now I'll go and sleep an hour or two,
And then I'll wake and play the whole night through."
    When the first cockcrow through the dark had come
Up rose this jolly lover Absolom
And dressed up smartly. He was not remiss
About the least point. He chewed licorice
And cardamom to smell sweet, even before
He combed his hair. Beneath his tongue he bore
A sprig of Paris like a truelove knot.
He strolled off to the carpenter's house, and got
Beneath the window. It came so near the ground
It reached his chest. Softly, with half a sound,
He coughed, "My honeycomb, sweet Alison,
What are you doing, my sweet cinnamon?
Awake, my sweetheart and my pretty bird,
Awake, and give me from your lips a word!
Little enough you care for all my woe,
How for your love I sweat wherever I go!
No wonder I sweat and faint and cannot eat
More than a girl; as a lamb does for the teat
I pine. Yes, truly, I so long for love
I mourn as if I were a turtledove."
    Said she, "You Jack-fool, get away from here!
So help me God, I won't sing 'Kiss me, dear!'
I love another more than you. Get on,
For Christ's sake, Absolom, or I'll throw a stone.
The devil with you! Go and let me sleep."
    "Ah, that true love should ever have to reap
So evil a fortune," Absolom said. "A kiss,
At least, if it can be no more than this,

Give me, for love of Jesus and of me."
    "And will you go away for that?" said she.
    "Yes, truly, sweetheart," answered Absolom.
    "Get ready then," she said, "for here I come,"
And softly said to Nicholas, "Keep still,
And in a minute you can laugh your fill."
    This Absolom got down upon his knee
And said, "I am a lord of pure degree,
For after this, I hope, comes more to savor.
Sweetheart, your grace, and pretty bird, your favor!"
    She undid the window quickly. "That will do,"
She said. "Be quick about it, and get through,
For fear the neighbors will look out and spy."
    Absolom wiped his mouth to make it dry.
The night was pitch dark, coal-black all about.
Her rear end through the window she thrust out.
He got no better or worse, did Absolom,
Than to kiss her with his mouth on the bare bum
Before he had caught on, a smacking kiss.
    He jumped back, thinking something was amiss.
A woman has no beard, he was well aware,
But what he felt was rough and had long hair.
    "Alas," he cried, "what have you made me do?"
    "Te-hee!" she said, and banged the window to.
    Absolom backed away a sorry pace.
    "You've bearded him!" said handy Nicholas.
"God's body, this is going fair and fit!"
    This luckless Absolom heard every bit,
And gnawed his mouth, so angry he became.
He said to himself, "I'll square you, all the same."
    But who now scrubs and rubs, who chafes his lips
With dust, with sand, with straw, with cloth and chips,
If not this Absolom? "The devil," says he,
"Welcome my soul if I wouldn't rather be
Revenged than have the whole town in a sack!
Alas," he cries, "if only I'd held back!"
His hot love had become all cold and ashen.
He didn't have a curse to spare for passion
From the moment when he kissed her on the ass.
That was the cure to make his sickness pass!
He cried as a child does after being whipped;
He railed at love. Then quietly he slipped
Across the street to a smith who was forging out
Parts that the farmers needed round about.
He was busy sharpening colter and plowshare

When Absolom knocked as though without a care.
  "Undo the door, Jervice, and let me come."
  "What? Who are you?"
                            "It is I, Absolom."
  "Absolom, is it! By Christ's precious tree,
Why are you up so early? Lord bless me,
What's ailing you? Some gay girl has the power
To bring you out, God knows, at such an hour!
Yes, by St. Neot, you know well what I mean!"
  Absolom thought his jokes not worth a bean.
Without a word he let them all go by.
He had another kind of fish to fry
Than Jervice guessed. "Lend me this colter here
That's hot in the chimney, friend," he said. "Don't fear,
I'll bring it back right off when I am through.
I need it for a job I have to do."
  "Of course," said Jervice. "Why, if it were gold
Or coins in a sack, uncounted and untold,
As I'm a rightful smith, I wouldn't refuse it.
But, Christ's foot! How on earth do you mean to use it?"
  "Let that," said Absolom, "be as it may.
I'll let you know tomorrow or next day,"
And took the colter where the steel was cold
And slipped out with it safely in his hold
And softly over to the carpenter's wall.
He coughed and then he rapped the window, all
As he had done before.
                          "Who's knocking there?"
Said Alison. "It is a thief, I swear."
  "No, no," said he. "God knows, my sugarplum,
My bird, my darling, it's your Absolom.
I've brought a golden ring my mother gave me,
Fine and well cut, as I hope that God will save me.
It's yours, if you will let me have a kiss."
  Nicholas had got up to take a piss
And thought he would improve the whole affair.
This clerk, before he got away from there,
Should give *his* ass a smack; and hastily
He opened the window, and thrust out quietly,
Buttocks and haunches, all the way, his bum.
Up spoke this clerk, this jolly Absolom:
"Speak, for I don't know where you are, sweetheart."
  Nicholas promptly let fly with a fart
As loud as if a clap of thunder broke,
So great he was nearly blinded by the stroke,

And ready with his hot iron to make a pass,
Absolom caught him fairly on the ass.

Off flew the skin, a good handbreadth of fat
Lay bare, the iron so scorched him where he sat.
As for the pain, he thought that he would die,
And like a madman he began to cry,
"Help! Water! Water! Help, for God's own heart!"

At this the carpenter came to with a start.
He heard a man cry "Water!" as if mad.
"It's coming now," was the first thought he had.
"It's Noah's flood, alas, God be our hope!"
He sat up with his ax and chopped the rope
And down at once the whole contraption fell.
He didn't take time out to buy or sell
Till he hit the floor and lay there in a swoon.

Then up jumped Nicholas and Alison
And in the street began to cry, "Help, ho!"
The neighbors all came running, high and low,
And poured into the house to see the sight.
The man still lay there, passed out cold and white,
For in his tumble he had broken an arm.
But he himself brought on his greatest harm,
For when he spoke he was at once outdone
By handy Nicholas and Alison
Who told them one and all that he was mad.
So great a fear of Noah's flood he had,
By some delusion, that in his vanity
He had bought himself these kneading troughs, all three,
And hung them from the roof there, up above,
And he had pleaded with them, for God's love,
To sit there in the loft for company.

The neighbors laughed at such a fantasy,
And round the loft began to pry and poke
And turned his whole disaster to a joke.
He found it was no use to say a word.
Whatever reason he offered, no one heard.
With oaths and curses people swore him down
Until he passed for mad in the whole town.
Wit, clerk, and student all stood by each other.
They said, "It's clear the man is crazy, brother."
Everyone had his laugh about this feud.
So Alison, the carpenter's wife, got screwed
For all the jealous watching he could try,
And Absolom, he kissed her nether eye,

And Nicholas got his bottom roasted well.
God save this troop! That's all I have to tell.

THE REEVE'S TALE

At Trumpington, near Cambridge, a brook flows;
Across this brook, moreover, a bridge goes,
And on the said brook stands a mill as well,
And sober truth is all this that I tell.
A miller lived there once for many a day
Who dressed up like a peacock, proud and gay.
He could bagpipe, wrestle, shoot his bow, and fish,
Mend nets, and lathe a wooden cup or dish.
He wore a long knife always at his belt;
Keen as a sharpened sword its edges felt.
A fancy dagger too he kept upon him,
And no man dared to put a finger on him.
He kept a Sheffield blade inside his hose.
He had a round face and a flattened nose.
His skull had no more hair than a bald ape.
He went to market looking for a scrape,
And anyone who was bold enough to lay
A hand on him he swore he'd soon repay.
He was for fact a thief of corn and meal,
And a sly one at that, well versed to steal.
He was christened Simon; Simkin by nickname.
As for his wife, from noble kin she came.
Her father was the parson of the town,
And handsome was the dowry he paid down,
For Simkin with his blood would be allied.
She was brought up in a convent; in his pride
Simkin refused to take a wife, he said,
Unless she were a maiden and well bred,
To keep up his position as a yeoman.
Proud as a jay she was and pert, this woman.
They made a sight together, did this pair.
On saints' days he would march in front of her,
The muffler of his hood tied round his head
While she came after in a cape of red,
And Simkin sported long hose of the same.
No one dared speak to her except as "Dame,"
And none so hardy walking by the way
Who dared make love or even so much as play,
Unless he would be killed, with Simkin's wife,
For fear of Simkin's cutlass or his knife.

These jealous men are dangerous, as we know;
At least they want their wives to think them so.
She suffered a smirch by being a priest's daughter,
And so she was as snotty as ditch water,
Hoity-toity and down-her-nose to spare.
A lady ought to carry herself with care,
She thought, what for the duty of maintaining
Her kinship and her stock of convent training.

    Between them they produced a daughter, grown
To twenty or so, and save for her alone
No other children except one, a mere
Babe in the cradle, of some half a year.
She was a plump, well-rounded wench, this lass,
Her nose was flat, her blue eyes clear as glass,
Her buttocks broad, her breasts were round and high.
But she had lovely hair, and that's no lie.

    This parson, seeing that the girl was fair,
Had it in mind to name her as his heir,
Both of his goods and dwelling in addition.
He made her marriage hard, for his ambition
Was to bestow her, hand and property,
On blood that came of worthy ancestry.
The things that are Holy Church's must be spent
On blood that Holy Church owns by descent;
He would not leave his holy blood in the lurch
Although he might devour the Holy Church.

    A heavy toll this miller took, past doubt,
Of wheat and barley all the land about.
He cheated the great college worst of all
That stands in Cambridge, King's or Soler Hall,
For he was given their malt and wheat to grind.

    They happened, on a certain day, to find
Their steward sick, and in a stupor lying.
They thought for certain that he must be dying,
And so this miller stole both meal and corn
More than he ever had since he was born
A hundredfold; he thieved it courteously
Before, but now he stole outrageously.
The provost stormed and raised a great affair,
But all this gave the miller little care.
He talked big, swearing, "Not so," on his oath.

    Two poor young students at that time were both
Residing in this hall of which I speak.
They loved their fun, and they were full of cheek,
And merely for a jaunt they busily

Begged the provost to let them go and see
Their corn ground at the mill. Each bet his neck
The miller wouldn't cost them half a peck
Whether by force or sleight he tried to thieve.
At last the provost granted them his leave.

John was the name of one, Alan the other.
Their birthplace was the same, a town called Strother,
Far to the north, I cannot tell you where.

Alan gathered his stuff for this affair,
And got a horse to put the grain sack on.
So off went Alan the student, off went John,
Each with a sword and buckler by his side.
John knew the way, he did not need a guide,
And at the mill the grain sack down he set.
Alan spoke first. "What ho, Simkin, well met!
How are your lovely daughter and your wife?"

"Alan!" said Simkin. "Welcome, on my life,
And also John. What are you doing here?"

"Simkin," said John, "without a slave, no fear,
A man slaves for himself, or he's a fool.
Necessity, say the learned, knows no rule.
Our steward, I expect, will soon be dead
His molars ache so steadily in his head.
That's why I'm here, and Alan too. We've come
To grind our corn, and then to carry it home.
Help us get off as quickly as may be."

"Just as you want it," Simkin said. "Trust me.
What will you do while this is going on?"

"By God, right by the hopper," answered John,
"I'll stand, and see just how the corn goes in.
I've never watched yet, by my father's kin,
The way the hopper jiggles to and fro."

"Is that," said Alan, "what you're going to do?
I'll be down underneath, then, by my hide,
And notice how the grain comes down the slide
Into the trough. That's what I'll do for sport,
For, John, the fact is that I'm of your sort,
I am as bad a miller as you can be."

The miller smiled at their simplicity,
And thought, "All this is done for stratagem.
They fancy no one can hornswoggle them.
But yet I'll let them have some dust in the eye
For all the sleight in their philosophy.
The better the trap, no matter how sly they make it,
The more I'll pilfer when I'm ready to take it.

Instead of flour I'll give them only bran.
'The greatest scholar is not the wisest man,'
As one time to the wolf remarked the mare.
For all their cunning a fig is what I care."

Out through the doorway he slipped quietly
When he perceived his time, in secrecy,
And up and down he looked until he found
The students' horse, where it was standing bound
Behind the mill beneath a clump of trees.
Up to the horse as easy as you please
He went, and stripped the bridle off, and when
The horse was loose he started for the fen
Where there were wild mares running, and thundered in,
"Wehee," whinnying on through thick and thin.

This miller came back, not a word he spoke,
But with the students he began to joke
And worked until the corn was all well ground.
And when the meal was in the sack and bound
This John goes out and finds no horse at all.
"Help! Help!" and "God's bones!" he began to call.
"Our horse is gone! Come out here, Alan, man!
Step on your feet! Get going, if you can!
Our provost's palfrey lost—here's a fine deal!"

This Alan, he forgot both corn and meal.
His husbandry was wholly put to rout.
"What, where was he heading?" he began to shout.

The miller's wife came leaping in on the run.
"Off to the fen," she said, "your horse has gone
With the wild mares, as fast as he can go,
And no thanks to the hand that tied him so.
He should have put a better knot in the reins."

"Alas," this John said, "Alan, for Christ's pains,
Put down your sword, and I'll put mine down too.
A roe can't run, by God, the way I do.
He can't shake both of us, he won't be able.
God's heart, why didn't you put him in the stable?
God, Alan, you're a fool! Look what you've done!"

Hell-bent away these hapless scholars run
Straight toward the fen, Alan, and with him John.
The miller, when he saw that they were gone,
Took of their flour half a bushel or so
And told his wife to knead it into dough.
"I think these students had their fears," he said,
"But a miller can beat a scholar, head for head,
For all his knowledge. Let them go their way!

Look where they go! Yes, let the children play.
They'll work before they catch him, I'll be bound!"
  These luckless students ran and thrashed around
With "Whoa! Whoa! Stand! This way! Behind, keep clear!
You go and whistle, and I'll hold him here!"
To cut it short, until the very night
They could not, though they worked with all their might,
Lay hands upon their nag, he ran so fast,
Until they caught him in a ditch at last.
  Weary and wet as a cow is in the rain
Alan, and with him John, came back again.
"A curse," said John, "on the day that I was born!
Now we'll be in for ribbing and for scorn.
Our meal is stolen, men will call us 'fool,'
Yes, both the provost and our friends at school,
And specially the miller, damn the day."
  With Bayard the horse in hand along the way
Back to the mill, thus John moaned in his ire.
He found the miller sitting by his fire,
For it was night. No farther could they go,
But begged him for the love of God to show
Some comfort and some shelter for their penny.
  The miller answered them, "If there is any,
Such as it is, you two shall have your part.
My house is small, but with your scholar's art
You can by syllogisms make a place
A mile wide out of twenty feet of space.
See if there's room in this place for us each,
Or as your way is, puff it up with speech."
  "Now, by St. Cuthbert, always a bright word,
Simon," said John. "Well answered! I have heard
'A man must always take one of two things,
Such as he finds, or else such as he brings.'
But specially, and this I beg you most,
Get us some meat and drink, make cheer, good host,
And we will pay in full, you understand.
A man can't lure a hawk with empty hand.
Look, here's our silver, ready to be spent."
  His daughter off to town the miller sent
For ale and bread, and roasted them a goose,
And tied their horse, no more to wander loose.
In his own room he made them up a bed
With sheets and Chalon blankets neatly spread
Not more than ten or twelve feet from his own.
His daughter in the same room slept alone,

All by herself, in another bed close by.
It was the best that could be done—and why?
There were no roomier quarters, that was clear.
They talked and ate their supper with good cheer,
And pulled hard on the strong ale, as seemed best.
And when the midnight came, they went to rest.

This miller was well oiled by now. His head—
He had drunk so much—was pale instead of red.
He hiccups, and his voice comes through his nose
As if he had a cold. To bed he goes,
And with him goes his wife, jolly and gay,
Light in the head and frisking like a jay
So well her merry whistle had been wet.
Under the footboard of their bed they set
The cradle, where the child could nurse and rock.
And when they finish all that's in the crock
The daughter goes to bed; when she is gone
To bed goes Alan and to bed goes John.
And that was all—they did not need a drug.

This sleeping miller had so plied the jug
He snorted like a horse, nor did he mind
What might be happening to his tail behind.
His wife kept up a counterbass in style.
You could have heard them snore for half a mile.
The wench snored with them, too, for company.

Alan, who listened to this melody,
Poked John and said, "Are you sleeping through this row?
Have you ever heard such music before now?
Here's a fine service to wind up the day
Between them all! I hope they burn away
With itch. Did ever such a racket rend
A poor man's ears? The best of a bad end
I'll give them, though. I see I'll have no rest
All the long night; no matter, it's for the best.
For, John, by all the wealth of church or bench,
If it can be done, I'm going to lay that wench.
The law itself some easement offers us,
For John, there is a maxim that goes thus:
If in one point of law a man's aggrieved,
Then in some other he shall be relieved.
Our corn is stolen; that we can't gainsay,
And we've been in a bad fix this whole day.
Now since my loss is past all cancellation,
I will accept instead some compensation.
By the soul of God," he said, "it shall be so."

"Alan," this John replied, "think twice! You know
This miller is a dangerous man," he said.
"And if he wakes and jumps up out of bed
He may do both of us an injury."

"I hold him," Alan answered, "a mere flea."
He rose, and toward the wench began to creep.
This wench lay stretched out flat and fast asleep.
He got so near she could not bat an eye
Before it was too late to raise a cry.
To cut the story short, they were at one.
Now make hay, Alan, and we'll turn to John.

This John lay quiet for a moment or so.
He brooded to himself, and nursed his woe.
"This is a wicked prank, and no escape.
I see that I'm no better than an ape.
My pal, here, for his troubles and his harms
Has got the miller's daughter in his arms.
He took a chance, and now his needs are fed
While like a sack of chaff I lie in bed.
People will joke about this exploit soon,
And I'll pass for a fool and a poltroon.
I'll rise and take my chance too, come what may,
For 'nothing venture, nothing have,' they say."
He rose, and to the cradle cautiously
He went, and picked it up, and quietly
He put it by his bed's foot on the floor.

Soon after this the good wife ceased to snore.
She went out for a leak, and coming back,
She missed the cradle. She felt first on one tack,
Then on another, but cradle there was none.
"Mercy," she said, "I've almost been undone!
I almost got into the students' bed.
Eh, bless me, then I would have been ill sped!"
And on she gropes until her fingers find
The cradle and the bed, and in her mind
She had no thought of anything but good,
For there right by the bed the cradle stood,
And since the night was dark, she could not see,
But by the student crawled in trustfully,
And lay quite still, and would have gone to sleep.
Presently John the student, with a leap,
Pitched into this good woman. Year in, year out,
She had not had for long so merry a bout,
For hard and deep he went; he thrust like mad.
Such was the jolly life these students had

Until the cocks were tuning up their choir
For the third time. Alan began to tire
As dawn came near, for he had worked all night.
"Molly," he whispered, "it will soon be light.
I can't stay any longer at your side.
But sweetheart, always, though I walk or ride,
I am your own forever, till I die."

   "Now, darling, go," said Molly, "and good-by.
But wait, I'm going to tell you something still.
On the way home, as you go past the mill,
Stop at the door, and there, right in behind,
A good half-bushel loaf of bread you'll find.
Kneaded it was and baked from your own meal,
The very same I helped my father steal.
And now God keep you safe, sweetheart, God keep——"
And she was almost in a state to weep.

   Alan got up. "Before it's day, I ought
To crawl in with my crony here," he thought,
And promptly felt the cradle with his hand.
"I'm all turned round, I don't know where I stand.
My head is fuzzy with my work tonight.
By God, I haven't got my bearings right.
The cradle makes it certain I've gone wrong.
Here's where the miller and his wife belong,"
And as the devil would have it, groped his way
Straight to the bed in which the miller lay,
And in with John, or so he thought, he eased him,
And lay down by the miller instead, and seized him
Around the neck, and speaking softly, said:
"Wake up, you John, wake up, you dull swine's head!
Listen, for Christ's soul, to some noble sport,
For, by St. James, although it has been short,
Flat on her back, three times in this one night,
I've rolled the miller's daughter, while for fright
You lay here!"

        "Have you so," the miller said,
"False thief? God's dignity, you shall be dead!
Traitor! You dared abuse a daughter of mine,
False scholar, and she comes of such a line?"
And he seized Alan by the Adam's apple,
And Alan desperately began to grapple
With him, and let him have it on the nose,
And down the miller's chest a red stream flows
And on the floor, with nose smashed and teeth broke
They heave and roll like two pigs in a poke,

And up they get and down again they go
Till on a stone the miller stubbed his toe
And took a backward tumble on his wife,
Who had no notion of this frenzied strife,
For she had quickly dozed off with this John
Who had not slept all night for what went on;
But with the fall her eyes popped open wide,
And "Holy cross of Bromholm, help!" she cried.
"Into Thy hands, O Lord—on Thee I call!
Wake, Simon! Fiends and devils on me fall!
My ribs are burst. Help! I'm as good as dead.
Someone is on my belly and my head.
Help, Simkin, for the wicked students fight!"
     This John sprang up as quickly as he might
And here and there along the walls he fumbled
To find a staff; and out she also tumbled
And knew the right nooks better than he could,
And by the wall she found a stick of wood,
And saw a tiny glimmering of light
Where through a crack the moon was shining bright,
And by this glint of light she saw the two,
But could not tell for certain who was who
Except for something pale that she made out.
Seeing this thing of white, she had no doubt
It was a nightcap that the student wore.
Closer and closer with her stick she bore,
Thinking to hit this Alan a good bop,
And fetched the miller one on his bald top.
He went down with a yelp, "Ow, I am dying!"
These students beat him up and left him lying,
And quickly dressed and got their meal and horse
And set out promptly on their homeward course,
And at the mill they found, as Molly had said,
Well baked, their good half-bushel loaf of bread.
     So this proud miller got himself a beating,
And lost his labor, what with all his cheating,
And paid for every bit they had to sup,
Alan and John, who soundly beat him up.
His wife got hers, so did his daughter too.
This comes of the cheating that false millers do!
True are the words of this old proverb still:
"Let him not look for good whose works are ill,"
For tricked himself shall every trickster be.
     And now may God, throned high in majesty,

Bring us, both great and small, into His glory.
Thus I have paid the Miller with my story.

PROLOGUE TO THE WIFE OF BATH'S TALE

"Experience, though all authority
Was lacking in the world, confers on me
The right to speak of marriage, and unfold
Its woes. For, lords, since I was twelve years old
—Thanks to eternal God in heaven alive—
I have married at church door no less than five
Husbands, provided that I can have been
So often wed, and all were worthy men.
But I was told, indeed, and not long since,
That Christ went to a wedding only once
At Cana, in the land of Galilee.
By this example he instructed me
To wed once only—that's what I have heard!
Again, consider now what a sharp word,
Beside a well, Jesus, both God and man,
Spoke in reproving the Samaritan:
'Thou hast had five husbands'—this for a certainty
He said to her—'and the man that now hath thee
Is not thy husband.' True, he spoke this way,
But what he meant is more than I can say
Except that I would ask why the fifth man
Was not a husband to the Samaritan?
To just how many could she be a wife?
I have never heard this number all my life
Determined up to now. For round and round
Scholars may gloze, interpret, and expound,
But plainly, this I know without a lie,
God told us to increase and multiply.
That noble text I can well understand.
My husband—this too I have well in hand—
Should leave both father and mother and cleave to me.
Number God never mentioned, bigamy,
No, nor even octogamy; why do men
Talk of it as a sin and scandal, then?
    "Think of that monarch, wise King Solomon.
It strikes me that *he* had more wives than one!
To be refreshed, God willing, would please me
If I got it half as many times as he!
What a gift he had, a gift of God's own giving,
For all his wives! There isn't a man now living

Who has the like. By all that I make out
This king had many a merry first-night bout
With each, he was so thoroughly alive.
Blessed be God that I have married five,
And always, for the money in his chest
And for his nether purse, I picked the best.
In divers schools ripe scholarship is made,
And various practice in all kinds of trade
Makes perfect workmen, as the world can see.
Five husbands have had turns at schooling me.
Welcome the sixth, whenever I am faced
With yet another. I don't mean to be chaste
At all costs. When a spouse of mine is gone,
Some other Christian man shall take me on,
For then, says the Apostle, I'll be free
To wed, in God's name, where it pleases me.
To marry is no sin, as we can learn
From him; better to marry than to burn,
He says. Why should I care what obloquy
Men heap on Lamech and his bigamy?
Abraham was, by all that I can tell,
A holy man; so Jacob was as well,
And each of them took more than two as brides,
And many another holy man besides.
Where, may I ask, in any period,
Can you show in plain words that Almighty God
Forbade us marriage? Point it out to me!
Or where did he command virginity?
The Apostle, when he speaks of maidenhood,
Lays down no law. This I have understood
As well as you, milords, for it is plain.
Men may advise a woman to abstain
From marriage, but mere counsels aren't commands.
He left it to our judgment, where it stands.
Had God enjoined us all to maidenhood
Then marriage would have been condemned for good.
But truth is, if no seed were ever sown,
In what soil could virginity be grown?
Paul did not dare command a thing at best
On which his Master left us no behest.
  "But now the prize goes to virginity.
Seize it whoever can, and let us see
What manner of man shall run best in the race!
But not all men receive this form of grace
Except where God bestows it by his will.

The Apostle was a maid, I know; but still,
Although he wished all men were such as he,
It was only *counsel* toward virginity.
To be a wife he gave me his permission,
And so it is no blot on my condition
Nor slander of bigamy upon my state
If when my husband dies I take a mate.
A man does virtuously, St. Paul has said,
To touch no woman—meaning in his bed.
For fire and fat are dangerous friends at best.
You know what this example should suggest.
Here is the nub: he held virginity
Superior to wedded frailty,
And frailty I call it unless man
And woman both are chaste for their whole span.
    "I am not jealous if maidenhood outweighs
My marriages; I grant it all the praise.
It pleases them, these virgins, flesh and soul
To be immaculate. I won't extol
My own condition. In a lord's household
You know that every vessel can't be gold.
Some are of wood, and serve their master still.
God calls us variously to do his will.
Each has his proper gift, of all who live,
Some this, some that, as it pleases God to give.
    "To be virgin is a high and perfect course,
And continence is holy. But the source
Of all perfection, Jesus, never bade
Each one of us to go sell all he had
And give it to the poor; he did not say
That all should follow him in this one way.
He spoke to those who would live perfectly,
And by your leave, lords, that is not for me!
The flower of my best years I find it suits
To spend on the acts of marriage and its fruits.
    "Tell me this also: why at our creation
Were organs given us for generation,
And for what profit were we creatures made?
Believe me, not for nothing! Ply his trade
Of twisting texts who will, and let him urge
That they were only given us to purge
Our urine; say without them we should fail
To tell a female rightly from a male
And that's their only object—say you so?
It won't work, as experience will show.

Without offense to scholars, I say this,
They were given us for both these purposes,
That we may both be cleansed, I mean, and eased
Through intercourse, where God is not displeased.
Why else in books is this opinion met,
That every man should pay his wife his debt?
Tell me with what a man should hope to pay
Unless he put his instrument in play?
They were supplied us, then, for our purgation,
But they were also meant for generation.

   "But none the less I do not mean to say
That all those who are furnished in this way
Are bound to go and practice intercourse.
The world would then grant chastity no force.
Christ was a maid, yet he was formed a man,
And many a saint, too, since the world began,
And yet they lived in perfect chastity.
I am not spiteful toward virginity.
Let virgins be white bread of pure wheat seed.
Barley we wives are called, and yet I read
In Mark, and tell the tale in truth he can,
That Christ with barley bread cheered many a man.
In the state that God assigned to each of us
I'll persevere. I'm not fastidious.
In wifehood I will use my instrument
As freely by my Maker it was lent.
If I hold back with it, God give me sorrow!
My husband shall enjoy it night and morrow
When it pleases him to come and pay his debt.
But a husband, and I've not been thwarted yet,
Shall always be my debtor and my slave.
From tribulation he shall never save
His flesh, not for as long as I'm his wife!
I have the power, during all my life,
Over his very body, and not he.
For so the Apostle has instructed me,
Who bade men love their wives for better or worse.
It pleases me from end to end, that verse!"

   The Pardoner, before she could go on,
Jumped up and cried, "By God and by St. John,
Upon this topic you preach nobly, Dame!
I was about to wed, but now, for shame,
Why should my body pay a price so dear?
I'd rather not be married all this year!"

   "Hold on," she said. "I haven't yet begun.

You'll drink a keg of this before I'm done,
I promise you, and it won't taste like ale!
And after I have told you my whole tale
Of marriage, with its fund of tribulation—
And I'm the expert of my generation,
For I myself, I mean, have been the whip—
You can decide then if you want a sip
Out of the barrel that I mean to broach.
Before you come too close in your approach,
Think twice. I have examples, more than ten!
'The man who won't be warned by other men,
To other men a warning he shall be.'
These are the words we find in Ptolemy.
You can read them right there in his *Almagest*."

    "Now, Madam, if you're willing, I suggest,"
Answered the Pardoner, "as you began,
Continue with your tale, and spare no man.
Teach us your practice—we young men need a guide."

    "Gladly, if it will please you," she replied.
"But first I ask you, if I speak my mind,
That all this company may be well inclined,
And will not take offense at what I say.
I only mean it, after all, in play.

    "Now, sirs, I will get onward with my tale.
If ever I hope to drink good wine or ale,
I'm speaking truth: the husbands I have had,
Three of them have been good, and two were bad.
The three were kindly men, and rich, and old.
But they were hardly able to uphold
The statute which had made them fast to me.
You know well what I mean by this, I see!
So help me God, I can't help laughing yet
When I think of how at night I made them sweat,
And I thought nothing of it, on my word!
Their land and wealth they had by then conferred
On me, and so I safely could neglect
Tending their love or showing them respect.
So well they loved me that by God above
I hardly set a value on their love.
A woman who is wise is never done
Busily winning love when she has none,
But since I had them wholly in my hand
And they had given me their wealth and land,
Why task myself to spoil them or to please
Unless for my own profit and my ease?

I set them working so that many a night
They sang a dirge, so grievous was their plight!
They never got the bacon, well I know,
Offered as prize to couples at Dunmow
Who live a year in peace, without repentance!
So well I ruled them, by my law and sentence,
They were glad to bring me fine things from the fair
And happy when I spoke with a mild air,
For God knows I could chide outrageously.
　"Now judge if I could do it properly!
You wives who understand and who are wise,
This is the way to throw dust in their eyes.
There isn't on the earth so bold a man
He can swear false or lie as a woman can.
I do not urge this course in every case,
Just when a prudent wife is caught off base;
Then she should swear the parrot's mad who tattled
Her indiscretions, and when she's once embattled
Should call her maid as witness, by collusion.
But listen, how I threw them in confusion:
　"'Sir dotard, this is how you live?' I'd say.
'How can my neighbor's wife be dressed so gay?
She carries off the honors everywhere.
I sit at home. I've nothing fit to wear.
What were you doing at my neighbor's house?
Is she so handsome? Are you so amorous?
What do you whisper to our maid? God bless me,
Give up your jokes, old lecher. They depress me.
When I have a harmless friend myself, you balk
And scold me like a devil if I walk
For innocent amusement to his house.
You drink and come home reeling like a souse
And sit down on your bench, worse luck, and preach.
Taking a wife who's poor—this is the speech
That you regale me with—costs grievously,
And if she's rich and of good family,
It is a constant torment, you decide,
To suffer her ill humor and her pride.
And if she's fair, you scoundrel, you destroy her
By saying that every lecher will enjoy her;
For chastity at best has frail protections
If a woman is assailed from all directions.
　"'Some want us for our wealth, so you declare,
Some for our figure, some think we are fair,
Some want a woman who can dance or sing,

Some want kindness, and some philandering,
Some look for hands and arms well turned and small.
Thus, by your tale, the devil may take us all!
Men cannot keep a castle or redoubt
Longer, you tell me, than it can hold out.
Or if a woman's plain, you say that she
Is one who covets each man she may see,
For at him like a spaniel she will fly
Until she finds some man that she can buy.
Down to the lake goes never a goose so gray
But it will have a mate, I've heard you say.
It's hard to fasten—this too I've been told—
A thing that no man willingly will hold.
Wise men, you tell me as you go to bed,
And those who hope for heaven should never wed.
I hope wild lightning and a thunderstroke
Will break your wizened neck! You say that smoke
And falling timbers and a railing wife
Drive a man from his house. Lord bless my life!
What ails an old man, so to make him chide?
We cover our vices till the knot is tied,
We wives, you say, and then we trot them out.
Here's a fit proverb for a doddering lout!
An ox or ass, you say, a hound or horse,
These we examine as a matter of course.
Basins and also bowls, before we buy them,
Spoons, spools, and such utensils, first we try them,
And so with pots and clothes, beyond denial;
But of their wives men never make a trial
Until they are married. After that, you say,
Old fool, we put our vices on display.

  " 'I am in a pique if you forget your duty
And fail, you tell me, to praise me for my beauty,
Or unless you are always doting on my face
And calling me "fair dame" in every place,
Or unless you give a feast on my birthday
To keep me in good spirits, fresh and gay,
Or unless all proper courtesies are paid
To my nurse and also to my chambermaid,
And my father's kin with all their family ties—
You say so, you old barrelful of lies!

  " 'Yet just because he has a head of hair
Like shining gold, and squires me everywhere,
You have a false suspicion in your heart
Of Jenkin, our apprentice. For my part

I wouldn't have him if you died tomorrow!
But tell me this, or go and live in sorrow:
That chest of yours, why do you hide the keys
Away from me? It's my wealth, if you please,
As much as yours. Will you make a fool of me,
The mistress of our house? You shall not be
Lord of my body and my wealth at once!
No, by St. James himself, you must renounce
One or the other, if it drives you mad!
Does it help to spy on me? You would be glad
To lock me up, I think, inside your chest.
"Enjoy yourself, and go where you think best,"
You ought to say; "I won't hear tales of malice.
I know you for a faithful wife, Dame Alice."
A woman loves no man who keeps close charge
Of where she goes. We want to be at large.
Blessed above all other men was he,
The wise astrologer, Don Ptolemy,
Who has this proverb in his *Almagest:*
"Of all wise men his wisdom is the best
Who does not care who has the world in hand."
Now by this proverb you should understand,
Since you have plenty, it isn't yours to care
Or fret how richly other people fare,
For by your leave, old dotard, you for one
Can have all you can take when day is done.
The man's a niggard to the point of scandal
Who will not lend his lamp to light a candle;
His lamp won't lose although the candle gain.
If you have enough, you ought not to complain.
    " 'You say, too, if we make ourselves look smart,
Put on expensive clothes and dress the part,
We lay our virtue open to disgrace.
And then you try to reinforce your case
By saying these words in the Apostle's name:
"In chaste apparel, with modesty and shame,
So shall you women clothe yourselves," said he,
"And not in rich coiffure or jewelry,
Pearls or the like, or gold, or costly wear."
Now both your text and rubric, I declare,
I will not follow as I would a gnat!
    " 'You told me once that I was like a cat,
For singe her skin and she will stay at home,
But if her skin is smooth, the cat will roam.
No dawn but finds her on the neighbors calling

To show her skin, and go off caterwauling.
If I am looking smart, you mean to say,
I'm off to put my finery on display.
    " 'What do you gain, old fool, by setting spies?
Though you beg Argus with his hundred eyes
To be my bodyguard, for all his skill
He'll keep me only by my own free will.
I know enough to blind him, as I live!
    " 'There are three things, you also say, that give
Vexation to this world both south and north,
And you add that no one can endure the fourth.
Of these catastrophes a hateful wife—
You precious wretch, may Christ cut short your life!—
Is always reckoned, as you say, for one.
Is this your whole stock of comparison,
And why in all your parables of contempt
Can a luckless helpmate never be exempt?
You also liken woman's love to hell,
To barren land where water will not dwell.
I've heard you call it an unruly fire;
The more it burns, the hotter its desire
To burn up everything that burned will be.
You say that just as worms destroy a tree
A wife destroys her spouse, as they have found
Who get themselves in holy wedlock bound.'
    "By these devices, lords, as you perceive,
I got my three old husbands to believe
That in their cups they said things of this sort,
And all of it was false; but for support
Jenkin bore witness, and my niece did too.
These innocents, Lord, what I put them through!
God's precious pains! And they had no recourse,
For I could bite and whinny like a horse.
Though in the wrong, I kept them well annoyed,
Or oftentimes I would have been destroyed!
First to the mill is first to grind his grain.
I was always the first one to complain,
And so our peace was made; they gladly bid
For terms to settle things they never did!
    "For wenching I would scold them out of hand
When they were hardly well enough to stand.
But this would tickle a man; it would restore him
To think I had so great a fondness for him!
I'd vow when darkness came and out I stepped,
It was to see the girls with whom he slept.

Under this pretext I had plenty of mirth!
Such wit as this is given us at our birth.
Lies, tears, and needlework the Lord will give
In kindness to us women while we live.
And thus in one point I can take just pride:
In the end I showed myself the stronger side.
By sleight or strength I kept them in restraint,
And chiefly by continual complaint.
In bed they met their grief in fullest measure.
There I would scold; I would not do their pleasure.
Bed was a place where I would not abide
If I felt my husband's arm across my side
Till he agreed to square accounts and pay,
And after that I'd let him have his way.
To every man, therefore, I tell this tale:
Win where you're able, all is up for sale.
No falcon by an empty hand is lured.
For victory their cravings I endured
And even feigned a show of appetite.
And yet in old meat I have no delight;
It made me always rail at them and chide them,
For though the Pope himself sat down beside them
I would not give them peace at their own board.
No, on my honor, I paid them word for word.
Almighty God so help me, if right now
I had to make my last will, I can vow
For every word they said to me, we're quits.
For I so handled the contest by my wits
That they gave up, and took it for the best,
Or otherwise we should have had no rest.
Like a mad lion let my husband glare,
In the end he got the worst of the affair.
   "Then I would say, 'My dear, you ought to keep
In mind how gentle Wilkin looks, our sheep.
Come here, my husband, let me kiss your cheek!
You should be patient, too; you should be meek.
Of Job and of his patience when you prate
Y*our* conscience ought to show a cleaner slate.
He should be patient who so well can preach.
If not, then it will fall on me to teach
The beauty of a peaceful wedded life.
For one of us must give in, man or wife,
And since men are more reasonable creatures
Than women are, it follows that *your* features
Ought to exhibit patience. Why do you groan?

You want my body yours, and yours alone?
Why, take it all! Welcome to every bit!
But curse you, Peter, unless you cherish it!
Were I inclined to peddle my *belle chose*,
I could go about dressed freshly as a rose.
But I will keep it for your own sweet tooth.
It's your fault if we fight. By God, that's truth!'
  "This was the way I talked when I had need.
But now to my fourth husband I'll proceed.
  "This fourth I married was a roisterer.
He had a mistress, and my passions were,
Although I say it, strong; and altogether
I was young and stubborn, pert in every feather.
If anyone took up his harp to play,
How I could dance! I sang as merry a lay
As any nightingale when of sweet wine
I had drunk my draft. Metellius, the foul swine,
Who beat his spouse until he took her life
For drinking wine, had I only been his wife,
He'd never have frightened me away from drinking!
But after a drink, Venus gets in my thinking,
For just as true as cold engenders hail
A thirsty mouth goes with a thirsty tail.
Drinking destroys a woman's last defense
As lechers well know by experience.
  "But, Lord Christ, when it all comes back to me,
Remembering my youth and jollity,
It tickles me to the roots. It does me good
Down to this very day that while I could
I took my world, my time, and had my fling.
But age, alas, that poisons everything
Has robbed me of my beauty and my pith.
Well, let it go! Good-by! The devil with
What cannot last! There's only this to tell:
The flour is gone, I've only chaff to sell.
Yet I'll contrive to keep a merry cheek!
But now of my fourth husband I will speak.
  "My heart was, I can tell you, full of spite
That in another he should find delight.
I paid him for this debt; I made it good.
I furnished him a cross of the same wood,
By God and by St. Joce—in no foul fashion,
Not with my flesh; but I put on such passion
And rendered him so jealous, I'll engage
I made him fry in his own grease for rage!

On earth, God knows, I was his purgatory;
I only hope his soul is now in glory.
God knows it was a sad song that he sung
When the shoe pinched him; sorely was he wrung!
Only he knew, and God, the devious system
By which outrageously I used to twist him.
He died when I came home from Jerusalem.
He is buried near the chancel, under the beam
That holds the cross. His tomb is less ornate
Than the sepulcher where Darius lies in state
And which the paintings of Apelles graced
With subtle work. It would have been a waste
To bury him lavishly. Farewell! God save
His soul and give him rest! He's in his grave.

"And now of my fifth husband let me tell.
God never let his soul go down to hell
Though he of all five was my scourge and flail!
I feel it on my ribs, right down the scale,
And ever shall until my dying day.
And yet he was so full of life and gay
In bed, and could so melt me and cajole me
When on my back he had a mind to roll me,
What matter if on every bone he'd beaten me!
He'd have my love, so quickly he could sweeten me.
I loved him best, in fact; for as you see,
His love was a more arduous prize for me.
We women, if I'm not to tell a lie,
Are quaint in this regard. Put in our eye
A thing we cannot easily obtain,
All day we'll cry about it and complain.
Forbid a thing, we want it bitterly,
But urge it on us, then we turn and flee.
We are chary of what we hope that men will buy.
A throng at market makes the prices high;
Men set no value on cheap merchandise,
A truth all women know if they are wise.

"My fifth, may God forgive his every sin,
I took for love, not money. He had been
An Oxford student once, but in our town
Was boarding with my good friend, Alison.
She knew each secret that I had to give
More than our parish priest did, as I live!
I told her my full mind, I shared it all.
For if my husband pissed against a wall
Or did a thing that might have cost his life,

To her, and to another neighbor's wife,
And to my niece, a girl whom I loved well,
His every thought I wouldn't blush to tell.
And often enough I told them, be it said.
God knows I made his face turn hot and red
For secrets he confided to his shame.
He knew he only had himself to blame.

"And so it happened once that during Lent,
As I often did, to Alison's I went,
For I have loved my life long to be gay
And to walk out in April or in May
To hear the talk and seek a favorite haunt
Jenkin the student, Alice, my confidante,
And I myself into the country went.
My husband was in London all that Lent.
I had the greater liberty to see
And to be seen by jolly company.
How could I tell beforehand in what place
Luck might be waiting with a stroke of grace?
And so I went to every merrymaking.
No pilgrimage was past my undertaking.
I was at festivals, and marriages,
Processions, preachings, and at miracle plays,
And in my scarlet clothes I made a sight.
Upon that costume neither moth nor mite
Nor any worm with ravening hunger fell.
And why, you ask? It was kept in use too well.

"Now for what happened. In the fields we walked,
The three of us, and gallantly we talked,
The student and I, until I told him he,
If I became a widow, should marry me.
For I can say, and not with empty pride,
I have never failed for marriage to provide
Or other things as well. Let mice be meek;
A mouse's heart I hold not worth a leek.
He has one hole to scurry to, just one,
And if that fails him, he is quite undone.

"I let this student think he had bewitched me.
(My mother with this piece of guile enriched me!)
All night I dreamed of him—this too I said;
He was killing me as I lay flat in bed;
My very bed in fact was full of blood;
But still I hoped it would result in good,
For blood betokens gold, as I have heard.
It was a fiction, dream and every word,

But I was following my mother's lore
In all this matter, as in many more.

   "Sirs—let me see; what did I mean to say?
Aha! By God, I have it! When he lay,
My fourth, of whom I've spoken, on his bier,
I wept of course; I showed but little cheer,
As wives must do, since custom has its place,
And with my kerchief covered up my face.
But since I had provided for a mate,
I did not cry for long, I'll freely state.
And so to church my husband on the morrow
Was borne away by neighbors in their sorrow.
Jenkin, the student, was among the crowd,
And when I saw him walk, so help me God,
Behind the bier, I thought he had a pair
Of legs and feet so cleanly turned and fair
I put my heart completely in his hold.
He was in fact some twenty winters old
And I was forty, to confess the truth;
But all my life I've still had a colt's tooth.
My teeth were spaced apart; that was the seal
St. Venus printed, and became me well.
So help me God, I was a lusty one,
Pretty and young and rich, and full of fun.
And truly, as my husbands have all said,
I was the best thing there could be in bed.
For I belong to Venus in my feelings,
Though I bring the heart of Mars to all my dealings.
From Venus come my lust and appetite,
From Mars I get my courage and my might,
Born under Taurus, while Mars stood therein.
Alas, alas, that ever love was sin!
I yielded to my every inclination
Through the predominance of my constellation;
This made me so I never could withhold
My chamber of Venus, if the truth be told,
From a good fellow; yet upon my face
Mars left his mark, and in another place.
For never, so may Christ grant me intercession,
Have I yet loved a fellow with discretion,
But always I have followed appetite,
Let him be long or short or dark or light.
I never cared, as long as he liked me,
What his rank was or how poor he might be.

   "What should I say, but when the month ran out,

This jolly student, always much about,
This Jenkin married me in solemn state.
To him I gave land, titles, the whole slate
Of goods that had been given me before;
But my repentance afterward was sore!
He wouldn't endure the pleasures I held dear.
By God, he gave me a lick once on the ear,
When from a book of his I tore a leaf,
So hard that from the blow my ear grew deaf.
I was stubborn as a lioness with young,
And by the truth I had a rattling tongue,
And I would visit, as I'd done before,
No matter what forbidding oath he swore.
Against this habit he would sit and preach me
Sermons enough, and he would try to teach me
Old Roman stories, how for his whole life
The man Sulpicius Gallus left his wife
Only because he saw her look one day
Bareheaded down the street from his doorway.

"Another Roman he told me of by name
Who, since his wife was at a summer's game
Without his knowledge, thereupon forsook
The woman. In his Bible he would look
And find that proverb of the Ecclesiast
Where he enjoins and makes the stricture fast
That men forbid their wives to rove about.
Then he would quote me this, you needn't doubt:
'Build a foundation over sands or shallows,
Or gallop a blind horse across the fallows,
Let a wife traipse to shrines that some saint hallows,
And you are fit to swing upon the gallows.'
Talk as he would, I didn't care two haws
For his proverbs or his venerable saws.
Set right by him I never meant to be.
I hate the man who tells my faults to me,
And more of us than I do, by your pleasure.
This made him mad with me beyond all measure.
Under his yoke in no case would I go.

"Now, by St. Thomas, I will let you know
Why from that book of his I tore a leaf,
For which I got the blow that made me deaf.

"He had a book, *Valerius*, he called it,
And Theophrastus, and he always hauled it
From where it lay to read both day and night
And laughed hard at it, such was his delight.

There was another scholar, too, at Rome
A cardinal, whose name was St. Jerome;
He wrote a book against Jovinian.
In the same book also were Tertullian,
Chrysippus, Trotula, Abbess Héloïse
Who lived near Paris; it contained all these,
Bound in a single volume, and many a one
Besides; the Parables of Solomon
And Ovid's *Art of Love*. On such vacation
As he could snatch from worldly occupation
He dredged this book for tales of wicked wives.
He knew more stories of their wretched lives
Than are told about good women in the Bible.
No scholar ever lived who did not libel
Women, believe me; to speak well of wives
Is quite beyond them, unless it be in lives
Of holy saints; no woman else will do.
Who was it painted the lion, tell me who?
By God, if women had only written stories
Like wits and scholars in their oratories,
They would have pinned on men more wickedness
Than the whole breed of Adam can redress.
Venus's children clash with Mercury's;
The two work evermore by contraries.
Knowledge and wisdom are of Mercury's giving,
Venus loves revelry and riotous living,
And with these clashing dispositions gifted
Each of them sinks when the other is uplifted.
Thus Mercury falls, God knows, in desolation
In the sign of Pisces, Venus's exaltation,
And Venus falls when Mercury is raised.
Thus by a scholar no woman can be praised.
The scholar, when he's old and cannot do
The work of Venus more than his old shoe,
Then sits he down, and in his dotage fond
Writes that no woman keeps her marriage bond!
 "But now for the story that I undertook—
To tell how I was beaten for a book.
 "Jenkin, one night, who never seemed to tire
Of reading in his book, sat by the fire
And first he read of Eve, whose wickedness
Delivered all mankind to wretchedness
For which in his own person Christ was slain
Who with his heart's blood bought us all again.
'By this,' he said, 'expressly you may find

That woman was the loss of all mankind.'
    "He read me next how Samson lost his hair.
Sleeping, his mistress clipped it off for fair;
Through this betrayal he lost both his eyes.
He read me then—and I'm not telling lies—
How Deianeira, wife of Hercules,
Caused him to set himself on fire. With these
He did not overlook the sad to-do
Of Socrates with *his* wives—he had two.
Xantippe emptied the pisspot on his head.
This good man sat as patient as if dead.
He wiped his scalp; he did not dare complain
Except to say 'With thunder must come rain.'
    "Pasiphaë, who was the Queen of Crete,
For wickedness he thought her story sweet.
Ugh! That's enough, it was a grisly thing,
About her lust and filthy hankering!
And Clytemnestra in her lechery
Who took her husband's life feloniously,
He grew devout in reading of her treason.
And then he told me also for what reason
Unhappy Amphiaraus lost his life.
My husband had the story of *his* wife,
Eriphyle, who for a clasp of gold
Went to his Grecian enemies and told
The secret of her husband's hiding place,
For which at Thebes he met an evil grace.
Livia and Lucilia, he went through
Their tale as well; they killed their husbands, too.
One killed for love, the other killed for hate.
At evening Livia, when the hour was late,
Poisoned her husband, for she was his foe.
Lucilia doted on her husband so
That in her lust, hoping to make him think
Ever of her, she gave him a love drink
Of such a sort he died before the morrow.
And so at all turns husbands come to sorrow!
    "He told me then how one Latumius,
Complaining to a friend named Arrius,
Told him that in his garden grew a tree
On which his wives had hanged themselves, all three,
Merely for spite against their partnership.
'Brother,' said Arrius, 'let me have a slip
From this miraculous tree, for, begging pardon,

I want to go and plant it in my garden.'[1]
   "Then about wives in recent times he read,
How some had murdered husbands lying abed
And all night long had let a paramour
Enjoy them with the corpse flat on the floor;
Or driven a nail into a husband's brain
While he was sleeping, and thus he had been slain;
And some had given them poison in their drink.
He told more harm than anyone can think,
And seasoned his wretched stories with proverbs
Outnumbering all the blades of grass and herbs
On earth. 'Better a dragon for a mate,
Better,' he said, 'on a lion's whims to wait
Than on a wife whose way it is to chide.
Better,' he said, 'high in the loft to bide
Than with a railing wife down in the house.
They always, they are so contrarious,
Hate what their husbands like,' so he would say.
'A woman,' he said, 'throws all her shame away
When she takes off her smock.' And on he'd go:
'A pretty woman, unless she's chaste also,
Is like a gold ring stuck in a sow's nose.'
Who could imagine, who would half suppose
The gall my heart drank, raging at each drop?
   "And when I saw that he would never stop
Reading all night from his accursed book,
Suddenly, in the midst of it, I took
Three leaves and tore them out in a great pique,
And with my fist I caught him on the cheek
So hard he tumbled backward in the fire.
And up he jumped, he was as mad for ire
As a mad lion, and caught me on the head
With such a blow I fell down as if dead.
And seeing me on the floor, how still I lay,
He was aghast, and would have fled away,
Till I came to at length, and gave a cry.
'Have you killed me for my lands? Before I die,
False thief,' I said, 'I'll give you a last kiss!'
   "He came to me and knelt down close at this,
And said, 'So help me God, dear Alison,
I'll never strike you. For this thing I have done
You are to blame. Forgive me, I implore.'
So then I hit him on the cheek once more

---

[1] See the story from *Gesta Romanorum* on page 105.

And said, 'Thus far I am avenged, you thief.
I cannot speak. Now I shall die for grief.'
But finally, with much care and ado,
We reconciled our differences, we two.
He let me have the bridle in my hand
For management of both our house and land.
To curb his tongue he also undertook,
And on the spot I made him burn his book.
And when I had secured in full degree
By right of triumph the whole sovereignty,
And he had said, 'My dear, my own true wife,
Do as you will as long as you have life;
Preserve your honor and keep my estate,'
From that day on we had settled our debate.
I was as kind, God help me, day and dark
As any wife from India to Denmark,
And also true, and so he was to me.
I pray the Lord who sits in majesty
To bless his soul for Christ's own mercy dear."

MASUCCIO (1420–1476)

Little is known about Masuccio's life beyond the fact that he was born in Salerno in 1420, that his family was noble, that he married and had four children, was secretary to a lord, and that he died in or shortly after 1476.

Called a prime imitator of Boccaccio, Masuccio resented the designation. He claimed that his aim was not so much entertainment as admonition; he scourged the evils of his age, especially the inconstancy of women, the power of the rich, the avarice of rulers, and the vices of the priesthood. "It is when Masuccio begins to deal with the offenses which spring from the corruption of this or that particular class or sex," wrote one of his commentators, "that he seems to find his true vocation." Nevertheless, it is as a storyteller rather than a critic that Masuccio continues to be read. His Novellino is an assembly of fifty stories but, unlike the Decameron and similar collections, there is no attempt at continuity or connecting device. Each tale is told for its own sake; each begins with an "exordium" or dedication to some noted person and ends with a commentary by the author. In this volume, the dedication and author's comments are omitted and only the stories are retained. The translation is by W. G. Waters.

FROM: THE NOVELLINO

THE MIRACULOUS BREECHES

It chanced that there arrived in Catania a minor friar called Fra Nicolo who, though he wore the garb of poverty (clattering along with a pair of wooden sandals like prison shackles, with a bent neck), was nevertheless a fresh-colored and comely young fellow. He had studied at Perugia and had gained considerable knowledge of the doctrine taught there, and was a far-famed preacher. He declared, moreover, that he had in his possession certain relics by virtue of which God had shown, and still continued to show, many miracles. On account of this, and of the devout name enjoyed by his order, he drew to his preaching a marvelous great crowd of listeners.

It happened that, on a certain morning when he was preaching, he espied, amongst the crowd of women in the church, Madonna Agata, who seemed to him to be as a carbuncle stone in the midst of a mass of the whitest pearls, and, letting fall upon her many glances from the tail of his eye without in any way interrupting his sermon, he said to himself over and over again that the man who should be held worthy to enjoy the love of such a beautiful young woman might indeed reckon himself most fortunate.

Agata kept her eyes steadily fixed on the preacher and, since he appeared to her to be a young man comely beyond ordinary, she breathed a wish to herself that her husband were made more in the likeness of this handsome friar, and at the same time she began to think and to deliberate that she would like to go someday to make confession to Fra Nicolo. And thus as soon as she saw him come down from the pulpit she threw herself in his way and besought him that he would vouchsafe to hear her. The friar, though he was inwardly overjoyed at her request, made answer to her, so as not to allow the corruption of his mind to show itself on his countenance, that it was no part of his duty to hear confessions. Whereupon the lady replied: "But may not I, for the sake of Maestro Rogero, my good husband, ask to enjoy some privilege at your hands?" To this the friar answered: "Ah, then you are the wife of our procurator? For the respect I bear to him I will willingly listen to your confession." And when they had withdrawn themselves somewhat aside, and the friar had taken up his position in the place where they were accustomed to hear confessions, and the lady had gone down on her knees before him, she began to confess herself according to the accustomed rule.

After she had laid bare a certain portion of her offenses, telling the friar of the inordinate jealousy of her husband, she begged him of his kindness to let her know if there were any means within his power by which he could manage thoroughly to clear out of her husband's head all such delusions as these, believing perhaps that such ailments might be healed by herbs and plasters as her husband was wont to heal the sick folk under his charge. The friar set gladly to work to take into consideration a proposition such as this, for it seemed to him that now his good fortune was about to open for him the door which would give him the means of entering the path he so keenly desired to tread; wherefore, after he had given Madonna Agata consolation in somewhat flowery terms, he thus answered her: "My daughter, it is no marvel that your husband should be so jealous of you; indeed, were his mood otherwise, he would be held by me, and by every other man as well, to be something less than the prudent gentleman he is. Nor ought he to be charged with fault on this account, seeing that this circumstance arises solely from the working of nature, who, having produced you adorned with so great and angelic loveliness, has rendered it impossible that anyone should ever be the possessor of you without suffering the sharpest pangs of jealousy."

The lady, smiling somewhat at these words, saw that the time had now come when it behooved her to return to the attendants who were awaiting her. So, after certain other soft words had been spoken, she begged the friar to give her absolution. He therefore, having heaved a deep sigh, turned toward her with a pitiful countenance, and thus made answer: "My daughter, no one who is himself bound can give release to another, and for the reason that you in so short space of time have made me a slave, I can neither absolve you, nor loose myself, without aid from you." The courteous lady, who was by birth a Sicilian, quickly comprehended the real meaning of this ambiguous speech, remarking besides what a good-looking young fellow he was and feeling no small gratification that he seemed to be so mightily taken by her beauty. Still she was somewhat surprised to find that friars took thought of such matters, because, on account of her youth and the careful guard kept over her by her husband, she had not only been kept from all dealing with religious persons of every sort, but had even been made to believe that the making of men into friars differed nought from the making of cocks into capons. However, she saw clearly enough that Fra Nicolo was more of a cock than a capon, and with a longing such as she had never before known, and with the firm resolve to give him her love at all hazard, she thus answered him: "My father, leave all your cares to me, forasmuch as I, coming here a free woman, must now return home the slave of you and of love."

To this speech the friar replied, his heart filled with the greatest joy he had ever known: "Since then our desires run towards the same point, can you not devise some way by which we both of us, breaking forth at the same moment from this cruel prison, may taste the full joy our lusty youth permits?" To this she answered that she would willingly agree to this, supposing that a way could be found for its accomplishment, adding these words: "And now at this moment I am reminded of a plan whereby, in spite of the inordinate jealousy of my husband, we may be enabled to carry out our intention. For you must know that almost every month I am wont to be afflicted with a very grave distemper of the heart, so severe that it robs me of all power of sensation, nor up to this present time have I been able in the least degree to remedy the same by any device of the physicians. Indeed, certain women of experience in such matters have declared that my ailment proceeds from the womb, because I am young and fit to bear children, but by reason of the age of my husband I am not able to do this. Wherefore I have thought that on one of those days when my husband goes to ply his calling in the country, I might feign to be taken ill with one of my accustomed attacks. Then, having sent for you in haste, I might beg you to lend me certain relics of San Griffone, and you, on your part, must be prepared to come with them to me secretly. Afterwards, by the aid of a trusty maid of mine, we can meet and take our pleasure together."

As soon as she had returned home, the lady made known to her maid the plan she had devised with the friar for their common gratification and pleasure; whereupon the maid, who was mightily pleased at the news, made answer that everything her mistress might command should straightway be prepared.

It chanced that fortune was kind to them, for when the very next morning Maestro Rogero betook himself to visit his patients outside the city, his wife at once began to call upon San Griffone to come to her aid, feigning to be afflicted with an attack of her customary distemper. Then straightway the maid addressed her, as if by way of counsel: "Why do you not send for those sacred relics of the saint which have such miraculous fame amongst men of all sorts?" Thereupon the lady, according to the plan they had arranged between themselves, making believe that she could speak only with great difficulty, turned towards the maid and spake thus: "Nay, I beseech you to send and fetch them," and to her the woman, as if she were filled with pity, replied: "I will go myself for them." So, having set forth at the top of her speed, and found the friar and given him the message which had been arranged, Fra Nicolo, together with a certain companion of his, a sprightly young fellow, and one well fitted for the business in hand, straightway set forth on his errand.

When they were come into the chamber, and when Fra Nicolo, with a very devout look upon his face, had drawn anear the side of the bed upon which the lady was lying alone, she, who was tenderly awaiting him, received him with the greatest humility, and said: "O Father, pray to God and to the glorious San Griffone on my behalf." To this the friar replied: "May the Creator make you worthy of what you ask; but you on your part must give evidence of devout behavior, and if you are willing to accept His grace through the virtue of the holy relics I have with me, it is right and becoming that first we should resort with hearts full of contrition to the holy rite of confession, so that the soul, being brought back to health, the body may with ease be cleansed of its distemper." The lady answering, said: "Of a truth I have anticipated, and never wished for aught else than what you speak of, and this grace I beg most earnestly at your hands."

When they had thus spoken together, they gave courteous dismissal to all such persons as chanced to be in the chamber, so that there remained therein no one else except the maid and the companion who had come with the friar. Then, having securely locked themselves in, so that they might be in no danger of interruption, each lover began incontinently to raise the flame of desire with his lady. Fra Nicolo got upon the bed, and deeming that he might reckon on perfect security, took off his breeches in order that he might the better use his legs when freed from such impediment, and flung the garments aforesaid on the head of the bed. Then, having folded the lovely young woman in a close embrace, he began with her the sport so full of delight and so keenly desired by them both. The friar, who did not meet with such good luck every day of his life, gave full proof of his manhood, and once and twice reaped the full harvest of his desire; but, just as he was preparing for a third essay, he and Madonna Agata were made aware that Maestro Rogero on horseback was down below, he having come back sooner than they had anticipated from his journey. The friar in great haste flung himself off the bed, overcome with fear and vexation, and forgetting entirely the breeches which he had laid at the bed's head. The waiting woman, not at all pleased that the business she had begun with the friar's companion must needs be abandoned, unfastened the door of the chamber and, having called to the people who were waiting in the hall without, bade them come in at their pleasure, adding that, by the grace of God, her lady was now well-nigh entirely healed of her ailment.

In this wise the matter stood when Maestro Rogero came into the chamber. As soon as he realized that something strange had happened, he was no less disturbed at finding that friars had begun to frequent his house than at the fresh indisposition of his beloved spouse. But she, observing at a glance that his humor was mightily changed, cried out: "Oh husband! of a truth I should have been a dead woman by this time if our good father the preacher had not come to my aid with the relics of the most blessed San Griffone. These, as soon as he brought them near to my heart, took away all the pain and agony I suffered, just as a plentiful flood of water quenches a little fire." The credulous husband, when he heard how a remedy had at last been found for an ailment hitherto deemed incurable, fell a-thanking God and San Griffone with no small satisfaction, and at last, turning to the friar, gave him unbounded thanks for the great benefit he had wrought. Thus, after exchanging certain other speeches in devout and saintly discourse, the friar and his companion took their leave and went their way back to the monastery.

As soon as the friars had left the chamber, Maestro Rogero, going close up to his wife's side and, caressing her neck and her bosom, demanded to know from her whether the pain which had molested her had caused her great suffering. In the course of their conversation over this and over other matters, it chanced that Maestro Rogero, stretching out his hand to compose the pillows under his wife's head, caught hold of the laces of the breeches which the friar had left there.

When he had drawn them forth and observed of a surety they were of the sort commonly worn by friars, he cried out with a face changed mightily:

"What the devil can be the meaning of this? O Agata! for what reason are these friar's breeches here?" But the young wife, who was very wary and prudent (and love, moreover, had recently aroused yet more her intelligence), made answer without delaying her speech a moment: "And what can be the meaning of the long story I have just told you, my husband, if these be not the miraculous breeches which formerly belonged to the glorious San Griffone, and which our good father, the preaching friar, brought hither this morning as one of the most famous relics of the saint? Wherefore Almighty God, by the virtue of these, has already shown me great favor, and though I was fully assured of being entirely freed from my trouble, yet for greater security, and for piety's sake as well, I besought Fra Nicolo, when he was about to take it away, that he would leave it with me until the time of vespers, at which hour he or some others should send for it."

The husband, when he heard this answer so ready and so well fitted for the occasion, either believed it in truth or made as if he believed it; but, having within him the nature of a jealous man, his brain was buffeted about without ceasing by the two contrary winds which this accident had stirred up; nevertheless, without giving any farther answer to the remarks of his wife, he held his peace. The wily young woman, being well assured that her husband was still somewhat disturbed in his mind, now began to scheme how she might by a new stratagem clear out entirely from his breast all the suspicious thoughts he there nursed; so turning towards her maid, she said: "Go now at once to the convent, and as soon as you shall have found the friar preacher, tell him to send and fetch the relics which he left with me, for by God's mercy I have had no occasion to use them more." The discreet waiting woman, comprehending fully what the lady in truth wanted to say, went with all speed to the convent, and bade them quickly summon the friar preacher, who came straightway to the door, deeming peradventure that she had come to bring back the keepsake which he had left behind him. But he put on a smiling face as he spake to her, and asked her what news she bore. "No good news, in sooth," she answered, with a very ill grace, "thanks to your carelessness, and it would have been worse but for the prudence of my mistress." "Tell me what it is," cried the friar; and then the girl related to him, point by point, all that had happened, adding that it seemed to her there was no better way out of the affair than that they should send from the monastery to fetch the aforesaid relics with a certain parade of ceremony without further delay.

Then the friar said, "Keep your mind at ease;" and, having taken leave of her and bidden her to hope that all things which had been ill done would straightway be repaired, he sought out the superior, and spake to him in these words: "Good father, I have just committed a most grievous sin, one for which in due time you can punish me as I deserve, but just now I beseech you to give me instant help, as the needs of the case demand, in order that this mischance may be set right without delay," and then Fra Nicolo set forth the whole story in as brief a fashion as possible. The superior, finding himself perturbed in no small measure over the affair, took the friar sharply to task for his imprudence, and thus addressed him: "See now what comes of working miracles! A clever fellow you are, in sooth! You fancied, indeed, that you could go safely to work; but, if you found you must needs take off your breeches, could you not think of some other way of hiding them, either in the sleeves or in the breast of your gown, or in some other secret place about your person? You, wonted as you are to be mixed up in such scandals as these, recked naught as to the great burden of conscience and obloquy of the world with which we of your order shall have to battle. Of a truth I know not what reason there is why I should not forthwith send you to prison as you richly deserve. Nevertheless, seeing that at the present moment it behooves us to endeavor to mend matters rather than to inflict punishment, and that the affair concerns especially the honor of the order, we will postpone your chastisement to some future time."

Then, having set ringing the bell of the chapter house, and let assemble all the friars, the superior told them how, in the house of Maestro Rogero, the physician, God had that very day wrought a most evident miracle by the virtue of the breeches which formerly belonged to San Griffone. Having told them the story in the fewest possible words, he persuaded them that it behooved them to go forthwith to the house of the aforesaid physician, and bring back therefrom the holy relic with high solemnities and a procession, whereby they might give honor and glory to God, and cause the miracles of the saint to be held in yet higher esteem.

The physician, when he marked how the whole congregation of friars was come thither with so great a show of devotion, at once settled in his mind that these holy men would never have gathered themselves together to work any ill purpose; so, accepting as gospel truth the fictitious reasons of the superior, and driving away entirely all suspicious thoughts from his mind, he spake thus: "In sooth, you are all right welcome;" and, having taken the friar preacher by the hand, he led him into the chamber where Madonna Agata still was. She, who had in no wise gone to sleep over the business, had now the breeches all ready and wrapped in a white and perfumed linen cloth. The superior, when they were displayed to him, kissed them with the deepest reverence, and made the physician and the lady do the same, and in the end all those who were assembled in the room kissed them likewise. Next, after they had placed the breeches in the tabernacle which they had brought with them for that purpose, and after a sign had been given to the company, they all began to sing in unison *Veni Creator Spiritus*, and in this order, traversing the city and accompanied by a huge crowd, they bore the relic back to their church and there placed it above the high altar, letting it remain several days in order that all those who had already heard of the miraculous occurrence might pay their devotions to it.

Maestro Rogero, being very keenly set on increasing the reverence of the people round about toward the order aforesaid, let pass no opportunity of telling the story to whatsoever gatherings of men he chanced to encounter as he went about his practice, both within and without the city, setting forth the solemn miracle which God had wrought through the healing power of the breeches of San Griffone. And while he occupied himself in the discharge of this office, Fra Nicolo and his friend in no wise forgot to make a fresh trial of that rich hunting ground which they had already explored, to the great delight both of the mistress and of the maid. Madonna Agata, independent of any sensual delight she might enjoy, came to the conclusion that this operation was in truth the only one of any service to cure her acute attacks; for the reason that it brought relief to the very seat of her distemper. Besides this, being the wife of a physician, she had often heard tell of that text of Avicenna in which he lays down the dictum, "that those remedies which are approximate and partial may give ease, but those which are continuous will work a cure."

THE CARPENTER'S WIFE AND HER THREE LOVERS

Once upon a time there lived in Naples a certain fellow, a carpenter by trade, whose handicraft found no greater scope than the making of wooden shoes. He occupied a house near the saddlers' quarters and had to wife a very fair and graceful dame, who, although as a young woman she showed herself in no wise coy or averse from the courtings of everyone of the well-nigh countless swarm of her admirers, had nevertheless chosen from amongst this numerous company three whom she—and she was called Viola by name—especially favored with her love. Of these one was a smith who lived hard by, another was a Genoese merchant, and the third was a friar; and, although I cannot now call to mind what his name was or what the color of his frock, I well remember that he was a famous courser after such game. On a certain day it happened that, without showing one greater favor than the other, she gave her promise to all of these three, that whenever her husband might chance to be away all night from home, she would do for them what they so ardently desired.

It happened before many days had passed the husband found that he must needs go to Ponte a Selece to bring back with him an assload of finished wooden shoes, in order that he might let polish the same in Naples, as was his wont; and, because on account of this business he would have perforce to remain there until the following day, his departure and his absence from home for the night soon became known to all three of the expectant wooers. Now, although each one of them had prepared himself for the meeting after his own fashion, nevertheless the first who appeared at the door of our Madonna Viola all ready for the fray was the Genoese, who was also perhaps the most ardent of the lovers. He besought her in most tender speech that at nightfall she would await his coming and give him a night's lodging and supper thereto, holding out to her the while the most lavish promises. Indeed, he discoursed in such wise that Viola, so as not to keep him longer in suspense, assured him that she would do her best to content him, but that he must take good care to keep away until the night should be dark enough to prevent his coming from being seen by any of the people of the quarter who might be about. To this request of hers the Genoese answered gaily, "So be it, in God's name." Having taken his leave, he bought a couple of excellent capons, fat and white and big, which he sent privily to the young woman's house, together with some new bread and excellent wine of divers sorts.

The friar, after he had let celebrate his sacred office, felt himself mightily anxious that the promise which had been made to him should be duly kept. Wherefore, making the ground fly from under his feet, and running through one street after another just as if he had been a greedy wolf falling upon some stray lamb which had wandered afar from the fold, he arrived in front of the house where Viola dwelt, and having called upon her aloud, he let her know that he was minded, come what might, to spend that night with her. Viola, being in no way disposed to break her faith with the Genoese, and knowing full well that she could not refuse to give to one so rash and importunate as this friar the satisfaction she had promised him, felt herself in a mighty turmoil of mind, and knew not what to do.

Still, like a prudent young woman, she soon hit upon a plan by which she might settle matters in seemly and convenient fashion. She gave the friar a pleasant answer, and told him that she would hold herself ready to do his will, but that he must on no account come to her before eleven at night, for the reason that she had abiding with her in the house a little cousin of hers who would not be fallen to sleep before that time, and that he should take himself off straightway.

Thereupon the friar, seeing that reception would indeed be granted to him, agreed to do all that she asked him, and, caring for naught else, went his way. The smith, who had been busied until late at the customhouse, whither he had gone to attend to the withdrawal therefrom of certain iron, took his way back to his house, and as he passed along he espied Viola at the window and said to her: "Now that your husband is away you can let me come to you, and it will be well for you if you do this, for be assured that I will mar the working of any other scheme of yours." Viola, who was mightily partial to the smith, and somewhat in awe of him to boot, now began to consider whether in the course of a long night she might not find plenty of time to let come and go all three of her customers. So, as she had provided accommodation for the first two, she determined to give reception also to the third, although he had come last; wherefore she addressed him thus: "My Mauro, you know well enough that I am looked at askance in this quarter, and that all the women— no doubt for some good and sufficient reason—seek to chase me hence, and every evening until midnight some one or other of them keeps a watch upon me; therefore, in order that no hurt may befall me from these traps of theirs, see that you delay your coming to me until the dawn, the hour when you are accustomed to rise. Then, if you will give me a signal, I will let you enter, and in this manner we may be together for a little space for our first meeting. In due time we will find for ourselves a more convenient method."

The smith, being well aware that Viola had plausible reason for what she said, and feeling sure that he would get everything he wanted, went away without another word, being well content to let the affair rest as it stood. As soon as night had fallen the Genoese stealthily made his way into Viola's house, and although he was met with a right jolly reception and got from her many kisses, nevertheless he was of such cold-blooded nature that he was unable to bring himself into the humor necessary for the occasion without the warmth of the bed and other incitements, so he disposed himself according to his liking and tried his powers; the capons meantime taking a mighty long time to roast. All this time the young woman was almost fainting with eagerness, fearing lest her second course should be set before her ere she had disposed of the first; and nine o'clock had already struck before they had so much as made a beginning of their supper.

While they were thus waiting, there came a knocking at the door; whereupon the Genoese, horribly frightened, cried out, "It seems to me that someone knocks at the door here!" The young woman answered, "Yes, what you say is right, and in good sooth I fear very much that it may be my brother. But be not afraid, for I will take care that he does not catch sight of you. Get out of this window, and sit down in the little window arbor which is outside."

The Genoese, who was vastly more overcome by fear than by the ardor of love, at once followed Viola's directions, what though the wind was very cold, and there was falling a fine rain so chilling that most people would have taken it for snow. Thereupon Viola locked him out; and, making a guess as to who was the one who knocked, she carefully hid the supper. When she had gone down to the outer door and had assured herself that it was the importunate priest, she said to him in a tone somewhat troubled, "You have come very early, and have not observed the directions I gave you. Bad luck to me indeed that you should be minded to be the death of me, just because you could not be kept waiting a little time." And with these and other similar words she opened the door to the friar; and he having come in, without even tarrying to make fast the door, gave her plenary absolution at once, not indeed by any authority committed to him by his superiors, but by the power of his own lusty nature. Whereupon Viola, thinking that he had by this time got enough to let him go away contented, as soon as she saw that he was making his way into the house, closed the door and followed him up the stairs, saying to him, "Go away at once, for the love of God! For my young cousin is not yet asleep, and he will hear you of a surety." But the friar, paying no heed to what she said, went up the stairs, and finding the fire still burning, warmed himself a little and then took hold of Viola once more and began to attune his strings for a fresh spell of dancing, making thereby a melody vastly more pleasing than that which the poor devil of a Genoese played with his teeth, which chattered grievously by reason of the excessive cold. He, forsooth, could see everything which was being brought to pass within, by peeping through a fissure of the window, and how greatly he was tormented by grief at what he beheld and by the fear of being discovered and by the cruel cold, everyone who likes to consider the question may decide for himself.

As he stood there he made up his mind over and over again to jump down from his post, but he was held back from this deed by his inability to judge of the height on account of the darkness, and by the hope that the friar, who in sooth had swallowed far more than his share of the sweet repast, would take his departure, seeing that Viola entreated him continually to be gone. But the friar, heated by the pleasurable touch of the beautiful young woman, would in no wise let her go out of his embrace, and went on to give to her a lesson in all sorts and kinds of dances which were in fashion, and he taught, not her alone, but also the Genoese, who looked on at the sport with mighty little pleasure. At last he made up his mind that he would not depart until he should be chased away by the dawning of the day. And thus they went on until four in the morning, and then the friar heard the blacksmith knocking at Viola's door and giving the sign which had been settled; whereupon he, turning toward the young woman, spoke thus, "Who is it who knocks at your door?" To this she made answer, "Oh! that is nothing but the constant trouble I have to put up with from the smith my neighbor, a fellow I have not been able to beat off either by fair words or foul." The friar, who was gifted with a merry humor of his own, forthwith began to cast about in his mind how he might devise some new sport or other; then he went quickly down to the door, and, speaking in a soft voice, and feigning to be Viola, he said, "Who art thou?" Then the smith replied, "It is I; do you not know me? Open quickly the door, I beg you, for I am getting wet to the skin with the rain." Then said the friar, still in a simulated voice, "Alas, woe is me, that I cannot open the door! For whenever I move it, it makes so much noise that, were I to open it now, some scandal or other would surely arise thereanent." Then the smith, knowing not where to bestow himself in order to escape the rain, called out to Viola to open the door to him straightway, inasmuch as he was dying of love for her.

The friar, who was mightily pleased at keeping the smith waiting outside so that he might get wet through, now said, "Dear soul of mine, give me just one kiss through this opening of the door, which methinks is wide enough, and then I will see whether I cannot move this accursed door without letting it make much noise." The smith took all these words for truth, and, overjoyed at his good fortune, at once disposed himself to kiss his beloved Viola; but in the meantime the friar had taken off his breeches, and now he thrust his hinder part close to the opening of the door. The smith, who thought he was about to take a kiss from the sweet lips of his Viola, was forthwith made aware, both by the touch and the odor, what thing it was he was in truth kissing, and came to the conclusion that this must be some other huntsman, who had showed himself the keener after the game, and had both robbed him of his anticipated delight and put this shameful trick upon him. So he determined at once not to suffer this insult to go unavenged and, feigning still to be caressing his love, he said, "My Viola, while you are busying yourself in opening the door, I will go fetch a cloak from my house, for I can no longer endure this rain." To this the friar replied, "Go, in God's name, and come back as soon as possible." And when he had said this, he and Viola fell to laughing so heartily that they found it hard work to stand upright on their feet.

Meantime the smith went back to his shop and quickly got ready a rod of iron in the form of a spit, which he straightway heated red-hot in the fire, saying to his apprentice the while, "Now, take good heed of what I say, and, as soon as I shall spit, come to me as softly as you can, and bring me this rod." Having thus spoken he went back to Viola's house to speed his plan for gaining entrance thereinto; and, passing on from one word to another, he said at last, "Kiss me once more." Whereupon the friar, who was as expert as a monkey in making such a change of front as was here called for, again put before the smith the same object to kiss. Then Mauro gave the signal to his apprentice, who at once handed to him the red-hot iron rod, which he took in his hand, and, watching his time, dealt the friar a prick with the same in his backside with such good will that it went into his flesh well-nigh a palm's breadth.

The friar, when he felt the cruel pain of this, uttered a howl loud enough to touch the heavens, and went on bellowing as if he had been a wounded bull. All the neighbors round about, having been aroused from sleep, flocked to the windows with lights in their hands, and each one demanded to know what might be the cause of this strange uproar. The wretched Genoese, who was so benumbed with cold that a very little more would have turned him into an icicle, when he heard all this clamor, and saw that lights were coming from all parts, and that the day was about to break, took heart at last and resolved to leap down from where he stood, in order that he might not be discovered standing there in shameful concealment as if he were a thief. But fortune so dealt with him that, as he came to the ground, he happened to alight upon a stone, and fell over the same in such manner that he broke one of his legs in two places. Being stricken with a pain no less cruel than that which the friar suffered, he likewise shouted his woes aloud.

The smith, hearing the noise, ran forward at once, and, when he came upon the Genoese and recognized him and likewise perceived the cause which made him cry out in such fashion, felt somewhat of pity for him and contrived by the aid of his apprentice to convey him within the smithy, although the task was by no means an easy one. After the smith had heard from the injured man in what manner the whole affair had come about, and the name of the friar, he rushed into the street at once and managed to silence the huge uproar which the neighbors were still making, saying that the cries had arisen from two of his apprentices who had wounded one another in a quarrel.

When everything was once more quiet, Viola, according to the wish of the friar, called softly to the smith to come; and he, having entered the house and found the wretched friar half dead, debated in his mind many and various plans for the ending of the affair. At last he and his apprentice took the friar on their shoulders and carried him to his monastery; and then, having returned, they set the Genoese upon the back of an ass and conveyed him to his lodging. As to the smith, he took his way back to the house of Viola, it being now broad daylight, and after feasting together with her off the capons, and over and beyond this attaining the full enjoyment he desired, he went back in high delight to wield his hammer. And in this wise Maestro Mauro, what though he was the last of the competitors, left the other two to suffer no slight disgrace and injury and pain.[1]

THE NEIGHBORS WHO HAD EVERYTHING IN COMMON

Not far from here is a rather shabby neighborhood inhabited by rather gross and shabby people. Among its dwellers were two young men; one was a miller called Augustino, the other was a cobbler named Petruccio. Now between these two men there had always existed the greatest friendliness, a comradeship as close as had ever knit two friends together. Each of them had married a young and comely wife, and between the women there was also so great and constant a familiarity that they were rarely to be seen one without the other.

It chanced one day that the cobbler, although his wife was very good to look on, longing perhaps for a change in pasturage, found his friend's wife more to his taste. So, when an opportunity presented itself, he made known to her his desire. As soon as Caterina, for so the miller's wife was named, understood the meaning of his request, she put on an air of disdain and answered nothing, although she was anything but offended. But the first time she met Salvaggia, wife of the cobbler, she let her know what amorous proposition her husband Petruccio had been making. Whereupon Salvaggia, the cobbler's leavings, as it were, although disturbed by the story she had heard, nevertheless kept her anger within bounds. Moreover, she hit upon a plan by which she might at the same time have vengeance upon her husband and keep intact the great friendship subsisting between herself and Caterina. So, after having made answer to her dear friend in many grateful words, she begged her to give a promise to Petruccio her husband that she would, on some particular night, wait for him to come to her in her bed, and that, in change for herself, she should let be in the bed the rascal's own wife. Then they would assuredly find great sport and pleasure in what would follow.

The miller's wife, being very anxious to humor her friend, agreed to do what she asked; and the result was that in the course of a few days Petruccio,

[1] One episode of this story is elaborated by Chaucer in "The Miller's Tale" on page 162.

finding himself alone with Caterina, made the same request as before, using stronger persuasion than he had used on the former occasion. After listening to him, and giving him many and various denials (which forsooth seemed to have but little heart in them), she showed herself ready to do his will, so that the trick which had been planned might be duly brought to an issue. Then, having had a discussion with him as to the when, the where, and the how, the young woman said, "In sooth I can find no time fitting for such an affair save when my husband may happen to be busied some night over his work at the mill. Then I could very well let you come to me while I am abed."

To this speech Petruccio made answer in very joyful wise, "I come just now from the mill, where there is so large a quantity of grain that two thirds of the night will assuredly be spent in the grinding of the same." Hearing this, Caterina said, "So be it, in God's name. Come, then, between the second and the third hour of the night, when I shall be awaiting you, and will leave open the door, as I am accustomed to leave it for my husband. Then, without saying a word of any sort, you must straightway get into bed. Tell me, however, by what means you will keep clear of your wife, for I fear her more than I fear death." To this Petruccio made answer, "I have already hatched a plan as to how I may borrow the ass of my good gossip the archpriest, and will tell my wife that I am minded to go away into the country." Then said she, "In sooth this plan of yours pleases me greatly."

As soon as they had made an end of their talk, Petruccio betook himself to the mill to get due assurance that his comrade had his hands full of business, and in the meantime Caterina gave to her friend full intelligence as to the plan which had been arranged. Petruccio, when he had ascertained that the miller was at work in the mill, went back to his house and, making believe that he was vastly busied over his affairs, told his wife that he had a mind to go forthwith to Policastro in order to buy some leather for the workshop. The wife, who knew well enough whither he was really bound, said to him, "Go at once then." But laughing to herself she said, "This time, forsooth, you will find you have bought leather of your own, instead of skin belonging to another man."

Petruccio, having made a show of departure, hid himself in a certain spot in the village and there tarried, waiting till the expected hour should come. Caterina, as soon as the night had fallen, went to the house of Salvaggia and, according to the plan settled between them, took up her abode there for the night; while Salvaggia went to Caterina's house, and having duly got into bed, waited with no little satisfaction the coming of her husband to that amorous battle which he so keenly desired.

Petruccio, when it seemed to him that the time was ripe, went with gentle steps toward his neighbor's house. But, just as he went about to enter therein, he saw that the miller was coming back home—the reason for his return being that the mill, for some cause which he could not determine, had broken down. On account of this Petruccio was stricken with fear and, ill content with this accident, stole back to his own house without having been seen or heard by anybody, saying to himself the while that, though the business had miscarried this time, it should be duly dispatched the next attempt. But because there yet remained to be spent a good part of this night which had proved so unlucky to him, he began at first softly and then aloud to knock at the door, and to call out to his wife to open it and let him in.

Caterina, perceiving who it was by the voice, not only refused to open to him, but, furthermore, without answering a word, kept herself as quiet as a mouse, so as not to let him get wind of the plot that had been laid for him. Petruccio, being mightily perturbed at this, plied the door so vigorously that at last he gained entry thereby, and, having gone in, went straight to the bed; and then, becoming aware of the presence of the woman, who was pretending to be fast asleep, he shook her by the arm and awakened her. Believing all the while she was his wife, he compounded a fresh story to account for the fact that his journey had been abandoned, and, having taken off his clothes, he lay down beside her. And seeing that he had already prepared himself for action, he set himself now to consider whether, after he had been frustrated in his plan of tilling his neighbor's vineyard, he might not as well do a stroke of work in his own. Wherefore, deeming that of a surety he had fast hold of his Salvaggia, he took Caterina in his arms and gave her a valorous proof of his powers, which the poor woman bore with due show of pleasure and patience in order to make him believe that she was in sooth his wife.

In the meantime the miller, who had gone back wearily and with lagging steps to his house and had laid himself down in bed in order to get some sleep, lay quite immovable without uttering a word. Salvaggia, being well assured that it was her husband who was with her, gave him a gladsome reception, keeping quite silent the while. After she had waited for some time without finding the lover giving any sign that he was disposed for the battle, she began to handle him amorously in order that she might not be mocked and befooled in the business she had undertaken. The miller, believing that he was abed with his wife, although he felt more need of a good night's rest than any desire for skirmishing of this sort, when he felt her lustful bitings and dallyings, was stirred to get to work, and duly set going the mill which was not his own.

Now when it appeared to the cobbler's neglected wife that the time had come for her to let forth the angry words she had prepared, she broke the silence and took him to task in these words: "Ah! Deceitful rogue, disloyal dog that you are! Who was it you deemed you were holding in your arms, the wife of your best friend, in whose field you thought this night to spend your labor, for the sake of friendship, peradventure? Here indeed you have gone to work with far more spirit than is your wont, proving yourself to be a man of mettle, while at home you are ever short of breath. But, God be thanked, this time you have missed the prize you dreamt of, and all the same I will take good care that you smart for your sins." And with discourse like this, and with words still more injurious, she importuned him and demanded his answer.

The poor miller, although he was as one dumb-stricken when he learned the conditions of affairs, understood nevertheless clearly enough, as soon as he caught the meaning of her words, that the woman abed with him was no other than the wife of his good friend. However, divining exactly how the matter had come to pass, the pleasure which he had felt heretofore was quickly turned into sorrow; but, by dint of resolutely keeping silence, he withdrew himself from her side, and, for the reason that it was not daylight, he made his way with all speed to the spot where he deemed for certain he would find his own wife. Having arrived there and called for his friend, bidding him come down on account of a pressing matter, Petruccio went forth, albeit mightily distrustful, and him the miller at once addressed in these terms: "Good brother of mine, it comes from your fault alone that we both of us have suffered injury, and have been put to shame, and have met with a mishap of a sort which renders it more seemly on our part to keep silence than to speak, while there is assuredly no need to bring about a quarrel over the same."

Then, with no small chagrin, the miller set forth the whole story in due order to his friend, giving him full description as to how everything had happened; adding, as his own judgment, that as Fortune had shown herself propitious to the cunning of their wives, she had likewise shown no disposition to vent her spite upon themselves by letting anything happen which might lessen the friendship that had lasted so many years. He further went on to say that the mishap which had just befallen them through trickery might be made to serve the common agreement and pleasure of all four of them, and that, as in times past they had possessed all their goods in common, so in the future they should likewise enjoy the possession of one another's wives.

Thus, from that time forward, neither in the matter of their wives nor goods of any kind whatsoever, was any distinction recognized between the two friends, and the agreement was carried out in such manner that the only parents the children knew for their very own were their mothers.[1]

FRANÇOIS VILLON (1431–1463?)

A street brawl changed the career of one of the most spectacular poets of the fifteenth century. François de Montcorbier, who, as the name indicates, claimed to be from an aristocratic family, entered the University of Paris at fifteen and was a brilliant as well as a precocious student. He received bachelor's and master's degrees from the Sorbonne while still in his teens. Un-

---

[1] A variation of this story was told with great relish by Boccaccio—it being the eighth story, told on the eighth day of the *Decameron*.

fortunately, his boon companions were not other serious scholars, but a group of raffish young bloods, libertines, and rakehells. He was scarcely twenty when a priest was assaulted and accidentally killed in a nocturnal revel, and the perpetrators (he among them) were exiled from Paris. Changing his name to François Villon, he crept back to the city and joined a notorious gang of purse snatchers, sneak thieves, debauched nuns, hired assassins, and prostitutes. He became their leader, was frequently arrested for minor depredations and major crimes until, after a particularly brutal murder, he was tortured by being made to swallow gallons of water—a drink which Villon swore was poison to him—and condemned to be hanged. Somehow he managed to have the sentence changed to banishment, and then disappeared. A few of his manuscripts floated back to Paris but, after his thirty-second year, nothing further was heard of him.

Far from dying with him, his poems, continually quoted during his lifetime, became immensely popular upon his death. Within the following eighty years, thirty-four editions of his works had been circulated, and a leading poet-scholar was put to work establishing an authentic text at the command of Francis I, who boasted that he knew all of Villon by heart. Centuries have not dimmed the bright colors nor softened the strength of Villon's verse. His Testaments still prickle with lively puns, pointed thrusts, and malicious "bequests"—he bequeaths long cloaks to chicken thieves to conceal their booty, lawless dissipation to monks and abbesses, and to prostitutes the right to hold night school where the teachers will be instructed by the pupils. His ballades are as gross and as gaily detailed as a Breughel painting; his manner is so unself-conscious that his lines have been cherished by ordinary readers as well as scholars for over five hundred years. Writers have turned Villon into an almost legendary figure. Swinburne apostrophized him as "Bird of the bitter bright grey golden morn" and "Villon, our sad bad glad mad brother's name." Victor Hugo enlarged the Villon saga by adding exploits of his own; Robert Louis Stevenson supplied a plausible, if fictional, portrait in Lodging for the Night; Justin Huntly McCarthy made him swaggeringly heroic in If I Were King, a novel that was turned into a play of the same name and, later, into an operetta romantically entitled The Vagabond King.

The first of the following translations of Villon's ballades, strictly rhymed in the precise French form, is by Algernon Charles Swinburne; the others are by John Payne.

COMPLAINT OF THE FAIR ARMORESS

> Meseemeth I heard cry and groan
>   The sweet who was the armorer's maid.
> For her young years she made sore moan,
>   And right upon this wise she said:
>   "Ah, fierce old age with foul bald head,
> To spoil fair things thou art ever fain.

Who holds me? Who? Would I were dead!
Would God I were well dead and slain!

"Lo, thou hast broken the sweet yoke
    That my high beauty held above
All priests and clerks and merchantfolk;
    There was not one but for my love
    Would give me gold and gold enough,
Though sorrow his very heart had riven,
    To win from me such wage thereof
As now no thief would take if given.

"I was right chary of the same,
    God wot it was my great folly,
For love of one sly knave of them,
    Good store of that same sweet had he;
    For all my subtle wiles, perdie,
God wot I loved him well enow;
    Right evilly he handled me,
But he loved well my gold, I trow.

"Though I gat bruises green and black,
    I loved him never the less a jot;
Though he bound burdens on my back,
    If he said 'Kiss me, and heed it not,'
    Right little pain I felt, God wot,
When that foul thief's mouth, found so sweet,
    Kissed me— Much good thereof I got!
I keep the sin and the shame of it.

"And he died thirty year agone.
    I am old now, no sweet thing to see;
By God, though, when I think thereon,
    And of that glad good time, woe's me,
    And stare upon my changed bodie,
Stark naked, that had been so sweet,
    Lean, wizened, like a small dry tree,
I am nigh mad with the pain of it.

"Where is my forehead's faultless white,
    The lifted eyebrows, soft gold hair,
Eyes wide apart and keen of sight,
    With subtle skill in the amorous air;
    The straight nose, great nor small, but fair,
The small carved ears of shapeliest growth,
    Chin dimpling, color good to wear,
And sweet red splendid kissing mouth.

"The shapely slender shoulders small,
  Long arms, hands wrought in glorious wise,
Round little breasts, the hips withal
  High, full of flesh, not scant in size,
  Fit for all amorous masteries;
Wide flanks, and the fresh sweet flower
  Of youth, between the perfect thighs,
That hides within its pretty bower.

"A wrinkled forehead, hair gone gray,
  Fallen eyebrows, eyes gone blind and red,
Their laughs and looks all fled away,
  Yea, all that smote men's hearts are fled;
  The bowed nose, fallen from goodlihead;
Foul flapping ears like water flags;
  Peaked chin, and cheeks all waste and dead,
And lips that are two skinny rags.

"Thus endeth all the beauty of us.
  The arms made short, the hands made lean,
The shoulders bowed and ruinous,
  The breasts, alack! all fallen in;
  The flanks too, like the breasts, grown thin;
The flower of love no longer sweet;
  For the lank thighs, no thighs but skin
That are speckled with spots like sausage meat.

"So we make moan for the old sweet days,
  Poor old light women, two or three
Squatting above the straw fire's blaze,
  The bosom crushed against the knee,
  Like fagots on a heap we be,
Round fires soon lit, soon quenched and done;
  And we were once so sweet—even we!
Thus fareth many and many an one!"

BALLADE OF VILLON AND FAT MARGOT

Because I love and serve a whore *sans glose,*
  Think not therefore a knave or fool am I.
She hath in her such goods as no man knows.
  For love of her, target and dirk I ply:
  When clients come, I hend a pot there nigh
And get me gone for wine, without word said:
Before them water, fruit, bread, cheese, I spread.
  If they pay well, I bid them "Well God aid!

Come here again, when you by lust are led,
   In this the brothel where we ply our trade."

But surely before long an ill wind blows
   When, coinless, Margot comes by me to lie.
I hate the sight of her, catch up her hose,
   Her gown, her surcoat and her girdle tie,
   Swearing to pawn them, meat and drink to buy.
She grips me by the throat and cuffs my head,
Cries "Antichrist!" and swears by Jesus dead,
   It shall not be; till I, to quell the jade,
A potsherd seize and score her nose with red,
   In this the brothel where we ply our trade.

Then she, peace made, to show we're no more foes,
   A hugeous crack of wind at me lets fly
And laughing sets her fist against my nose,
   Bids me "Go to" and claps me on the thigh;
   Then, drunk, like logs we sleep till, by and by,
Awaking, when her womb is hungered,
To spare the child beneath her girdle stead,
   She mounts on me, flat as a pancake laid.
With wantoning she wears me to the thread,
   In this the brothel where we ply our trade.

ENVOI

Hail, rain, freeze, ready baked I hold my bread:
Well worth a lecher with a wanton wed!
Which is the worse? They differ not a shred.
   Ill cat to ill rat; each for each was made.
We flee from honor; it from us hath fled:
Lewdness we love, that stands as well in stead,
   In this the brothel where we ply our trade.

BALLADE OF LADIES' LOVE

Whoso in love would bear the bell,
   Needs must he prank him gallantly,
Swagger and ruffle it, bold and snell,
   And when to his lady's sight comes he,
   Don cloth of gold and embroidery;
For ladies liken a goodly show.
   This should serve well; but, by Marie,
   Not all can nick it that will, heigho!

Once on a season in love I fell
   With a lady gracious and sweet to see,
Who spoke me fair, that she liked me well
   And gladly would hearken to my plea,
   But first I must give to her for fee
Fifty gold crowns, not less nor mo'.
   Fifty gold crowns?—O' right good gree!
Not all can nick it that will, heigho!

To bed I went with the damsel
   And there four times right merrily
I did to her what I may not tell
   In less than an hour and a half, perdie.
   Then with a failing voice she said,
"Once more, I prithee! my heart is woe."
   Once more, quotha, sweetheart? Ah me,
Not all can nick it that will, heigho!

ENVOI

Great God of love, I crave of thee,
   If ever again I lay her low,
Ne'er let my lance untempered be,
Not all can nick it that will, heigho!

BALLADE OF THE FAIR HELM-MAKER
TO THE LIGHT O' LOVES

Now think on't, Nell the glover fair,
   That wont my scholar once to be,
And you, Blanche Slippermaker there,
   Your case in mine I'd have you see:
   Look all to right and left take ye;
Forbear no man; for trulls that bin
   Old have nor course nor currency,
No more than money that's called in.

You, sausage-huckstress debonair,
   That dance and trip it brisk and free,
And Guillemette Upholstress, there,
   Look you transgress not Love's decree:
   Soon must you shut up shop, perdie;
Soon old you'll grow, faded and thin,
   Worth, like some old priest's visnomy,
No more than money that's called in.

Jenny the hatter, have a care
  Lest some false lover hamper thee;
And Kitty Spurmaker, beware,
  Deny no man that proffers fee;
  For girls that are not bright o' blee
Men's scorn and not their service win:
  Foul age gets neither love nor gree,
No more than money that's called in.

ENVOI

Wenches, give ear and list (quoth she)
  Wherefore I weep and make this din:
'Tis that there is no help for me—
  No more than money that's called in.

BALLADE OF EASE

Athwart a hole in the arras, t'other day,
  I saw a fat priest lie on a down bed,
Hard by a fire; and by his side there lay
  Dame Sydonie, full comely, white and red:
  By night and day a goodly life they led.
I watched them laugh and kiss and play, drink high
Of spicèd hypocras; then, putting by
  Their clothes, I saw them one another seize,
To take their bodies' pleasure. Thence knew I
  There is no treasure but to have one's ease.

If, with his mistress Helen, Franc-Gontier
  Had all their life this goodly fashion sped,
With cloves of garlic, rank of smell alway,
  They had no need to rub their oaten bread:
  For all their curds (*sans malice* be it said)
No jot I care, nor all their cakes of rye.
If they delight beneath the rose to lie,
  What say you? Must we couch afield like these?
Like you not better bed and chair there nigh?
  There is no treasure but to have one's ease.

They eat coarse bread of barley, sooth to say,
  And drink but water from the heavens shed:
Not all the birds that singen all the way
  From here to Babylon could me persuade
  To spend one day so harbored and so fed.

For God's sake let Franc-Gontier none deny
To play with Helen 'neath the open sky!
   Why should it irk me, if they love the leas?
But, vaunt who will the joys of husbandry,
   There is no treasure but to have one's ease.

ENVOI

Prince, be you judge betwixt us all: for my
   Poor heart I mind me (so it none displease)
Whilst yet a child, I heard folk testify,
   There is no treasure but to have one's ease.

MARGARET, QUEEN OF NAVARRE (1492–1549)

Born in the momentous year of 1492, daughter of royal blood on both her mother's and father's sides, sister of Francis I, King of France, Margaret of Navarre was one of the most remarkable of Renaissance women. She was well educated, as befitted a woman of her station, and spoke several languages fluently; she had presence, charm, and authority, as well as a superior mind. At seventeen, she was married to Charles, Duke of Alençon; at twenty-three she was a childless widow. Her brother had need of her gifts for diplomacy and she served him brilliantly in the troubled affairs of state. Her second husband was Henry of Navarre, a king without a kingdom but with extensive estates, as had Margaret. For the rest of her life, Margaret was greatly occupied with the management of these properties; her one child, a daughter, was, for state reasons, brought up away from her. The Queen of Navarre maintained something of a court, and her sympathies with Reformation attitudes and art attracted to it some of the most gifted men of the time. Rabelais, whom she knew from the court of Francis I, dedicated the third book of Pantagruel to her. Her own literary output was considerable: poems, dramatic works, epistles, and songs, as well as the seventy-two stories that constitute the Heptameron.

Margaret intended to write a hundred stories, ten for each of ten days, candidly modeling her collection on the Decameron, which her secretary had translated into French and which, along with most things Italian, was then the rage. As framework for her storytelling, she devised a company of aristocrats, isolated in an abbey because of a flood. To pass the time, they have Bible readings in the morning (Margaret was a devout woman, critical of monkish abuses) and storytelling in the afternoon. The work was never completed, but she had got as far as the second story of the eighth day when she died at the age of fifty-seven.

In common with similar collections, many of the plots of the Heptameron *were taken from earlier sources; some of them were adaptations of scandals, escapades, and occurrences concerning actual people Margaret knew, or knew of. But her retelling gave them a flavor of their own, a blending, as George Saintsbury says in an essay on the work, "of positive religious devotion . . . and secondly, the infusing into it of the peculiar Renaissance contrast of love and death, passion and piety, voluptuous enjoyment and sombre anticipation."*

FROM: THE HEPTAMERON

THE PLEASURE OF THE INNOCENTS

There was at Tours a shrewd, cunning fellow, who was upholsterer to the late Duke of Orleans, son of King Francis I. Though this upholsterer had become deaf in consequence of a severe illness, he nevertheless retained the full use of his wits, and was so well endowed in that respect that there was not a man in his trade more cunning than himself. As for other matters, you shall see from what I am about to relate to you how he contrived to acquit himself. He had married a good and honorable woman, with whom he lived very peaceably. He was greatly afraid of displeasing her, and she also studied to obey him in all things. But for all the great affection the husband had for his wife, he was so charitable that he often gave his female neighbors what belonged to her; but this he always did as secretly as possible. They had a good stout wench as a servant, with whom the upholsterer fell in love. Fearing, however, lest his wife should perceive it, he affected often to scold her, saying she was the laziest creature he had ever seen; but that he did not wonder at it since her mistress never beat her.

One day, when they were talking of giving the Innocents,[1] the upholsterer said to his wife, "It would be a great charity to give the ceremonial whippings to that lazy jade of yours; but it would not do for her to receive them from your hand, for it is too weak and your heart is too tender. If I were to put my own hand to the job, we should be better served by her than we are." The poor woman, suspecting nothing, begged that he would perform the operation, confessing that she had neither the heart nor the strength to do it. The husband willingly undertook the commission; and, as if he intended to flog the wench soundly, he bought the finest rods he could procure; and to show that he had no mind to spare her, he steeped them in pickle, so that

[1] The learned Gregory observes that "it hath been a custom to whip the children upon Innocents' Day morning, that the memorie of Herod's murder of the Innocents might stick the closer, and in a moderate proportion to act over the crueltie again in kinde." That which was at first a serious parody of the martyrdom of Bethlehem, afterward degenerated into a jocular usage, and persons past the age of childhood, young women especially, were made to play the part of the Innocents.

the poor woman felt more compassion for her servant than suspicion of her husband.

Innocents' Day being come, the upholsterer rose betimes, went to the upper room where the servant lay alone, and gave her the Innocents in a very different manner from that he had talked of to his wife. The servant fell a-crying, but her tears were of no avail. For fear, however, that his wife should come up, he began to whip the bedpost at such a rate that he made the rods fly in pieces, and then he carried them broken as they were to his wife. "I think, my dear," said he, showing them to her, "that your servant will not soon forget the Innocents."

The upholsterer having gone out of doors, the servant went and threw herself at her mistress' feet, and complained that her husband had behaved to her in the most shameful way that ever a servant was treated. The good woman, imagining that she spoke of the flogging she had received, interrupted her and said, "My husband has done well, and just as I have been begging him to do this month and more. If he has made you smart I am very glad of it. You may lay it all to me. He has not given you half as much as he ought."

When the girl perceived that her mistress approved of such an act, she concluded that it was not such a great sin as she had supposed, seeing that a woman who was considered so virtuous was the cause of it; and so she never ventured to complain of it again. The upholsterer, seeing that his wife was as glad to be deceived as he was to deceive her, resolved frequently to give her the same satisfaction, and gained the servant's consent so well that she cried no more for getting the Innocents. He continued the same course for a long time without his wife's knowing anything of the matter until winter came, and there was a great fall of snow. As he had given his servant the Innocents in the garden on the green grass, he took a fancy to give them to her also on the snow; and one morning before anyone was awake, he took her out into the garden in her shift, to make the crucifix on the snow. They romped and pelted each other, and among the sports that of the Innocents was not forgotten.

One of the neighbors meanwhile had gone to her window to see what sort of weather it was. The window looked right over the upholsterer's garden, and the woman saw the game of the Innocents that was going on there and was so shocked that she resolved to inform her good gossip, that she might no longer be the dupe of such a wicked husband and vicious servant. After the upholsterer had finished his fine game, he looked round to see if he had been noticed by anyone, and to his great vexation he saw his neighbor at her window. As he knew how to give all sorts of colors to his tapestry, so he thought he should be able to put such a color on this fact that his neighbor would be no less deceived than his wife. No sooner had he got to bed again than he made his wife get up in her shift, and took her to the very spot where he had been toying with the servant. He frolicked awhile with her at snowball throwing, as he had done with the servant. Next he gave her the Innocents as he had done to the other; and then they went back to bed.

The next time the upholsterer's wife went to mass, her neighbor and good friend failed not to meet her there, and entreated her with very great earnestness, but without saying more, to discharge her servant, who was a good-for-nothing, dangerous creature. The upholsterer's wife said she would do no such thing, unless the other told her why she thought the wench so good for nothing and dangerous. The neighbor, thus pressed, stated at last that she had seen her one morning in the garden with her husband.

"It was I, gossip dearie," replied the good woman, laughing.

"What!" cried the neighbor. "Stripped to your shift in the garden at four o'clock in the morning?"

"Yes, gossip," said the upholsterer's wife. "In good sooth, it was myself."

"They pelted each other with snow," continued the neighbor, "and he played with her teaties and all that sort of thing as familiarly as you please."

"Yes, gossip, it was myself."

"But, gossip," rejoined the neighbor, "I saw them do upon the snow a thing that seems to me neither decent nor proper."

"That may be, gossip dearie," replied the upholsterer's wife. "But as I told you before and tell you again, it was myself and no one else that did all this; for my good husband and I divert ourselves in that way together. Don't be shocked, pray. You know that we are bound to please our husbands."

The end of the matter was that the neighbor went home much more disposed to wish that she had such a husband than to pity her good friend. When the upholsterer came home, his wife repeated to him the whole conversation she had had with her neighbor. "It is well for you, my dear," he replied, "that you are a good and sensible woman; but for that, we should have been separated long ago. But I trust that by God's grace we shall love each other in time to come as much as we have in the past, and that to His glory, and to our own comfort and satisfaction."

"Amen, my dear," said the good woman. "I hope too that you will never find me fail to do my part towards maintaining the good understanding between us."

THE TOO-CLEVER COUNTESS

At the court of one of the kings of France, named Charles (I will not say which of them, for the honor of the lady of whom I am about to speak and whom I shall also abstain from naming), there was a foreign countess of very good family. As new things please, this lady at once attracted all eyes, both by the novelty of her costume and by its richness and magnificence. Though she was not a beauty of the first order, she possessed, nevertheless, so much grace, such a lofty deportment and a manner of speaking which inspired so much respect, that no one ventured to attempt her except the

King, who was very much in love with her. That he might enjoy her society more freely, he gave the count, her husband, a commission which kept him a long time away from the court, and during that interval the King diverted himself with the countess.

Several of the King's gentlemen, seeing that their master was well treated by the countess, took the liberty to speak to her on the subject; among the rest, one named Astillon, an enterprising and handsome man. At first she answered him with great dignity, and thought to frighten him by threatening to complain to the King his master. But he, who was not a man to be moved by the menaces of an intrepid captain, made light of those which the lady held forth, and pressed her so closely that she consented to grant him a private interview and even told him what he should do in order to reach her chamber; a lesson which he failed neither to remember nor to practice. To prevent any suspicion on the King's part, he made a pretense of a journey to obtain leave of absence for some days, and actually took his departure from the court, but quitted his retinue at the first stage and returned at night to receive the favors which the countess had promised him. She fulfilled her promise; and he was so satisfied with his reception that he was content to remain seven or eight days shut up in a small room, living on nothing but aphrodisiacs.

During the time he was thus confined, one of his comrades, named Duracier, came to make love to the countess. She went through the same ceremonies with this second wooer as with the first, spoke to him at first sternly and haughtily, softened to him only by degrees; and on the day she let the first prisoner go, she put the second into his place. Whilst he was there, a third came, named Valbenon, and had the same treatment as his two predecessors. After these three came two or three others, who also had part in that sweet captivity. And so it went on for a long while, the intrigue being so nicely conducted that not one of the whole number knew anything of the adventures of the rest. They heard plenty of talk, indeed, of the passion of every one of them for the countess, but there was not one of them but believed himself to be the only favored lover, and laughed in his sleeve at his disappointed rivals.

One day, all these gentlemen being met together at an entertainment at which they made very good cheer, they began to talk about their adventures and the prisons in which they had been during the wars. Valbenon, who was not the man to keep a secret which flattered his vanity, said to the others, "I know in what prisons you have been; but as for me, I have been in one for sake of which I will speak well of prisons in general as long as I live; for I don't believe there is a pleasure in the world equal to that of being a prisoner."

Astillon, who had been the first prisoner, at once suspected what prison he meant. "Under what jailer," he asked, "were you so well treated that you were so fond of your prison?"

"Be the jailer who he may," replied Valbenon, "the prison was so agreeable that I was very loath to leave it so soon, for I never was better treated or more comfortable than there."

Duracier, who hitherto had said nothing, shrewdly suspected that the prison in question was that in which he had been confined, as well as the other two. "Tell me," said he to Valbenon, "what sort of food did they give you in that same prison you praise so highly?"

"Food? The King has not better, or more nutritive," was the reply.

"But I should like to know, too," returned Duracier, "did not the person who kept you prisoner make you earn your bread?"

"Hah! Bentrebleu!" cried Valbenon, who saw that the spark was hit. "Have I had comrades? I thought myself the only one."

"Well," said Astillon, laughing, "we are all companions and friends from our youth, and all serve the same master. If we all share alike in the same good fortune, we may well laugh in company. But in order to know if what I imagine is true, pray let me interrogate you, and all of you tell me the truth. If what I suppose has happened to us, it is the oddest and most amusing adventure that could ever be imagined."

All swore they would speak the truth, at least if matters were so that they could not help doing so. "I will relate my adventure to you," said Astillon, "and you will each answer me yes or no, if yours is like it or not."

Everyone having agreed to this, "In the first place," said Astillon, "I asked leave of absence of the King, under pretense of a journey."

"And so did we," said the others.

"When I was two leagues from the court, I left my retinue, and went and surrendered myself a prisoner."

"And so did we."

"I remained for seven or eight days hid in a tiny room, where I was fed upon nothing but restoratives, and the best viands I ever tasted. At the end of eight days, my keepers let me go, much weaker than I had come."

They all swore that they had been served just the same way.

"My imprisonment ended on such-and-such a day," continued Astillon.

"Mine began the very day yours ended," said Duracier, "and lasted until such a day."

Valbenon now lost patience and began to swear. "By the Lord," said he, "I find I was the third, though I thought myself the first and the only one; for I entered such a day, and left such another."

The other three who were at table swore that they had entered and departed successively in the same order.

"Since that is the case," said Astillon, "I will describe our jailer. She is married, and her husband is away."

"The very same," said all the others.

"As I was the first enrolled," continued Astillon, "I will be the first to name her for our common relief. She is the countess, who was so haughty that in winning her I thought I had done as great a feat as if I had vanquished Caesar. To the devil with the slut that made us toil so hard and deem ourselves so fortunate in having won her. There never was a more infernal woman. Whilst she had one of us caged, she was trapping another, so that the place might never be vacant. I would rather die than not have my revenge."

They all asked Duracier what he thought of the matter and in what manner she ought to be punished, adding that they were ready to put their hands to the work.

"It strikes me," said he, "that we ought to tell the facts to the King our master, who esteems her as a goddess."

"We will not do that," said Astillon; "we can revenge ourselves very well without our master's aid. Let us wait for her tomorrow when she goes to mass, every man with an iron chain round his neck; and when she enters the church, we will salute her as is fitting."

This suggestion was unanimously approved. Everyone provided himself with a chain, and next morning, dressed all in black, with their chains round their necks, they presented themselves to the countess as she was going to church. When she saw them in that trim she burst out laughing, and said to them, "Whither go these people that look in such doleful plight?"

"As your poor captive slaves, madam," said Astillon, "we are come to do you service."

"You are not my captives," she replied, "and I know no reason why you should be bound more than others to do me service."

Valbenon then advanced. "We have so long eaten your bread, madam," he said, "that we should be very ungrateful not to do you service."

She pretended not to have the least idea of what he meant and preserved an unruffled air, thinking thereby to disconcert them. But they played their parts so well that she could not but be aware that the thing was discovered. Nevertheless, she quite baffled them, for as she had lost honor and conscience, she did not take to herself the shame they sought to put upon her; but as one who preferred her pleasure to all the honor in the world, she showed them no worse a countenance for what they had done and carried her head as high as ever, whereat they were so astounded that they felt themselves as much ashamed as they had meant to make her.

THE MAN WHO MADE HIMSELF A CUCKOLD

In the county of Alletz there lived a man named Bornet, who, being married to an upright and virtuous wife, had great regard for her honor and reputation. But although he desired that she should be true to him, he was not willing that the same law should apply to both, for he fell in love with his maidservant, from whom he had nothing to gain save the pleasure afforded by a diversity of viands.

Now he had a neighbor of the same condition as his own, named Sandras, a taborer and tailor by trade, and there was such friendship between them that, excepting Bornet's wife, they had all things in common. It thus hap-

pened that Bornet told his friend of the enterprise he had in hand against
the maidservant; and Sandras not only approved of it, but gave all the assistance he could to further its accomplishment, hoping that he himself might
share in the spoil.

The maidservant, however, was loath to consent, and finding herself hard
pressed, she went to her mistress, told her of the matter, and begged leave
to go home to her kinsfolk, since she could no longer endure to live in such
torment. Her mistress, who had great love for her husband and had often
suspected him, was well pleased to have him thus at a disadvantage, and to
be able to show that she had doubted him justly. Accordingly, she said to the
servant:

"Remain, my girl, but lead my husband on by degrees, and at last make
an appointment to lie with him in my closet. Do not fail to tell me on what
night he is to come, and see that no one knows anything about it."

The maidservant did all that her mistress had commanded her, and her
master in great content went to tell the good news to his friend. The latter
then begged that, since he had been concerned in the business, he might have
part in the result. This was promised him, and, when the appointed hour
was come, the master went to lie, as he thought, with the maidservant. But
his wife, yielding up the authority of commanding for the pleasure of obeying, had put herself in the servant's place and she received him, not in the
manner of a wife, but after the fashion of a frightened maid. This she did
so well that her husband suspected nothing.

I cannot tell you which of the two was the better pleased, he at the thought
that he was deceiving his wife, or she at really deceiving her husband. When
he had remained with her, not as long as he wished but according to his
powers, which were those of a man who had long been married, he went out
of doors, found his friend, who was much younger and lustier than himself,
and told him gleefully that he had never met with better fortune. "You know
what you promised me," said his friend to him.

"Go quickly then," replied the husband, "for she may get up, or my wife
have need of her."

The friend went off and found the supposed maidservant, who, thinking
her husband had returned, denied him nothing that he asked of her, or
rather took, for he durst not speak. He remained with her much longer than
her husband had done, whereat she was greatly astonished, for she had not
been accustomed to pass such nights. Nevertheless, she endured it all with
patience, comforting herself with the thought of what she would say to him
on the morrow, and of the ridicule that she would cast upon him.

Towards daybreak the man rose from beside her, and toying with her as
he was going away, snatched from her finger the ring with which her husband
had espoused her and which the women of that part of the country guard
with great superstition. She who keeps it till her death is held in high honor;
while she who chances to lose it is thought lightly of as a person who has
given her faith to some other than her husband. The wife, however, was

very glad to have it taken, thinking it would be a sure proof of how she had deceived her husband.

When the friend returned, the husband asked him how he had fared. He replied that he was of the same opinion as himself and that he would have remained longer had he not feared to be surprised by daybreak. Then they both went to the friend's house to take as long a rest as they could. In the morning, while they were dressing, the husband perceived the ring that his friend had on his finger and saw that it was exactly like the one he had given to his wife at their marriage. He thereupon asked his friend from whom he had received the ring, and when he heard he had snatched it from the servant's finger, he was confounded and began to strike his head against the wall, saying: "Ah! good Lord! Have I made myself a cuckold without my wife knowing anything about it?"

"Perhaps," said his friend in order to comfort him, "your wife gives her ring into the maid's keeping at nighttime."

The husband made no reply, but took himself home, where he found his wife fairer, more gaily dressed, and merrier than usual, like one who rejoiced at having saved her maid's conscience, and tested her husband to the full, at no greater cost than a night's sleep. Seeing her so cheerful, the husband said to himself: "If she knew of my adventure she would not show me such a pleasant countenance."

Then, whilst speaking to her of various matters, he took her by the hand, and on noticing that she no longer wore the ring, which she had never been accustomed to remove from her finger, he was quite overcome.

"What have you done with your ring?" he asked her in a trembling voice.

She, well pleased that he gave her an opportunity to say what she desired, replied: "O wickedest of men! From whom do you imagine you took it? You thought it was from my maidservant, for love of whom you expended more than twice as much of your substance as you ever did for me! The first time you came to bed I thought you as much in love as it was possible to be; but after you had gone out and were come back again, you seemed to be a very devil. Wretch! Think how blind you must have been to bestow such praises on my person and lustiness, which you have long enjoyed without holding them in any great esteem. 'Twas, therefore, not the maidservant's beauty that made the pleasure so delightful to you, but the grievous sin of lust which so consumes your heart and so clouds your reason that in the frenzy of your love for the servant you would, I believe, have taken a she-goat in a nightcap for a comely girl! Now, husband, it is time to amend your life and, knowing me to be your wife and an honest woman, to be as content with me as you were when you took me for a pitiful strumpet. What I did was to turn you from your evil ways, so that in your old age we might live together in true love and repose of conscience. If you purpose to continue your past life, I had rather be severed from you than daily see before my eyes the ruin of your soul, body, and estate. But if you will acknowledge the evil of your ways, and resolve to live in fear of God and obedience to His commandments, I will forget all your past sins, as I trust God will forget my ingratitude in not loving Him as I ought to do."

If ever man was reduced to despair it was this unhappy husband. Not only had he abandoned this sensible, fair, and chaste wife for a woman who did not love him, but, worse than this, he had without her knowledge made her a strumpet by causing another man to participate in the pleasure which should have been for himself alone; and thus he had made himself horns of everlasting derision.

However, seeing his wife in such wrath by reason of the love he had borne his maidservant, he took care not to tell her of the evil trick that he had played her; and entreating her forgiveness, with promises of full amendment of his former evil life, he gave her back the ring which he had recovered from his friend. He entreated the latter not to reveal his shame. But, as what is whispered in the ear is always proclaimed from the house top, after a while the truth became known, and men called him cuckold without imputing any shame to his wife.

THE DESPERATE REMEDY

There was at Amboise a saddler named Brimbaudlier, who worked for the Queen of Navarre. It was enough to see the man's red nose to be assured that he was more a servant to Bacchus than to Diana. He had married a worthy women, with whom he was very well satisfied, and who managed his children and his household with great discretion. One day he was told that his good wife was very ill, at which he was greatly afflicted. He went home with speed, and found her so far gone that she had more need of a confessor than of a doctor, whereat he made the most doleful lamentations that ever were heard. After he had rendered her all the good offices he could, she asked for the cross, which was brought her. The good man, seeing this, threw himself on a bed howling and crying and ejaculating with his thick tongue: "O Lord, I am losing my poor wife. Was there ever such a misfortune? What shall I do?" and so forth. At last, there being no one in the room but a young servant, rather a good-looking girl, he called her to him in a faint voice and said, "I am dying, my dear, and worse than if I was dead all out, to see your mistress dying. I know not what to say or do, only that I look for help to you and beg you to take care of my house and my children. Take the keys that hang at my side. Do everything in the house for the best, for I am not in a condition to attend to such things."

The poor girl pitied and tried to comfort him, begging him not to be so cast down, lest besides losing her mistress she should lose her good master also. "It can't be helped, my dear," said he, "for I am dying. See how cold my face is; put your cheeks to mine to warm them." As she did so he put his hand on her bosom, whereat she offered to make some difficulty, but he begged her not be alarmed, for they must by all means see each other more closely. Thereupon he laid hold of her and threw her on the bed. His wife, who was left alone with the cross and the holy water and who had not spoken for two days, began to cry out: "Ah! Ah! Ah! I am not dead yet!" And threatening them with her hand, she repeated, "Wicked wretches, I am not dead yet!"

The husband and the servant jumped up instantly; but the sick woman was so enraged with them that her anger consumed the catarrhal humor that hindered her from speaking, so that she poured out upon them all the abuse she could think of. From that moment she began to amend; but her husband had often to endure her reproaches for the little love he had shown for her.

THE HYPOCRITICAL MISTRESS

A princess of great eminence lived in a very handsome chateau, and had with her a lady named Jambicque, of a haughty and audacious spirit, who was, nevertheless, such a favorite with her mistress that she did nothing except, by her advice, believing her to be the most discreet and virtuous lady of her time. This Jambicque used to inveigh loudly against illicit love; and if ever she saw that any gentleman was enamored with one of her companions, she used to reprimand the pair with great bitterness and tell a very bad tale of them to her mistress, so that she was much more feared than loved. As for her, she never spoke to a man except aloud, and with so much haughtiness, that she was universally regarded as an inveterate foe to love. In her heart, however, she was quite otherwise. In fact, there was a gentleman in her mistress' service with whom she was as much in love as a woman could be. But so dear to her was her good name and the reputation she had made herself that she entirely dissembled her passion.

After suffering for a year without choosing to solace herself like other women, by means of her eyes and her tongue, her heart became so inflamed that she was driven to seek the ultimate remedy; and she made up her mind that it was better to satisfy her desire, provided none but God knew her heart, than to confide it to one who might betray her secret. Having come to this resolution, one day when she was in her mistress' chamber and was looking out on a terrace, she saw the gentleman she loved so much walking there. After gazing on him until darkness concealed him from her sight, she called her little page, and, pointing out the gentleman to him, "Do you see," she said, "that gentleman in a crimson satin doublet and a robe trimmed with lynx fur? Go and tell him that a friend of his wishes to see him and is waiting for him in the gallery in the garden."

Whilst the page was doing his errand, she went out the back way and went to the gallery, after putting on her mask and pulling down her hood. When the gentleman entered the gallery, she first fastened both the doors so that no one should come in upon them and then, embracing him with all her might, she said in a low whisper, "This long time, my friend, the love I have for you has made me long for place and time to speak with you; but my fear for my honor has been so great that I have been constrained, in spite of myself, to conceal my passion. But at last love has prevailed over fear; and as your honor is known to me, I declare that if you will promise to love me, and never to speak of it to anyone, or inquire whom I am, I will be all my life your faithful and loving friend; and I assure you I will never love any but you; but I would rather die than tell you who I am."

The gentleman promised all she asked, and thereby encouraged her to treat him in the same way—that is to say, refuse him nothing. It was in winter, about five or six o'clock in the evening, when of course he could not see much. But if his eyes were of little service to him on the occasion, his hands were not so. Touching her clothes he found they were of velvet, a costly stuff in those times, and not worn every day, except by ladies of high family. As far as the hand could judge, all beneath was neat and in the best condition. Accordingly he tried to regale her to the best of his ability, she too performed her part equally well, and the gentleman easily perceived she was married.

When she was about to return to the place whence she came, the gentleman said to her, "Highly do I prize the favor you have conferred on me without my deserving it; but that will be still more precious to me which you will grant at my entreaty. Enchanted as I am by your gracious favor, I beg you will tell me if I am to expect a continuance of it, and in what manner I am to act; for, not knowing you, how am I to address you elsewhere to solicit the renewal of my happiness?"

"Give yourself no concern about that," replied the fair one, "but rely upon it that every evening after my mistress has supped, I shall be sure to send for you, if you are on the terrace where you were just now. But, above all things, do not forget what you have promised. When I simply send word that you are wanted, you will understand that I await you in the gallery. But if you hear speak of our going to dine, you may either retire or come to our mistress' apartment. Above all, I beg you never to attempt to know who I am, unless you wish to break our friendship."

The lady and the gentleman then went their several ways. Their intrigue lasted a long while without his ever being able to know who she was, though he had a marvelous longing to satisfy his curiosity on the point. He wearied his imagination in vain to guess who she might be, and could not conceive that there was a woman in the world who did not choose to be seen and loved. As he had heard some stupid preacher say that no one who had seen the face of the devil would ever love him, he imagined that she might possibly be some evil spirit. To clear up his doubts, he resolved to know who she was who received him so graciously.

The next time, therefore, that she sent for him, he took some chalk, and in the act of embracing her, marked her shoulder without her perceiving it. As soon as she had left him, he hastened to the princess' chamber, and stationed himself at the door to observe the shoulders of the ladies who entered. It was not long before he saw that same Jambicque advance to the door, with such an air of lofty disdain, that he durst not think of scrutinizing her like the others, feeling assured that she could not be the person he sought.

But when her back was turned, he could not help seeing the mark of the chalk, though such was his astonishment he could hardly believe his own eyes. However, after having well considered her figure, which corresponded precisely to that he was in the habit of touching in the dark, he was convinced that it was she herself; and he was very glad to see that a woman who had never been suspected of having a gallant, and was renowned for having refused so many worthy gentlemen, had at last fixed upon him alone.

Love, which never remains in one mood, could not suffer him long to enjoy that satisfaction. The gentleman conceived such a good opinion of his own powers of pleasing and flattered himself with such fair hopes that he resolved to make his love known to her, imagining that when he had done so, he should have reason to love her still more passionately. One day, when the princess was walking in the garden, the Lady Jambicque turned into an alley by herself. The gentleman, seeing her alone, went to converse with her, and feigning not to have seen her elsewhere, said to her, "I have long loved you, mademoiselle, but durst not tell you so, for fear of offending you. This constraint is so irksome to me that I must speak or die; for I do not believe that anyone can love you as I do."

Here the Lady Jambicque cut him short, and looking sternly upon him, "Have you ever heard," she said, "that I had a lover? I think not; and I am amazed at your presumption in daring to address such language to a lady of my character. You have seen enough of me here to be aware that I shall never love anyone but my husband. Beware, then, how you venture again to speak to me in any such way."

Astonished at such profound hyprocrisy, the gentleman could not help laughing. "You have not always been so rigid, madam," he said. "What is the use of dissembling with me? Is it not better we should love perfectly than imperfectly?"

"I neither love you perfectly nor imperfectly," replied Jambicque, "but regard you just as I do my mistress' other servants. If you continue to speak to me in this manner, I am very likely to hate you in such sort that you will repent of having given me provocation."

The gentleman, pushing his point, rejoined, "Where are the caresses, mademoiselle, which you bestow upon me when I cannot see you? Why deprive me of them now that day reveals your exquisite beauty to me?"

"You are out of your senses," exclaimed Jambicque, making a great sign of the cross, "or you are the greatest liar in the world; for I don't believe I ever bestowed on you more or less caresses than I do this moment. What is it you mean, pray?"

The poor gentleman, thinking to force her from her subterfuges, named the place where he had met her and told her of the mark he had put upon her with chalk in order to recognize her. Her exasperation was then so excessive that, instead of confessing, she told him he was the most wicked of men to have invented such an infamous lie against her, but that she would try to make him repent it. Knowing what influence she had with her mistress, he tried to appease her, but all in vain. She rushed from him in fury and went to where her mistress was walking, who quitted the company with her to converse with Jambicque, whom she loved as herself. The princess, seeing her so agitated, asked her what was the matter. Jambicque concealed nothing, but told her all the gentleman had said, putting it in so artful a manner and so much to the poor gentleman's disadvantage that his mistress that very evening sent him orders to go home instantly, without saying a word to anyone, and to remain there until further orders. He obeyed for fear of worse. As long as Jambicque was with the princess he remained in exile, and never heard from Jambicque, who had warned him truly that he should lose her if ever he tried to know her.

THE REMARKABLY SOLICITOUS WIFE

There was at Tours a handsome and discreet bourgeoise, who, for her virtues, was not only loved but feared by her husband. However, as husbands are frail and often grow tired of always eating good bread, hers fell in love with one of his female share croppers. He used frequently to go from Tours to visit his share cropper, always remained there two or three days, and always came back so jaded and out of sorts that his poor wife had trouble enough to set him up again. But no sooner was he himself once more, than back he would go to his share cropper, where pleasure made him forget all his ailments.

His wife, who loved his life and health above all things, seeing him always come back in such a bad plight, went to the share cropper, where she found the young woman whom her husband loved. The wife then said to her, not angrily but in the gentlest manner possible, that she knew her husband often visited her but was sorry she treated him so badly as invariably to send him home ill. The poor woman, constrained by respect for her mistress and by the force of truth, had not courage to deny the fact, and besought pardon. The lady of Touraine desired to see the room and the bed in which her husband slept. The room struck her as so cold and dirty that she was struck with pity, and sent straightway for a good bed, fine blankets, sheets, and counterpane after her husband's taste. She had the room made clean and neat and hung with tapestry, gave the woman a handsome service of plate, a pipe of good wine, sweetmeats, and confections, and begged her for the future not to send her husband back to her in so broken-down a condition.

It was not long before the husband went to see the share cropper as usual; and great was his surprise to find the sorry room become so neat, but still greater was it when she gave him a silver cup to drink out of. He asked her where it came from, and the poor woman told him with tears that it was his wife who, pitying his poor entertainment, had thus furnished the house, enjoining her to be careful of his health. Struck by the great goodness of his wife, who thus returned so much good for so much evil, the gentleman reproached himself for ingratitude as great as his wife's generosity. He gave his paramour money, begged her thenceforth to live like an honest woman, and went back to his wife. He confessed the whole truth to her, and told her that her gentleness and goodness had withdrawn him from a bad course, from which it was impossible he should ever have escaped by any other means; and forgetting the past, they lived thenceforth together in peace and concord.

FRANÇOIS RABELAIS (1495?–1553)

Victor Hugo said that Rabelais enthroned "a dynasty of big bellies" and called him "The Aeschylus of grub"; Voltaire spoke of him as "a drunken philosopher who wrote only when he was intoxicated"; the historian Hippolyte Taine found him so excessive and eccentric that he could be understood only by drunkards—or scholars. On the other hand, Balzac considered his mind "the greatest in modern humanity" and ranked Rabelais with Aristotle and Dante, while Coleridge classed him "among the deepest as well as the boldest thinkers of his age . . . even with the greatest creative minds of the world."

Since most of the facts concerning François Rabelais were compiled many years after his death, the results are not too trustworthy. The very date of his birth is conjectural; the seventeenth-century authorities agreed on 1495, although recent researches favor 1490. The place of his birth seems to have been established as a farm near Chinon in Touraine. Rabelais' people were well to do—the family included a lawyer and an apothecary—and young François was educated in a monastery, became a Franciscan priest, and emerged as an author with a rhymed epistle to the poet Jean Bouchet. In his thirties he exchanged the Franciscan robe for that of a Benedictine; then, revolting against convent life, became a secular priest, studied medicine, got a degree, lectured on Galen and Hippocrates, and turned to the writing of literature.

The legend of a fearsome but not necessarily evil giant was popular in the Middle Ages. The Great and Inestimable Chronicles of the Enormous Giant Gargantua, a collation of some of the legends, appeared in 1532. Although Rabelais did not write it, it is believed that he edited it, and his own enlargement of the myth was published a few years later. It was signed "Alcofribas Nasier," an anagram of his name. The material was not only embellished and enriched but enlivened with that inexhaustible flow of language and that irresistible spirit which we know as Rabelaisian. The humor was rough and the speech was coarse; but so were the language and literature of his times, to say nothing of many songs, paintings, and carved figures on churches.

Nevertheless, the book was attacked and, although Rabelais received absolution from the Pope, the author was involved in various irregularities. He became the father of a son born out of wedlock but, as George Saintsbury delicately reminds us in his introduction, "Nothing is known about the child and its mother; it is enough to say that the existence of the former would have been by the manners and morals of the time very easily condoned."

The story of the rest of Rabelais' life is a series of conjectures. It is probable that he served the community as doctor and priest, although his title of "the curate of Meudon" is apocryphal. Apocryphal, too, is the account of adversities in his fifties and the touching detail that he was allowed to do nothing but teach the plain song to children. The date of his death, usually given as January 9, 1553, is uncertain; so is the legend of his deathbed aphorisms. As the priest administered Extreme Unction, it is said Rabelais remarked, "I go to seek the Great Perhaps," and after a pause, "The farce is played out."

In spite of Churchly disapproval—or possibly because of it—Rabelais' work was immensely popular; more than sixty editions were printed in the fifty years following his death. When the monks clamored that the book should be suppressed, Francis I commanded that it be read to him. He was delighted with its energy and extravagances. "I find no passage in it which could be mistrusted," he concluded gravely.

The following chapters are the classic seventeenth-century translations by Sir Thomas Urquhart, whose task was completed by the Anglicized Frenchman, Peter Motteux.

FROM: THE BOOK OF GARGANTUA

HOW GARGANTUA WAS CARRIED ELEVEN MONTHS IN HIS MOTHER'S BELLY

Grangousier was a good fellow in his time, and notable jester; he loved to drink neat, as much as any man that then was in the world, and would willingly eat salt meat. To this intent he was ordinarily well furnished with gammons of bacon, both of Westphalia, Mayence and Bayonne, with store of dried neat's tongues, plenty of links, chitterlings and puddings in their season; together with salt beef and mustard, a good deal of hard roes of powdered mullet called botargos, great provision of sausages, not of Bolonia (for he feared the Lombard Boccone), but of Bigorre, Longaulnay, Brene, and Rouargue. In the vigor of his age he married Gargamelle, daughter to the King of the Parpaillons, a jolly pug, and well-mouthed wench. These two did oftentimes do the two-backed beast together, joyfully rubbing and frotting their bacon 'gainst one another in so far, that at last she became great with child of a fair son, and went with him unto the eleventh month; for so long, yea longer, may a woman carry her great belly, especially when it is some masterpiece of nature, and a person predestinated to the performance, in his due time, of great exploits. As Homer says, that the child, which Neptune begot upon the nymph, was born a whole year after the conception, that is, in the twelfth month. For, as Aulus Gellius saith, Lib. 3, this long time was suitable to the majesty of Neptune, that in it the child might receive his perfect form. For the like reason Jupiter made the night, wherein he lay with Alcmena, last forty-eight hours, a shorter time not being sufficient for the forging of Hercules, who cleansed the world of the monsters and tyrants wherewith it was suppressed. My masters, the ancient Pantagruelists, have confirmed that which I say, and withal declared it to be not only possible, but also maintained the lawful birth and legitimation of the infant born of a woman in the eleventh month after the decease of her husband.

According to ancient laws, the widows may, without danger, play at the close-buttock game with might and main, and as hard as they can for the space of the first two months after the decease of their husbands. I pray you, my good lusty springal lads, if you find any of these females, that are worth the pains of untying the codpiece point, get up, and bring them to me; for if they happen within the third month to conceive, the child shall be heir to the deceased, and the mother shall pass for an honest woman.

When she is known to have conceived, thrust forward boldly, spare her not, whatever betide you, seeing the paunch is full. As Julia, the daughter of the Emperor Octavian, never prostituted herself to her belly-bumpers, but when she found herself with child; after the manner of ships that receive not their steersman till they have their ballast and lading. And if any blame the women for that after pregnancy they still continue buxom, and push for more; whereas any beast, a cow or mare will kick and flounce, and admit no farther courtship from the bull or stallion: the answer will be, these are beasts and know no better: but the other are women, and understand the glorious right they have to the pretty perquisite of a superfoetation, as Populia heretofore answered, according to the relation of Macrobius, Lib. 2. Saturnal. If the devil will not have them to bagge, he must wring hard the spigot, and stop the bung-hole.

HOW GARGAMELLE, BEING BIG WITH GARGANTUA, DID EAT A HUGE DEAL OF TRIPES

The occasion and manner how Gargamelle was brought to bed, and delivered of her child, was thus: and if you do not believe it I wish your bum-gut may fall out. Her bum-gut indeed, or fundament escaped her in an afternoon, on the third day of February, with having eaten at dinner too many godebillios: godebillios are the fat tripes of coiros: coiros are beeves fattened in the ox-stalls, and guimo meadows: guimo meadows are those that may be mowed twice a year; of those fat beeves they had killed three hundred sixty-seven thousand and fourteen, to be salted at Shrovetide; that in the entering of the spring they might have plenty of powdered beef, wherewith to season their mouths at the beginning of their meals, and to taste their wine the better.

They had abundance of tripes as you have heard, and they were so delicious that every one licked his fingers. But, as the devil would have it, there was no possibility of keeping them long sweet, and to let them stink was not so commendable or handsome; it was therefore concluded, that they should be all of them gulched up, without any waste. To this effect they invited all the burghers of Sainais, of Suillé, of the Roche Clermaud, of Vaugaudry, without omitting Coudray, Monpensier, the Gué de Vede, and other their neighbours; all stiff drinkers, brave fellows, and good players at nine-pins. The good man Grangousier took great pleasure in their company, and commanded there should be no want nor pinching for anything: nevertheless he bade his wife eat sparingly, because she was near her time, and that these tripes were no very commendable meat; they would fain (said he) be at the chewing of ordure, who eat the bag that contained it. Notwithstanding these admonitions, she did eat sixteen quarters, two bushels, three pecks, and a pipkin full. What a filthy deal of loblolly was here, to swell and wamble in her guts?

After dinner they all went tag-rag together to the willow-grove, where, on the green grass, to the sound of merry flutes and pleasant bagpipes, they danced so gallantly that it was a sweet and heavenly sport to see them so frolic.

HOW GARGANTUA WAS BORN IN A STRANGE MANNER

Whilst they were discoursing of drinking, Gargamelle began to be a little unwell in her lower parts. Whereupon Grangousier arose from the grass, and fell to comfort her very honestly and kindly, suspecting that she was in travail, and told her that it was best for her to sit down upon the grass, under the willows, because she was like very shortly to see young feet; and that, therefore, it was convenient she should pluck up her spirits, and take a good heart at the new coming of her baby; saying to her withal, that although the pain was somewhat grievous to her, it would be but of short continuance; and that the succeeding joy would quickly remove that sorrow, in such sort that she should not so much as remember it. "On with a sheep's courage," quoth he; "dispatch this boy, and we will speedily fall to work for the making of another." "Ha!" said she, "so well as you speak at your own ease, you that are men: well, then, in the name of God, I'll do my best, seeing you will have it so; but would to God that it were cut off from you." "What?" said Grangousier. "Ha!" said she, "you are a good man indeed—you understand it well enough." "What, my member?" said he. "Udzookers, if it please you, that shall be done instantly; bid 'em bring hither a knife." "Alas!" said she, "the Lord forbid; I pray Jesus to forgive me; I did not say it from my heart: do it not any kind of harm, neither more nor less, for my speaking: but I am like to have work enough today, and all for your member; yet God bless both you and it."

"Courage, courage," said he; "take you no care of the matter; let the four foremost oxen do the work. I will yet go drink one whiff more, and if, in the meantime, anything befall you, I will be so near that, at the first whistling in your fist, I shall be with you." A little while after, she began to groan, lament, and cry: then suddenly came the midwives from all quarters, who, groping her below, found some *peloderies* of a bad savor indeed: this they thought had been the child; but it was her fundament that was slipped out with the mollification of her *intestinum rectum*, which you call the bum-gut, and that merely by eating of too many tripes, as we have shewed you before. Whereupon an old, ugly trot in the company, who was reputed a notable physician, and was come from Brispaille, near to St. Gnou, threescore years before, made her so horrible a restrictive and binding medicine, whereby all her arse-pipes were so oppilated, stopped, obstructed, and contracted, that you could hardly have opened and enlarged them with your teeth, which is a terrible thing to think upon, seeing the devil at mass at St. Martin's was puzzled with the like task, when with his teeth he lengthened out the parchment whereon he wrote the tittle-tattle of two young mangy whores.

The effect of this was, that the *cotyledons* of her matrix were all loosened above, through which the child sprung up and leaped, and so entering into the hollow vein, did climb by the *diaphragm* even above her shoulders (where that vein divides itself into two), and, from thence taking his way towards the left side, issued forth at her left ear. As soon as he was born, he cried, not as other babes use to do, "*mies, mies, mies;*" but, with a high, sturdy, and big voice, shouted "Give us drink! Drink! Drink!" as though inviting the world to share it with him. The noise thereof was exceedingly great, so that it was heard at the same time in two counties, Beauce and Bibarois. I doubt me that you may not thoroughly believe the truth of this strange nativity. Though you believe it or not, I care not much; but an honest man, and one of good judgment, believeth what is told him and that which he finds written.

Is this beyond our law or our faith? Is it against reason or the Holy Scripture? For my part I find nothing in the sacred Bible that is against it. But tell me, if it had been the will of God, would you say that he could not do it? Ha, for favor sake, I beseech you, never emberlucock or inpulregafize your spirits with these vain thoughts and idle conceits; for I tell you, it is not impossible with God, and, if he pleased, all women henceforth should bring forth their children at the ear. Was not Bacchus engendered out of the very thigh of Jupiter? Did not Roquetaillade come out at his mother's heel, and Crocmoush from the slipper of his nurse? Was not Minerva born of the brain, even through the ear of Jove? Adonis, of the bark of a myrrh tree; and Castor and Pollux of the doupe of that egg which was laid and hatched by Leda? But you would wonder more, and with far greater amazement, if I should now present you with that chapter of Plinius, wherein he treateth of strange births, and contrary to nature, and yet am not I so impudent a liar as he was. Read the seventh book of his *Natural History*, Chap. 3, and trouble not my head any more about this.

HOW THEY APPARELED GARGANTUA

(*This chapter is a rollicking account of the monstrous accouterments designed for and worn by Gargantua. It also contains a hilarious description of
the enormous and elaborate codpiece Gargantua wears and which makes frequent appearances throughout the several books. Rabelais puts into print details prominently featured in the rowdy scenes painted by Breughel and the
elegant portraits by Bronzino.*)

Being of this age, his father ordained to have clothes made for him in his
own livery, which was white and blue. To work then went the tailors, and
with great expedition were those clothes made, cut, and sewed, according to
the fashion that was then in vogue. I find by the ancient records, to be seen
in the chamber of accounts at Montsoreau, that he was accoutered in manner
as followeth: To make one shirt of his there were taken up nine hundred ells
of Chasteleraud linen, and two hundred for the gussets, in manner of cushions, which they put under his armpits; his shirt was not gathered nor plaited,
for the plaiting of shirts was not found out till the seamstresses (when the
point of their needles was broken) began to work and occupy with the tail.
There were taken up for his doublet eight hundred and thirteen ells of white
satin, and for his codpiece points, fifteen hundred and nine dog skins and a
half. Then was it that men began to tie their breeches to their doublets, and
not their doublets to their breeches; for it is against nature, as hath most
amply been shewed by Ockam.

For his breeches, were taken up eleven hundred and five ells and a third
of white broadcloth. They were cut in form of pillars, chamfred, channeled,
and pinked behind, that they might not overheat his reins; and were, within
the panes, puffed out with the lining of as much blue damask as was needful;
and remark, that he had very good knee-rollers, proportionable to the rest of
his stature.

For his codpiece were used sixteen ells and a quarter of the same cloth,
and it was fashioned on the top like unto a triumphant arch, most gallantly
fastened with two enameled clasps, in each of which was set a great emerald
as big as an orange; for, as says Orpheus, *Lib. de lapidibus*, and Pliny *Lib.
ultimo*, it hath an erective virtue and comfortative of the natural member.
The ject, or outstanding of his codpiece, was of the length of a yard, jagged
and pinked, and withal bagging, and strutting out with the blue damask lining, after the manner of his breeches. But had you seen the fair embroidery of
the small needlework purl, and the curiously interlaced knots, by the goldsmith's art, set out and trimmed with rich diamonds, precious rubies, fine
turquoises, costly emeralds, and Persian pearls, you would have compared it
to a fair cornucopia, or horn of abundance, such as you see in antiques, or
as Rhea gave to the two nymphs, Amalthea and Ida, the nurses of Jupiter.

And like to that horn of abundance, it was still gallant, succulent, droppy,
sappy, pithy, lively, always flourishing, always fructifying, full of juice, full of

flower, full of fruit, and all manner of delight. Blessed lady! It would have done one good to have seen it: but I will tell you more of it in the book which I have made of the dignity of codpieces. One thing I will tell you, that as it was both long and large, so was it well furnished and provided within, nothing like unto the hypocritical codpieces of some fond wooers and wench-courters, which are stuffed only with wind, to the great prejudice of the female sex.

For his shoes, were taken up four hundred and six ells of blue crimson velvet, and were very neatly cut by parallel lines, joined in uniform cylinders: for the soling of them were made use of eleven hundred hides of brown cows, shapen like the tail of a keeling.

For his coat, were taken up eighteen hundred ells of blue velvet, dyed in grain, embroidered in its borders with fair gilliflowers, in the middle decked with silver purl, intermixed with plaits of gold, and store of pearls, hereby showing that in his time he would prove an especial good fellow, and singular whip-can.

His girdle was made of three hundred ells and a half of silken serge, half white and half blue, if I mistake it not. His sword was not of Valentia, nor his dagger of Saragosa, for his father could not endure these *Hidalgos borrachos maranisados como diablos*; but he had a fair sword made of wood, and the dagger of boiled leather, as well painted and gilded as any man could wish.

His purse was made of the cod of an elephant, which was given him by Her Pracontal, proconsul of Lybia.

For his gown, were employed nine thousand six hundred ells, wanting two-thirds, of blue velvet, as before, all so diagonally purled, that by true perspective issued thence an unnamed color, like that you see in the necks of turtle-doves or turkey-cocks, which wonderfully rejoiceth the eyes of the beholders. For his bonnet, or cap, were taken up three hundred two ells and a quarter of white velvet, and the form thereof was wide and round, of the bigness of his head; for his father said, that the caps of the Marrabaise fashion, made like the cover of a pasty, would, one time or other, bring a mischief on those that wore them. For his plume, he wore a fair great blue feather, plucked from an Onocrotal of the country of Hircania the Wild, very prettily hanging down over his right ear: for the jewel or broach, which in his cap he carried, he had in a cake of gold, weighing threescore and eight marks, a fair piece of enameled work, wherein were portrayed a man's body with two heads, looking towards one another; four arms, four feet, two arses, such as Plato, in Symposio, says was the mystical beginning of man's nature; and about it was written in Ionic letters, "Charity seeketh not her own."

To wear about his neck he had a golden chain, weighing twenty-five thousand and sixty-three marks of gold, the link thereof being made after the manner of great berries, amongst which were set in work green jaspers, engraven, and cut dragon-like, all environed with beams and sparks, as King Nicepsos of old was wont to wear them, and it reached down to the very bust of the rising of his belly, whereby he reaped great benefit all his life long, as the

Greek physicians knew well enough. For his gloves, were put in work sixteen otters' skins, and three of *loupgarous*, or men-eating wolves, for the bordering of them: and of this stuff were they made, by the appointment of the Cabalists of Sanlouand. As for the rings which his father would have him to wear, to renew the ancient mark of nobility, he had on the forefinger of his left hand a carbuncle as big as an ostrich's egg, enchased very daintly in gold of the fineness of a Turkey seraph. Upon the middle finger of the same hand he had a ring made of four metals together, of the strangest fashion that ever was seen; so that the steel did not crash against the gold, nor the silver crush the copper. All this was made by Captain Chappuys, and Alcofribas, his good agent. On the medical finger of his right hand he had a ring made spirewise, wherein was set a perfect Balas ruby, a pointed diamond, and a Physon emerald, of an inestimable value. For Hans Carvel, the king of Melinda's jeweler, esteemed them at the rate of threescore nine millions, eight hundred ninety-four thousand, and eighteen French crowns of Berry, and at so much did the Foucres of Augsburg prize them.

HOW GARGANTUA PAID HIS RESPECTS TO THE PARISIANS
AND HOW HE TOOK AWAY THE GREAT BELLS OF OUR LADY'S CHURCH

(While completing his education in Paris, Gargantua's desire to escape the scrutiny of the curious leads to one of the most famous as well as one of the most scurrilous episodes in the book. It relates, moreover, how the giant stole the great bells of Notre Dame and how Paris got its name.)

Some few days after that they had refreshed themselves, he went to see the city, and was beheld of everybody there with great admiration: for the people of Paris are such fools, such puppies, and naturals, that a juggler, a carrier of indulgencies, a sumpter-horse, a mule with his bells, a blind fiddler in the middle of a cross lane, shall draw a greater confluence of people together than an evangelical preacher. And they pressed so hard upon him, that he was constrained to rest himself upon the steeple of our Lady's church; at which place, seeing so many about him, he said with a loud voice, "I believe that these buzzards will have me to pay them here my welcome hither, and my beverage: it is but good reason. I will now give them their wine, but it shall be only a *par ris*, that is, in sport." Then smiling, he untied his goodly codpiece, and lugging out his Roger into the open air, he so bitterly all-to-be-pissed them, that he drowned two hundred and sixty thousand four hundred and eighteen, besides the women and little children.

Some, nevertheless, of the company escaped this piss-flood by mere speed of foot, who when they were at the higher end of the university, sweating, coughing, spitting, and out of breath, they began to swear and curse, some in good hot earnest, and others *par ris, carimari, carimara; golynoly, golynolo;* "ods-bodikins, we are washed *par ris*," from whence that city hath been ever since called Paris; whose name formerly was Leucotia (as Strabo testifieth,

Lib. quarto), which in Greek is whiteness, because of the white thighs of the ladies of that place. And forasmuch as at this imposition of a new name, all the people that were there swore, every one by the Sancts of his parish, the Parisians, which are patched up of all nations, and all manner of men, are by nature good at swearing, and not a little domineering; whereupon Joanninus de Barrauco, *libro de copiositate reverentiarum*, thinks that they are called Parisians from the Greek, as one would say, bold talkers.

This done, he considered the great bells which were in the said steeple, and made them ring very harmoniously: which whilst he was doing it came into his mind that they would serve very well for tingling tantans to hang about his mare's neck, when she should be sent back to his father (as he intended) loaded with Brie cheese and fresh herring; and, indeed, he forthwith carried them to his lodging. In the meanwhile there came a master beggar of the friars of St. Anthony, for some hogs' purtenance; who, that he might be heard afar off, and to make the bacon shake in the very chimneys, had a mind to these bells, and made account to filch them away privily. Nevertheless, he left them behind him very honestly, not for that they were too hot, but that they were somewhat too heavy for his carriage.

All the city was in an uproar, they being (as you know, upon any slight occasion) so ready to uproars and insurrections, that foreign nations wonder at the patience of the kings of France, who do not by good justice restrain them from such tumultuous courses, seeing the manifold inconveniences which thence arise from day to day. Would to God I knew the shop wherein are forged these divisions, and factious combinations, that I might bring them to light in the confraternities of my parish! Believe for a truth, that the place wherein the people gathered together, were thus sulphured, hopurymated, moiled, and bepissed, was called Nesle, where then was, but now is no more, the oracle of Leucotia. There was the case proposed, and the inconvenience showed of the transporting of the bells. After they had well ergoted pro and con, they concluded in baralipton, that they should send the oldest and most sufficient of the faculty unto Gargantua, to signify unto him the great and horrible prejudice they sustain by the want of those bells.

FROM: THE BOOK OF PANTAGRUEL

OF THE ORIGIN AND ANTIQUITY OF PANTAGRUEL

It will not be an idle or unprofitable thing, seeing we are at leisure, to put you in mind of the fountain and original source, whence is derived unto us the good Pantagruel: for I see that all good historiographers have thus handled their chronicles, not only the Arabians, Barbarians, and Latins, but also the gentle Greeks, who were eternal drinkers. You must therefore remark, that at the beginning of the world, I speak of a long time, it is above forty quarantans of nights, according to the supputation of the ancient

Druids, a little after that Abel was killed by his brother Cain, the earth embrued with the blood of the just, was one year so exceedingly fertile in those fruits which it usually produceth to us, and especially in medlars, that, ever since, throughout all ages, it hath been called the year of the great medlars, for three of them did fill a bushel. In that year the calends were found by the Grecian almanacks. There was that year nothing of the month of March in the time of Lent, and the middle of August was in May. In the month of October, as I take it, or at least September, that I may not err, for I will carefully take heed of that, was the week so famous in the annals, which they call the week of the three Thursdays; for it had three of them, by means of the irregular leap-years, occasioned by the sun's having tripped and stumbled a little towards the left hand, like a debtor afraid of serjeants; and the moon varied from her course above five fathom; and there was manifestly seen the motion of trepidation in the firmament called Aplanes, so that the middle Pleiade, leaving her follows, declined toward the equinoctial; and the star named Spica left the constellation of the Virgin, withdrawing itself towards the Balance: which are cases very terrible, and matters so hard and difficult, that astrologians cannot set their teeth in them; and indeed their teeth had been pretty long if they could have reached thither.

However, account you it for a truth, that everybody did then most heartily eat of these medlars, for they were fair to the eye, and in taste delicious. But even as Noah, that holy man, to whom we are so much beholden, bound, and obliged, for that he planted to us the vine, from whence we have that nectarian, delicious, precious, heavenly, joyful, and deific liquor, which they call the piot, or tiplage, was deceived in the drinking of it, for he was ignorant of the great virtue and power thereof; so likewise the men and women of that time did delight much in the eating of that fair great fruit; but divers and very different accidents did ensue thereupon: for there fell upon them all in their bodies a most terrible swelling, but not upon all in the same place; for some were swollen in the belly, and their belly strouted out big like a great tun; of whom it is written, *ventrem omnipotentem;* who were all very honest men, and merry blades: and of this race came St. Fatgulch and Shrovetuesday. Others did swell at the shoulders, who in that place were so crump and knobby that they were therefore called Montifers, which is as much to say as Hill-carriers, of whom you see some yet in the world, of divers sexes and degrees. Of this race came Æsop, some of whose excellent words and deeds you have in writing. Some other puffs did swell in length by the member which they call the laborer of nature, in such sort that it grew marvelous long, fat, great, lusty, stirring, and crest-risen, in the antique fashion, so that they made use of it as of a girdle, winding it five or six times about their waist: but if it happened the aforesaid member to be in good case, spooming with a full sail bunt fair before the wind, then to have seen those strutting champions, you would have taken them for men that had their lances settled on their rest to run at the ring or tilting whintam [quintain]. Of these, believe me, the race is utterly lost and quite extinct, as the women say; for they do lament continually that there are none extant now of those great, &c. You know the rest of the song. Others did grow in matter of ballocks so enormously that three of them would well fill a sack able to contain five quarters of wheat. From them are descended the ballocks of Lorrain, which never dwell in codpieces, but fall down to the bottom of the breeches. Others grew in the legs, and to see them you would have said they had been cranes, or the reddish-long-billed-storklike-scrank-legged sea-fowls called flamans, or else men walking upon stilts or scatches. The little grammar-school boys, known by the name of Grimos, called those leg-grown slangams Jambus, in allusion to the French word jambe, which signifieth a leg. In others, their nose did grow so, that it seemed to be the beak of a limbeck, in every part thereof most variously diapered with the twinkling sparkles of crimson blisters budding forth, and purpled with pimples all enameled with thickest wheals of a sanguine colour, bordered with gules; and such have you seen the Canon or Prebend Panzoult, and Woodenfoot, the physician of Angiers. Of which race there were few that liked the ptisane, but all of them were perfect lovers of the pure Septembral juice. Naso and Ovid had their extraction from thence, and all those of whom it is written, Ne reminiscaris. Others grew in ears, which they had so big that out of one would have been stuff enough got to make a doublet, a pair of breeches, and a jacket, whilst with the other they might have covered themselves as with a Spanish cloak: and they say that in Bourbonnois this race remaineth yet. Others grew in length of body, and of these came the giants, and of them Pantagruel.

HOW PANURGE SERVED A PARISIAN LADY A TRICK THAT DID NOT PLEASE HER VERY WELL

(*Panurge, Pantagruel's boon companion and a desperate rake, has been rejected by a haughty Parisian lady. He revenges himself upon her with a humiliating and almost incredible act of rowdiness.*)

Now you must note that the next day was the great festival of Corpus Christi, called the sacre, wherein all women put on their best apparel; and on that day the said lady was cloathed in a rich gown of crimson satin, under which she wore a very costly white velvet petticoat.

Now on the vigil, Panurge searched so long of one side and another, that he found a hot or salt bitch, which, when he had tied her with his girdle, he led her to his chamber, and fed her very well all that day and night; in the morning thereafter he killed her, and took that part of her which the Greek geomancers know, and cut it into several pieces as small as he could: then carrying it away as close as might be, he went to the place where the lady was to come along to follow the procession, as the custom is upon the said holy-day. And when she came in, Panurge sprinkled some holy water on her, saluting her very courteously. Then, a little while after she had said her petty devotions, he sat down close by her upon the same bench, and gave her this roundelay in writing, in manner as followeth:

A *Roundelay*

> Lady, for once, because my case
> I told you, am I out of grace?
> That you should so severely call
> Me to be gone for good-and-all,
> Who never had deserved your frown
> By word, deed, letter, or lampoon.
> You might deny me what I sought,
> And not have call'd me all to nought,
> Because I would have had a bout,
> > Lady, for once.
>
> It hurts you not that I complain
> Of my intolerable pain;
> Of bloody wound, and deadly dart,
> Wherewith your beauty thrills my heart:
> And since from thence my torment came,
> O grant some little of that same,
> > Lady, for once.

As she was opening this paper to see what it was, Panurge very promptly and lightly scattered the drug that he had upon her in divers places, but especially in the pleats of her sleeves, and of her gown. Then said he unto her, "Madam, the poor lovers are not always at ease. As for me, I hope that those heavy nights, those pains and troubles, which I suffer for love of you, shall be a deduction to me of so much pain in purgatory; yet, at the least, pray to God to give me patience in my misery." Panurge had no sooner spoke this but all the dogs that were in the church came running to this lady with the smell of the drugs that he had strewed upon her, both small and great, big and little, all came, laying out their member, smelling to her, and pissing everywhere upon her—it was the greatest villainy in the world. Panurge made the fashion of driving them away; then took his leave of her and withdrew himself into some chapel or oratory of the said church to see the sport; for these villainous dogs did compiss all her habiliments, and left none of her attire unbesprinkled with their staling; insomuch that a tall greyhound pissed upon her head, others in her sleeves, others on her crupper-piece, and the little ones pissed upon her pataines; so that all the women that were round about her had much ado to save her. Whereat Panurge very heartily laughing, he said to one of the lords of the city, "I believe that same lady is hot, or else that some greyhound hath covered her lately." And when he saw that all the dogs were flocking about her, yarring at the retard-ment of their access to her, and every way keeping such a coil with her, as they are wont to do about a proud or salt bitch; he forthwith departed from thence, and went to call Pantagruel; not forgetting in his way along the streets through which he went, where he found any dogs, to give them a bang with his foot, saying, "Will you not go with your fellows to the wedding? Away hence! avant! avant! with a devil avant!" And being come home, he said to Pantagruel, "Master, I pray you come and see all the dogs of the country, how they are assembled about a lady, the fairest in the city, and would duffle and line her." Whereunto Pantagruel willingly condescended, and saw the mystery, which he found very pretty and strange. But the best was at the procession, in which were seen above six hundred thousand and fourteen dogs about her, which did very much trouble and molest her; and whithersoever she passed, those dogs that came afresh, tracing her footsteps, followed her at the heels, and pissed in the way where her gown had touched. All the world stood gazing at this spectacle, considering the action of those dogs, who leaping up, got about her neck, and spoiled all her gorgeous accouterments; for the which she could find no remedy, but to retire unto her house, which was a palace. Thither she went, and the dogs after her: she ran to hide herself, but the chambermaids could not abstain from laughing. When she was entered into the house, and had shut the door upon herself, all the dogs came running, of half a league round, and did so well bepiss the gate of her house, that there they made a stream with their urine wherein a duck might very well have swum; and it is the same current that now runs at St. Victor, in which Gobelin dyeth scarlet by the specifical virtue of these piss-dogs.

HOW PANTAGRUEL DEPARTED FROM PARIS

(In an extremely short chapter Rabelais packs an unblushing account of soldierly sexuality—which, he says, accounts for the shortness of French leagues.)

A little while after Pantagruel heard news that his father Gargantua had been translated into the land of the fairies by Morgue, as heretofore were Ogier and Arthur; as also, that the report of his translation being spread abroad, the Dipsodes, had issued out beyond their borders, with inroads had wasted a great part of Utopia, and at that very time had besieged the great city of the Amaurots. Whereupon departing from Paris without bidding any man farewell, for the business required diligence, he came to Rouen.

Now Pantagruel in his journey seeing that the leagues of that little territory about Paris called France were very short in comparison to those of other countries, demanded the cause and reason of it from Panurge, who told him a story which Marotus of the Lac set down in the Acts of the Kings of Canarre, saying that in old times countries were not distinguished into leagues, miles, furlongs, nor parasangs, until that King Pharamond divided them, which was done in manner as followeth: The said king chose at Paris a hundred fair, gallant, lusty, brisk young men, all resolute and bold adventurers in Cupid's duels, together with a hundred comely, pretty, handsome, lovely and well-complexioned wenches of Picardy, all whom he caused to be well entertained and highly fed for the space of eight days. Then having called for them, he delivered to every one of the young men his wench, with store of money to defray their charges, and this injunction besides, to go unto divers places here and there. And wheresoever they should biscot and thrum their wenches, that, they setting a stone there, it should be accounted for a league. Thus went away those brave fellows and sprightly blades most merrily, and because they were fresh and had been at rest, they very often jummed and fanfreluched almost at every field's end, and this is the cause why the leagues about Paris are so short. But when they had gone a great way, and were now as weary as poor devils, all the oil in their lamps being almost spent, they did not chink and duffle so often, but contented themselves (I mean for the men's part) with one scurvy paltry bout in a day, and this is that which makes the leagues in Brittany, Delanes, Germany, and other more remote countries so long. Other men give other reasons for it, but this seems to me of all others the best.

MIGUEL DE CERVANTES (1547–1616)

A chivalrous Spanish soldier, Miguel de Cervantes wrote the world's most famous satire on chivalry. Its hero, Don Quixote, had drugged himself with so many books about noble knights and damsels in distress that he resolved not only to rescue all unfortunates but to right the wrongs of the entire world. His mad idealism, contrasted with the materialism of his servant, Sancho Panza, gave literature a prime synonym for the impractical crusader and enriched our vocabulary with the word "quixotic." In his efforts to save those who are oppressed, Don Quixote attacks windmills under the delusion that they are giants, fights with peasants whom he mistakes for ruffians, and transforms flocks of sheep into armies, country wenches into countesses, and tawdry inns into castles.

It is at one of the inns that the Knight of the Doleful Countenance (Sancho Panza's title for his master) has one of his most boisterous and most lamentable experiences. He and his bony horse, romantically christened Rozinante, have been beaten by a pack of "bloody-hearted and evil villains" (actually harmless carriers) after Don Quixote has made another of his simple-minded mistakes. Bruised and wretched, but by no means discouraged, the lean, impoverished knight reaches an inn which the inveterate dreamer, as usual, takes to be a castle. What follows is a nightmare of false identifications, general confusion, and bawdy pandemonium.

The translation is a revision of Charles Jarvis's version.

FROM: DON QUIXOTE

WHAT HAPPENED TO DON QUIXOTE AT THE INN

When the inn-keeper saw Don Quixote lying upon the ass, he inquired of Sancho Panza what was wrong with his master. Sancho replied that it was nothing serious, just a fall from a rock which had bruised his ribs. The inn-keeper's wife, whose disposition was different from that of most inn-keepers' wives, was kindly and sympathetic to the misfortunes of her neighbors. She prepared to do something for the poor stranger at once and made her daughter, a comely girl, assist her.

There also was a servant at the inn, a broad-faced, flat-nosed, blunt-headed Asturian wench; she was half blind in one eye and squinted with the other. She made up for these defects by having an elegant body, whose allure consisted of heavy shoulders, a squat carriage, and slouching walk—all of her measuring about three feet. This delectable maiden helped the daughter attend to Don Quixote, and the two of them arranged a bed for the shaken knight in the garret which had once served as a hayloft.

This garret also lodged a carrier, whose bed was a little further from the door than Don Quixote's, and, though it consisted of nothing more luxurious than his mules' saddles and blankets, it was decidedly more comfortable than the knight's, which was nothing more than four rough boards held up by a pair of uneven trestles, a mattress thin as a quilt and full of lumps—each lump being as hard as a pebble—two sheets made of discarded leather, and an old rug whose every thread could have been counted without missing a single frayed yarn. In this wretched bed was Don Quixote laid; after which the hostess and her daughter plastered him from head to foot. Maritornes (for so the Asturian wench was called) at the same time held the light. And, as the hostess was thus employed, perceiving Don Quixote to be mauled in every part, she said that his bruises seemed the effect of hard drubbing, rather than of a fall. "Not a drubbing," said Sancho; "but the knobs and sharp points of the rock every one of which has left its mark. And, now that I think of it," added he, "pray spare a morsel of that tow, as somebody may find it useful—indeed, I suspect that my sides would be glad of a little of it." "What, you have had a fall too, have you?" said the hostess. "No," replied Sancho, "not a fall, but a fright, on seeing my master tumble, which so affected my whole body that I feel as if I had received a thousand blows myself." "That may be," said the damsel, "for I have often dreamed that I was falling down from some high tower, and could never come to the ground; and, when I awoke, I have found myself as much bruised and battered as if I had really fallen." "But here is the point, mistress," answered Sancho Panza, "that I, without dreaming at all, and more awake than I am now, find myself with almost as many bruises as my master Don Quixote." "What do you say is the name of this gentleman?" quoth the Asturian. "Don Quixote de la Mancha," answered Sancho Panza. "He is a knight-errant, and one of the

best and most valiant that has been seen for this long time in the world."
"What is a knight-errant?" said the wench. "Are you such a novice as not to
know that?" answered Sancho Panza. "You must know, then, that a knight-
errant is a thing that, in two words, is cudgeled and made an emperor.
Today he is the most unfortunate wretch in the world; and tomorrow will
have two or three crowns of kingdoms to give to his squire." "How comes
it then to pass that you, being squire to this worthy gentleman," said the
hostess, "have not yet, as it seems, got so much as an earldom?" "It is early
days yet," answered Sancho, "for it is but a month since we set out in quest
of adventures, and hitherto we have met with none that deserve the name.
And sometimes we look for one thing, and find another. But the truth is,
if my master Don Quixote recovers of this wound or fall, and I am not
disabled thereby, I would not trade my hopes for the best title in Spain."

To all this conversation Don Quixote had listened attentively, and now,
raising himself up in the bed as well as he could, and taking the hand of his
hostess, he said to her: "Believe me, beauteous lady, you may esteem yourself fortunate in having entertained me in this your castle, being such a
person that, if I say little of myself, it is because, as the proverb declares,
self-praise depreciates. But my squire will inform you who I am. I only say
that I shall retain the service you have done me eternally engraven on my
memory, and be grateful to you as long as my life shall endure. And, had
it pleased the high heavens that Love had not held me so enthralled and
subject to his laws, and to the eyes of that beautiful ingrate whose name
I silently pronounce, those of this lovely virgin had become enslavers of my
liberty."

The hostess, her daughter, and the good Maritornes, stood confounded at
this harangue, which they understood just as much as if he had spoken Greek,
although they guessed that it all tended to compliments and offers of service; and, not being accustomed to such kind of language, they gazed at him
with surprise, and thought him another sort of man than those now in
fashion. Then, after thanking him, in their inn-like phrase, for his offers,
they left him. The Asturian Maritornes doctored Sancho, who stood in no
less need of plasters than his master. The carrier and she, it appeared, had
agreed to pass that night together; and she had given him her word that,
when the guests were all quiet and her master and mistress asleep, she would
share his bed with him. And it is said of this honest wench that she never
made the like promise but she performed it, even though she had made it
on a mountain, without any witness; for she valued herself upon her gentility,
and thought it no disgrace to be employed in such service at an inn, since
misfortunes and accidents, as she affirmed, had brought her to that state.

Don Quixote's hard, scanty, beggarly, crazy bed stood first in the middle
of the hayloft; and close by it Sancho had placed his own, which consisted
only of a rush mat, and a rug that seemed to be rather of beaten hemp than
of wool. Next to the squire's stood that of the carrier, made up, as hath

been said, of the saddles and blankets of his mules: for he possessed twelve in number, sleek, fat, and stately.

After the carrier had visited his mules, and given them their second course, he laid himself down in expectation of his usually prompt Maritornes. Sancho was already plastered and in bed; and, though he tried to sleep, the pain of his ribs would not allow him; and Don Quixote, from the same cause, kept his eyes wide open as those of a hare. The whole inn was in profound silence, and contained no other light than that from a lamp which hung in the middle of the entry. This marvelous stillness, and the thoughts of our knight, which incessantly recurred to those adventures so common in the annals of chivalry, brought to his imagination one of the strangest whims that can well be conceived. He imagined that he was now in some famous castle, and that the daughter of its lord, captivated by his fine appearance, had become enamored of him, and had promised to steal that night privately to him, and pass some time with him. Then, taking all this fantasy formed by himself for reality, he began to feel some alarm, reflecting on the dangerous trial to which his fidelity was on the point of being exposed; but resolved in his heart not to commit disloyalty against his lady Dulcinea del Toboso, though Queen Ginebra herself should present herself before him.

Whilst his thoughts were occupied by these extravagances, the hour—an unlucky one to him—arrived when the gentle Asturian, mindful of her promise, entered the room, undressed and bare-footed, with her hair tucked up under a fustian kerchief, and, with silent and cautious step, advanced towards the couch of her beloved. But scarcely had she passed the threshold of the door when Don Quixote heard her; and, sitting up in his bed, in spite of plasters and the pain of his ribs, stretched out his arms to receive his beauteous damsel, who, crouching, and holding her breath as she went, with hands extended feeling for her lover, encountered the arms of Don Quixote, who caught first hold of her by the wrist, and, drawing her towards him (she not daring to speak a word), made her sit down on the bed. On touching her only garment, though it was of sacking, it seemed to him to be of the finest and softest lawn; the glass beads that encircled her wrists, to his fancy were precious oriental pearls; her hairs, not unlike those of a horse's mane, he took for threads of the brightest gold of Arabia, whose splendor obscures that of the sun itself; and though her breath smelt of the last night's stale salt-fish, he fancied himself inhaling a delicious and aromatic odor. In short, his imagination painted her to him in the very form and manner of some princess described in his books, who comes thus adorned to visit the wounded knight with whom she is in love. And so great was the poor gentleman's infatuation that neither the touch, nor the breath, nor other things the wench had about her, could undeceive him, although enough to make any one but a carrier sick. So far from this, he imagined that he held the goddess of beauty in his arms; and, clasping her fast, in a low and amorous voice he said to her: "O! that I were in a state, beautiful and exalted lady, to return so vast a favor as this you confer upon me by your charming presence! But fortune, never weary of persecuting the good, is pleased to lay me on this bed, so bruised and disabled that, how much soever I may be inclined to convince you of my devotion, it is impossible. To which is added another still greater impossibility—the plighted faith I have sworn to the peerless Dulcinea del Toboso, sole mistress of my thoughts! Had not these things intervened, I should not have been so insensible a knight as to let slip the happy opportunity with which your great goodness has favored me."

Maritornes was in the utmost vexation at being thus held by Don Quixote and, not hearing or attending to what he said, she struggled, without speaking a word, to release herself. The good carrier, whom lustful thoughts had kept awake, having heard his fair one from the first moment she entered the door, listened attentively to all that Don Quixote said; and, suspecting that the Asturian nymph had played false with him, he advanced towards Don Quixote's bed, and stood still, in order to discover the tendency of his discourse, which, however, he could not understand. But, seeing that the wench struggled to get from him, and that Don Quixote labored to hold her, and also not liking the jest, he lifted up his arm, and discharged so terrible a blow on the lean jaws of the enamored knight, that his mouth was bathed in blood. Not content with this, he mounted upon his ribs, and paced them somewhat above a trot from one end to the other. The bed, which was crazy, and its foundations none of the strongest, being unable to bear the additional weight of the carrier, came down to the ground with such a crash that the inn-keeper awoke; and, having called aloud to Maritornes without receiving an answer, he immediately conjectured it was some affair in which she was concerned. With this suspicion he arose, and, lighting a candle, went to the place where he had heard the bustle.

The wench, seeing her master coming, and knowing his furious disposition, retreated in terror to Sancho Panza's bed, who was now asleep; and there rolled herself into a ball. The inn-keeper entered, calling out, "Where are you, strumpet? for these are some of your doings!" Sancho, was now disturbed, and feeling such a mass upon him, fancied he had got the nightmare, and began to lay about him on every side; and not a few of his blows reached Maritornes, who, provoked by the smart, cast aside all decorum, and made Sancho such a return in kind that she effectually roused him from sleep, in spite of his drowsiness. The squire finding himself thus treated, and without knowing by whom, raised himself up as well as he could, and grappled with Maritornes, and there began between them the most obstinate and delightful skirmish in the world. The carrier, perceiving, by the light of the host's candle, how it fared with his mistress, quitted Don Quixote, and ran to her assistance. The landlord followed him, but with a different intention; for it was to chastise the wench, concluding that she was the sole occasion of all this discord. And so, as the proverb says, the cat chased the rat, the rat chased the rope, and the rope chased the post. The carrier belabored Sancho, Sancho the wench, the wench Sancho, and the inn-keeper the wench; all redoubling their blows without intermission: and the best of it was, the landlord's candle went out; when, being left in the dark, they indiscriminately thrashed each other, and with so little mercy that every blow left its mark.

It happened that there lodged that night in the inn, an officer belonging to the Holy Brotherhood of Toledo; who, hearing the strange noise of the scuffle, seized his wand and the tin-box which held his commission, and entered the room in the dark, calling out, "Forbear, in the name of justice; forbear in the name of the Holy Brotherhood." And the first he encountered was the battered Don Quixote, who lay senseless on his demolished bed, stretched upon his back; and, laying hold of his beard as he was groping about, he cried out repeatedly, "I charge you to aid and assist me." But, finding that the person whom he held was motionless, he concluded that he was dead, and that the people in the room were his murderers. Upon which he raised his voice still louder, crying, "Shut the inn-doors, and let none escape; for here is a man murdered!" These words startled them all, and the conflict instantly ceased. The landlord withdrew to his chamber, the carrier to his bed, and the wench to her straw. The unfortunate Don Quixote and Sancho alone were incapable of moving.

The Elizabethans
and the Age of Wit

WILLIAM SHAKESPEARE (1564–1616)

In 1947 Eric Partridge published Shakespeare's Bawdy, a serious study of the sexuality, homosexuality, and bawdiness in the works of the poet-playwright. Apropos of the reception of such a volume the author wrote: "In the 18th century this book could have been published; in the Victorian period, not; up till (say) 1930, it would have been deprecated; nowadays it will—or should—be taken very much as a matter of course." Partridge went on to quote a relevant paragraph from the London Times Literary Supplement: "We have given up supposing that Shakespeare's sensational plots and bawdy jokes were only a high-brow's concessions to the groundlings. The modern consciousness of responsibility to the public will incline the large-minded artist to make the most of everything in him which is common to all men."

Shakespeare's power of making "the most of everything in him which is common to all men" is proved again and again by passages which contrast the heights of nobility and the depths of degradation, the ultimate in lyric ecstasy and the limit in vulgar clowning. For example, the very opening of the poignant Romeo and Juliet consists of a series of rowdy puns culminating in jokes about the heads of the Montague maids and maidenheads. In the fourth act of King Lear the horror of the old monarch's madness is accentuated by a wild speech full of images of adultery and symbols of copulation. The comedy of Measure for Measure attains a particular ribaldry when, in Act Three, Lucio launches into a plea for leniency toward lechery—"Why, what a ruthless thing is this—for the rebellion of a codpiece to take away the life of a man!" The rude badinage of the old nurse in the midst of the lyrical Romeo and Juliet is notorious, and the tragic progress of Hamlet is intensified by dialogues in which the double meanings are as surprising as they are shameless.

Painfully significant is the revelation that when Ophelia loses her sanity she also loses her sense of modesty. Freed of what the Freudians call "the moral censor," she sings songs that are not only full of a sense of loss but full of inverted wish fulfillments.

OPHELIA'S SONG

To-morrow is Saint Valentine's day
  All in the morning betime,
And I a maid at your window,
  To be your Valentine.

Then up he rose, and donn'd his clothes,
  And dupp'd the chamber-door;

Let in the maid, that out a maid
  Never departed more.

By Gis and by Saint Charity,
  Alack, and fie for shame!
Young men will do 't, if they come to 't;
  By cock, they are to blame.

Quoth she, before you tumbled me,
  You promised me to wed.
So would I ha' done, by yonder sun,
  An thou hadst not come to my bed.

The Shakespeare comedies are naturally more concerned with the physical appetites than are the tragedies. There is a continual mingling of pagan frankness and breathless poetry in the wanton Troilus and Cressida, *with Pandarus' mocking innuendoes and Ulysses' satirical thrusts; in* The Taming of the Shrew *with its game of wit and double-entendres; in* Much Ado About Nothing, *especially in the pre-wedding sallies among the naughty Beatrice, Hero's maid Margaret, and Hero herself.* Pericles *alternates between shocking crises and extreme coarseness. The murky violence of* Macbeth *is made more lurid not only by the witches but by the porter and his discourse on the provocations of liquor and lechery.*

Shakespeare the poet cannot be considered apart from Shakespeare the dramatist. But it is apparent that the romancer luxuriated in poems which gave full play to his love of legendry. Venus and Adonis, *the most famous of these, is a riot of erotic imagery. Notable is the passage in which the immortal Queen of Love, with her arm around the beautiful youth, attempts to seduce the reluctant boy.*

FROM: VENUS AND ADONIS

O, what a war of looks was then between them!
Her eyes petitioners to his eyes suing;
His eyes saw her eyes as they had not seen them;
Her eyes woo'd still, his eyes disdain'd the wooing:
  And all this dumb play had his acts made plain
  With tears, which chorus-like her eyes did rain.

Full gently now she takes him by the hand,
A lily prison'd in a gaol of snow,
Or ivory in an alabaster band;
So white a friend engirts so white a foe:
  This beauteous combat, wilful and unwilling,
  Show'd like two silver doves that sit a-billing.

Once more the engine of her thoughts began:
"O fairest mover on this mortal round,
Would thou wert as I am, and I a man,
My heart all whole as thine, thy heart my wound;
　　For one sweet look thy help I would assure thee,
　　Though nothing but my body's bane would cure thee!"

"Give me my hand," saith he, "why dost thou feel it?"
"Give me my heart," saith she, "and thou shalt have it;
O, give it me, lest thy hard heart do steel it,
And being steel'd, soft sighs can never grave it:
　　Then love's deep groans I never shall regard,
　　Because Adonis' heart hath made mine hard.

.　　.　　.　　.　　.

"Who sees his true-love in her naked bed,
Teaching the sheets a whiter hue than white,
But, when his glutton eye so full hath fed,
His other agents aim at like delight?
　　Who is so faint, that dare not be so bold
　　To touch the fire, the weather being cold?"

.　　.　　.　　.　　.

"I know not love," quoth he, "nor will not know it,
Unless it be a boar, and then I chase it;
'Tis much to borrow, and I will not owe it;
My love to love is love but to disgrace it;
　　For I have heard it is a life and death,
　　That laughs and weeps, and all but with a breath.

.　　.　　.　　.　　.

"You hurt my hand with wringing; let us part,
And leave this idle theme, this bootless chat:
Remove your siege from my unyielding heart;
To love's alarms it will not ope the gate:
　　Dismiss your vows, your feignèd tears, your flattery;
　　For where a heart is hard they make no battery."

"What! canst thou talk?" quoth she, "hast thou a tongue?
O, would thou hadst not, or I had no hearing!
Thy mermaid's voice hath done me double wrong;
I had my load before, now press'd with bearing:
　　Melodious discord, heavenly tune harsh-sounding,
　　Ear's deep-sweet music, and heart's deep-sore wounding.

"Had I no eyes but ears, my ears would love
That inward beauty and invisible;
Or were I deaf, thy outward parts would move
Each part in me that were but sensible:
   Though neither eyes nor ears, to hear nor see,
   Yet should I be in love by touching thee."

      .   .   .   .   .

And at his look she flatly falleth down,
For looks kill love and love by looks reviveth;
A smile recures the wounding of a frown;
But blessed bankrupt, that by love so thriveth!
   The silly boy, believing she is dead,
   Claps her pale cheek, till clapping makes it red;

And all amazed brake off his late intent,
For sharply he did think to reprehend her,
Which cunning love did wittily prevent:
Fair fall the wit that can so well defend her!
   For on the grass she lies as she were slain,
   Till his breath breatheth life in her again.

He wrings her nose; he strikes her on the cheeks;
He bends her fingers; holds her pulses hard;
He chafes her lips; a thousand ways he seeks
To mend the hurt that his unkindness marr'd.
   He kisses her; and she, by her good will,
   Will never rise, so he will kiss her still.

The night of sorrow now is turn'd to day:
Her two blue windows faintly she up-heaveth,
Like the fair sun, when in his fresh array
He cheers the morn, and all the earth relieveth:
   And as the bright sun glorifies the sky,
   So is her face illumined with her eye.

      .   .   .   .   .

"O, where am I?" quoth she, "in earth or heaven,
Or in the ocean drench'd, or in the fire?
What hour is this? or morn or weary even?
Do I delight to die, or life desire?
   But now I lived, and life was death's annoy;
   But now I died, and death was lively joy.

"O, thou didst kill me: kill me once again:
Thy eyes' shrewd tutor, that hard heart of thine,
Hath taught them scornful tricks and such disdain,
That they have murder'd this poor heart of mine;
    And these mine eyes, true leaders to their queen,
    But for thy piteous lips no more had seen.

.   .   .   .   .

"A thousand kisses buys my heart from me;
And pay them at thy leisure, one by one.
What is ten hundred touches unto thee?
Are they not quickly told and quickly gone?
    Say, for non-payment that the debt should double,
    Is twenty hundred kisses such a trouble?"

"Fair queen," quoth he, "if any love you owe me,
Measure my strangeness with my unripe years:
Before I know myself, seek not to know me;
No fisher but the ungrown fry forbears:
    The mellow plum doth fall, the green sticks fast,
    Or being early pluck'd is sour to taste.

.   .   .   .   .

"Now let me say 'Good night,' and so say you;
If you will say so, you shall have a kiss."
"Good night," quoth she; and, ere he says "Adieu,"
The honey fee of parting tender'd is:
    Her arms do lend his neck a sweet embrace;
    Incorporate then they seem; face grows to face.

Till, breathless, he disjoin'd, and backward drew
The heavenly moisture, that sweet coral mouth,
Whose precious taste her thirsty lips well knew,
Whereon they surfeit, yet complain on drouth:
    He with her plenty press'd, she faint with dearth,
    Their lips together glued, fall to the earth.

Now quick desire hath caught the yielding prey,
And glutton-like she feeds, yet never filleth;
Her lips are conquerors, his lips obey,
Paying what ransom the insulter willeth;
    Whose vulture thought doth pitch the price so high,
    That she will draw his lips' rich treasure dry:

And having felt the sweetness of the spoil,
With blindfold fury she begins to forage;
Her face doth reek and smoke, her blood doth boil,
And careless lust stirs up a desperate courage,
    Planting oblivion, beating reason back,
    Forgetting shame's pure blush and honor's wrack.

Hot, faint, and weary, with her hard embracing,
Like a wild bird being tamed with too much handling,
Or as the fleet-foot roe that's tired with chasing,
Or like the froward infant still'd with dandling,
    He now obeys, and now no more resisteth,
    While she takes all she can, not all she listeth.

      ·   ·   ·   ·   ·   ·

For pity now she can no more detain him;
The poor fool prays her that he may depart:
She is resolved no longer to restrain him;
Bids him farewell, and look well to her heart,
    The which, by Cupid's bow she doth protest,
    He carries thence incagèd in his breast.

"Sweet boy," she says, "this night I'll waste in sorrow,
For my sick heart commands mine eyes to watch.
Tell me, Love's master, shall we meet to-morrow?
Say, shall we? shall we? wilt thou make the match?"
    He tells her, no; to-morrow he intends
    To hunt the boar with certain of his friends.

"The boar!" quoth she; whereat a sudden pale,
Like lawn being spread upon the blushing rose,
Usurps her cheek; she trembles at his tale,
And on his neck her yoking arms she throws:
    She sinketh down, still hanging by his neck,
    He on her belly falls, she on her back.

Now is she in the very lists of love,
Her champion mounted for the hot encounter:
All is imaginary she doth prove,
He will not manage her, although he mount her;
    That worse than Tantalus' is her annoy,
    To clip Elysium and to lack her joy.

Even as poor birds, deceived with painted grapes,
Do surfeit by the eye and pine the maw,
Even so she languisheth in her mishaps,
As those poor birds that helpless berries saw.

The warm effects which she in him finds missing
She seeks to kindle with continual kissing.

But all in vain; good queen, it will not be:
She hath assay'd as much as may be proved;
Her pleading hath deserved a greater fee;
She's Love, she loves, and yet she is not loved.
    "Fie, fie," he says, "you crush me; let me go;
    You have no reason to withhold me so."

"Thou hadst been gone," quoth she, "sweet boy, ere this,
But that thou told'st me thou wouldst hunt the boar.
O, be advised! thou know'st not what it is
With javelin's point a churlish swine to gore,
    Whose tushes never sheathed he whetteth still,
    Like to a mortal butcher bent to kill.

.   .   .   .   .   .

"Lie quietly, and hear a little more;
Nay, do not struggle, for thou shalt not rise:
To make thee hate the hunting of the boar,
Unlike myself thou hear'st me moralize,
    Applying this to that, and so to so;
    For love can comment upon every woe.

"Where did I leave?" "No matter where," quoth he,
"Leave me, and then the story aptly ends:
The night is spent." "Why, what of that?" quoth she.
"I am," quoth he, "expected of my friends;
    And now 'tis dark, and going I shall fall."
    "In night," quoth she, "desire sees best of all."

The Rape of Lucrece, A Lover's Complaint, The Passionate Pilgrim, *and
many of the* Sonnets *are couched in phrases that are alternately amorous and
scornful of amour. The impassioned stanzas of* Venus and Adonis *did not
exhaust Shakespeare's fondness for the theme of the infatuated goddess and
the resisting mortal. Shakespeare turned the singing stanzas into sonnets.*

FROM: THE PASSIONATE PILGRIM

IV

Sweet Cytherea, sitting by a brook
With young Adonis, lovely, fresh, and green,
Did court the lad with many a lovely look,
Such looks as none could look but beauty's queen.

She told him stories to delight his ear;
She show'd him favors to allure his eye;
To win his heart, she touch'd him here and there;
Touches so soft still conquer chastity.
But whether unripe years did want conceit,
Or he refused to take her figured proffer,
The tender nibbler would not touch the bait,
But smile and jest at every gentle offer:
  Then fell she on her back, fair queen, and toward:
  He rose and ran away; ah, fool too froward!

·   ·   ·   ·   ·

XI

Venus, with young Adonis sitting by her
Under a myrtle shade, began to woo him:
She told the youngling how god Mars did try her,
And as he fell to her, so fell she to him.
"Even thus," quoth she, "the warlike god embraced me,"
And then she clipp'd Adonis in her arms;
"Even thus," quoth she, "the warlike god unlaced me,"
As if the boy should use like loving charms;
"Even thus," quoth she, "he seized on my lips,"
And with her lips on his did act the seizure:
And as she fetched breath, away he skips,
And would not take her meaning nor her pleasure.
  Ah, that I had my lady at this bay,
  To kiss and clip me till I run away!

Even in the midst of his most delicate songs and speeches, Shakespeare permitted himself light ribaldries. Perhaps the best known example is the charming tribute to spring in Love's Labour's Lost *in which, voicing the very gladness of the awakening season, the sly poet adds a humorously discordant note by sounding the punning implications of "cuckoo" and "cuckold."*

SPRING SONG

When daisies pied and violets blue
And lady-smocks all silver-white
And cuckoo-buds of yellow hue
Do paint the meadows with delight,
The cuckoo then, on every tree,
Mocks married men; for thus sings he, Cuckoo;
Cuckoo, cuckoo: O word of fear,
Unpleasing to a married ear!

When shepherds pipe on oaten straws
And merry larks are ploughmen's clocks,
When turtles tread, and rooks, and daws,
And maidens bleach their summer smocks,
The cuckoo then, on every tree,
Mocks married men; for thus sings he, Cuckoo;
Cuckoo, cuckoo: O word of fear,
Unpleasing to a married ear!

THE DELIGHTS AND DANGERS OF DRINKING

THE THIRSTY SOUL

Crudely carved, this drinking cup
Marks one who loved to lap it up.
Her whole life passed, the lucky lass,
With nose half-buried in her glass.
She mourns not for her children pale
Nor friends, but only for her ale.
Deep in the dusty earth, I think
She still cries out, poor soul, for drink.

AUTHOR UNKNOWN (From: *The Greek Anthology*)
Translated by L.U.

THE SOBER COMPANION

More than the Pleiades' setting
More than the yammering surf at the point of the jetty
More than the frenzied lightning that scores the vast arch of the sky
I fear the man who drinks water
And so remembers this morning what the rest of us said last night.

AUTHOR UNKNOWN (From *The Greek Anthology*)
Translated by DUDLEY FITTS

LIVE MY FOLLIES O'ER AGAIN

'Tis true, my fading years decline.
Yet can I quaff the brimming wine,
As deep as any stripling fair,
Whose cheeks the flush of morning wear;

And if, amidst the wanton crew,
I'm called to wind the dance's clue,
Then shalt thou see this vigorous hand,
Not faltering on the Bacchant's wand,
But brandishing a rosy flask,
The only thyrsus e'er I'll ask!

Let those who pant for Glory's charms,
Embrace her in the field of arms;
While my inglorious, placid soul
Breathes not a wish beyond this bowl.
Then fill it high, my ruddy slave,
And bathe me in its brimming wave.
For though my fading years decay,
Though manhood's prime hath passed away,
Like old Silenus, sire divine,
With blushes borrowed from my wine,
I'll wanton 'mid the dancing train,
And live my follies o'er again!

ANACREON, *translated by* THOMAS MOORE

AWAY WITH RULES

Away, away, ye men of rules,
What have I to do with schools?
They'd make me learn, they'd make me think,
But would they make me love and drink?
Teach me this, and let me swim
My soul upon the goblet's brim;
Teach me this, and let me twine
Some fond, responsive heart to mine,
For age begins to blanch my brow,
I've time for nought but pleasure now.

Fly, and cool my goblet's glow
At yonder fountain's gelid flow;
I'll quaff, my boy, and calmly sink
This soul to slumber as I drink.
Soon, too soon, my jocund slave,
You'll deck your master's grassy grave;
And there's an end—for ah, you know
They drink but little wine below!

ANACREON, *translated by* THOMAS MOORE

IN PRAISE OF ALE

I cannot eat but little meat,
   My stomach is not good;
But sure I think that I can drink
   With him that wears a hood.
Though I go bare, take ye no care,
   I nothing am a-cold;
I stuff my skin so full within
   Of jolly good ale and old.
      Back and side go bare, go bare;
      Both foot and hand go cold;
      But, belly, God send thee good ale enough,
      Whether it be new or old.

JOHN STILL (1543–1608)

A SONG FOR DRINKING

Would you be a man of fashion?
   Would you live a life divine?
Take a little dram of passion
   In a lusty dose of wine.

If the nymph have no compassion,
   Vain it is to sigh and groan:
Love was but put in for fashion,
   Wine will do the work alone.

AUTHOR UNKNOWN (Seventeenth century)

BALLADE OF GOOD DOCTRINE

Peddle indulgences as you may:
   Cog the dice for your cheating throws:
Try if counterfeit coin will pay,
   At risk of roasting at last, like those
   That deal in treason. Lie and glose,
Rob and ravish: what profits it?
   Who gets the purchase, do you suppose?
Taverns and wenches, every whit.

Rhyme, rail, wrestle and cymbals play:
   Flute and fool it in mummers' shows:
Along with the strolling players stray
   From town to city, without repose;

Act mysteries, farces, imbroglios:
Win money at gleek or a lucky hit
    At the pins: like water, away it flows;
Taverns and wenches, every whit.

Turn from your evil courses, I pray,
    That smell so foul in a decent nose;
Earn your bread in some honest way.
    If you have no letters, nor verse nor prose,
    Plough or groom horses, beat hemp or toze.
Enough you shall have if you think but fit:
    But cast not your wage to the wind that blows—
Taverns and wenches, every whit.

ENVOI

Doublets, pointlace, and silken hose,
    Gowns and linen, woven or knit,
Ere your wede's worn, away it goes:
    Taverns and wenches, every whit.

FRANÇOIS VILLON, *translated by* JOHN PAYNE

A MERRY BALLADE OF VINTNERS

By dint of dart, by push of sharpened spear,
    By sweep of scythe or thump of spike-set mace,
By poleaxe, steel-tipped arrowhead, or shear
    Of double-handed sword or well-ground ace,
    By dig of dirk or tuck with double face,
Let them be done to death; or let them light
On some ill stead, where brigands lurk by night,
    That they the hearts from out their breasts may tear,
    Cut off their heads, then drag them by the hair
And cast them on the dunghill to the swine,
    That sows and porkers on their flesh may fare,
The vintners that put water in our wine.

Let Turkish quarrels run them through the rear
    And rapiers keen their guts and vitals lace;
Singe their perukes with Greek fire, ay, and sear
    Their brains with levins; string them brace by brace
    Up to the gibbet; or for greater grace,
Let gout and dropsy slay the knaves outright:
Or else let drive into each felon wight
    Irons red-heated in the furnace-flare:
    Let half a score of hangmen flay them bare;

And on the morrow, seethed in oil or brine,
   Let four great horses rend them then and there,
The vintners that put water in our wine.

Let some great gunshot blow their heads off sheer;
   Let thunders catch them in the market-place;
Let rend their limbs and cast them far and near,
   For dogs to batten on their bodies base;
   Or let the lightning-stroke their sight efface.
Frost, hail and snow let still upon them bite;
Strip off their clothes and leave them naked quite,
   For rain to drench them in the open air;
   Lard them with knives and poniards and then bear
Their carrion forth and soak it in the Rhine;
   Break all their bones with mauls and do not spare
The vintners that put water in our wine.

ENVOI

Prince, may God curse their vitals is my prayer,
   And may they burst with venom all, in fine,
These traitorous thieves, accursèd and unfair,
   The vintners that put water in our wine!

FRANÇOIS VILLON, *translated by* JOHN PAYNE

THE DISCOURSE OF THE DRINKERS

(FROM: THE BOOK OF GARGANTUA)

Then did they fall upon the chat of victuals and some belly furniture to be snatched at in the very same place. Which purpose was no sooner mentioned, but forthwith began flagons to go, gammons to trot, goblets to fly, great bowls to ting, glasses to ring. Draw, reach, fill, mix, give it me without water. So, my friend, so, whip me off this glass neatly, bring me hither some claret, a full weeping glass till it run over. A cessation and truce with thirst. Ha, thou false fever, wilt thou not be gone? By my figgins, godmother, I cannot as yet enter in the humor of being merry, nor drink so currently as I would. You have catched a cold, gammer? Yea, forsooth, sir. By the belly of Sanct Buff, let us talk of our drink: I never drink but at my hours, like the Pope's mule. And I never drink but in my breviary, like a fair father guardian. Which was first, thirst or drinking? Thirst, for who in the time of innocence would have drunk without being athirst? Nay, sir, it was drinking; for *privatio præsupponit habitum.* I am learned, you see; *Fæcundi calices quem non fecere disertum?* We poor innocents drink but too much without thirst. Not I truly, who am a sinner, for I never drink without thirst, either present or future. To prevent it, as you know, I drink for the thirst to come. I drink eternally. This is to me an eternity of drinking, and drinking of eternity. Let us sing, let us drink, and tune up our roundelays. Where is my funnel? What, it seems I do not drink but by an attorney? Do you wet yourselves to dry, or do you dry to wet you? Pish, I understand not the rhetoric (theoric, I should say), but I help myself somewhat by the practice. *Baste!* enough! I sup, I wet, I humect, I moisten my gullet, I drink, and all for fear of dying. Drink always and you shall never die. If I drink not, I am a-ground, dry, graveled and spent. I am stark dead without drink, and my soul ready to fly into some marsh amongst frogs; the soul never dwells in a dry place, drouth kills it. O you butlers, creators of new forms, make me of no drinker a drinker, a perennity and everlastingness of sprinkling and bedewing me through these my parched and sinewy bowels. He drinks in vain that feels not the pleasure of it. This entereth into my veins—the pissing tools and urinal vessels shall have nothing of it. I would willingly wash the tripes of the calf which I appareled this morning. I have pretty well now ballasted my stomach and stuffed my paunch. If the papers of my bonds and bills could drink as well as I do, my creditors would not want for wine when they come to see me, or when they are to make any formal exhibition of their rights to what of me they can demand. This hand of yours spoils your nose. O how many other such will enter here before this go out! What, drink so shallow? It is enough to break both girds and petrel. This is called a cup of dissimulation, or flagonal hypocrisy.

What difference is there between a bottle and a flagon. Great difference; for the bottle is stopped and shut up with a stopple, but the flagon with a vice. Bravely and well played upon the words! Our fathers drank lustily, and emptied their cans. Well cacked, well sung! Come, let us drink; will you send nothing to the river? Here is one going to wash the tripes. I drink no more than a sponge. I drink like a Templar knight. . . . Give me a synonym for a gammon of bacon. It is the compulsory of drinkers; it is a pulley. By a pulley-rope wine is let down into a cellar, and by a gammon into the stomach. Hey! now, boys, hither, some drink, some drink! There is no trouble in it. If I could get up as well as I can swallow down, I had been long ere now very high in the air.

FRANÇOIS RABELAIS

SHAKESPEARIANA

> And let me the canakin clink, clink;
> And let me the canakin clink:
>> A soldier's a man;
>> A life's but a span:
> Why, then, let a soldier drink.

From *Othello*

MACDUFF: Was it so late, friend, ere you went to bed, that you do lie so late?

PORTER: 'Faith sir, we were carousing till the second cock; and drink, sir, is a great provoker of three things.

MACDUFF: What three things does drink especially provoke?

PORTER: Marry, sir, nose-painting, sleep, and urine. Lechery, sir, it provokes, and unprovokes; it provokes the desire, but it takes away the performance. Therefore much drink may be said to be an equivocator with lechery. It makes him, and it mars him; it sets him on, and it takes him off; it persuades him, and disheartens him; makes him stand to, and not stand to; in conclusion, equivocates him in a sleep, and, giving him the lie, leaves him.

From Macbeth

> The master, the swabber, the boatswain and I,
> 　The gunner and his mate
> Loved Mall, Meg and Marian and Margery,
> 　But none of us cared for Kate;
> 　For she had a tongue with a tang,
> 　Would cry to a sailor, Go hang!
> She loved not the savor of tar nor of pitch,
> Yet a tailor might scratch her where'er she did itch:
> 　Then to sea, boys, and let her go hang!

Drinking Song: From *The Tempest*

MEMOIRS AND LETTERS

Five drunkards agreed to drink the King's health in their blood, and that each of them should cut off a piece of his buttock and fry it upon the gridiron; which was done by four of them, of whom one did bleed so exceedingly that they were fain to send for a chirurgeon and so were discovered. The wife of one of them hearing that her husband was amongst them, came to the room, and, taking up a pair of tongs, laid about her, and so saved the cutting of her husband's flesh.

From Memorials of English Affairs, 1682

Lord Mansfield was very desirous of long life, and, whenever he had old men to examine, he generally asked them what their habits of living had been. To this interrogatory an aged person replied that he had never been drunk in his life. "See, gentlemen," said his Lordship, turning to the younger barristers, "what temperance will do." The next, of equally venerable appearance, gave a very different account of himself; he had not gone to bed sober one night for fifty years. "See, my Lord," said the young barristers, "what a cheerful glass will do." "Well, gentlemen," replied his Lordship, "it only proves, that some sorts of timber keep better when they are wet, and others when they are dry."

From *Memoir of Joseph Brasbridge*, 1824

5 January 1767

That very evening I gave a supper to two or three of my acquaintance, having before I left Scotland, layed a guinea that I should not catch the venereal disorder for three years, which bet I had most certainly lost and now was paying. We drank a great deal till I was so much intoxicated that instead of going home, I went to a low house in one of the alleys of Edinburgh where I knew a common girl lodged and, like a brute as I was, I lay all night with her. . . . Next morning I was like a man ordered for ignominious execution. But by noon I was worse; for I discovered that some infection had reached me. Was not this dreadful? I had an assignation in the evening with my charmer. How lucky was it that I knew my misfortune in time. I might have polluted her sweet body. Bless me! What a risk! But how could I tell her my shocking story? I took courage. I told how drunk I had been. I told the consequences. I lay down and kissed her feet. I said I was unworthy of any other favour. But I took myself. I gloried that I had ever been firmly constant to her while I was myself. I hoped she would consider my being drunk as a fatal accident which I should never again fall into. I called her my friend in whom I had confidence and intreated she would comfort me——

How like you the eloquence of a young barrister? It was truly the eloquence of love. She bid me rise; she took me by the hand. She kissed me. She gently upbraided me for entertaining any unfavourable ideas of her. She bid me take great care of myself and in time coming never drink upon any account. Own to me, Temple, that this was noble—and all the time her beauty enchanted me more than ever. May I not then be hers? In the meantime I must shut up, and honest Thomas must be my guardian.

From *Letters*, JAMES BOSWELL (1740–1795)

18 March 1775

There is a handsome maid at this inn (at Grantham) who interrupts me by coming sometimes into the room. I have no confession to make, my priest; so be not curious, I am too many as the phrase is, for one woman; and a certain transient connection I am persuaded does not interfere with that attachment which a man has for a wife, and which I have as much as any man that ever lived, though some of my qualifications are not valued by her, as they have been by other women—ay, and well educated women too. Concubinage is almost universal. If it was morally wrong, why was it permitted to the most pious men under the Old Testament? Why did our Saviour never say a word against it?

From *Letters,* JAMES BOSWELL (1740–1795)

Doctor Fordyce sometimes drank a good deal at dinner. He was summoned one evening to see a lady patient when he was more than half-seas-over, and conscious that he was so. Feeling her pulse, and finding himself unable to count its beats, he muttered, "Drunk, by God!" Next morning, recollecting the circumstance, he was greatly vexed: and just as he was thinking what explanation of his behaviour he should offer to the lady, a letter from her was put into his hand. "She too well knew," said the letter, "that he had discovered the unfortunate condition in which she was when he last visited her; and she entreated him to keep the matter secret in consideration of the enclosed: a hundred-pound bank-note."

From *Table Talk,* SAMUEL ROGERS (1763–1855)

HUSBAND AND WIFE

Hear then, ye wives, who to a male incline,
Nor blush to heighten your repast with wine;
And let the spouse agreeing in the end,
Drink moderate, and social glasses blend:
For nature, when she molded woman's frame,
Gave moisture to her womb, her temper, flame;
And these exalted by the vinous heat,
A proper mixture for a male complete.
Nor yet too frequent to the liquor press;
The juice is noxious taken to excess:
It floats in heavy and unactive streams,
And damps the native heat with sickly steams.
Nature oppress'd in her foundation fails,
Too gross from thence to form the vig'rous males.
Remember how once Bacchus fluster'd came,
And hot with wine compress'd the Cyprian Dame:
Folding the Goddess in his drunken arms,
Glowing he kiss'd, and rioted in charms.
The crude warm seed thus immaturely wrought,
A foul, obscene disfigur'd daughter brought;
The Gout her name, of pale and squalid face;
Limping she walk'd, and hobbled in her pace.

Let prudence then thy flowing cup restrain,
And golden moderation hold the rein.

From *Callipaedia*: or *The Art of Begetting Beautiful Children*, 1733,
by CLAUDIUS QUILLET, *translated by* MR. SEWELL

THREE EPITAPHS

She drank ale, porter, punch, and wine,
And lived to the age of ninety-nine.

John Adams lies here, of the parish of Southwell,
A carrier who carried his can to his mouth well.
He carried so much, and he carried so fast,
He could carry no more, and was carried at last:
For the liquor he drank, being too much for one,
He could not carry off—so he's now carri-on.

Here lies poor Burton;
    He was both 'ale and stout.
Death laid him on his bitter bier;
    And now in heaven he hops about.

JOHN BARLEYCORN

There were three kings into the east
    Three kings both great and high
And they hae sworn a solemn oath
    John Barleycorn must die.

They took a plough and plough'd him down,
    Put clods upon his head;
And they hae sworn a solemn oath
    John Barleycorn was dead.

But the cheerful spring came kindly on,
    And showers began to fall:
John Barleycorn got up again,
    And sore surprised them all.

The sultry suns of summer came,
    And he grew thick and strong;
His head weel arm'd wi' pointed spears,
    That no one should him wrong.

The sober autumn enter'd mild,
    When he grew wan and pale;
His bending joints and drooping head
    Show'd he began to fail.

His colour sicken'd more and more,
    He faded into age;
And then his enemies began
    To show their deadly rage.

They've ta'en a weapon, long and sharp,
    And cut him by the knee;
And tied him fast upon a cart,
    Like a rogue for forgerie.

They laid him down upon his back,
    And cudgell'd him full sore;
They hung him up before the storm,
    And turn'd him o'er and o'er.

They fillèd up a darksome pit
    With water to the brim:
They heavèd in John Barleycorn,
    There let him sink or swim.

They laid him out upon the floor,
    To work him further woe:
And still, as signs of life appear'd,
    They toss'd him to and fro.

They wasted o'er a scorching flame
    The marrow of his bones;
But a miller used him worst of all—
    He crush'd him 'tween two stones.

And they hae ta'en his very heart's blood,
    And drank it round and round,
And still the more and more they drank,
    Their joy did more abound.

John Barleycorn was a hero bold,
    Of noble enterprise;
For if you do but taste his blood,
    'Twill make your courage rise.

'Twill make a man forget his woe;
    'Twill heighten all his joy:
'Twill make the widow's heart to sing,
    Though the tear were in her eye.

Then let us toast John Barleycorn,
    Each man a glass in hand;
And may his great posterity
    Ne'er fail in any land.

ROBERT BURNS

FIVE REASONS FOR DRINKING

If all be true that I do think,
There are five reasons why we should drink:
Good wine—a friend—or being dry—
Or lest we should be by and by—
Or any other reason why.

HENRY ALDRICH

AFTERWARDS

When Father Time swings round his scythe,
    Intomb me 'neath the bounteous vine,
So that its juices red and blithe
    May cheer these thirsty bones of mine.

EUGENE FIELD

ROBERT HERRICK (1591–1674)

Like Laurence Sterne (see page 377), Robert Herrick was an ordained priest and, also like Sterne, a lighthearted profligate. Unlike Sterne, however, Herrick paraded a multiplicity of mistresses, most of whom were imaginary. His tributes to them are playful and petulant but seldom passionate. Even when Herrick complains of frustration (a frequent theme) he does not ache with pain; his protest is little more than a pout. One of the most graceful of poets, he charms us not only with prettiness but with a kind of mocking purity. His verse may be licentious but it is seldom lewd; the tone may be carnal but it is never gross.

Born in London in 1591, apprenticed to his uncle as a jeweler, educated at Cambridge, Herrick spent ten years alternately preparing for the ministry and enjoying the temptations of the metropolis. At thirty-eight he became vicar of Dean Prior in rural Devonshire and retired to the countryside. Although he longed for the city it was the country Muse that inspired him, and if his Julias, Antheas, Electras, Corinnas, Dianemes, Perennas, and Silvias are stereotypes—the not-too-differentiated composites of a conventionalized pattern—the models are as graceful as they are "cleanly wanton." They are, it is true, too coy, too bloodless, too perfectly simple to be real, but they are as haunting as a recurring dream.

Forgotten for more than a hundred years, Herrick was rediscovered in the late eighteenth century. Frail though the substance of his work may be, it is superbly finished; nicety and naughtiness are joined in a set of happy incongruities. Herrick himself expressed the paradox in a wishful if not altogether accurate couplet:

> To his book's end this last line he'd have placed:
> Jocund his Muse was, but his life was chaste.

Herrick's poetry is a triumph of tiny significances; never has a writer done so much with so little. It may be said that Herrick trifled his way from light verse into lasting poetry.

UPON JULIA'S WASHING HERSELF IN THE RIVER

> How fierce was I when I did see
> My Julia wash herself in thee!
> So lilies thorough crystal look,
> So purest pebbles in the brook,
> As in the river Julia did,
> Half with a lawn of water hid.
> Into thy stream myself I threw
> And struggling there I kissed thee too;
> And more had done, it is confessed,
> Had not the waves forbade the rest

CLOTHES DO BUT CHEAT AND COZEN US

> Away with silks, away with lawn;
> I'll have no screens or curtains drawn.
> Give me my mistress as she is,
> Dressed in her nak'd simplicities.
> For as my heart, e'en so my eye
> Is won with flesh, not drapery.

TO ELECTRA: THE VISION

> I dreamed we both were in a bed
> Of roses almost smotherèd:
> The warmth and sweetness had me there
> Made lovingly familiar,

But that I heard thy sweet breath say,
"Faults done by night will blush by day."
I kissed thee, panting, and I call
Night to the record, that was all.
But ah! if empty dreams so please,
Love, give me more such nights as these.

TO JULIA: THE NIGHT-PIECE

Her eyes the glow-worm lend thee;
The shooting stars attend thee;
    And the elves also,
    Whose little eyes glow
Like the sparks of fire, befriend thee.

No will-o'-th'-wisp mislight thee,
Nor snake or slow-worm bite thee;
    But on, on thy way,
    Not making a stay,
Since ghost there's none to affright thee.

Let not the dark thee cumber;
What though the moon does slumber?
    The stars of the night
    Will lend thee their light
Like tapers clear, without number.

Then, Julia, let me woo thee,
Thus, thus, to come unto me;
    And when I shall meet
    Thy silvery feet,
My soul I'll pour into thee.

UPON THE NIPPLES OF JULIA'S BREAST

Have ye beheld (with much delight)
A red rose peeping through a white?
Or else a cherry (double graced)
Within a lily's centre placed?
Or ever marked the pretty beam,
A strawberry shows half drowned in cream?
Or seen rich rubies blushing through
A pure smooth pearl, and orient too?
So like to this, nay all the rest,
Is each neat niplet of her breast.

TO DIANEME

Show me thy feet, show me thy legs, thy thighs,
Show me those fleshy principalities;
Show me that hill where smiling love doth sit,
Having a living fountain under it;
Show me thy waist; then let me there withal,
By the ascension of thy lawn, see all.

TO PERENNA

When I thy parts run o'er, I can't espy
In any part the least indecency,
But every line and limb diffusèd thence,
A fair and unfamiliar excellence:
So that the more I look, the more I prove
There's still more cause why I the more should love.

WHAT KIND OF MISTRESS HE WOULD HAVE

Be the mistress of my choice
Clean in manners, clear in voice;
Be she witty, more than wise;
Pure enough, though not precise:
Be she showing in her dress,
Like a civil wilderness;
That the curious may detect
Order in a sweet neglect:
Be she rolling in her eye,
Tempting all the passers-by;
And each ringlet of her hair
An enchantment, or a snare
For to catch the lookers on,
But herself held fast by none.
Let her Lucrece all day be,
Thaïs in the night, to me.
Be she such, as neither will
Famish me, nor over-fill.

TO HIS MISTRESSES

Help me! help me! now I call
To my pretty witchcrafts all:
Old I am, and cannot do
That I was accustomed to.

Bring your magics, spells, and charms,
To enflesh my thighs and arms.
Is there no way to beget
In my limbs their former heat?
Æson had, as poets fain,
Baths that made him young again:
Find that medicine, if you can,
For your dry, decrepit man;
Who would fain his strength renew,
Were it but to pleasure you.

THE VINE

I dreamed this mortal part of mine
Was metamorphosed to a vine,
Which, crawling one and every way,
Enthralled my dainty Lucia.
Methought, her long small legs and thighs
I with my tendrils did surprise;
Her belly, buttocks, and her waist
By my soft nervelets were embraced:
About her head I writhing hung,
And with rich clusters hid among
The leaves, her temples I behung:
So that my Lucia seemed to me
Young Bacchus ravished by his tree.
My curls about her neck did crawl,
And arms and hands they did enthrall,
So that she could not freely stir,
All parts there made one prisoner.
But when I crept with leaves to hide
Those parts which maids keep unespied,
Such fleeting pleasures there I took
That with the fancy I awoke;
And found, ah me! this flesh of mine
More like a stock than like a vine.

TO THE VIRGINS, TO MAKE MUCH OF TIME

Gather ye rosebuds while ye may,
    Old Time is still a-flying:
And this same flower that smiles to-day
    To-morrow will be dying.

The glorious lamp of heaven, the sun,
    The higher he's a-getting,
The sooner will his race be run,
    And nearer he's to setting.

That age is best which is the first,
    When youth and blood are warmer;
But being spent, the worse, and worst
    Times still succeed the former.

Then be not coy, but use your time,
    And while ye may, go marry:
For having lost but once your prime,
    You may for ever tarry.

JEAN DE LA FONTAINE (1621–1695)

Son of a forest ranger, born in Château-Thierry, Jean de La Fontaine was always his own opposite. Something of a peasant, he became something of a patrician. Prepared for the Church, he left the seminary for a life of irresponsibility. At twenty-six he was wed to a girl of fifteen and, though she brought him a large dowry, he left her, to spend most of his time in Paris. (One of his biographers puts it quaintly: "He married, in compliance with the wishes of his family, a beautiful and chaste woman, who drove him to despair.") In the metropolis he found many patronesses who were glad to serve in the combined roles of mother and mistress. His biographer refers to "two high-born Ladies who kept him from experiencing the pangs of poverty"; they were the Dowager Duchess of Orleans and the Duchess de la Sablière, with whom he lived openly for twenty years.

Although most of his life was devoted to pleasure, he found time to write a great quantity of stories, and if few are original, all are turned with nimble reason and agile rhyme. His Fables, founded on Aesop, is his most famous work; but the Tales and Novels, with plots borrowed from his beloved Boccaccio, Margaret of Navarre, and earlier sources, are his most diverting. Some of them are spicy retellings of contemporary scandals; others are slightly elaborated jokes with odd denouements. Resenting the charge that his Tales were licentious, La Fontaine wrote: "One must conform one's self to the nature of the things about which one writes. . . . He who would reduce Boccaccio to the same modesty as Virgil will produce nothing worth having." As for propriety, La Fontaine reminded the reader of Cicero's remark that "propriety consists in saying what is appropriate to the time, the place, and the person to whom one is speaking."

Age, however, changed his point of view. At seventy, afflicted with a severe

*illness, he repented his amoralities, became reconciled to the Church, and
swore never to write another lubricious incident. Instead he adapted some
Psalms, gave himself up to moral meditations, and died at seventy-four in
the odor of sanctity. He was buried in sacred ground by the side of Molière.*

FROM: TALES AND NOVELS

THE GASCON PUNISHED

A Gascon, being heard one day to swear
That he'd possessed a certain lovely fair,
Was played a wily trick and nicely served;
'Twas clear from truth he shamefully had swerved.
The dame indeed the Gascon only jeered,
Denied herself to him when he appeared;
For when she met the man who sought to shine
And called her "angel, beauteous and divine,"
She fled and hastened to a female friend.
Where she could laugh and at her ease unbend.

Near Phillis, (our fair fugitive) there dwelled
One Eurilas, his nearest neighbor held;
His wife was Cloris—'twas with *her* our dove
Took shelter from the Gascon's forward love,
Whose name was Dorilas—and Damon young
(The Gascon's friend) on whom gay Cloris hung.

Sweet Phillis, by her manner, you might see,
From sly amours and dark intrigues was free;
The value to possess her no one knew,
Though all admired the lovely belle at view.
Just twenty years she counted at the time,
And now a widow was, though in her prime,
(Her spouse, an aged dotard, worth a plum—
Of those whose loss to mourn no tears e'er come.)

Our seraph fair, such loveliness possessed,
In num'rous ways a Gascon could have blessed;
Above, below, appeared angelic charms;
'Twas Paradise, 'twas Heav'n, within her arms!

The Gascon was—a *Gascon*—would you more?
Who knows a Gascon knows at least a score.
I need not say what solemn vows he made;
Alike with Normans Gascons are portrayed;

Their oaths, indeed, won't pass for Gospel truth;
But we believe that Dorilas (the youth)
Loved Phillis to his soul, our lady fair,
Yet he would fain be thought *successful* there.

One day, said Phillis, with unusual glee
(Pretending with the Gascon to be free)
"Do me a favor—nothing very great—
Assist to dupe one jealous of his mate.
You'll find it very easy to be done,
And doubtless 'twill produce a deal of fun.
'Tis my request (the plot you'll say is deep),
That you this night with Cloris' husband sleep.
Some disagreement with her gay gallant
Requires that she at least a night should grant
To settle diff'rences. Now I desire
That you'll to bed with Eurilas retire.
There's not a doubt he'll think his Cloris near;
He never touches her, so nothing fear.
For whether jealousy or other pains,
He constantly from intercourse abstains,
Snores through the night and, if a cap he sees,
Believes his wife in bed and feels at ease.
We'll properly equip you as a belle,
And I will certainly reward you well."

To gain but Phillis' smiles, the Gascon said
He'd with the very devil go to bed.

The night arrived, our man the chamber traced;
The lights extinguished; Eurilas, too, placed.
The Gascon 'gan to tremble in a trice,
And soon with terror grew as cold as ice;
Durst neither spit nor cough; still less encroach;
And seemed to shrink, lest t'other should approach;
Crept near the edge; would scarcely room afford,
And could have passed the scabbard of a sword.

Oft in the night his bed-fellow turned round;
At length a finger on his nose he found,
Which Dorilas exceedingly distressed;
But more inquietude was in his breast,
For fear the husband amorous should grow,
From which incalculable ills might flow.

Our Gascon ev'ry minute knew alarm;
'Twas now a leg stretched out, and then an arm;

He even thought he felt the husband's beard;
But presently arrived what more he feared.

A bell, conveniently, was near the bed,
Which Eurilas to ring was often led;
At this the Gascon swooned, so great his fear,
And swore for ever he'd renounce his dear.
But no one coming, Eurilas once more
Resumed his place, and 'gan again to snore.

At length, before the sun his head had reared,
The door was opened, and a torch appeared.
Misfortune then he fancied full in sight;
More pleased he'd been to rise without a light,
And clearly thought 'twas over with him now;
The flame approached—the drops ran o'er his brow;
With terror he for pardon humbly prayed.
"You have it," cried a fair. "Be not dismayed."
'Twas Phillis spoke, who Eurilas's place
Had filled, throughout the night, with wily grace,
And now to Damon and his Cloris flew,
With ridicule the Gascon to pursue;
Recounted all the terrors and affright,
Which Dorilas had felt throughout the night.
To mortify still more the silly swain,
And fill his soul with every poignant pain,
She gave a glimpse of beauties to his view,
And from his presence instantly withdrew.

THE KISS RETURNED

As William walking with his wife was seen,
A man of rank admired her lovely mien.
"Who gave you such a charming fair?" he cried.
"May I presume to kiss your beauteous bride?"
"With all my heart," replied the humble swain.
"You're welcome, sir. I beg you'll not refrain.
She's at your service. Take the boon I pray;
You will not get such offers every day."

The gentleman proceeded as desired.
To get a kiss alone he had aspired;
Howe'er, so fervently he pressed her lip
That Petronella blushed at every sip.

A week had scarcely run when, to his arms,
The noble took a wife with seraph charms;
And William was allowed to take a kiss
That filled his soul with soft, ecstatic bliss.
"I wish," cried he, "and truly I am grieved,
That when the gentleman a kiss received
From her I love, he'd gone to greater height
And with my Petronella spent the night."

THE PACK-SADDLE

A famous painter, jealous of his wife,
Whose charms he valued more than fame or life,
When going on a journey used his art
To paint an ASS upon a certain part,
(Umbilical, 'tis said) and like a seal:
Impressive token, nothing thence to steal.

A brother painter, favored by the dame,
Now took advantage and declared his flame:
The ASS effaced, but God knows how 'twas done.
Another soon howe'er he had begun,
And finished well, upon the very spot
(In painting, few more praises ever got),
But want of recollection made him place
A saddle, where before he none could trace.

The husband, when returned, desired to look
At what he drew, when leave he lately took.
"Yes, see my dear," the wily wife replied.
"The ASS is witness, faithful I abide."
"Zounds!" said the painter, when he got a sight,
"What!—you'd persuade me ev'ry thing is right?
I wish the witness you display so well,
And him who saddled it, were both in Hell!"

THE EAR-MAKER AND THE MOULD-MENDER

When William went from home (a trader styled),
Six months his better half he left with child,
A simple, comely, modest, youthful dame,
Whose name was Alice; from Champaign she came.
Her neighbor Andrew visits now would pay;
With what intention, needless 'tis to say:
A master who but rarely spread his net,
But, first or last, with full success he met;

And cunning was the bird that 'scaped his snare,
Without surrendering a feather there.

Quite raw was Alice; for his purpose fit;
Not overburdened with a store of wit;
Of this indeed she could not be accused,
And Cupid's wiles by her were never used;
Poor lady, all with her was honest part,
And naught she knew of stratagem or art.

Her husband then away, and she alone,
This neighbor came, and in a whining tone,
To her observed, when compliments were o'er—
"I'm all astonishment, and you deplore,
To find that neighbor William's gone from hence,
And left your child's completing in suspense,
Which now you bear within, and much I fear,
That when 'tis born you'll find it wants an ear.
Your looks sufficiently the fact proclaim,
For many instances I've known the same."
"Good heav'ns!" replied the lady in a fright;
"What say you, pray?—the infant won't be right?
Shall I be mother to a one-eared child?
And know you no relief that's certain styled?"
"Oh yes, there is," rejoined the crafty knave,
"From such mishap I can the baby save;
Yet solemnly I vow, for none but you
I'd undertake the toilsome job to do.
The ills of others, if I may be plain,
Except your husband's, never give me pain;
But him I'd serve for ever, while I've breath;
To do him good I'd e'en encounter death.
Now let us see, without more talk or fears,
If I know how to forge the bantling ears."
"Remember," cried the wife, "to make them like."
"Leave that to me," said he, "I'll justly strike."
Then he prepared for work—the dame gave way;
Not difficult she proved—well pleased she lay;
Philosophy was never less required,
And Andrew's process much the fair admired,
Who, to his work extreme attention paid;
'Twas now a tendon; then a fold he made,
Or cartilage, of which he formed enough,
And all without complaining of the stuff.
"Tomorrow we will polish it," said he:
"Then in perfection soon the whole will be;

And from repeating this so oft, you'll get
As perfect issue as was ever met."
"I'm much obliged to you," the wife replied,
"A friend is good in whom we may confide."

Next day, when tardy Time had marked the hour,
That Andrew hoped again to use his pow'r,
He was not plunged in sleep, but briskly flew,
His purpose with the charmer to pursue.
Said he, "All other things aside I've laid,
This ear to finish, and to lend you aid."
"And I," the dame replied, "was on the eve,
To send and beg you not the job to leave;
Above stairs let us go": away they ran,
And quickly recommenced as they began.
The work so oft was smoothed that Alice showed
Some scruples lest the ear he had bestowed
Should do too much, and to the wily wight,
She said, "So little you the labor slight,
'Twere well if ears no more than two appear";
"Of that," rejoined the other, "never fear;
I've guarded thoroughly against defects,
Mistakes like that shall ne'er your senses vex."

The ear howe'er was still in hand the same,
When from his journey home the husband came.
Saluted Alice, who with anxious look,
Exclaimed, "Your work how finely you forsook,
And, but for neighbor Andrew's kindness here,
Our child would incomplete have been—an ear.
I could not let a thing remain like this,
And Andrew would not be to friends remiss,
But, worthy man, he left his thriving trade,
And for the babe a proper ear has made."

The husband, not conceiving how his wife,
Could be so weak and ignorant of life,
The circumstances made her fully tell,
Repeat them o'er and on each action dwell.
Enraged at length, a pistol by the bed
He seized and swore at once he'd shoot her dead.
The belle with tears replied, howe'er she'd swerved,
Such cruel treatment never she deserved.
Her innocence, and simple, gentle way,
At length appeared his frantic rage to lay.
"What injury," continued she, "is done?

The strictest scrutiny I would not shun;
Your goods and money, ev'ry thing is right;
And Andrew told me, nothing he would slight;
That you would find much more than you could want;
And this I hope to me you'll freely grant;
If falsehood I advance, my life I'll lose;
Your equity, I trust, will me excuse."

A little cooled, then William thus replied,
"We'll say no more; you have been drawn aside;
What passed you fancied acting for the best,
And I'll consent to put the thing at rest;
To nothing good such altercations tend;
I've but a word: to that attention lend;
Contrive tomorrow that I here entrap
This fellow who has caused your sad mishap;
You'll utter not a word of what I've said.
Be secret, or at once I'll strike you dead.
Adroitly you must act. For instance, say
I'm on a second journey gone away;
A message or a letter to him send,
Soliciting that he'll on *you* attend,
That something you have got to let him know—
To come, no doubt, the rascal won't be slow;
Amuse him then with converse most absurd,
But of the EAR remember—not a word;
That's finished now, and nothing can require;
You'll carefully perform what I desire."
Poor innocent! the point she nicely hit;
Fear oft gives simpletons a sort of wit.

The arch gallant arrived; the husband came:
Ascended to the room where sat his dame;
Much noise he made, his coming to announce;
The lover, terrified, began to bounce;
Now here, now there, no shelter could he meet;
Between the bed and wall he put his feet,
And lay concealed, while William loudly knocked;
Fair Alice readily the door unlocked,
And, pointing with her hand, informed the spouse,
Where he might easily his rival rouse.

The husband ev'ry way was armed so well,
He four such men as Andrew could repel;
In quest of succor howsoe'er he went:
To kill him surely William never meant,

But only take an ear, or what the Turks,
Those savage beasts, cut off from Nature's works,
Which doubtless must be infinitely worse:
Infernal practice and continual curse.
'Twas this he whispered should be Andrew's doom,
When with his easy wife he left the room;
She nothing durst reply: the door he shut,
And our gallant 'gan presently to strut
Around and round, believing all was right,
And William unacquainted with his plight.

The latter having well the project weighed,
Now changed his plan, and other schemes surveyed;
Proposed within himself revenge to take,
With less parade: less noise it then would make,
And better fruit the action would produce
Than if he were apparently profuse.
Said he to Alice, "Go and seek his wife;
To her relate the whole that caused our strife;
Minutely all from first to last detail;
And then the better on her to prevail,
To hasten here, you'll hint that you have fears,
That Andrew risks the loss of—more than ears,
For I have punishment severe in view,
Which greatly she must wish I should not do;
But if an ear-maker, like this, is caught,
The worst of chastisement is always sought;
Such horrid things as scarcely can be said:
They make the hair to stand upon the head;
That he's upon the point of suff'ring straight,
And only for her presence things await;
That though she cannot all proceedings stay
Perhaps she may some portion take away.
Go. Bring her instantly. Haste quickly. Run.
And if she comes, I'll pardon what's been done."

With joy to Andrew's house fair Alice went;
The wife to follow her appeared content;
Quite out of breath, alone she ran up stairs,
And, not perceiving him who shared her cares,
Believed he was imprisoned in a room;
And while with fear she trembled for his doom,
The master (having laid aside his arms)
Now came to compliment the lady's charms;
He gave the belle a chair, who looked most nice:
Said he, "Ingratitude's the worst of vice;

To me your husband has been wondrous kind;
So many services has done I find,
That, ere you leave this house, I'd wish to make
A like return, and this you will partake.
When I was absent from my loving dear,
Obligingly he made her babe an ear.
The compliment of course I must admire;
Retaliation is what I desire,
And I've a thought—your children all have got
The nose a little short, which is a blot;
A fault within the mould no doubt's the cause,
Which I can mend, and any other flaws.
The business now let's execute I pray,"
On which the dame he took without delay,
And placed her near where Andrew hid his head,
Then 'gan to operate as he was led.

The lady patiently his process bore,
And blessed her stars that Andrew's risk was o'er:
That she had thus the dire return received,
And saved the man for whom her bosom grieved.
So much emotion William seemed to feel,
No grace he gave, but all performed with zeal;
Retaliated ev'ry way so well,
He measure gave for measure—ell for ell.

How true the adage, that revenge is sweet!
The plan he followed clearly was discrete;
For since he wished his honor to repair—
Of any better way I'm not aware.

The whole without a murmur Andrew viewed,
And thanked kind Heav'n that nothing worse ensued;
One ear most readily he would have lost,
Could he be certain *that* would pay the cost.
He thought 'twould lucky be, could he get out,
For all considered, better 'twere no doubt,
Howe'er ridiculous the thing appears,
To have a pair of horns than lose his ears.

JOHN AUBREY (1626–1697)

*During his lifetime John Aubrey was considered an unimportant fellow.
He had no head for business, was always in debt, and never gained authority*

in any profession. The one thing he did with application—the one thing he did well—was to collect odd bits of information about people and places.

During his student years at Oxford and at the Middle Temple in London, he came to know many of the notables of seventeenth-century England, or those who knew them, or who talked about them as though they knew them. Aubrey had an instinct that the common talk about uncommon men, the curious items of gossip that were whispered around, were worth jotting down. The style in which he recorded them was so artless as to be enduring art. The pages of Aubrey's Brief Lives and other works, are like a keyhole to their time. Put your ear to it and you can hear Elizabethan England, at ease and unexpurgated.

In the following excerpts from these abbreviated biographies the spelling has been modernized.

FROM: BRIEF LIVES

SIR THOMAS MORE . . . In his Utopia his law is that the young people are to see each other stark-naked before marriage. Sir William Roper, of Eltham in Kent, came one morning, pretty early, to my lord, with a proposal to marry one of his daughters. My lord's daughters were then both together abed in a truckle-bed in their father's chamber asleep. He carries Sir William into the chamber and takes the sheet by the corner and suddenly whips it off. They lay on their backs, and their smocks up as high as their armpits. This awakened them, and immediately they turned on their bellies. Quoth Roper, "I have seen both sides," and so gave a pat on her buttock he made choice of, saying, "Thou art mine." Here was all the trouble of the wooing. This account I had from my honoured friend, old Mistress Tyndale, whose grandfather, Sir William Stafford, was an intimate acquaintance of this Sir W. Roper, who told him the story. . . .

GEORGE MONK, DUKE OF ALBERMARLE . . . George Monk was born in Devon, a second son of an ancient family, and which had about Henry VIII's time £10,000 per annum (as he himself said). He was a strong, lusty, well-set young fellow; and in his youth happened to slay a man, which was the occasion of his flying into the Low Countries, where he learned to be a soldier. He was first an ensign and after a captain in the Low Countries, and for making false musters was like to have been cashiered. At the beginning of the late civil wars, he came over to the king's side, where he had command.

He was prisoner in the Tower, where his seamstress, Nan Clarges (a blacksmith's daughter), was kind to him in a double capacity. (The shop is still of that trade; the corner shop, the first turning on the right hand as you come out of the Strand into Drury Lane; the house is now built of brick.)

It must be remembered that he was taken prisoner by the Parliament forces, and kept in the Tower; and the truth was he was forgotten and neglected at Court, that they did not think of exchanging him, and he was in want, and she assisted him. Here she was got with child. She was not at all handsome, nor cleanly. Her mother was one of the five women barbers.

. . . There was a married woman in Drury Lane that had clapt (i.e., given the pox to) a woman's husband, a neighbour of hers. She complained of this to her neighbour gossips. So they concluded on this revenge, *viz.*, to get her and whip her and to shave all the hair off her pudenda; which severities were executed and put into a ballad. 'Twas the first ballad I ever cared for the reading of: the burden of it was thus:

> Did ye ever hear the like
> Or ever heard the same
> Of five women barbers
> That lived in Drury Lane?

Her brother, Thomas Clarges, came ashipboard to G.M. and told him his sister was brought to bed. "Of what?" said he. "Of a son." "Why then," said he, "she is my wife." He had only this child.

EDWARD DE VERE, EARL OF OXFORD . . . Mr. Thomas Henshawe, *Regiae Societatis Socius*, tells me that Nicholas Hill was secretary to the great Earl of Oxford, who spent forty thousand pounds per annum in seven years' travel. He lived at Florence in more grandeur than the Duke of Tuscany. This Earl of Oxford, making of his low obeisance to Queen Elizabeth, happened to let a fart at which he was so abashed that he went to travel seven years. At his return the queen welcomed him home and said, "My lord, I had forgot the fart" . . .

JOHN OVERALL . . . Dr. Overall was dean of St. Paul's, London. . . . I know not what he wrote or whether he was any more than a common-prayer doctor; but most remarkable by his wife, who was the greatest beauty in her time in England. That she was so I have it attested from the famous limner Mr. Hoskins and other old painters, besides old courtiers. She was not more beautiful than she was obliging and kind, and was so tender-hearted that (truly) she could scarce deny any one. She had (they told me) the loveliest eyes that ever were seen, but wondrous wanton. When she came to Court or to the playhouse, the gallants would flock around her. Richard, the Earl of Dorset, and his brother Edward, since Earl, both did mightily adore her. And by their reports, he must have had a hard heart that did not admire her. Bishop Hall says in his *Meditations* that "there is none so old that a beautiful person loves not: nor so young whom a lovely feature moves not."

The good old dean, notwithstanding he knew well enough that he was

horned, loved her infinitely: in so much that he was willing she should enjoy
what she had a mind to.

Among others who were charmed by her was Sir John Selby of Yorkshire.
In 1656, old Mistress Tyndale (of the Priory near Easton Piers), who knew
her, remembers a song made of her and Sir John, part where of was this,
viz.:

> The dean of Paul's did search for his wife,
> And where d'ye think he found her?
> Even upon Sir John Selby's bed,
> As flat as any flounder.

On these two lovers was made this following copy of pastoral verses:

> Down lay the shepherd swain
>   So sober and demure,
> Wishing for his wench again
>   So bonny and so pure,
> With his head on hillock low
>   And his arms akimbo,
> And all was for the loss of his
>   Hey nonny nonny no.
>
> Sweet she was, as kind a love
>   As ever fetter'd swain;
> Never such a dainty one
>   Shall man enjoy again.
> Set a thousand on a row,
>   I forbid that any show
> Ever the like of her
>   Hey nonny nonny no.
>
> Face she had of filbert hue,
>   And bosom'd like a swan;
> Back she had of bended ewe,
>   And waisted by a span.
> Hair she had as black as crow
>   From the head unto the toe
> Down, down, all over her
>   Hey nonny nonny no.
>
> With her mantle tucked up high
>   She foddered her flock
> So buxom and alluringly,
>   Her knee upheld her smock
> So nimbly did she use to go
>   So smooth she danced on tiptoe,
> That all men were fond of her
>   Hey nonny nonny no.

To sport it on the merry down,
     To dance the lively hay,
To wrestle for a green gown
     In heat of all the day,
Never would she say me no
     Yet methought I had though
Never enough of her
     Hey nonny nonny no.

But gone she is, the prettiest lass
     That ever trod on plain.
Whatever hath betide of her
     Blame not the shepherd swain.
For why? She was her own foe
     And gave herself the overthrow.
By being so frank of her
     Hey nonny nonny no.

SIR WALTER RALEIGH . . . My old friend James Harrington, Esq. was well acquainted with Sir Benjamin Ruddyer, who was an acquaintance of Sir Walter Raleigh's. He told Mr. J. H. that Sir Walter Raleigh being invited to dinner to some great person where his son was to go with him, he said to his son, "Thou art expected today at dinner to go along with me, but thou art such a quarrelsome, affronting— that I am ashamed to have such a bear in my company." Mr. Walter humbled himself to his father, and promised he would behave himself mighty mannerly. So away they went (and Sir Benjamin, I think, with them). He sat next to his father and was very demure at least half dinner time. Then said he, "I, this morning, not having the fear of God before my eyes, but by the instigation of the devil, went to a whore. I was very eager of her, kissed and embraced her, and went to enjoy her, but she thrust me from her, and vowed I should not, 'for your Father lay with me but an hour ago.'" Sir Walter being strangely surprised and put out of his countenance at so great a table, gives his son a damned blow over his face. His son, as rude as he was, would not strike his father, but strikes over the face the gentleman that sat next to him and said, "Box about: 'twill come to my father anon!" 'Tis now a common-used proverb . . .

WILLIAM WYCHERLEY (1640–1716)

The so-called Restoration plays came by their name appropriately; for when the London theaters, after having been closed by the Puritans for about eighteen years, were reopened in 1660 by Charles II, the world of the theater was restored to the people. Since, after every period of prohibition, reaction was intense, the raffish playwrights, protected by a particularly dissolute royal patron, filled the stage with rogues and libertines, high-class courtesans and low-class wenches, who progressed from one adultery to another. They mirrored a society where wit and wickedness were bedfellows and where beauty was esteemed only if it was sufficiently bawdy.

Artificiality went hand in hand with gallantry in the plays of this period. Genuine emotion was practically taboo; the couples involved in the action took part in a series of amorous maneuvers in which cuckoldry was a main objective; the word "passion" was bandied about, but love was an amusing game rather than a driving force. It was a strictly amoral-fashionable world that was reflected, and its playful code was rigidly conventionalized. Everything was to be treated with clever scorn and cynical epigrams; nothing was to be taken seriously. "Those who professed the code and did not abide by it were even more amusing than the unfortunates who made no attempt to follow it," says Brice Harris in an introduction to the Modern Library edition of Restoration Plays. *"Country people, clergymen, scholars and poets, merchants and tradesmen, in fact anybody who worked for his living, had no time to engage in such activities. But dancing across the stage was an entire generation of fops and dunces, coquettes and mistresses, pseudo-wits and social enthusiasts of various orders that rocked the theater audiences with laughter."*

The Restoration comedies of manners reached their high point (or, as the Puritans charged, their low mark) in the brilliant and brittle plays of George Etherege, George Farquhar, William Congreve, and William Wycherley. Wycherley's The Country Wife *epitomizes these plays and takes on impudently fresh life with every revival. Its author, whose scandalous* Love in a Wood *delighted the notorious Duchess of Cleveland, the King's senior mistress, has been widely condemned—Macaulay considered his work "licentious and indecent"—but contemporaries called him "manly Wycherley." He, however, was bland about the fact that wit, like virtue, was its own reward; one of his characters says: "By what I've heard, 'tis a pleasant, well-bred, complaisant, free, frolic, good-natured, pretty age. And if you do not like it, leave it to us that do."*

The Country Wife is a play about a rake's progress, without any of Hogarth's grim details but, contrariwise, with a cynically "happy ending." Its hero, Mr. Horner (a rather obvious pun), devotes himself to turning husbands into cuckolds. This he does with ease by spreading information that, as the result of an operation, he is a eunuch. Believing in his impotence, husbands not only permit him to squire their spouses but to entertain them in his rooms. Thus he acquires various paramours, including Mrs. Squeamish, Mrs. Dainty Fidget, Lady Fidget, who feels that a constant use of the word "honor" is all that is needed to defend what she has not got, and Mrs. Pinchwife, the naïve but extremely clever little country wife who, by means of quaint double-dealing, makes even adultery seem innocent. Perhaps the two most famous scenes are those in Horner's lodging where the ladies go to examine "china" and where, later, they discover that Horner, pretending to be faithful to only one, has been free with all. Wycherley delights to ridicule all those who stick to conventional morality; he is, writes John Harold Wilson in The Court Wits of the Restoration, *"against surly husbands who keep charming wives locked up; against foolish women who make much of their honor; against the nice institutions and customs of society which hamper the devotees of Venus; against everything, in short, which went then or now by the name of respectability.* The Country Wife *is a knavish and laughable piece of work, and one to make Mrs. Grundy scream with horror."*

FROM: THE COUNTRY WIFE

ACT IV, SCENE III. *Horner's Lodging*

QUACK: Well, Sir, how fadges the new design? Have you not the luck of all your brother prospectors, to deceive only yourself at last?

HORN: No, good Domine Doctor, I deceive you, it seems, and others too; for the grave matrons, and old, rigid husbands think me as unfit for love as they are; but their wives, sisters, and daughters know, some of 'em, better things already.

QUACK: Already!

HORN: Already, I say. Last night I was drunk with half-a-dozen of your civil persons, as you call 'em, and people of honour, and so was made free of their society and dressing-rooms for ever hereafter; and am already come to the privileges of sleeping upon their pallets, warming smocks, tying shoes and garters, and the like, Doctor, already, already, Doctor.

QUACK: You have made use of your time, Sir.

HORN: I tell thee, I am now no more interruption to 'em when they sing, or talk, bawdy, than a little squab French page who speaks no English.

QUACK: But do civil persons and women of honour drink, and sing bawdy songs?

HORN: Oh, amongst friends, amongst friends. For your bigots in honour are just like those in religion; they fear the eye of the world more than the eye of Heaven, and think there is no virtue but railing at vice, and no sin but giving scandal. They rail at a poor little kept player, and keep themselves some young modest pulpit comedian to be privy to their sins in their closets, not to tell 'em of them in their chapels.

QUACK: Nay, the truth on't is priests, amongst the women now, have quite got the better of us lay-confessors, physicians.

HORN: And they are rather their patients; but——

(*Enter* MY LADY FIDGET, *looking about her.*)

Now we talk of women of honour, here comes one. Step behind the screen there, and but observe if I have not particular privileges with the women of reputation already, Doctor, already.

(QUACK retires.)

LADY FID: Well, Horner, am not I a woman of honour? You see, I'm as good as my word.

HORN: And you shall see, Madam, I'll not be behindhand with you in honour; and I'll be as good as my word too, if you please but to withdraw into the next room.

LADY FID: But first, my dear Sir, you must promise to have a care of my dear honour.

HORN: If you talk a word more of your honour, you'll make me incapable to wrong it. To talk of honour in the mysteries of love, is like talking of Heaven or the Deity in an operation of witchcraft just when you are employing the devil: it makes the charm impotent.

LADY FID: Nay, fy! let us not be smutty. But you talk of mysteries and bewitching to me; I don't understand you.

HORN: I tell you, Madam, the word money in a mistress's mouth, at such a nick of time, is not a more disheartening sound to a younger brother, than that of honour to an eager lover like myself.

LADY FID: But you can't blame a lady of my reputation to be chary.

HORN: Chary! I have been chary of it already, by the report I have caused of myself.

LADY FID: Ay, but if you should ever let other women know that dear secret, it would come out. Nay, you must have a great care of your conduct; for my acquaintance are so censorious (oh, 'tis a wicked, censorious world, Mr. Horner!), I say, are so censorious and detracting that perhaps they'll talk to the prejudice of my honour, though you should not let them know the dear secret.

HORN: Nay, Madam, rather than they shall prejudice your honour, I'll prejudice theirs; and, to serve you, I'll lie with 'em all, make the secret their own, and then they'll keep it. I am a Machiavel in love, Madam.

LADY FID: Oh, no, Sir, not that way.

HORN: Nay, the devil take me if censorious women are to be silenced any other way.

LADY FID: A secret is better kept, I hope, by a single person than a multitude; therefore pray do not trust anybody else with it, dear, dear Mr. Horner. (*embracing him*)

(*Enter* SIR JASPER FIDGET.)

SIR JASP: How now!

LADY FID: (*aside*) Oh my husband!—prevented—and what's almost as bad, found with my arms about another man—that will appear too much—what shall I say?—(*aloud*) Sir Jasper, come hither: I am trying if Mr. Horner were ticklish, and he's as ticklish as can be. I love to torment the confounded toad; let you and I tickle him.

SIR JASP: No, your ladyship will tickle him better without me, I suppose. But is this your buying china? I thought you had been at the china-house.

HORN: (*aside*) China-house! that's my cue, I must take it.—(*aloud*) A pox! can't you keep your impertinent wives at home? Some men are troubled with the husbands, but I with the wives; but I'd have you to know, since I cannot be your journeyman by night, I will not be your drudge by day, to squire your wife about, and be your man of straw, or scarecrow only to pies and jays, that would be nibbling at your forbidden fruit; I shall be shortly the hackney gentleman-usher of the town.

SIR JASP: (*aside*) He! he! he! poor fellow, he's in the right on't, faith. To squire women about for other folks is as ungrateful an employment, as to tell money for other folks.—(*aloud*) He! he! he! be'n't angry, Horner.

LADY FID: No, 'tis I have more reason to be angry, who am left by you, to go abroad indecently alone; or, what is more indecent, to pin myself upon such ill-bred people of your acquaintance as this is.

SIR JASP: Nay, prithee, what has he done?

LADY FID: Nay, he has done nothing.

SIR JASP: But what d'ye take ill, if he has done nothing?

LADY FID: Ha! ha! ha! faith, I can't but laugh however; why, d'ye think the unmannerly toad would come down to me to the coach? I was fain to come up to fetch him, or go without him, which I was resolved not to do; for he knows china very well, and has himself very good, but will not let me see it, lest I should beg some; but I will find it out, and have what I came for yet.

HORN: (*apart to* LADY FIDGET, *as he follows her to the door*) Lock the door, Madam.—(*exit* LADY FIDGET, *and locks the door*)—(*aloud*) So, she has got into my chamber and locked me out. Oh the impertinency of woman-kind! Well, Sir Jasper, plain-dealing is a jewel; if ever you suffer your wife to trouble me again here, she shall carry you home a pair of horns; by my lord mayor she shall; though I cannot furnish you myself, you are sure, yet I'll find a way.

SIR JASP: Ha! ha! he!—(*aside*) At my first coming in, and finding her arms about him, tickling him it seems, I was half jealous, but now I see my folly. —(*aloud*) He! he! he! poor Horner.

HORN: Nay, though you laugh now, 'twill be my turn ere long. Oh, women, more impertinent, more cunning, and more mischievous than their monkeys, and to me almost as ugly!—Now is she throwing my things about and rifling all I have; but I'll get in to her the back way, and so rifle her for it.

SIR JASP: Ha! ha! ha! poor angry Horner.

HORN: Stay here a little, I'll ferret her out to you presently, I warrant. (*Exit at t'other door.*)

(SIR JASPER *calls through the door to his Wife; she answers from within.*)

SIR JASP: Wife! my lady Fidget! wife! he is coming in to you the back way.

LADY FID: Let him come, and welcome, which way he will.

SIR JASP: He'll catch you, and use you roughly, and be too strong for you.

LADY FID: Don't you trouble yourself, let him if he can.

QUACK: (*behind*) This indeed I could not have believed from him, nor any but my own eyes.

(*Enter* MRS. SQUEAMISH.)

MRS. SQUEAM: Where's this woman-hater, this toad, this ugly, greasy, dirty sloven?

SIR JASP: (*aside*) So, the women all will have him ugly: methinks he is a comely person, but his wants make his form contemptible to 'em; and 'tis e'en as my wife said yesterday, talking of him, that a proper handsome eunuch was as ridiculous a thing as a gigantic coward.

MRS. SQUEAM: Sir Jasper, your servant: where is the odious beast?

SIR JASP: He's within in his chamber, with my wife; she's playing the wag with him.

MRS. SQUEAM: Is she so? and he's a clownish beast, he'll give her no quarter, he'll play the wag with her again, let me tell you: come, let's go help her.— What, the door's locked?

SIR JASP: Ay, my wife locked it.

MRS. SQUEAM: Did she so? Let's break it open then.

SIR JASP: No, no; he'll do her no hurt.

MRS. SQUEAM: No.—(*aside*) But is there no other way to get in to 'em? Whither goes this? I will disturb 'em. (*Exit* MRS. SQUEAMISH *at another door.*)

(*Enter* OLD LADY SQUEAMISH.)

LADY SQUEAM: Where is this harlotry, this impudent baggage, this rambling tomrigg? O, Sir Jasper, I am glad to see you here. Did you not see my vile grandchild come in hither just now?

SIR JASP: Yes.

LADY SQUEAM: Ay, but where is she then? where is she? Lord, Sir Jasper, I have e'en rattled myself to pieces in pursuit of her: but can you tell what she makes here? they say below, no woman lodges here.

SIR JASP: No.

LADY SQUEAM: No! what does she here then? say, if it be not a woman's lodging, what makes she here? But are you sure no woman lodges here?

SIR JASP: No, nor no man neither, this is Mr. Horner's lodging.

LADY SQUEAM: Is it so, are you sure?

SIR JASP: Yes, yes.

LADY SQUEAM: So; then there's no hurt in't, I hope. But where is he?

SIR JASP: He's in the next room with my wife.

LADY SQUEAM: Nay, if you trust him with your wife, I may with my Biddy.

They say, he's a merry harmless man now, e'en as harmless a man as ever came out of Italy with a good voice, and as pretty, harmless company for a lady, as a snake without his teeth.

SIR JASP: Ay, ay, poor man.

(*Re-enter* MRS. SQUEAMISH.)

MRS. SQUEAM: I can't find 'em.—Oh, are you here, grandmother? I followed, you must know, my Lady Fidget hither; 'tis the prettiest lodging, and I have been staring on the prettiest pictures——

(*Re-enter* LADY FIDGET *with a piece of china in her hand, and* HORNER *following.*)

LADY FID: And I have been toiling and moiling for the prettiest piece of china, my dear.

HORN: Nay, she has been too hard for me, do what I could.

MRS. SQUEAM: Oh, lord, I'll have some china too. Good Mr. Horner, don't think to give other people china, and me none; come in with me too.

HORN: Upon my honour, I have none left now.

MRS. SQUEAM: Nay, nay, I have known you deny your china before now, but you shan't put me off so. Come.

HORN: This lady had the last there.

LADY FID: Yes indeed, Madam, to my certain knowledge, he has no more left.

MRS. SQUEAM: O, but it may be he may have some you could not find.

LADY FID: What, d'ye think if he had had any left, I would not have had it too? for we women of quality never think we have china enough.

HORN: Do not take it ill, I cannot make china for you all, but I will have a roll-waggon for you too, another time.

MRS. SQUEAM: Thank you, dear toad.

LADY FID: (*to* HORNER *aside*) What do you mean by that promise?

HORN: (*apart to* LADY FIDGET) Alas, she has an innocent, literal understanding.

LADY SQUEAM: Poor Mr. Horner! he has enough to do to please you all, I see.

HORN: Ay, Madam, you see how they use me.

LADY SQUEAM: Poor gentleman, I pity you.

HORN: I thank you, Madam: I could never find pity but from such reverend ladies as you are; the young ones will never spare a man.

MRS. SQUEAM: Come, come, beast, and go dine with us; for we shall want a man at ombre after dinner.

HORN: That's all their use of me, Madam, you see.

MRS. SQUEAM: Come, sloven, I'll lead you, to be sure of you. (*pulls him by the cravat*)

LADY SQUEAM: Alas, poor man, how she tugs him! Kiss, kiss her; that's the way to make such nice women quiet.

HORN: No, Madam, that remedy is worse than the torment; they know I dare suffer anything rather than do it.

LADY SQUEAM: Prithee kiss her, and I'll give you her picture in little, that you admired so last night; prithee do.

HORN: Well, nothing but that could bribe me: I love a woman only in effigy and good painting, as much as I hate them. I'll do't, for I could adore the devil well painted. (*kisses* MRS. SQUEAMISH)

MRS. SQUEAM: Foh, you filthy toad! nay, now I've done jesting.

LADY SQUEAM: Ha! ha! ha! I told you so.

MRS. SQUEAM: Foh! a kiss of his——

SIR JASP: Has no more hurt in't than one of my spaniel's.

MRS. SQUEAM: Nor no more good neither.

QUACK: (*behind*) I will now believe anything he tells me.

(*Enter* PINCHWIFE.)

LADY FID: O Lord! Here's a man! Sir Jasper, my mask, my mask! I would not be seen here for the world!

SIR JASP: What! Not when I am with you?

LADY FID: No, no, my honour—let's be gone.

MRS. SQUEAM: Oh grandmother, let's be gone; make haste, make haste, I know not how he may censure us.

LADY FID: Be found in the lodging of anything like a man!—Away.

(*Exeunt* SIR JASPER FIDGET, LADY FIDGET, OLD LADY SQUEAMISH, *and* MRS. SQUEAMISH.)

QUACK: What's here? another cuckold? he looks like one, and none else sure have any business with him. (*aside*)

HORN: Well, what brings my dear friend hither?

PINCH: Your impertinency.

HORN: My impertinency!—why, you gentlemen that have got handsome wives, think you have a privilege of saying anything to your friends, and are as brutish as if you were our creditors.

PINCH: No, Sir, I'll ne'er trust you any way.

HORN: But why not, dear Jack? why diffide in me thou know'st so well?

PINCH: Because I do know you so well.

HORN: Han't I been always thy friend, honest Jack, always ready to serve thee, in love or battle, before thou wert married, and am so still?

PINCH: I believe so, you would be my second now, indeed.

HORN: Well then, dear Jack, why so unkind, so grum, so strange to me? Come, prithee kiss me, dear rogue: gad, I was always, I say, and am still as much thy servant as——

PINCH: As I am yours, Sir. What, you would send a kiss to my wife, is that it?

HORN: So, there 'tis—a man can't show his friendship to a married man, but presently he talks of his wife to you. Prithee, let thy wife alone, and let thee and I be all one, as we were wont. What, thou art as shy of my kindness as a Lombard Street alderman of a courtier's civility at Locket's!

PINCH: But you are over-kind to me, as kind as if I were your cuckold already; yet I must confess you ought to be kind and civil to me, since I am so kind so civil to you, as to bring you this: look you there, Sir. (*delivers him a letter*)

HORN: What is't?

PINCH: Only a love-letter, Sir.

HORN: From whom?—how! this is from your wife—hum—and hum—— (*reads*)

PINCH: Even from my wife, Sir: am I not wondrous kind and civil to you now too?—(*aside*) But you'll not think her so.

HORN: Ha! is this is a trick of his or hers? (*aside*)

PINCH: The gentleman's surprised I find.—What, you expected a kinder letter?

HORN: No faith, not I, how could I?

PINCH: Yes, yes, I'm sure you did. A man so well made as you are must needs be disappointed, if the women declare not their passion at first sight or opportunity.

HORN: (*aside*) But what should this mean? Stay, the postscript.—(*reads aside*) "Be sure you love me, whatsoever my husband says to the contrary, and let him not see this, lest he should come home and pinch me, or kill my squirrel."—It seems he knows not what the letter contains.

PINCH: Come, ne'er wonder at it so much.

HORN: Faith, I can't help it.

PINCH: Now, I think I have deserved your infinite friendship and kindness, and have showed myself sufficiently an obliging kind friend and husband; am I not so, to bring a letter from my wife to her gallant?

HORN: Ay, the devil take me, art thou, the most obliging, kind friend and husband in the world, ha! ha!

PINCH: Well, you may be merry, Sir; but in short I must tell you, Sir, my honour will suffer no jesting.

HORN: What dost thou mean?

PINCH: Does the letter want a comment? Then, know, Sir, though I have been so civil a husband as to bring you a letter from my wife, to let you kiss and court her to my face, I will not be a cuckold, Sir, I will not.

HORN: Thou art mad with jealousy. I never saw thy wife in my life but at the play yesterday, and I know not if it were she or no. I court her, kiss her!

PINCH: I will not be a cuckold, I say; there will be danger in making me a cuckold.

HORN: Why, wert thou not well cured of thy last clap?

PINCH: I wear a sword.

HORN: It should be taken from thee, lest thou shouldst do thyself a mischief with it; thou art mad, man.

PINCH: As mad as I am, and as merry as you are, I must have more reason from you ere we part. I say again, though you kissed and courted last night my wife in man's clothes, as she confesses in her letter—

HORN: (*aside*) Ha!

PINCH: Both she and I say, you must not design it again, for you have mistaken your woman, as you have done your man.

HORN: (*aside*) O—I understand something now—(*aloud*) Was that thy wife! Why wouldst thou not tell me 'twas she? Faith, my freedom with her was your fault, not mine.

PINCH: Faith, so 'twas.

HORN: Fy! I'd never do't to a woman before her husband's face, sure.

PINCH: But I had rather you should do't to my wife before my face, than behind my back; and that you shall never do.

HORN: No—you will hinder me.

PINCH: If I would not hinder you, you see by her letter she would.

HORN: Well, I must e'en acquiesce then, and be contented with what she writes.

PINCH: I'll assure you 'twas voluntarily writ; I had no hand in't you may believe me.

HORN: I do believe thee, faith.

PINCH: And believe her too, for she's an innocent creature, has no dissembling in her: an so fare you well, Sir.

HORN: Pray, however, present my humble service to her, and tell her, I will obey her letter to a tittle, and fulfil her desires, be what they will, or with what difficulty soever I do't; and you shall be no more jealous of me, I warrant her, and you.

PINCH: Well then, fare you well; and play with any man's honour but mine, kiss any man's wife but mine, and welcome. (*exit*)

HORN: Ha! ha! ha! Doctor.

QUACK: It seems, he has not heard the report of you, or does not believe it.

HORN: Ha! ha!—now, Doctor, what think you?

QUACK: Pray let's see the letter—hum—"for—dear—love you——" (*reads the letter*)

HORN: I wonder how she could contrive it! What say'st thou to't? 'tis an original.

QUACK: So are your cuckolds too originals: for they are like no other common cuckolds, and I will henceforth believe it not impossible for you to cuckold the Grand Signior amidst his guards of eunuchs, that I say.

HORN: And I say for the letter, 'tis the first love-letter that ever was without flames, darts, fates, destinies, lying and dissembling in't.

(*Enter* SPARKISH *pulling in* PINCHWIFE.)

SPARK: Come back, you are a pretty brother-in-law, neither go to church nor to dinner with your sister bride!

PINCH: My sister denies her marriage, and you see is gone away from you dissatisfied.

SPARK: Pshaw! upon a foolish scruple, that our parson was not in lawful orders, and did not say all the common prayer; but 'tis her modesty only I believe. But let women be never so modest the first day, they'll be sure to come to themselves by night, and I shall have enough of her then. In the meantime, Harry Horner, you must dine with me: I keep my wedding at my aunt's in the Piazza.

HORN: Thy wedding! what stale maid has lived to despair of a husband, or what young one of a gallant?

SPARK: Oh, your servant, Sir—this gentleman's sister then—no stale maid.

HORN: I'm sorry for't.

PINCH: (*aside*) How comes he so concerned for her?

SPARK: You sorry for't? Why, do you know any ill by her?

HORN: No, I know none but by thee; 'tis for her sake, not yours, and another man's sake that might have hoped, I thought.

SPARK: Another man! another man! What is his name?

HORN: Nay, since 'tis past, he shall be nameless.—(*aside*) Poor Harcourt! I am sorry thou hast missed her.

PINCH: (*aside*) He seems to be much troubled at the match.

SPARK: Prithee, tell me—— Nay, you shan't go, Brother.

PINCH: I must of necessity, but I'll come to you to dinner. (*Exit* PINCH-WIFE.)

SPARK: But, Harry, what, have I a rival in my wife already? But with all my heart, for he may be of use to me hereafter; for though my hunger is now my sauce, and I can fall on heartily without, the time will come when a rival will be as good sauce for a married man to a wife, as an orange to veal.

HORN: O thou damned rogue! thou hast set my teeth on edge with thy orange.

SPARK: Then let's to dinner—there I was with you again. Come.

HORN: But who dines with thee?

SPARK: My friends and relations, my brother, Pinchwife, you see, of your acquaintance.

HORN: And his wife?

SPARK: No, 'gad, he'll ne'er let her come amongst us good fellows; your stingy country coxcomb keeps his wife from his friends, as he does his little firkin of ale, for his own drinking, and a gentleman can't get a smack on't; but his servants, when his back is turned, broach it at their pleasures, and dust it away, ha! ha! ha!—'Gad, I am witty, I think, considering I was married to-day, by the world; but come——

HORN: No, I will not dine with you, unless you can fetch her too.

SPARK: Pshaw! what pleasure canst thou have with women now, Harry?

HORN: My eyes are not gone; I love a good prospect yet, and will not dine with you unless she does too; go fetch her, therefore, but do not tell her husband 'tis for my sake.

SPARK: Well, I'll go try what I can do; in the meantime, come away to my aunt's lodging, 'tis in the way to Pinchwife's.

HORN: The poor woman has called for aid, and stretched forth her hand, Doctor; I cannot but help her over the pale out of the briars. (*Exeunt*)

ACT V, SCENE IV. *Horner's Lodging. A table, banquet, bottles.*

(*Enter* LADY FIDGET, MRS. DAINTY FIDGET, MRS. SQUEAMISH.)

HORN: (*aside*) A pox! They are come too soon—before I have sent back my new mistress. All I have now to do is to lock her in, that they may not see her.

LADY FID: That we may be sure of our welcome, we have brought our entertainment with us, and are resolved to treat thee, dear toad.

MRS. DAIN: And that we may be merry to purpose, have left Sir Jasper and my old Lady Squeamish quarrelling at home at backgammon.

MRS. SQUEAM: Therefore let us make use of our time, lest they should chance to interrupt us.

LADY FID: Let us sit then.

HORN: First, that you may be private, let me lock this door and that, and I'll wait upon you presently.

LADY FID: No, Sir, shut 'em only, and your lips for ever; for we must trust you as much as our women.

HORN: You know all vanity's killed in me; I have no occasion for talking.

LADY FID: Now, ladies, supposing we had drank each of us our two bottles, let us speak the truth of our hearts.

MRS. DAIN: and MRS. SQUEAM: Agreed.

LADY FID: By this brimmer, for truth is nowhere else to be found—(*aside to* HORNER) not in thy heart, false man!

HORN: (*aside to* LADY FIDGET) You have found me a true man, I'm sure.

LADY FID: (*aside to* HORNER) Not every way.—But let us sit and be merry. (LADY FIDGET *sings.*)

1

> Why should our damn'd tyrants oblige us to live
> On the pittance of pleasure which they only give?
> We must not rejoice
> With wine and with noise:
> In vain we must wake in a dull bed alone,
> Whilst to our warm rival, the bottle, they're gone.
> Then lay aside charms,
> And take up these arms.[1]

[1] The glasses of wine.

2

'Tis wine only gives 'em their courage and wit;
Because we live sober, to men we submit.
  If for beauties you'd pass,
  Take a lick of the glass,
'Twill mend your complexions, and when they are gone,
  The best red we have is the red of the grape:
Then, sisters, lay't on,
   And damn a good shape.

MRS. DAIN: Dear brimmer! Well, in token of our openness and plain-dealing, let us throw our masks over our heads.

HORN: So, 'twill come to the glasses anon. (*aside*)

MRS. SQUEAM: Lovely brimmer! let me enjoy him first.

LADY FID: No, I never part with a gallant till I've tried him. Dear brimmer! that makest out husbands short-sighted.

MRS. DAIN: And our bashful gallants bold.

MRS. SQUEAM: And, for want of a gallant, the butler lovely in our eyes.—Drink, eunuch.

LADY FID: Drink, thou representative of a husband. Damn a husband!

MRS. DAIN: And, as it were a husband, an old keeper.

MRS. SQUEAM: And an old grandmother.

HORN: And an English bawd, and a French surgeon.

LADY FID: Ay, we have all reason to curse 'em.

HORN: For my sake, ladies?

LADY FID: No, for our own; for the first spoils all young gallants' industry.

MRS. DAIN: And the other's art makes 'em bold only with common women.

MRS. SQUEAM: And rather run the hazard of the vile distemper amongst them, than of a denial amongst us.

MRS. DAIN: The filthy toads choose mistresses now as they do stuffs, for having been fancied and worn by others.

MRS. SQUEAM: For being common and cheap.

LADY FID: Whilst women of quality, like the richest stuffs, lie untumbled, and unasked for.

HORN: Ay, neat, and cheap, and new, often they think best.

MRS. DAIN: No, Sir, the beasts will be known by a mistress longer than by a suit.

MRS. SQUEAM: And 'tis not for cheapness neither.

LADY FID: No; for the vain fops will take up druggets and embroider 'em. But I wonder at the depraved appetites of witty men; they used to be out of the common road, and hate imitation. Pray tell me, beast, when you were a man, why you rather chose to club with a multitude in a common house for an entertainment, than to be the only guest at a good table.

HORN: Why, faith, ceremony and expectation are unsufferable to those that are sharp bent. People always eat with the best stomach at an ordinary, where every man is snatching for the best bit.

LADY FID: Though he get a cut over the fingers.—But I have heard people eat most heartily of another man's meat, that is, what they do not pay for.

HORN: When they are sure of their welcome and freedom; for ceremony in love and eating is as ridiculous as in fighting: falling on briskly is all should be done on those occasions.

LADY FID: Well then, let me tell you, Sir, there is nowhere more freedom than in our houses; and we take freedom from a young person as a sign of good breeding; and a person may be as free as he pleases with us, as frolic, as gamesome, as wild as he will.

HORN: Han't I heard you all declaim against wild men?

LADY FID: Yes; but for all that, we think wildness in a man as desirable a quality as in a duck or rabbit: a tame man! foh!

HORN: I know not, but your reputations frightened me as much as your faces invited me.

LADY FID: Our reputation! Lord, why should you not think that we women make use of our reputation, as you men of yours, only to deceive the world with less suspicion? Our virtue is like the stateman's religion, the Quaker's word, the gamester's oath, and the great man's honour—but to cheat those that trust us.

MRS. SQUEAM: And that demureness, coyness, and modesty that you see in our faces in the boxes at plays, is as much a sign of a kind woman, as a vizard-mask in the pit.

MRS. DAIN: For, I assure you, women are least masked when they have the velvet vizard on.

LADY FID: You would have found us modest women in our denials only.

MRS. SQUEAM: Our bashfulness is only the reflection of the men's.

MRS. DAIN: We blush when they are shamefaced.

HORN: I beg your pardon, ladies, I was deceived in you devilishly. But why that mighty pretence to honour?

LADY FID: We have told you; but sometimes 'twas for the same reason you men pretend business often, to avoid ill company, to enjoy the better and more privately those you love.

HORN: But why would you ne'er give a friend a wink then?

LADY FID: Faith, your reputation frightened us as much as ours did you, you were so notoriously lewd.

LADY FID: Was that all that deterred you?

HORN: And so expensive—you allow freedom, you say.

LADY FID: Ay, ay.

HORN: That I was afraid of losing my little money, as well as my little time, both which my other pleasures required.

LADY FID: Money! foh! you talk like a little fellow now: do such as we expect money?

HORN: I beg your pardon, Madam, I must confess, I have heard that great ladies, like great merchants, set but the higher prices upon what they have, because they are not in necessity of taking the first offer.

MRS. DAIN: Such as we make sale of our hearts?

MRS. SQUEAM: We bribed for our love? foh!

HORN: With your pardon, ladies, I know, like great men in offices, you seem to exact flattery and attendance only from your followers; but you have receivers about you, and such fees to pay, a man is afraid to pass your grants. Besides, we must let you win at cards, or we lose your hearts; and if you make an assignation, 'tis at a goldsmith's, jeweller's, or china-house; where for your honour you deposit to him, he must pawn his to the punctual cit, and so paying for what you take up, pays for what he takes up.

MRS. DAIN: Would you not have us assured of our gallants' love?

MRS. SQUEAM: For love is better known by liberality than by jealousy.

LADY FID: For one may be dissembled, the other not.—(*aside*) But my jealousy can be no longer dissembled, and they are telling ripe.—(*aloud*) Come, here's to our gallants in waiting, whom we must name, and I'll begin. This is my false rogue. (*claps him on the back*)

MRS. SQUEAM: How!

HORN: (*aside*) So, all will out now.

MRS. SQUEAM: (*aside to* HORNER) Did you not tell me, 'twas for my sake only you reported yourself no man?

MRS. DAIN: (*aside to* HORNER) Oh, wretch! did you not swear to me, 'twas for my love and honour you passed for that thing you do?

HORN: So, so.

LADY FID: Come, speak, ladies: this is my false villain.

MRS. SQUEAM: And mine too.

MRS. DAIN: And mine.

HORN: Well then, you are all three my false rogues too, and there's an end on't.

LADY FID: Well then, there's no remedy; sister sharers, let us not fall out, but have a care of our honour. Though we get no presents, no jewels of him, we are savers of our honour, the jewel of most value and use, which shines yet to the world unsuspected, though it be counterfeit.

HORN: Nay, and is e'en as good as if it were true, provided the world think so; for honour, like beauty now, only depends on the opinion of others.

LADY FID: Well, Harry Common, I hope you can be true to three. Swear. But 'tis to no purpose to require your oath, for you are as often forsworn as you swear to new women.

HORN: Come, faith, Madam, let us e'en pardon one another; for all the difference I find betwixt we men and you women, we forswear ourselves at the beginning of an amour, you as long as it lasts.

DANIEL DEFOE (1660–1731)

Born in 1660 in London, son of a humble butcher, James Foe, Daniel supported himself as a youth by selling hosiery. Disliking the trade as well as his name, he abandoned the former for soldiering, politics, and pamphleteering, and changed the latter from the pedestrian Foe to the aristocratic Defoe. Beginning as a dissenter, he became a wavering opportunist. Engaged as a secret agent, his loyalty was suspected and his political activities landed him in jail.

None of this interfered with his literary activities, which were immense. He expressed all sides of himself—the shifty politician and the convinced liberal, the unscrupulous journalist and the ardent moralist—in more than two hundred and fifty works. His religious tracts, travel book, poems, and such guides as The Complete English Gentleman *are forgotten. But Defoe's essential qualities—his liveliness, candor, and sympathy with human weakness—live for us not only in* Robinson Crusoe, *his most popular work which has become a children's classic, but in* Roxana, the Fortunate Mistress *and* Moll Flanders.

The plot of the last is suggested by the full title of the original: The Fortunes and Misfortunes of the famous Moll Flanders, &c., who was born in Newgate, and during a life of continued variety, for threescore years, besides her childhood, was twelve years a Whore, five times a Wife (whereof once to her own brother), twelve years a Thief, eight years a transported Felon in Virginia, at last grew rich, lived honest, and died a Penitent.

Moll's repentance is not only belated but suspiciously smug. "The publishing of this account of my life," Defoe has her say, "is for the sake of the just moral of every part of it, and for instruction, caution, warning, and improvement to every reader." However, most readers, unaffected by the "warning," are more fascinated by the wicked life and the spirited, plain-speaking picture of an age which took its morals as well as its immorality lightly.

FROM: MOLL FLANDERS

LIAISON IN BATH

(Moll Flanders' fortunes are at a low ebb when she decides to reside at Bath, "where men find a mistress sometimes, but very rarely look for a wife." There she meets a man who is married but separated from his insane wife. Understanding that Moll is a widow he makes "no professions to her but of an extraordinary respect." He has come to the noted watering place for his health and Moll, winning his confidence as well as his respect, acts as his nurse.)

After some time he gathered strength and grew well apace, and I would have removed my pallet-bed, but he would not let me, till he was able to venture himself without anybody to sit up with him, when I removed to my own chamber.

He took many occasions to express his sense of my tenderness for him; and when he grew well he made me a present of fifty guineas for my care, and, as he called it, hazarding my life to save his.

And now he made deep protestations of a sincere inviolable affection for me, but with the utmost reserve for my virtue and his own. I told him I was fully satisfied of it. He carried it that length that he protested to me, that if he was naked in bed with me, he would as sacredly preserve my virtue as he would defend it, if I was assaulted by a ravisher. I believed him, and told him I did so; but this did not satisfy him. He would, he said, wait for some opportunity to give me an undoubted testimony of it.

It was a great while after this that I had occasion, on my business, to go to Bristol, upon which he hired me a coach, and would go with me; and now indeed our intimacy increased. From Bristol he carried me to Glouces-ter, which was merely a journey of pleasure, to take the air; and here it was our hap to have no lodgings in the inn, but in one large chamber with two beds in it. The master of the house going with us to show his rooms, and coming into that room, said very frankly to him, "Sir, it is none of my busi-ness to inquire whether the lady be your spouse or no; but if not, you may lie as honestly in these two beds as if you were in two chambers," and with that he pulls a great curtain which drew quite across the room, and effectually divided the beds. "Well," says my friend, very readily, "these beds will do; and as for the rest, we are too near akin to lie together, though we may lodge near one another;" and this put an honest face on the thing too. When we came to go to bed, he decently went out of the room till I was in bed, and then went to bed in the other bed, but lay there talking to me a great while.

At last, repeating his usual saying, that he could lie naked in the bed with me and not offer me the least injury, he starts out of his bed. "And now, my dear," says he, "you shall see how just I will be to you, and that I can keep my word," and away he comes to my bed.

I resisted a little, but I must confess I should not have resisted him much, if he had not made those promises at all. So, after a little struggle, I lay still and let him come to bed. When he was there he took me in his arms, and so I lay all night with him, but he had no more to do with me, or offered anything to me, other than embracing me, as I say, in his arms, no, not the whole night, but rose up and dressed him in the morning, and left me as innocent for him as I was the day I was born.

This was a surprising thing to me, and perhaps may be so to others, who know how the laws of nature work; for he was a vigorous, brisk person. Nor did he act thus on a principle of religion at all, but of mere affection; in-sisting on it, that, though I was to him the most agreeable woman in the world, yet, because he loved me, he could not injure me.

I own it was a noble principle, but as it was what I never saw before, so it was perfectly amazing. We travelled the rest of the journey as we did before, and came back to Bath, where, as he had opportunity to come to me when he would, he often repeated the same moderation, and I frequently lay with him, and although all the familiarities of man and wife were common to us, yet he never once offered to go any farther, and he valued himself much upon it. I do not say that I was so wholly pleased with it as he thought I was, for I own I was much wickeder than he.

We lived thus near two years, only with this exception, that he went three times to London in that time, and once he continued there four months; but, to do him justice, he always supplied me with money to subsist on very handsomely.

Had we continued thus, I confess we had had much to boast of; but, as wise men say, it is ill venturing too near the brink of a command. So we found it; and here again I must do him the justice to own that the first breach was not on his part. It was one night that we were in bed together warm and merry, and having drunk, I think, a little more both of us than usual, though not in the least to disorder us, when, after some other follies which I cannot name, and being clasped close in his arms, I told him (I repeat it with shame and horror of soul) that I could find in my heart to discharge him of his engagement for one night and no more.

He took me at my word immediately, and after that there was no resisting him; neither indeed had I any mind to resist him any more.

Thus the government of our virtue was broken, and I exchanged the place of friend for that unmusical, harsh-sounding title of whore. In the morning we were both at our penitentials. I cried very heartily, he expressed himself very sorry; but that was all either of us could do at that time, and the way being thus cleared, and the bars of virtue and conscience thus removed, we had the less to struggle with.

It was but a dull kind of conversation that we had together for all the rest of that week; I looked on him with blushes, and every now and then started that melancholy objection, "What if I should be with child now? What will become of me then?" He encouraged me by telling me that as long as I was true to him, he would be so to me; and since it was gone such a length (which indeed he never intended), yet if I was with child, he would take care of that and me too. This hardened us both. I assured him if I was with child, I would die for want of a midwife rather than name him as the father of it; and he assured me I should never want if I should be with child. These mutual assurances hardened us in the thing, and after this we repeated the crime as often as we pleased, till at length, as I feared, so it came to pass, and I was indeed with child.

After I was sure it was so, and I had satisfied him of it too, we began to think of taking measures for the managing it, and I proposed trusting the secret to my landlady, and asking her advice, which he agreed to. My landlady, a woman (as I found) used to such things, made light of it; she said she knew it would come to that at last, and made us very merry about it. As I said above, we found her an experienced old lady at such work; she undertook everything, engaged to procure a midwife and a nurse, to satisfy all inquiries, and bring us off with reputation, and she did so very dexterously indeed.

When I grew near my time, she desired my gentleman to go away to London, or make as if he did so. When he was gone, she acquainted the parish officers that there was a lady ready to lie in at her house, but that she knew her husband very well, and gave them, as she pretended, an account of his name, which she called Sir Walter Cleave; telling them he was a worthy gentleman, and that she would answer for all inquiries, and the like. This satisfied the parish officers presently, and I lay in in as much credit as I could have done if I had really been my Lady Cleave; and was assisted in my travail by three or four of the best citizens' wives of Bath, which, however, made me a little the more expensive to him. I often expressed my concern to him about that part, but he bid me not be concerned at it.

As he had furnished me very sufficiently with money for the extraordinary expenses of my lying-in, I had everything very handsome about me, but did not affect to be so gay or extravagant neither; besides, knowing the world, as I had done, and that such kind of things do not often last long, I took care to lay up as much money as I could for a wet day, as I called it; making him believe it was all spent upon the extraordinary appearance of things in my lying-in.

By this means, with what he had given me as above, I had at the end of my lying-in two hundred guineas by me, including also what was left of my own.

I was brought to bed of a fine boy indeed, and a charming child it was; and when he heard of it, he wrote me a very kind, obliging letter about it, and then told me he thought it would look better for me to come away for London as soon as I was up and well; that he had provided apartments for me at Hammersmith, as if I came only from London; and that after a while I should go back to Bath, and he would go with me.

I liked his offer very well, and hired a coach on purpose, and taking my child and a wet-nurse to tend and suckle it, and a maid-servant with me, away I went for London.

He met me at Reading in his own chariot, and taking me into that, left the servant and the child in the hired coach, and so he brought me to my new lodgings at Hammersmith; with which I had abundance of reason to be very well pleased, for they were very handsome rooms.

And now I was indeed in the height of what I might call prosperity, and I wanted nothing but to be a wife, which, however, could not be in this case, and therefore on all occasions I studied to save what I could, as I said above, against the time of scarcity; knowing well enough that such things as these do not always continue; that men that keep mistresses often change them, grow weary of them, or jealous of them, or something or other; and sometimes the ladies that are thus well used, are not careful by a prudent conduct to preserve the esteem of their persons, or the nice article of their fidelity, and then they are justly cast off with contempt.

But I was secured in this point, for as I had no inclination to change, so I had no manner of acquaintance, so no temptation to look any farther. I kept no company but in the family where I lodged, and with a clergyman's lady at next door; so that when he was absent I visited nobody, nor did he ever find me out of my chamber or parlour whenever he came down; if I went anywhere to take the air, it was always with him.

The living in this manner with him, and his with me, was certainly the most undesigned thing in the world. He often protested to me that when he became first acquainted with me, and even to the very night when we first broke in upon our rules, he never had the least design of lying with me; that he always had a sincere affection for me, but not the least real inclination to do what he had done. I assured him I never suspected him; that if I had I should not so easily have yielded to the freedoms which brought it on, but that it was all a surprise, and was owing to our having yielded too far to our mutual inclinations that night; and indeed I have often observed since, and leave it as a caution to the readers of this story, that we ought to be cautious of gratifying our inclinations in loose and lewd freedoms, lest we find our resolutions of virtue fail us in the juncture when their assistance should be most necessary.

It is true that from the first hour I began to converse with him, I resolved to let him lie with me, if he offered it; but it was because I wanted his help, and knew of no other way of securing him. But when we were that night together, and, as I have said, had gone such a length, I found my weakness; the inclination was not to be resisted, but I was obliged to yield up all even before he asked it.

However, he was so just to me that he never upbraided me with that; nor did he ever express the least dislike of my conduct on any other occasion, but always protested he was as much delighted with my company as he was the first hour we came together.

LOVERS AND LIBERTINES

A LITTLE ANTHOLOGY OF AMOROUS POEMS

For two hundred years, between 1600 and 1800, the writing of love poems was an art which went to extremes of the natural and the artificial. The latter strain predominated. A few poets, such as the metaphysical John Donne, the salacious Thomas Carew, and the licentious Earl of Rochester, wrote out of conviction rather than convention. But the tendency was toward prettiness instead of passion, delicacy instead of intensity. Since infidelity was to be expected and promiscuity was a light pursuit, most of the amatory writing became a formula where even frankness was an affectation. The leading lyricists wrote songs about unlikely people in an unreal world; women were not women but nymphs, idealized shepherdesses, painted figurines that went by such pastoral pseudonyms as Phyllis, Chloris, Corinna, Lesbia, Althea, Lucasta, Lydia, Electra.

Although the emphasis was on carnal love—the triumph of the senses, or the victory of one body over another—the tone was light, and even the sensual appeal was limited. The late Elizabethan singers, and to a still greater extent the Restoration poets, pictured a realm in which amour was completely conventionalized, a world of pretty languors and no apparent labor, a world in which the poet's lady—whether she was a court nymph or a country Nell—was in herself a formula, a literary stock in trade. The very language had its conventions. Many of the erotic songs were vulgar to the point of pornography, but most of them hid or half concealed their meanings in neatly manipulated double-entendres. For example, the word "die" was almost always used as a euphemism; lovers were continually dying or expiring in the final moment of ecstasy.

The selections which follow run through an unusually wide gamut. They range from pure and concentrated passion, such as the poignant four lines which begin the section and which antedate the Elizabethans, to sheer play and impudent persiflage, the mock-pastorals and seductive society verses of the Restoration wits.

O WESTERN WIND

> O western wind, when wilt thou blow
> That the small rain down can rain?
> Christ! that my love were in my arms!
> And I in my bed again!

AUTHOR UNKNOWN. *Sixteenth century*

BEAUTY'S SELF

> My love in her attire doth show her wit,
>   It doth so well become her;
> For every season she hath dressings fit,
>   For winter, spring, and summer.
> No beauty she doth miss
>   When all her robes are on;
> But Beauty's self she is
>   When all her robes are gone.

AUTHOR UNKNOWN. *Sixteenth century*

O STAY, SWEET LOVE

O stay, sweet love; see here the place of sporting;
　　These gentle flowers smile sweetly to invite us,
And chirping birds are hitherward resorting,
　　Warbling sweet notes only to delight us:
Then stay, dear love, for, tho' thou run from me,
Run ne'er so fast, yet I will follow thee.

I thought, my love, that I should overtake you;
　　Sweet heart, sit down under this shadowed tree,
And I will promise never to forsake you,
　　So you will grant to me a lover's fee.
Whereat she smiled, and kindly to me said,
"I never meant to live and die a maid."

AUTHOR UNKNOWN. *Sixteenth century*

MAID AND MISTRESS

One day, as Madam took her rest,
　　His Lordship entertained her maid,
Who, young and ardent, did her best
　　To prove his efforts well repaid.
At length Lizette, who worried lest
　　Her silence might seem impolite,
Said, "Grant, Milord, one small request:
　　Now, will you tell me, honor bright,
Does she, or I, display more zest?"
　　"Oh, you, of course, to play *this* game."
"Then, surely, I must pass the test,
　　For everybody says the same!"

MELLIN DE SAINT-GELAIS (1491–1558)
Translated by DEEMS TAYLOR

AGAINST FULFILLMENT OF DESIRE

There is not half so warm a fire
In the fruition as desire.
When I have got the fruit of pain
Possession makes me poor again:
Expected forms and shapes unknown
Whet and make sharp temptatiòn.
Sense is too niggardly for bliss,
And pays me dully with what is;

But fancy's liberal and gives all
That can within her vastness fall.
Veil therefore still, while I divine
The treasure of this hidden mine,
And make imagination tell
What wonder doth in beauty dwell.

AUTHOR UNKNOWN. Sixteenth century

THE FORSAKEN LOVER

They flee from me, that sometime did me seek,
With naked foot stalking within my chamber:
Once have I seen them gentle, tame, and meek,
That now are wild, and do not once remember,
That sometime they have put themselves in danger
To take bread at my hand; and now they range
Busily seeking with a continual change.

Thanked be Fortune, it hath been otherwise
Twenty times better; but once in special,
In thin array, after a pleasant guise,
When her loose gown did from her shoulders fall,
And she me caught in her arms long and small,
And therewithal so sweetly did me kiss,
And softly said, "Dear heart, how like you this?"

It was no dream; for I lay broad awaking:
But all is turned now through my gentleness
Into a bitter fashion of forsaking,
And I have leave to go of her goodness,
And she also to use new-fangledness.
But since that I unkindly so am served,
"How like you this?"— What hath she now deserved?

SIR THOMAS WYATT (1503?–1542)

IT FELL ON A SUMMER'S DAY

It fell on a summer's day,
While sweet Bessy sleeping lay
In her bower on her bed,
Light with curtains shadowèd,
Jamie came; she him spies,
Opening half her heavy eyes.

Jamie stole in through the door,
She lay slumbering as before,
Softly to her he drew near;
She heard him, but would not hear.
Bessy vowed not to speak;
He resolved that dump[1] to break.

First a soft kiss he did take;
She lay still and would not wake.
Then his hands learned to woo;
She dreamt not what he would do,
But still slept, while he smiled
To see love by sleep beguiled.

Jamie then began to play;
Bessy as one buried lay,
Gladly still through this sleight
Deceivèd in her own deceit.
And since this trance begun,
She sleeps every afternoon.

THOMAS CAMPION (1567–1620)

I CARE NOT FOR THESE LADIES

I care not for these ladies,
That must be wooed and prayed:
Give me kind Amarillis,
The wanton country maid.
Nature art disdaineth,
Her beauty is her own,
  Her when we court and kiss,
  She cries, "Forsooth, let go!"
  But when we come where comfort is,
  She never will say "No!"

If I love Amarillis,
She gives me fruit and flowers:
But if we love these ladies,
We must give golden showers.
Give them gold that sell love;
Give me the nut-brown lass,
  Who, when we court and kiss,
  She cries, "Forsooth, let go!"
  But when we come where comfort is,
  She never will say "No!"

[1] Dump: depressed condition.

These ladies must have pillows,
And beds by strangers wrought;
Give me a bower of willows,
Of moss and leaves unbought,
And fresh Amarillis,
With milk and honey fed;
  Who, when we court and kiss,
  She cries, "Forsooth, let go!"
  But when we come where comfort is,
  She never will say "No!"

THOMAS CAMPION (1567–1620)

FAIN WOULD I WED A FAIR YOUNG MAN

Fain would I wed a fair young man that day and night could please me,
When my mind or body grieved that had the power to ease me.
Maids are full of longing thoughts that breed a bloodless sickness,
And that, oft I hear men say, is only cured by quickness,
Oft I have been wooed and prayed, but never could be moved;
Many for a day or so I have most dearly loved,
But this foolish mind of mine straight loathes the thing resolved;
If to love be sin in me that sin is soon absolved.
Sure I think I shall at last fly to some holy order;
When I once am settled there then can I fly no farther.
Yet I would not die a maid, because I had a mother;
As I was by one brought forth I would bring forth another.

THOMAS CAMPION (1567–1620)

COME, MY CELIA

Come, my Celia, let us prove,
While we can, the sports of love.
Time will not be ours for ever;
He, at length, our good will sever.
Spend not then his gifts in vain:
Suns that set may rise again.
But if once we lose this light,
'Tis with us perpetual night.
Why should we defer our joys?
Fame and rumour are but toys.
Cannot we delude the eyes
Of a few poor household spies?
Or his easier ears beguile,
Thus removèd by our wile?

'Tis no sin love's fruits to steal,
But the sweet thefts to reveal;
To be taken, to be seen,
These have crimes accounted been.

BEN JONSON (1573–1637)

TO HIS MISTRESS GOING TO BED

Come, madam, come, all rest my powers defy,
Until I labour, I in labour lie.
The foe ofttimes having the foe in sight,
Is tired with standing though he never fight.
Off with that girdle, like heaven's zone glittering,
But a far fairer world encompassing.
Unpin that spangled breastplate which you wear,
That th'eyes of busy fools may be stopped there.
Unlace yourself, for that harmonious chime,
Tells me from you that now it is bed-time.
Off with that happy busk, which I envie,
That still can be, and still can stand so nigh.
Your gown going off, such beauteous state reveals,
As when from flowery meads th'hills shadow steals.
Off with that wiry coronet and show
The hairy diadem which on you doth grow:
Now off with those shoes, and then safely tread
In this love's hallowed temple, this soft bed.
In such white robes, heaven's angels used to be
Received by men. Thou, angel, bring'st with thee
A heaven like Mahomet's paradise; and though
Ill spirits walk in white, we easily know,
By this these angels from an evil sprite:
Those set our hairs, but these our flesh upright.
    License my roving hands, and let them go,
Before, behind, between, above, below.
O my America! my New-found-land,
My kingdom, safeliest when with one man manned.
My mine of precious stones, my empery,
How blest am I in this discovering thee!
To enter in these bonds, is to be free;
Then where my hand is set, my seal shall be.
    Full nakedness! All joys are due to thee,
As souls unbodied, bodies unclothed must be,
To taste whole joys. Gems which you women use
Are like Atlanta's ball, cast in men's views,

That when a fool's eye lightest on a gem,
His earthly soul may covet that, not them.
Like pictures, or like books' gay coverings made
For laymen, are all women thus arrayed;
Themselves are mystic books, which only we
(Whom their imputed grace will dignify)
Must see revealed. Then since that I may know,
As liberally as to a midwife, show
Thyself: cast all, yea, this white linen hence;
There is no penance due to innocence.
    To teach thee, I am naked first. Why, then,
What need'st thou have more covering than a man?

JOHN DONNE (1573–1631)

SONG

Go and catch a falling star,
    Get with child a mandrake root,
Tell me where all past years are,
    Or who cleft the devil's foot;
Teach me to hear mermaids' singing,
Or to keep off envy's stinging,
        And find
        What wind
Serves to advance an honest mind.

If thou be'st born to strange sights,
    Things invisible to see,
Ride ten thousand days and nights
    Till Age snow white hairs on thee;
Thou, when thou return'st, wilt tell me
All strange wonders that befell thee,
        And swear
        Nowhere
Lives a woman true and fair.

If thou find'st one, let me know;
    Such a pilgrimage were sweet.
Yet do not; I would not go,
    Though at next door we might meet.
Though she were true when you met her,
And last till you write your letter,
        Yet she
        Will be
False, ere I come, to two or three.

JOHN DONNE (1573–1631)

FROM: A RAPTURE

  Come, then, and mounted on the wings of Love
We'll cut the flitting air and soar above
The monster's[1] head, and in the noblest seats
Of those blest shades quench and renew our heats.
There shall the queens of love and innocence,
Beauty and Nature, banish all offence
From our close ivy-twines; there I'll behold
Thy bared snow and thy unbraided gold;
There my enfranchised hand on every side
Shall o'er thy naked polish'd ivory slide.
No curtain there, though of transparent lawn,
Shall be before thy virgin-treasure drawn;
But the rich mine, to the enquiring eye
Exposed, shall ready still for mintage lie,
And we will coin young Cupids. There a bed
Of roses and fresh myrtles shall be spread,
Under the cooler shade of cypress groves;
Our pillows of the down of Venus' doves,
Whereon our panting limbs we'll gently lay,
In the faint respites of our active play:
That so our slumbers may in dreams have leisure
To tell the nimble fancy our past pleasure.
And so our souls, that cannot be embraced,
Shall the embraces of our bodies taste.
Meanwhile the bubbling stream shall court the shore,
Th'enamoured chirping wood-choir shall adore
In varied tunes the deity of love;
The gentle blasts of western winds shall move
The trembling leaves, and through their close boughs breathe
Still music, whilst we rest ourselves beneath
Their dancing shade; till a soft murmur, sent
From souls entranced in amorous languishment,
Rouse us, and shoot into our veins fresh fire,
Till we in their sweet ecstasy expire.
  Then, as the empty bee that lately bore
Into the common treasure all her store,
Flies 'bout the painted field with nimble wing,
Deflow'ring the fresh virgins of the spring,
So will I rifle all the sweets that dwell
In my delicious paradise, and swell
My bag with honey, drawn forth by the power
Of fervent kisses from each spicy flower.

[1] The "monster" is Honor.

I'll seize the rose-buds in their perfumed bed,
The violet knots, like curious mazes spread
O'er all the garden; taste the ripen'd cherry,
The warm firm apple, tipped with coral berry:
Then will I visit with a wand'ring kiss
The vale of lilies and the bower of bliss;
And where the beauteous region doth divide
Into two milky ways, my lips shall slide
Down those smooth alleys, wearing as they go
A tract for lovers on the printed snow;
Thence climbing o'er the swelling Apennine,
Retire into thy grove of eglantine,
Where I will all those ravish'd sweets distil
Through Love's alembic, and with chemic skill
From the mix'd mass one sovereign balm derive,
Then bring that great elixir to thy hive.
  Now in more subtle wreaths I will entwine
My sinewy thighs, my legs and arms with thine;
Thou like a sea of milk shalt lie display'd
Whilst I the smooth calm ocean invade
With such a tempest, as when Jove of old
Fell down on Danaë in a storm of gold;
Yet my tall pine shall in the Cyprian strait
Ride safe at anchor and unlade her freight:
My rudder with thy bold hand, like a tried
And skilful pilot, thou shalt steer, and guide
My bark into love's channel, where it shall
Dance, as the bounding waves do rise or fall.
Then shall thy circling arms embrace and clip
My willing body, and thy balmy lip
Bathe me in juice of kisses, whose perfume
Like a religious incense shall consume,
And send up holy vapours to those powers
That bless our loves and crown our sportful hours,
That with such halcyon calmness fix our souls
In steadfast peace, as no affright controls.
There no rude sounds shake us with sudden starts;
No jealous ears, when we unrip our hearts,
Such our discourse in; no observing spies
This blush, that glance traduce; no envious eyes
Watch our close meetings; nor are we betray'd
To rivals by the bribèd chambermaid.
No wedlock bonds unwreathe our twisted loves,
We seek no midnight arbor, no dark groves
To hide our kisses: there, the hated name

Of husband, wife, lust, modest, chaste, or shame,
Are vain and empty words, whose very sound
Was never heard in the Elysian ground.
All things are lawful there, that may delight
Nature or unrestrainèd appetite.
Like and enjoy, to will and act is one:
We only sin when Love's rites are not done.

THOMAS CAREW (1595–1639)

TO PHYLLIS: A PLEA FOR PROMISCUITY

Phyllis, why should we delay
Pleasures shorter than the day?
Could we (which we never can!)
Stretch our lives beyond their span,
Beauty like a shadow flies,
And our youth before us dies.
Or, would youth and beauty stay,
Love hath wings, and will away.
Love hath swifter wings than Time:
Change in love to Heaven does climb.
Gods, that never change their state,
Vary oft their love and hate.

Phyllis, to this truth we owe
All the love betwixt us two:
Let not you and I inquire
What has been our past desire;
On what shepherd you have smiled,
Or what nymphs I have beguiled.
Leave it to the planets, too,
What we shall hereafter do.
For the joys we now may prove,
Take advice of present love.

EDMUND WALLER (1606–1668)

THE CONSTANT LOVER

Out upon it, I have loved
    Three whole days together!
And am like to love three more,
    If it prove fair weather.

Time shall moult away his wings
　　Ere he shall discover
In the whole wide world again
　　Such a constant lover.

But the spite on't is, no praise
　　Is due at all to me:
Love with me had made no stays,
　　Had it been but she.

Had it any been but she,
　　And that very face,
There had been at least ere this
　　A dozen in her place.

SIR JOHN SUCKLING (1609–1642)

THE REJECTED OFFER

It is not four years ago
　　I offered forty crowns
To lie with her a night or so.
　　She answered me with frowns.

Not two years since, she, meeting me,
　　Did whisper in my ear
That she would at my service be,
　　If I contented were.

I told her I was cold as snow
　　And had no great desire,
But should be well content to go
　　To twenty, but no higher.

Some three months since or thereabout,
　　She that so coy had been,
Bethought herself and found me out,
　　And was content to sin.

I smiled at that, and told her I
　　Did think it somewhat late,
And that I'd not repentance buy
　　At more than half the rate.

This present morning early she
　　Forsooth came to my bed,
And gratis there she offered me
　　Her high-prized maidenhead.

I told her that I thought it then
  Far dearer than I did,
When I at first the forty crowns
  For one night's lodging bid.

SIR JOHN SUCKLING (1609–1642)

TO HIS COY MISTRESS

Had we but world enough, and time,
This coyness, lady, were no crime.
We would sit down, and think which way
To walk, and pass our long love's day.
Thou by the Indian Ganges' side
Should'st rubies find: I by the tide
Of Humber would complain. I would
Love you ten years before the Flood,
And you should, if you please, refuse
Till the conversion of the Jews.
My vegetable love should grow
Vaster than empires, and more slow.
An hundred years should go to praise
Thine eyes, and on thy forehead gaze:
Two hundred to adore each breast:
But thirty thousand to the rest;
An age at least to every part,
And the last age should show your heart.
For, lady, you deserve this state,
Nor would I love at lower rate.
  But at my back I always hear
Time's wingèd chariot hurrying near:
And yonder all before us lie
Deserts of vast eternity.
Thy beauty shall no more be found;
Nor, in thy marble vault, shall sound
My echoing song: then worms shall try
That long-preserved virginity,
And your quaint honor turn to dust,
And into ashes all my lust.
The grave's a fine and private place,
But none, I think, do there embrace.
  Now, therefore, while the youthful hue
Sits on thy skin like morning dew,
And while thy willing soul transpires
At every pore with instant fires,

Now let us sport us while we may:
And now, like amorous birds of prey,
Rather at once our Time devour,
Than languish in his slow-chapt power.
Let us roll all our strength and all
Our sweetness up into one ball,
And tear our pleasures with rough strife
Through the iron gates of life.
Thus, though we cannot make our Sun
Stand still, yet we will make him run.

ANDREW MARVELL (1621–1678)

ALICE

Alice is tall and upright as a pine,
White as blanched almonds or the falling snow,
Sweet as are damask roses when they blow,
And doubtless fruitful as the swelling vine.

Ripe to be cut and ready to be pressed,
Her full-cheeked beauties very well appear;
And a year's fruit she loses every year,
Wanting a man to improve her to the best.

Full fain she would be husbanded; and yet,
Alas, she cannot a fit labourer get
To cultivate her to his own content.

Fain would she be (God wot) about her task,
And yet (forsooth) she is too proud to ask,
And (which is worse) too modest to consent.

CHARLES COTTON (1630–1687)

MARGARET

Margaret of humbler stature by the head
Is (as it oft falls out with yellow hair)
Than her fair sister, yet so much more fair
As her pure white is better mixed with red.

This, hotter than the other ten to one,
Longs to be put unto her mother's trade,
And loud proclaims she lives too long a maid,
Wishing for one to untie her virgin zone.

She finds virginity a kind of ware
That's very, very troublesome to bear,
And being gone she thinks will ne'er be missed:

And yet withal the girl has so much grace,
To call for help I know she wants the face,
Though, asked, I know not how she would resist.

CHARLES COTTON (1630–1687)

BENEATH A MYRTLE SHADE

(From: The Conquest of Granada)

Beneath a myrtle shade,
Which love for none but happy lovers made,
I slept; and straight my love before me brought
Phyllis, the object of my waking thought;
Undressed she came my flames to meet,
While Love strowed flowers beneath her feet;
Flowers which, so pressed by her, became more sweet.

From the bright vision's head
A careless veil of lawn was loosely spread:
From her white temples fell her shaded hair,
Like cloudy sunshine, not too brown nor fair:
Her hands, her lips, did love inspire;
Her every grace my heart did fire:
But most her eyes, which languished with desire.

"Ah, charming fair," said I,
"How long can you my bliss and yours deny?
By nature and by love this lonely shade
Was for revenge of suff'ring lovers made.
Silence and shades with love agree:
Both shelter you and favour me;
You cannot blush, because I cannot see."

"No, let me die," she said,
"Rather than lose the spotless name of maid!"
Faintly, methought, she spoke; for all the while
She bid me not believe her, with a smile.
"Then die," said I: she still denied:
"And is it thus, thus, thus," she cried,
"You use a harmless maid?"—and so she died!

I waked, and straight I knew
I loved so well, it made my dream prove true:

Fancy, the kinder mistress of the two,
Fancy had done what Phyllis would not do!
Ah, cruel nymph, cease your disdain;
While I can dream, you scorn in vain—
Asleep or waking, you must ease my pain.

JOHN DRYDEN (1631–1700)

WHILST ALEXIS LAY PREST

(From: Marriage a la Mode)

Whilst Alexis lay prest
    In her arms he loved best,
With his hands round her neck,
    And his head on her breast,
He found the fierce pleasure too hasty to stay,
And his soul in the tempest just flying away.

When Celia saw this,
With a sigh and a kiss,
She cried, "Oh, my dear, I am robbed of my bliss!
'Tis unkind to your love, and unfaithfully done,
To leave me behind you, and die all alone."

The youth, though in haste,
And breathing his last,
In pity died slowly, while she died more fast;
Till at length she cried, "Now, my dear, now let us go:
Now die, my Alexis, and I will die too!"

Thus entranced they did lie,
Till Alexis did try
To recover new breath, that again he might die:
Then often they died; but the more they did so,
The nymph died more quick, and the shepherd more slow.

JOHN DRYDEN (1631–1700)

LOVE'S FANCY

(From: An Evening's Love)

After the pangs of a desperate lover,
When a day and night I have sighed all in vain,
Ah, what a pleasure it is to discover,
In her eyes pity who causes my pain,

When with unkindness our love at a stand is,
And both have punish'd our selves with the pain,
Ah, what a pleasure the touch of her hand is!
Ah, what a pleasure to touch it again!

When the denial comes fainter and fainter,
And her eyes give what her tongue does deny,
Ah, what a trembling I feel when I venture,
Ah, what a trembling does usher my joy!

When, with a sigh, she accords me the blessing
And her eyes twinkle 'twixt pleasure and pain,
Ah, what a joy 'tis beyond all expressing!
Ah, what a joy to hear, "Shall we again?"

JOHN DRYDEN (1631–1700)

BENEATH A COOL SHADE

Beneath a cool shade, where some here have been,
Convenient for lovers, most pleasant and green,
Alexis and Chloris lay pressing soft flowers,
She close in his arms with her head on his breast,
And fainting with pleasure; you guess at the rest:
She blushed and she sighed with a joy beyond measure,
All ravished with billing and dying with pleasure.

But while thus in transports extended they lay,
A handsome young shepherd was passing that way.
She saw him and cried, "Oh, Alexis, betrayed!
Oh what have you done? You have ruined a maid!"
But the shepherd, being modest, discreetly past by,
And left them again at their leisure to die.
And often they languished with joy beyond measure,
All ravished with billing and dying with pleasure.

APHRA BEHN (1640–1689)

INDIAN SUMMER

Now that my Madelon knows at last
    That I'm wearing specs and slippers,
She is secretly bidding—fast—
    For one of the other skippers.

Well, you could say, the cargo shifts;
    But I'm used to such surprises.

Any vessel tosses and drifts
When the mast no longer rises.

N. BERTHELOT (about 1646)
Translated by DEEMS TAYLOR

UPON LEAVING HIS MISTRESS

'Tis not that I am weary grown
Of being yours, and yours alone;
But with what face can I incline
To damn you to be only mine—
You, whom some kinder power did fashion,
By merit, and by inclination,
The joy at least of a whole nation?

Let meaner spirits of your sex
With humble aims their thoughts perplex,
And boast if by their arts they can
Contrive to make one happy man;
While, moved by an impartial sense,
Favours, like Nature, you dispense
With universal influence.

See, the kind seed-receiving earth
To every grain affords a birth:
On her no showers unwelcome fall;
Her willing womb retains them all.
And shall my Celia be confined?
No, live up to thy mighty mind,
And be the mistress of mankind!

JOHN WILMOT, EARL OF ROCHESTER (1647–1680)

THE IMPERFECT ENJOYMENT

Naked she lay, clasped in my longing arms,
I filled with love, and she all over charms,
Both equally inspired with eager fire,
Melting through kindness, flaming in desire.
With arms, lips, legs close clinging to embrace,
She clips me to her breast, and sucks me to her face.
The nimble tongue (love's lesser lightning) played
Within my mouth, and to my thoughts conveyed
Swift orders that I should prepare to throw
The all-dissolving thunderbolt below.

My fluttering soul, sprung with the pointed kiss,
Hangs hovering o'er her balmy limbs of bliss.
But whilst her busy hand would guide that part
Which should convey my soul up to her heart,
In liquid raptness I dissolve all o'er,
Melting in love, such joys ne'er felt before.
A touch from any part of her had done't,
Her hand, her foot, her very looks had charms upon't.
Smiling, she chides in a soft murmuring noise,
And sighs to feel the too-too hasty joys;
When with a thousand kisses, wand'ring o'er
My panting breast—and is there then no more?
She cries: All this to love and raptures due,
Must we not pay a debt to pleasure too?

But I the most forlorn, lost man alive
To show my wish'd obedience vainly strive.
I sigh, alas, and kiss, but cannot drive.
Eager desires confound my first intent,
Succeeding shame does more success prevent,
And rage at last confirms me impotent.
Even her fair hands which might bid heat return
To frozen age, and make cold hermits burn,
Applied to my dead cinder warms no more
Than fire to ashes could past flames restore.
Trembling, confused, despairing, limber, dry,
A wishing, weak, unmoving lump I lie.
This dart of love, whose piercing point oft tried
With virgin blood, a hundred maids has dyed,
Which nature still directed with such art
That it, through every port, reached every heart.
Stiffly resolved, turned careless I invade,
Where it essayed, nor ought its fury stayed,
Where e'er it pierced, entrance it found or made,
Now languid lies, in this unhappy hour,
Shrunk up and sapless, like a withered flower.

Thou treacherous, base, deserter of my flame,
False to my passion, fatal to my fame,
By what mistaken magic dost thou prove
So true to lewdness, so untrue to love?
What oyster, cinder, beggar, common whore,
Didst thou e'er fail in all thy life before?
When vice, disease, and scandal led the way
With what officious haste didst thou obey?
Like a rude-roaring Hector in the streets

That scuffles, cuffs, and ruffles all he meets;
But if his King or country claim his aid
The rascal villain shrinks and hides his head;
E'en so is thy brutal valour displayed,
Breaks every stews, does each small crack invade,
But if great love the onset does command,
Base recreant to thy Prince, thou dost not stand.
Worst part of me and henceforth hated most,
Through all the town the common rubbing-post,
On whom each wretch relieves her lustfull want,
As hogs on goats do rub themselves and grunt,
May'st thou to ravenous shankers be a prey,
Or in consuming weepings waste away;
May stranguries and stone thy days attend.
May'st thou not piss who did'st so much offend
When all my joys did on false thee depend.
And may ten thousand abler men agree
To do the wrong'd Corinna right for thee.

JOHN WILMOT, EARL OF ROCHESTER (1647–1680)

MAN IS FOR WOMAN MADE

Man is for woman made,
And the woman made for man;
As the spur is for the jade,
As the scabbard for the blade,
As for digging is the spade,
As for liquor is the can,
So man is for the woman made
And the woman made for man.

As the sceptre's to be swayed,
As for night's the serenade,
As for pudding is the pan
And to cool us is the fan,
So man is for the woman made
And the woman made for man.

Be she widow, wife, or maid,
Be she wanton, be she staid,
Be she well or ill arrayed,
Whore, or bawd, or harridan,
Yet man is for the woman made
And the woman made for man.

PETER ANTHONY MOTTEUX (1660–1718)

TELL ME NO MORE

Tell me no more I am deceived,
    That Chloe's false and common;
By Heaven! I all along believed
    She was a very woman;
As such I liked, as such caressed,
She was constant—when possessed;
    She could do more for no man.

But oh! her thoughts on others ran,
    And that you think a hard thing?
Perhaps she fancied you the man?
    Why, what care I one farthing?
You think she's false, I'm sure she's kind,
I'll take her body, you her mind:
    Who has the better bargain?

WILLIAM CONGREVE (1670–1729)

ALL OR NOTHING

Pious Selinda goes to prayers
    If I but ask the favour;
And yet the tender fool's in tears
    When she believes I'll leave her.

Would I were free from this restraint,
    Or else had hopes to win her;
Would she could make of me a saint,
    Or I of her a sinner!

WILLIAM CONGREVE (1670–1729)

THE GERANIUM

In the close covert of a grove,
By nature formed for scenes of love,
Said Susan in a lucky hour,
Observe yon sweet geranium flower;
How straight upon its stalk it stands,
And tempts our violating hands:
Whilst the soft bud as yet unspread,
Hangs down its pale declining head:
Yet, soon as it is ripe to blow,
The stems shall rise, the head shall glow.

Nature, said I, my lovely Sue,
To all her followers lends a clue;
Her simple laws themselves explain,
As links of one continued chain;
For her the mysteries of creation,
Are but the works of generation:
Yon blushing, strong, triumphant flower,
Is in the crisis of its power:
But short, alas! its vigorous reign,
He sheds his seed, and drops again;
The bud that hangs in pale decay,
Feels, not, as yet, the plastic ray;
Tomorrow's sun shall bid him rise,
Then, too, he sheds his seed and dies:
But words, my love, are vain and weak,
For proof, let bright example speak;
Then straight before the wondering maid,
The tree of life I gently laid;
Observe, sweet Sue, his drooping head,
How pale, how languid, and how dead;
Yet, let the sun of thy bright eyes,
Shine but a moment, it shall rise;
Let but the dew of thy soft hand
Refresh the stem, it straight shall stand:
Already, see, it swells, it grows,
Its head is redder than the rose,
Its shrivelled fruit, of dusky hue,
Now glows, a present fit for Sue:
The balm of life each artery fills,
And in o'erflowing drops distils.
Oh me! cried Susan, when is this?
What strange tumultuous throbs of bliss!
Sure, never mortal, till this hour,
Felt such emotion at a flower:
Oh, serpent! cunning to deceive,
Sure, 'tis this tree that tempted Eve;
The crimson apples hang so fair,
Alas! what woman could forbear?
Well, hast thou guessed, my love, I cried,
It is the tree by which she died;
The tree which could content her,
All nature, Susan, seeks the centre;
Yet, let us still, poor Eve forgive,
It's the tree by which we live;
For lovely woman still it grows,

And in the centre only blows.
But chief for thee, it spreads its charms,
For paradise is in thy arms.—
I ceased, for nature kindly here
Began to whisper in her ear:
And lovely Sue lay softly panting,
While the geranium tree was planting.
'Til in the heat of amorous strife,
She burst the mellow tree of life.
"Oh, heaven!" cried Susan, with a sigh,
"The hour we taste—we surely die;
Strange raptures seize my fainting frame,
And all my body glows with flame;
Yet let me snatch one parting kiss
To tell my love I die with bliss:
That pleased, thy Susan yields her breath;
Oh! who would live if this be death!"

RICHARD BRINSLEY SHERIDAN (1751–1816)

A LAMENTABLE CASE

Ye famed physicians of this place,
Hear Strephon's and poor Chloe's case
    Nor think that I am joking;
When she would, he cannot comply;
When he would drink, she's not a-dry.
    And is this not provoking?

At night, when Strephon comes to rest,
Chloe receives him on her breast,
    With fondly folding arms:
Down, down he hangs his drooping head,
Falls fast asleep, and lies as dead,
    Neglecting all her charms.

Reviving when the morn returns,
With rising flames young Strephon burns,
    And then, would fain be doing:
But Chloe, now asleep or sick,
Has no great relish for the trick,
    And sadly balks his wooing.

O cruel and disastrous case,
When in the critical embrace
    That only one is burning!
Dear doctors, set this matter right;

> Give Strephon spirits over night,
>   Or Chloe in the morning.

CHARLES HANBURY-WILLIAMS (?–1764)

SODGER LADDIE

> I once was a maid, tho' I cannot tell when,
> An' still my delight is in proper young men;
> Some one of a troop of dragoons was my daddie,
> No wonder I'm fond of a sodger laddie.
>
> The first of my loves was a swaggering blade,
> To rattle the thundering drum was his trade;
> His leg was so tight, and his cheek was so ruddy,
> Transported I was with my sodger laddie.
>
> But the godly old chaplain left him in the lurch,
> The sword I forsook for the sake of the church,
> He ventured the soul, and I risk'd the body,
> 'Twas then I proved false to my sodger laddie.
>
> Full soon I grew sick of my sanctified sot.
> The regiment at large for a husband I got;
> From the gilded spontoon to the life I was ready,
> I asked no more but a sodger laddie.
>
> But the peace it reduced me to beg in despair,
> Till I met my old boy at a Cunningham fair;
> His rags regimental they fluttered so gaudy,
> My heart it rejoiced at my sodger laddie.
>
> An' now I have lived—I know not how long,
> An' still I can join in a cup or a song;
> But whilst with both hands I can hold the glass steady,
> Here's to thee, my hero, my sodger laddie.

ROBERT BURNS (1759–1796)

GODLY GIRZIE

> The night it was a holy night,
>   The day had been a holy day;
> Kilmarnock gleam'd wi' candle light,
>   As Girzie hameward took her way,
> A man of sin, ill may he thrive!
>   And never holy meeting see!
> With godly Girzie met belyve,
>   Among the Craigie hills sae hie.

The chiel' was wight, the chiel' was stark,
    He was na wait to chap nor ca',
And she was faint wi' holy wark;
    She had no pith to say him na.
But ay she glowr'd up to the moon,
    And ay she sigh'd most piouslie,
"I trust my heart's in heaven aboon,
    "Whare'er your sinfu' pintle be."

ROBERT BURNS (1759–1796)

FROM: THE FESTIVAL OF LOVE (1789)

THE CAUTIOUS STRUGGLE

Be quiet, sir! Begone, I say!
Lord bless us, how you romp and tear!
        There!
        I swear!
Now you have laid my bosom bare!

I do not like such boisterous play,
So take that saucy hand away. . . .
Why! Now you're ruder than before!
Nay, I'll be hanged if I comply—
        Fie!
        I'll cry!
Oh, I can't bear it—I shall die!
I vow I'll never see you more!
But—are you sure you shut the door?

AUTHOR UNKNOWN

A LOGICAL SONG

Why, Chloe, thus squander your prime
    In debate between fear and temptation?
If adulterous love be a crime,
    Why quarrel with plain fornication?

Your beauties with age you may lose;
    Then seize the short moment of joy.
If not, then with confidence use
    What by using you cannot destroy.

Come, come, bid our raptures begin
    Ere we lose both our youth and our leisure.

'Tis better repenting a sin
   Than regretting the loss of a pleasure.

AUTHOR UNKNOWN

THE DISAPPOINTED MAID

As Dolly and her favorite swain
Were interrupted by the rain,
From tedding out the fragrant hay;
Beneath a sheltering cock they lay:
When thus the lovely, longing jade,
Unto the drowsy shepherd said,
"Nay, prithee Lobby, why so sleepy?
Indeed, upon my word I'll nip ye.
How pretty might we sit and chat,
Tell o'er old stories, and all that.
But you—O Lord, the careless beast!
As if folks lie down to take rest."

Lob, half asleep, made no replies,
Or answered with a grunt her sighs.
While she to be revenged, arose,
And played a tickler on his nose.
(But come, the virgin to disgrace,
We'll say, 'twas in another place.)
Be that as 'twill, she waked the swain,
And tickled him with words again.
"Come sweeting, Lobby, come my dear,
I'm sure that nobody is near;
Indeed we may, pray be'n't afraid,
Poor I am, but an harmless maid.
For since you're so disposed to rest,
Pray take a nap upon my breast.
You see time, leisure, place, and all
For such enjoyment seem to call.
And you remember people say,
When the sun shines, then make your hay."

"Augh! augh!" quoth Lob, waked with surprise,
To see the sun flame in his eyes.
"Heigh Ho! Come Doll, for as you say.
The sun shines, we must make our hay.
So reach me there my rake and prong,
'Twas well you waked—we've slept too long."

WILLIAM PATTISON (Eighteenth century)

THE PENITENT NUN

Dame Jane a sprightly nun and gay,
And formed of very yielding clay,
Had long with resolution strove
To guard against the shafts of love.
Fond Cupid smiling, spies the fair,
And soon he baffles all her care;
In vain she tries her pain to smother,
The nymph too frail becomes a mother.

But once these little follies o'er,
She firmly vows she'll sin no more;
No more to vice will fall a prey,
But spend in prayer each fleeting day.
Close in her cell immured she lies,
Nor from the cross removes her eyes;
While sisters crowding at the gate,
Spend all their time in worldly prate.

The abbess, overjoyed to find
This happy change in Jenny's mind,
The rest, with air composed, addressing,
"Daughters, if you expect a blessing,
From pious Jane, example take,
The world and all its joys forsake."
"We will," they all replied as one,
"But first let's do as Jane has done."

JOHN LOCKMAN (Eighteenth century)

VOLTAIRE (1694–1778)

François Marie Arouet, who wrote under the name of Voltaire, died as he had lived, scoffing. He was born in Paris toward the end of the seventeenth century and was in ill health and trouble most of his life. Poet, dramatist, philosopher, essayist and historian, he was a consistent non-conformer in every field, a thorn in every respectable side. His godfather was a clergyman, the Abbé of Chateauneuf, who introduced him to the literary and aristocratic world, with which Voltaire immediately took issue. At twenty-two he wrote a libelous lampoon and was exiled from Paris. A few years later he served on a rather dubious diplomatic mission. At thirty-two he crossed swords with an influential noble, was imprisoned, and ran off to

England. There he met Pope and Swift, who greatly influenced him, and, on his return, Voltaire introduced Shakespeare to France. Soon after this he was again in trouble. This time two of his books offended the authorities; they were burned and Voltaire was once more an exile. He found important patrons but quarreled with them. He was fifty-seven when he went to Berlin at the invitation of Frederick of Prussia, but he was no happier in Germany than he had been in France. He saw rivals everywhere, sneered at Lessing, the favorite dramatist, and resented the King himself.

What began as an intellectual partnership between an ideal monarch and a challenging intellectual degenerated into recriminations, and after three years Voltaire retired to a small town near Geneva, Switzerland, where he became known as "the Squire of Ferney." There he devoted himself to unremitting warfare against all forms of intolerance, superstition, injustice, organized religion and oppressive orthodoxy. At eighty-four he returned to Paris, which he had not seen in thirty years, and was received with so much honor and so many ceremonies that the shock was too much for him. He died, it is said, of excitement. When the priests arrived to administer the last sacrament and reclaim the renegade, Voltaire refused absolution, saying, "Let me die in peace," and closed his eyes.

Candide, his masterpiece, is a philosophical fairy tale, an extended burlesque, a rough satire on the school of optimists, which maintains that "all is for the best in this best of all possible worlds." A relentless foe of complacency and the status quo, Voltaire sends his guileless hero, Candide, through a cruel world attended by his tutor, Dr. Pangloss, who is the epitome of Pope's belief that "whatever is, is right." One calamity after another happens: rapes, murders, earthquakes, plagues, drownings, and unspeakable outrages. But nothing disturbs the travelers' equanimity, and at last Candide marries ugly Cunégonde, the once-beautiful sweetheart of his youth, and placidly settles down to cultivate his garden.

FROM: CANDIDE

HOW CANDIDE WAS BROUGHT UP IN A SPLENDID CASTLE AND HOW HE WAS EXPELLED FROM IT

In a Westphalian castle belonging to the Baron Thunder-ten-Tronckh, there lived a young man endowed by nature with the finest character. His face was the mirror of his soul. He combined honest judgment with simplicity of spirit—this, I suspect, being the reason he was called Candide. The old family servants thought he was the son of the Baron's sister by a respectable gentleman of the neighborhood, but whom the lady would never marry because his coat of arms could boast only seventy-one quarterings, the rest of his genealogical tree having been lost due to the ravages of time.

The Baron was one of the most powerful lords in all Westphalia, for his castle had not only a gate but windows. His Great Hall actually showed a piece of tapestry. The farmyard dogs became a pack of hounds whenever necessary, the grooms were his huntsmen, and the village curate was his Grand Almoner. Everyone called him "My Lord" and laughed at his stories.

The Baroness weighed about three hundred and fifty pounds; therefore she was greatly respected. She did the honors of the house with a dignity that made her still more an object of respect. Her daughter Cunégonde was seventeen years old, comely, fresh-colored, prettily plump, and in every way desirable. The Baron's son was altogether worthy of his father. The tutor Pangloss was the oracle of the family, and little Candide heard his lessons with all the good faith of his age and character.

Pangloss was professor of metaphysicotheologico-cosmolonigology. He proved admirably that there is no effect without a cause, and that, in this best of all possible worlds, the Baron's castle was the most magnificent of castles, and his lady the best of all possible baronesses.

"It is demonstrable," said he, "that things cannot be otherwise than as they are; for all being created for an end, all is necessarily for the best end. Observe, that the nose has been formed to bear spectacles—thus we have spectacles. Legs are visibly designed for stockings—and we have stockings. Stones were made to be hewn, and to construct castles—therefore my lord has a magnificent castle; for the greatest baron in the province ought to be the best lodged. Pigs were made to be eaten—therefore we eat pork all the year round. Consequently they who assert that all is well have said a foolish thing, they should have said all is for the best."

Candide listened attentively and believed innocently; for he thought Miss Cunégonde extremely beautiful, though he never had the courage to tell her so. He concluded that after the happiness of being born Baron of Thunder-ten-Tronckh, the second degree of happiness was to be Miss Cunégonde, the third that of seeing her every day, and the fourth that of hearing Master Pangloss, the greatest philosopher of the whole province, and consequently of the whole world.

One day Cunégonde, while walking near the castle in a little wood which they called a park, saw Dr. Pangloss in the bushes, giving a lesson in experimental physics to her mother's chambermaid, a little brown wench, very pretty and very docile. As Miss Cunégonde had a great disposition for the sciences, she breathlessly observed the repeated experiments of which she was a witness; she clearly perceived the force of the doctor's reasons, the effects, and the causes; she turned back greatly flurried, quite pensive, and filled with the desire to be learned; dreaming that she might well be a sufficient reason for young Candide, and he for her.

She met Candide on reaching the castle and blushed; Candide blushed also; she wished him good morrow in a faltering tone, and Candide spoke to her without knowing what he said. The next day after dinner, as they went from table, Cunégonde and Candide found themselves behind a screen; Cunégonde let fall her handkerchief, Candide picked it up, she took him innocently by the hand, the youth as innocently kissed the young lady's hand with particular vivacity, sensibility, and grace; their lips met, their eyes sparkled, their knees trembled, their hands strayed. Baron Thunder-ten-Tronckh passed near the screen and beholding this cause and effect chased Candide from the castle with great kicks on the backside. Cunégonde fainted away; she was boxed on the ears by the Baroness as soon as she came to herself; and all was consternation in this most splendid and most agreeable of all possible castles.

THE ADVENTURES OF THE OLD WOMAN

"I did not always have bleary eyes and red eyelids," said the old woman, "neither did my nose always touch my chin; nor was I always a servant. I am the daughter of Pope Urban X and the Princess of Palestrina. Until I was fourteen I was brought up in a palace, to which all the castles of your German barons would scarcely have served for stables; and one of my robes was worth more than all the magnificence of Westphalia. As I grew up I improved in beauty, wit, and every graceful accomplishment, in the midst of pleasures, hopes and respectful homage. Already I inspired love. My throat was formed—and such a throat!—white, firm, and shaped like that of the Venus of Medici. And what eyes! What eyelids! What black eyebrows! Such flames darted from my dark pupils that they eclipsed the scintillation of the stars, as I was told by the poets in our part of the world. My waiting women, when dressing and undressing me, used to fall into an ecstasy, whether they viewed me before or behind. How glad would the gentlemen have been to perform that office for them!

"I was betrothed to the most excellent Prince of Massa Carara. Such a prince! As handsome as myself, sweet-tempered, agreeable, brilliantly witty, and sparkling with love. I loved him as one loves for the first time—with idolatry, with transport. The nuptials were prepared. There was surprising pomp and magnificence; there were fetes, revels, routs, continual comic operas. All Italy composed sonnets in my praise, though not one of them was passable. I was just upon the point of reaching the summit of bliss, when an old marchioness who had been mistress to the Prince, my husband, invited him to drink chocolate with her. He died in less than two hours of most terrible convulsions. But this is only a bagatelle. My mother, in despair, and scarcely less afflicted than myself, determined to absent herself for some time from so fatal a place. She had a very fine estate in the neighborhood of Gaeta. We embarked on board a galley of the country which was gilded like the great altar of St. Peter's at Rome. A Sallee corsair swooped down and boarded us. Our men defended themselves like the Pope's soldiers; they flung themselves upon their knees and threw down their arms, begging of the corsair an absolution *in articulo mortis*.

"Instantly they were stripped as bare as monkeys; my mother, our maids of honor, and myself were all served in the same manner. It is amazing with what expedition those gentry undress people. But what surprised me most was that they thrust their fingers into the part of our bodies which the generality of women suffer no other instrument but—pipes to enter. It appeared to me a very strange kind of ceremony; but thus one judges of things when one has not seen the world. I afterward learned that it was to try whether we had concealed any diamonds. This is the practice established from time immemorial among civilized nations that scour the seas. I was informed that the very religious knights of Malta never fail to make this search when they take any Turkish prisoners of either sex. It is a law of nations from which they never deviate.

"I need not tell *you* how great a hardship it was for a young princess and her mother to be made slaves and carried to Morocco. You may easily imagine all we had to suffer on board the pirate vessel. My mother was still very handsome; our maids of honor, and even our waiting women, had more charms than are to be found in all Africa. As for myself, I was ravishing, was exquisite, grace itself, and I was a virgin! I did not remain so long; this flower, which had been reserved for the handsome Prince of Massa Carara, was plucked by the corsair captain. He was an abominable Negro and yet believed that he did me a great deal of honor. Certainly the Princess of Palestrina and myself must have been very strong to go through all that we experienced until our arrival at Morocco. But let us pass on; these are such common things as not to be worth mentioning.

"Morocco swam in blood when we arrived. Fifty sons of the Emperor Muley-Ismael had each their adherents; this produced fifty civil wars, of blacks against blacks, and blacks against tawnies, and tawnies against tawnies, and mulattoes against mulattoes. In short it was a continual carnage throughout the empire.

"No sooner were we landed, than the blacks of a contrary faction to that of my captain attempted to rob him of his booty. Next to jewels and gold we were the most valuable things he had. I was witness to such a battle as you have never seen in your European climates. The northern nations have not that heat in their blood, nor that raging lust for women, so common in Africa. It seems that you Europeans have only milk in your veins; but it is vitriol, it is fire which runs in those of the inhabitants of Mount Atlas and the neighboring countries. They fought with the fury of the lions, tigers, and serpents of the country, to see who should have us. A Moor seized my mother by the right arm, while my captain's lieutenant held her by the left; a Moorish soldier had hold of her by one leg and one of our corsairs held her by the other. Thus almost all our women were drawn in quarters by four men. My captain concealed me behind him and with his drawn scimitar cut and slashed every one that opposed his fury. At length I saw all our Italian women and my mother herself torn, mangled, massacred, by the monsters who disputed over them. The slaves, my companions, those who had taken them, soldiers, sailors, blacks, whites, mulattoes, and at last my captain, all were killed, and I remained dying on the heap of dead. Such scenes as this were transacted through an extent of three hundred leagues—and yet they never failed to recite the five prayers a day ordained by Mahomet.

"With great difficulty I disengaged myself from such a heap of slaughtered bodies, and crawled to a large orange tree on the bank of a neighboring rivulet where I fell, oppressed with fright, fatigue, horror, despair, and hunger. Immediately after, my senses, overpowered, gave themselves up to sleep, which was yet more swooning than repose. I was in this state of weakness and insensibility, between life and death, when I felt myself pressed by something that moved upon my body. I opened my eyes and saw a white man of good appearance who sighed, and who said between his teeth: '*O che sciagura d'essere senza coglioni!*'[1]

"Astonished and delighted to hear my native language, and no less surprised at what this man said, I made answer that there were much greater misfortunes than that of which he complained. I told him in a few words of the horrors which I had endured and fainted a second time. He carried me to a neighboring house, put me to bed, gave me food, waited upon me, consoled me, flattered me; he told me that he had never seen any one so beautiful as I and that he never so much regretted the loss of what it was impossible to recover.

" 'I was born at Naples,' said he. 'There they geld two or three thousand children every year. Some die of the operation; others acquire a voice more beautiful than that of women; and others are raised to offices of state. This operation was performed on me with great success and I was chapel musician to madam, the Princess of Palestrina.'

" 'To my mother!' cried I.

" 'Your mother!' cried he, weeping. 'What! can you be that young princess whom I brought up until the age of six years, and who promised so early to be as beautiful as you?'

" 'It is I, indeed; but my mother lies four hundred yards hence, torn in quarters, under a heap of dead bodies.'

"I told him all my adventures and he made me acquainted with his; telling me that he had been sent to the Emperor of Morocco by a Christian power, to conclude a treaty with that prince, in consequence of which he was to be furnished with military stores and ships to help to demolish the commerce of other Christian governments.

" 'My mission is done,' said the honest eunuch; 'I go to embark for Ceuta, and will take you to Italy. *Ma che sciagura d'essere senza coglioni!*'

"I thanked him with tears of commiseration; and instead of taking me to Italy he conducted me to Algiers where he sold me to the Dey. Scarcely was I sold, than the plague which had made the tour of Africa, Asia, and Europe, broke out with great malignancy in Algiers. You have seen earthquakes; but pray, miss, have you ever had the plague?"

"Never," answered Cunégonde.

---

[1] 'Oh, what a misfortune to be a eunuch!'

"If you had," said the old woman, "you would acknowledge that it is far more terrible than an earthquake. It is common in Africa, and I caught it. Imagine to yourself the distressed situation of the daughter of a Pope, only fifteen years old, who, in less than three months, had felt the miseries of poverty and slavery, had been ravished almost every day, had beheld her mother drawn in quarters, had experienced famine and war, and was dying of the plague in Algiers. I did not die, however, but my eunuch, and the Dey, and almost the whole seraglio of Algiers perished.

"As soon as the first fury of this terrible pestilence was over, a sale was made of the Dey's slaves; I was purchased by a merchant, and carried to Tunis; this man sold me to another merchant, who sold me again to another at Tripoli; from Tripoli I was sold to Alexandria, from Alexandria to Smyrna, and from Smyrna to Constantinople. At length I became the property of an aga of the Janissaries, who was soon ordered away to the defence of Azof, then besieged by the Russians.

"The Aga, who was a very gallant man, took his whole seraglio with him, and lodged us in a small fort on the Palus Méotides, guarded by two black eunuchs and twenty soldiers. The Turks killed prodigious numbers of the Russians, but the latter had their revenge. Azof was destroyed by fire, the inhabitants put to the sword, neither sex nor age was spared; until there remained only our little fort and the enemy wanted to starve us out. The twenty Janissaries had sworn they would never surrender. The extremities of famine to which they were reduced obliged them to eat our two eunuchs, for fear of violating their oath. And at the end of a few days they resolved also to devour the women.

"We had a very pious and humane Iman, who preached an excellent sermon, exhorting them not to kill us all at once.

"'Only cut off a buttock of each of those ladies,' said he, 'and you'll fare extremely well; if you must go to it again, there will be the same entertainment a few days hence; heaven will accept of so charitable an action, and send you relief.'

"He had great eloquence; he persuaded them; we underwent this terrible operation. The Iman applied the same balsam to us as he does to children after circumcision; and we all nearly died.

"Scarcely had the Janissaries finished the repast with which we had furnished them, than the Russians came in flat-bottomed boats; not a Janissary escaped. The Russians paid no attention to the condition we were in. There are French surgeons in all parts of the world; one of them who was very clever took us under his care—he cured us; and as long as I live I shall remember that as soon as my wounds were healed he made proposals to me. He bid us all be of good cheer, telling us that the like had happened in many sieges and that it was according to the laws of war.

"As soon as my companions could walk they were obliged to set out for Moscow. I fell to the share of a boyard who made me his gardener and gave me twenty lashes a day. But this nobleman having in two years' time been broke upon the wheel along with thirty more boyards for some broils at court, I profited by that event; I fled. I traversed all Russia; I was a long time an innholder's servant at Riga, the same at Rostock, at Vismar, at Leipzig, at Cassel, at Utrecht, at Leyden, at The Hague, at Rotterdam. I waxed old in misery and disgrace, having only one half of my posteriors, and always remembering I was a Pope's daughter. A hundred times I was upon the point of killing myself; but still I loved life. This ridiculous foible is perhaps one of our most fatal characteristics; for is there anything more absurd than to wish to carry continually a burden which one can always throw down, to detest existence and yet to cling to one's existence—in brief, to caress the serpent which devours us, till he has eaten our very heart?

"In the different countries which it has been my lot to traverse and the numerous inns in which I have been a servant, I have taken notice of a vast number of people who held their own existence in abhorrence, and yet I never knew of more than eight who voluntarily put an end to their misery; three Negroes, four Englishmen, and a German professor named Robek. I ended by being servant to the Jew, Don Issachar, who placed me near your presence, my fair lady. I am determined to share your fate and have been much more affected with your misfortunes than with my own. I would never even have spoken to you of my misfortunes had you not piqued me a little, and if it were not customary to tell stories on board ship in order to pass away the time. In short, Miss Cunégonde, I have had experience, I know the world. Therefore I advise you to divert yourself and prevail upon each passenger to tell his story. And if there be one of them all that has not cursed his life many a time, that has not frequently looked upon himself as the unhappiest of mortals, I give you leave to throw me headfirst into the sea."

FROM: THE PHILOSOPHICAL DICTIONARY

The Philosophical Dictionary *voices some of the irony of* Candide *in penetrating, bitter, and often heretical epigrams. In these condensed thoughts Voltaire's wisdom, wit, and wicked commentary are inextricably interwoven. The adaptation, from the Peter Pauper Press volume entitled* Voltaire's Alphabet of Wit, *is by Paul McPharlin.*

ADULTERY

This term is not heard in good company. We do not say, "Madame la Duchesse lives in adultery with Monsieur le Chevalier," or "Madame la Marquise has criminal relations with Monsieur l'Abbé." We say, "This week Monsieur l'Abbé is the lover of Madame la Marquise." Ladies discussing with their friends their adulteries remark, "I confess I'm rather fond of him." They used to confess they felt "some esteem," but since the time a certain wife told her confessor that she had esteem for a high official, and he asked how many proofs of esteem there had been given, ladies of quality have esteemed no one—and gone but little to confession.

About the year 1764 a French judge was so unfortunate as to marry a woman who had been led astray by a priest, and who continued to waver of her own accord. He was obliged to leave her. Being, however, but forty and in lusty health, he needed a companion. Too scrupulous to seek another man's wife, and too fearful to consort with prostitutes, he pleaded earnestly with the Church:

"My wife erred and I am the one to suffer. A woman is necessary to me. Without one how can I keep my virtue? Yet you refuse her to me; I cannot marry another. You compel me to take pleasure which you reprobate or consolation which you condemn. You force me to be a criminal. Your priests and monks may abstain from women if need be; I have no objections. It checks the increase in population. They suffer misfortune they have contrived for themselves. But I, a judge who serves mankind all day, have need of a little womankind at night."

Then there was the Countess D'Arcira of Portugal, a wife who made this plea before a junta: "The Gospels forbid adultery both to my husband and me. He has been guilty of fifty infidelities—he gave my necklace to one woman, my earrings to another—and I have imitated him only once, and then with the handsomest young man in Lisbon. Must I then answer questions before a panel of men, any one of whom would lose no time in such nonsense if he were alone with me? Must I have this lovely hair cut off? Must I be confined with nuns? Must I be deprived of the fortune I brought my husband so that he can go on with his seductions and adulteries? Is this justice?"

It would appear that, in order to assure a just verdict in an action for adultery, the jury should be composed of six men and six women, and—in the event of a tie—a hermaphrodite to cast the deciding vote.

IMPOTENCE

The canon law made considerable to-do of the question of impotence. Might a man who was prevented by sorcery from consummating his first marriage, after being divorced and having children by a second wife—might he, on the death of the second, still reject his first wife should she lay claim to him? All the great canonists decided in the negative: De Nevo, Alberic, Turrecremata, Soto, and fifty more.

It is impossible to help admiring the sagacity exhibited by the canonists, especially for the knowledge those irreproachable celibates had of the mysteries of sexual intercourse. There is no aberration, however strange, on which they did not hold forth. They discussed at length all the cases in which capability may exist at one time, and impotence in another. They inquired into all the ingenious devices to assist nature, and with the avowed object of pronouncing what is allowable and what is not, exposed all which might have remained veiled.

Sanchez especially distinguished himself by collecting cases of conscience which the boldest wife would hesitate to submit to her most prudent confidante. One query led to another in interminable succession, until the ultimate was reached in the extraordinary examination of the manner of communication of the Holy Ghost with the Virgin Mary.

Such exhaustive researches had never before been made, and could never have been made save by theologians.

In the Gospels divorce is spoken of as allowable for adultery alone. Jewish law permitted a husband to repudiate a wife who displeased him, without specifying the cause—"if she found no favor in his eyes." This law says nothing of impotence. It would appear, remarks a casuist, that God provided no impotence among a people who were to multiply like the sands on the shore, and to inherit the vast territory between the Nile and the Euphrates; indeed, to become lords of the earth. To fulfill divine promises, every honest Jew would have to labor unceasingly at the great work of propagation. There was certainly a curse upon impotence. The time had not yet arrived for the devout to live as eunuchs for the kingdom of heaven.

Marriage having arrived in the course of time at the dignity of a sacrament, the ecclesiastics naturally became judges of all which took place between husband and wife, and not only that, but also all which did *not* take place.

The most important proof of capability required from persons accused of impotence was that called "the congress." This combat in an enclosed field was adopted in France in the fourteenth century. It was not conducted exactly as people have imagined. It was supposed that a conjugal consummation took place under the inspection of physicians, surgeons, and midwives, but such was not the case. The parties went to bed in the usual manner, and at a proper time the inspectors, waiting in the next room, were called in to pronounce upon the case.

In the famous process of the Marquis de Langeais, decided in 1659, he demanded the congress; but thanks to the management of his lady, Marie de St. Simon, did not succeed. He demanded a second trial but the judges, tired of the outcries of the superstitious, the plaints of the prudes, and the raillery of the wits, refused it. They declared the Marquis impotent and his marriage void, forbade him to marry again, and allowed his wife to take another husband.

The Marquis disregarded this sentence, married the lovely Diana de Navailles, and by her had seven children!

INCUBI

Have there ever been incubi and succubi? Even though you doubt it, our learned jurisconsults and demonologists have proved both to exist.

It is supposed that Satan, always a very busy person, spends time producing heated dreams in young ladies and gentlemen, and by a sort of double process achieves the same end which resulted in so many heroes and demigods of old. He certainly took superfluous trouble, for he could have left the young people alone, and without his assistance the world would have been sufficiently supplied with heroes.

The ancient gods frequently disguised themselves, in the pursuit of human girls, as eagles, pigeons, swans, horses, or showers of gold, but the goddesses assumed no disguise, having only to show themselves to gain their objective. It is presumed that, whatever shapes the gods assumed, they consummated their loves in the convenient and more compatible form of men.

In accepting a demonistic scheme (less noble and decorous than that of the deities of antiquity) we believed a girl might be rendered pregnant by the ministry of the devil. We cannot doubt that this is possible, for the Sorbonne decided it to be true in 1318, and the decision has never been revoked. We are bound to believe in incubi and succubi, because our professors have evidently always believed in them. And not only they. Bodin, in his book about sorcerers, tells of Jean Hervilier, a native of Verberie, who was condemned by the Parliament of Paris to be burned alive for having prostituted his daughter to the devil. We learn that the embraces of this personage, who appeared as a big black man, were attended with a sensation of cold, which would seem rather contrary to his constitution.

The celebrated Picus of Mirandola—a prince never lies—says he knew an old man of eighty who had slept half his life with a female demon, and another of seventy who had enjoyed a similar felicity. Both are buried at Rome. That proves beyond doubt the existence of incubi and succubi. At least it is impossible to disprove it. If a demon can enter our bodies, why can he not take the same liberty with our wives and daughters? If there are demons, there must of course be demonesses. For the one to beget children on our women, there must be the other for us to use likewise. The empire of the devil is indeed universal.

Or was, until reason unthroned him.

LOVE

There are so many kinds of love that, in defining it, one must be specific. Some apply the term to a caprice of a few days, a connection without attachment, a passion without affection, a pretense, a gallantry, a mere ceremony, a romantic fancy, a taste followed quickly by distaste. It is applied to innumerable fantasies.

Should a philosopher be inclined to make an exhaustive research into a subject so unphilosophical, he might begin with Plato's *Symposium*, wherein Socrates, the decent and honorable lover of Alcibiades and Agathon, converses with them on the metaphysics of love. Lucretius speaks of it as a philosopher; so does Virgil.

It is an imaginative embroidery on the stuff of nature. Look at the sparrows in your garden; see your doves; observe the bull as he meets the heifer; regard that powerful, spirited stallion which a couple of your grooms are leading to the mare who quietly waits, evidently pleased at his approach; catch the flash in his eye, hear his resonant, melodious neighing, notice his springing and curveting, his pointed ears, his mouth open and convulsively gasping, his distended nostrils, his fiery breath, his erect, waving mane, and the impetuous dash with which he rushes toward what nature has destined for him; do not, however, envy him his pleasure, but reflect on the advantages which the human species have in love, as a compensation for the strength, beauty and celerity of mere animals.

Most of the animals which copulate take pleasure through but a single sense; when appetite is satisfied, all is over. No animal but man knows fondling; his whole body is sensitive to it; his lips particularly experience an unwearying delight which belongs to his species alone; finally, he is alive to the endearments of love at all seasons, while mere animals know them only for limited periods. If you reflect on this lofty preëminence, you will agree with the Earl of Rochester's remark that love would impel a whole nation of atheists to worship God.

As men have a faculty of perfecting what nature has bestowed, they have improved upon the gift of love. Cleanliness, good care, and health render the body more sensitive and increase its capacity for pleasure. All amiable and estimable qualities merge into love, as metals amalgamate with gold; friendship and respect rally to its support; excellence both of mind and body strengthens its bonds.

Such are the advantages possessed by man over the animals. But if he has pleasures unknown to them, how many pains does he have that they are free of! The most dreadful of these come from a disease to which man alone is subject, which has poisoned the pleasures of love and sources of life over most of the globe. This is not, like other maladies, a consequence of excess. It was not introduced through debauchery. The Phrynes and Laïses, the Floras and Messalinas, never had it. It originated in islands where man dwelt in innocence, whence it has spread throughout the civilized world. If nature could be accused of despising her own work, thwarting her own scheme, and quarreling with her own impulses it would be in this horrible scourge. And can this then be, in the best of all possible worlds? If Caesar and Anthony and Octavius never had the disease, why should Francis I have died of it? Things seem to be so ordered—unfortunately for those to whom Rabelais dedicated his book.

NAKEDNESS

Why do we hasten to lock up a man found naked in the street, when we take no offense at statues in the same state, or paintings of Jesus and Mary Magdalen in certain churches? It is probable that man got along for a good while before he discovered raiment. In more than one South Sea island, and in America, there are still people ignorant of the art of the tailor.

The more civilized primitive peoples deck their privy parts with leaves, rushwork, and feathers. Is this the concealment of modesty or the veiling of what nature provokes our desire to discover?

There are saints of Islam who go about bare as apes. It is possible that such madmen think it more proper to present themselves before the Deity as He made them, than under disguises of their own invention. They may have exposed themselves in an ecstasy of chastity, for there are so few well-made specimens of either sex that nakedness does nothing to arouse desire.

In even more polished levels of culture there are sects which, in worshiping God, deprive themselves of clothing. Such have been the Adamites and the Abelians, who assembled naked to sing the praises of God. It is also recorded that the Abelians renounced marriage. If they had very many lusty youths or amorous maidens, they could not have been too much like St. Adhelm or the happy Robert D'Arbriselle, who lay with the most luscious of ladies only to prove the strength of their continence.

I must confess to thinking that it must have been pleasant to see a hundred naked Helens and Parises singing anthems, giving one another the kiss of peace, and performing the ceremonies of the *agape*.[1]

BENJAMIN FRANKLIN (1706-1790)

Prototype of the ideal American, Benjamin Franklin was an itinerant journalist who became a universal figure, a great statesman, a printer who was also a poet as well as a philosopher, a humorist, scientist, and well-loved man of the world. He invented things as varied as the lightning rod, bifocal glasses, a new kind of stove, musical instruments and incidentally, it has been said, the Republic. Sent to France at the time of the Declaration of Independence, Franklin was so successful a diplomat that he raised sixty million dollars to finance the Revolution; his reputation in Europe was greater than that of Newton or Voltaire.

All this was achieved by a man who had no important family connections, no influential friends, and practically no education. The tenth of seventeen children, son of a candlemaker, Franklin had to quit school at the age of ten to help his father. When he was seventeen he was apprenticed to a printer and sent off to Philadelphia with a dollar in his pocket. He was in his mid-twenties when he started one of the first circulating libraries in the United States and, under the pseudonym of Richard Saunders, wrote and published the first issue of Poor Richard's Almanac, *a paper which was to run for a*

[1] The agape was a love feast among the early Christians. It ended with a "holy kiss."

quarter of a century. In between his editorial chores he managed to acquire conversational French, Spanish, Italian, and a working knowledge of Latin. At thirty he served as clerk of the General Assembly, became postmaster at Philadelphia, organized the first fire company and police force in America, built hospitals, started debating societies, was both a signer and framer of the Declaration of Independence. At seventy he was the world's most widely respected American.

A favorite story concerns a public meeting between Voltaire and Franklin, who was accompanied by his grandson. Both men conversed in English until they realized that those around them did not understand what was being said. Whereupon Voltaire informed the company in French that he would give the boy his blessing and, turning to the lad, he said in English: "God and Liberty," whereupon Franklin repeated the words in French.

Franklin, the author, was as distinctive as Franklin, the statesman. He had a style of his own, sharp but without malice, lively, loose, and genial. His Autobiography, revered as a classic and enjoyed as a living document, reveals the humanist and wit who was a natural Jack-of-all-trades and master of every one. His versatility is shown in the following selections: little whimsical pieces, "bagatelles," which, though not well known, are highly characteristic of his diverting and lightly ribald vein.

ADVICE ON THE CHOICE OF A MISTRESS

Philadelphia, June 25, 1745

My dear Friend:

I know of no medicine fit to diminish the violent natural inclinations you mention, and if I did, I think I should not communicate it to you. Marriage is the proper remedy. It is the most natural state of man, and therefore the state in which you are most likely to find solid happiness. Your reasons against entering into it at present appear to me not well founded. The circumstantial advantages you have in view by postponing it are not only uncertain, but they are small in comparison with that of the thing itself, the being married and settled. It is the man and woman united that make the complete human being. Separate, she wants his force of body and strength of reason; he, her softness, sensibility, and acute discernment. Together they are more likely to succeed in the world. A single man has not nearly the value he would have in the state of union. He is an incomplete animal. He resembles the odd half of a pair of scissors. If you get a prudent, healthy wife, your industry in your profession, with her good economy, will be a fortune sufficient.

But if you will *not* take this counsel and persist in thinking a commerce with the sex inevitable, then I repeat my former advice, that in all your amours you should prefer old women to young ones.

You call this a paradox and demand my reasons. They are these:

1. Because they have more knowledge of the world and their minds are better stored with observations, their conversation is more improving and more lastingly agreeable.

2. Because when women cease to be handsome they study to be good. To maintain their influence over men, they supply the diminution of beauty by an augmentation of utility. They learn to do a thousand services small and great, and are the most tender and useful of friends when you are sick. Thus they continue amiable. And hence there is hardly such a thing to be found as an old woman who is not a good woman.

3. Because there is no hazard of children, which irregularly produced may be attended with much inconvenience.

4. Because through more experience they are more prudent and discreet in conducting an intrigue to prevent suspicion. The commerce with them is therefore safer with regard to your reputation. And with regard to theirs, if the affair should happen to be known, considerate people might be rather inclined to excuse an old woman, who would kindly take care of a young man, form his manners by her good counsels, and prevent his ruining his health and fortune among mercenary prostitutes.

5. Because in every animal that walks upright the deficiency of the fluids that fill the muscles appears first in the highest part. The face first grows lank and wrinkled; then the neck; then the breast and arms; the lower parts continuing to the last as plump as ever: so that covering all above with a basket, and regarding only what is below the girdle, it is impossible of two women to tell an old one from a young one. And as in the dark all cats are gray, the pleasure of corporal enjoyment with an old woman is at least equal, and frequently superior; every knack being, by practice, capable of improvement.

6. Because the sin is less. The debauching a virgin may be her ruin, and make her for life unhappy.

7. Because the compunction is less. The having made a young girl miserable may give you frequent bitter reflection; none of which can attend the making an old woman happy.

8th and lastly. They are so grateful!

Thus much for my paradox. But still I advise you to marry directly; being sincerely

Your affectionate friend,

Benjamin Franklin

WHAT ARE THE POOR YOUNG WOMEN TO DO?

THE SPEECH OF POLLY BAKER

The speech of Miss Polly Baker before a court of judicature, at Connecticut near Boston in New England; where she was prosecuted the fifth time for having a bastard child: Which influenced the court to dispense with her punishment, and which induced one of her judges to marry her the next day by whom she had fifteen children.

"May it please the honorable bench to indulge me in a few words: I am a poor, unhappy woman, who have no money to fee lawyers to plead for me, being hard put to it to get a living. I shall not trouble your honors with long speeches; for I have not the presumption to expect that you may, by any means, be prevailed on to deviate in your sentence from the law, in my favor. All I humbly hope is that your honors would charitably move the governor's goodness on my behalf, that my fine may be remitted. This is the fifth time, gentlemen, that I have been dragged before your court on the same account; twice I have paid heavy fines, and twice have been brought to public punishment, for want of money to pay those fines. This may have been agreeable to the laws, and I don't dispute it. But since laws are sometimes unreasonable in themselves, and therefore repealed; and others bear too hard on the subject in particular circumstances, and therefore there is left a power somewhere to dispense with the execution of them; I take the liberty to say that I think this law, by which I am punished, both unreasonable in itself, and particularly severe with regard to me, who have always lived an inoffensive life in the neighborhood where I was born, and defy my enemies (if I have any) to say I ever wronged any man, woman, or child. Abstracted from the law, I cannot conceive (may it please your honors) what the nature of my offense is. I have brought five fine children into the world, at the risk of my life; I have maintained them well by my own industry, without burdening the township, and would have done it better if it had not been for the heavy charges and fines I have paid. Can it be a crime (in the nature of things, I mean) to add to the King's subjects, in a new country, that really wants people? I own it, I should think it rather a praiseworthy than a punishable action. I have debauched no other woman's husband, nor enticed any other youth; these things I never was charged with; nor has anyone the least cause of complaint against me, unless, perhaps, the ministers of justice, because I have had children without being married, by which they have missed a wedding fee. But can this be a fault of mine? I appeal to your honors. You are pleased to allow I don't want sense; but I must be stupefied to the last degree, not to prefer the honorable state of wedlock to the condition I have lived in. I always was, and still am, willing to enter into it; and doubt not my behaving well in it, having all the industry, frugality, fertility, and skill in economy appertaining to a good wife's character. I defy anyone to say I ever refused an offer of the sort: on the contrary, I readily consented to the only proposal of marriage that ever was made me, which was when I was a virgin, but too easily confiding in the person's sincerity that made it, I unhappily lost my honor by trusting to his; for he got me with child, and then forsook me.

"That every person, you all know, he is now become a magistrate of this country; and I had hopes he would have appeared this day on the bench, and have endeavored to moderate the court in my favor; then I should have scorned to have mentioned it; but I must now complain of it, as unjust and unequal, that my betrayer and undoer, the first cause of all my faults and miscarriages (if they must be deemed such), should be advanced to honor and power in this government that punishes my misfortunes with stripes and infamy. I should be told, 'tis like, that were there no act of assembly in the case, the precepts of religion are violated by my transgressions. If mine is a religious offense, leave it to religious punishments. You have already excluded me from the comforts of your church communion. Is not that sufficient? You believe I have offended heaven, and must suffer eternal fire: Will not that be sufficient? What need is there then of your additional fines and whipping? I own I do not think as you do, for, if I thought what you call a sin was really such, I could not presumptuously commit it. But, how can it be believed that heaven is angry at my having children, when to the little done by me toward it, God has been pleased to add his divine skill and admirable work-manship in the formation of their bodies, and crowned the whole by furnish-ing them with rational and immortal souls?

"Forgive me, gentlemen, if I talk a little extravagantly on these matters; I am no divine, but if you, gentlemen, must be making laws, do not turn natural and useful actions into crimes by your prohibitions. But take into your wise consideration the great and growing number of bachelors in the country, many of whom, from the mean fear of the expenses of a family, have never sincerely and honorably courted a woman in their lives; and by their manner of living leave unproduced (which is little better than murder) hundreds of their posterity to the thousandth generation. Is not this a greater offense against the public good than mine? Compel them, then, by law, either to marriage, or to pay double the fine of fornication every year. What must poor young women do, whom customs and nature forbid to solicit the men, and who cannot force themselves upon husbands, when the laws take no care to provide them any, and yet severely punish them if they do their duty without them; the duty of the first and great command of nature and nature's God, *increase and multiply*; a duty, from the steady performance of which nothing has been able to deter me, but for its sake I have hazarded the loss of the public esteem, and have frequently endured public disgrace and punishment; and therefore ought, in my humble opinion, instead of a whipping, to have a statue erected to my memory."

ON PERFUMES

A LETTER TO THE ROYAL ACADEMY OF BRUSSELS

Gentlemen:

I have perused your late mathematical prize question, proposed in lieu of one in natural philosophy for the ensuing year. . . . I conclude therefore that you have given this question instead of a philosophical, or, as the learned express it, a *physical* one, because you could not at the time think of a physi-

cal one that promised greater *utility*. . . . Permit me then humbly to
propose one of that sort for your consideration, and through you, if you approve it, for the serious inquiry of learned physicians, chemists, etc., of this
enlightened age.

It is universally well known that, in digesting our common food, there is
created or produced in the bowels of human creatures a great quantity of
wind.

That the permitting this air to escape and mix with the atmosphere is
usually offensive to the company, from the fetid smell that accompanies it.

That all well-bred people, therefore, to avoid giving such offense, forcibly
restrain the efforts of nature to discharge that wind.

That so retained contrary to nature it not only gives frequently great present pain, but occasions future diseases such as habitual cholics, ruptures,
tympanies, etc., often destructive of the constitution, and sometimes of life
itself.

Were it not for the odiously offensive smell accompanying such escapes,
polite people would probably be under no more restraint in discharging such
wind in company than they are in spitting or in blowing their noses.

My prize question therefore should be: To discover some drug, wholesome and not disagreeable, to be mixed with our common food, or sauces,
that shall render the natural discharges of wind from our bodies not only inoffensive, but agreeable as perfumes.

That this is not a chimerical project and altogether impossible, may appear
from these considerations. That we already have some knowledge of means
capable of *varying* that smell. He that dines on stale flesh, especially with
much addition of onions, shall be able to afford a stink that no company
can tolerate; while he that has lived for some time on vegetables only, shall
have that breath so pure as to be insensible to the most delicate noses; and
if he can manage so as to avoid the report, he may anywhere give vent to his
griefs, unnoticed. But as there are many to whom an entire vegetable diet
would be inconvenient, and as a little quicklime thrown into a jakes will
correct the amazing quantity of fetid air arising from the vast mass of putrid
matter contained in such places, and render it rather pleasing to the smell,
who knows but that a little powder of lime (or some other thing equivalent),
taken in our food, or perhaps a glass of limewater drunk at dinner, may have
the same effect on the air produced in and issuing from our bowels? This is
worth the experiment. Certain it is also that we have the power of changing
by slight means the smell of another discharge, that of our water. A few stems
of asparagus eaten shall give our urine a disagreeable odor; and a pill of
turpentine no bigger than a pea shall bestow on it the pleasing smell of
violets. And why should it be thought more impossible in nature to find
means of making perfume of our wind than of our water?

For the encouragement of this inquiry (from the immortal honor to be
reasonably expected by the inventor), let it be considered of how small importance to mankind, or to how small a part of mankind have been useful

those discoveries in science that have heretofore made philosophers famous. Are there twenty men in Europe this day the happier, or even the easier, for any knowledge they have picked out of Aristotle? What comfort can the vortices of Descartes give to a man who has whirlwinds in his bowels! The knowledge of Newton's mutual *attraction* of the particles of matter, can it afford ease to him who is racked by their mutual *repulsion*, and the cruel distensions it occasions? The pleasure arising to a few philosophers, from seeing, a few times in their lives, the threads of light untwisted, and separated by the Newtonian prism into seven colors, can it be compared with the ease and comfort every man living might feel seven times a day, by discharging freely the wind from his bowels? Especially if it be converted into a perfume; for the pleasures of one sense being little inferior to those of another, instead of pleasing the *sight*, he might delight the *smell* of those about him, and make numbers happy, which to a benevolent mind must afford infinite satisfaction. The generous soul, who now endeavors to find out whether the friends he entertains like best claret or Burgundy, champagne or Madeira, would then inquire also whether they chose musk or lily, rose or bergamot, and provide accordingly. And surely such a liberty of *ex-pressing one's scentiments, and pleasing one another*, is of infinitely more importance to human happiness than that liberty of the *press*, or of *abusing one another*, which the English are so ready to fight and die for.

In short, this invention, if completed, would be, as Bacon expresses it, *bringing philosophy home to men's business and bosoms.* And I cannot but conclude that in comparison therewith for *universal* and *continual utility*, the science of the philosophers abovementioned, even with the addition, gentlemen, of your "*figure quelconque*," and the figures inscribed in it, are, all together, scarcely worth a

Fart-hing

A BUNDLE OF BALLADS

Although there have been many artfully conceived and skillfully constructed narrative poems, the best and most enduring have been the so-called "popular ballads," popular in the sense that they are truly vox populi, *the voice (and therefore the poetry) of the people. It was among the common people rather than among the princes and proud nobles that ballads had their origin, and it was the people of the taverns and market places and street corners who enjoyed them in greater numbers and with lustier appreciation than lords and ladies in courts and castles.*

There are various reasons for the ballad's continuing popularity. For one thing the language was simple and forthright rather than florid and intellectual. For another thing the ballad maker was a storyteller, not a preacher;

he rarely philosophized or raised his voice or ruined the tale by adding a moral. Speaking to everyday people who relished lively gossip, a juicy scandal, or a desperate deed, he refused to be shocked by illicit love, violent betrayal, or bloody murder. Moreover, no time was lost in preliminaries; the manner of telling was as direct as the pace was swift. Essentially the ballad was made for crowd consumption and its greatest appeal was that everyone could comprehend it at first hearing.

The old ballads have attracted numerous scholars and researchers, including such notables as Bishop Percy in the eighteenth century and, more recently, Francis James Child. The following examples have been taken from The Roxburghe Ballads *and later collections.*

THE COURTEOUS KNIGHT

Yonder comes a courteous knight,
    Lustily raking over the hay,
He was well 'ware of a bonny lass,
    As she came wandering over the way:

"Jove you speed, fair lady," he said,
    "Amongst the leaves that be so green;
If I were a king, and wore a crown,
    Full soon, fair lady, should thou be a queen.

"Also Jove save you, fair lady,
    Among the roses that be so red:
If I have not my will of you,
    Full soon, fair lady, shall I be dead."

Then he looked East, then he looked West,
    He looked North, so did he South:
He could not find a private place,
    For all lay in the Devil's mouth.

"If you will carry me, gentle sir,
    A maid, unto my father's hall;
Then you shall have your will of me
    Under purple and under pall."

He sat her high upon a steed,
    And himself upon another;
All the day he rode her by,
    As tho' they had been sister and brother.

When she came to her father's hall,
    It was well walled round about;
She rode in at the wicket gate,
    And shut the four-eared fool without.

"You had me (quoth she) abroad in the field,
  Among the corn, amidst the hay,
Where you might had your will of me,
  For, in good faith, sir, I ne'er said nay.

"You had me also amid the field,
  Among the rushes that were so brown;
Where you might had your will of me,
  But you had not the face to lay me down."

He pulled out his nut-brown sword,
  And wiped the rust off with his sleeve:
And said, "Jove's curse come to his heart
  That any woman would believe."

When you have your own true love,
  A mile or twain out of town,
Spare not for her gay clothing,
  But lay her body flat on the ground.

THE FIRE-SHIP

As I strolled out one evening, out for a night's career,
I spied a lofty fire-ship, and after her I steered.
I hoisted her my siganals which she very quickly knew,
And when she see'd my bunting fly, she immediately hove too.
  She'd a dark and a rolling eye,
  And her hair hung down in ringalets.
  She was a nice girl, a decent girl,
  But one of the rakish kind.

O sir, you must excuse me for being out so late,
For if my parents knew of it, then sad would be my fate,
My father he's a minister, a true and honest man,
My mother she's a Methodist, and I do the best I can.
  She'd a dark and a rolling eye, etc.

I took her to a tavern and I treated her to wine,
Little did I think she belonged to the rakish kind;
I handled her, I dandled her, and found to my surprise,
She was nothing but a fire-ship rigged up in a disguise.
  She'd a dark and a rolling eye,
  And her hair hung down in ringalets.
  She was a nice girl, a decent girl,
  But one of the rakish kind.

A-ROVING

In Plymouth Town there lived a maid,
   (Bless you young women)
In Plymouth Town there lived a maid,
   (O, mind what I do say)
In Plymouth Town there lived a maid,
And she was mistress of her trade;
I'll go no more a-roving with you, fair maid.

I took this fair maid for a walk
   (Bless you young women)
I took this fair maid for a walk
   (O, mind what I do say)
I took this fair maid for a walk
And we had such a loving talk;
I'll go no more a-roving with you, fair maid.

And didn't I tell her stories too,
   (Bless you young women)
And didn't I tell her stories too,
   (O, mind what I do say)
And didn't I tell her stories too
Of the gold I found in Timbuctoo!
I'll go no more a-roving with you, fair maid.

But when we'd spent my blooming screw,
   (Bless you young women)
But when we'd spent my blooming screw,
   (O, mind what I do say)
But when we'd spent my blooming screw,
She cut her stick and vanished too.
I'll go no more a-roving with you, fair maid.

We only had one night, and yet
   (Bless you young women)
We only had one night, and yet
   (O, mind what I do say)
We only had one night, and yet
She gave me something I won't forget.
I'll go no more a-roving with you, fair maid.
   A-roving, a-roving,
     Since roving's been my ru-i-in,
I'll go no more a-roving with you, fair maid.

IT'S THE SAME THE WHOLE WORLD OVER

She was poor but she was honest,
Victim of a rich man's game;
For she met the village squire,
And she lost her maiden name.

It's the same the whole over;
It's the poor as gets the blame;
It's the rich as has the pleasure.
Ain't it all a bleeding shame.

So she hastened up to London
For to hide her grief and pain;
There she met an army captain,
And she lost her name again.

See him riding in his carriage
Past the gutter where she stands;
He has made a stylish marriage
While she wrings her ringless hands.

See him in the House of Commons,
Passing laws to put down crime;
While the girl as he has ruined
Slinks away to hide her shame.

See him laugh at the theayter
In the front row with the best;
While the girl as he has ruined
Entertains a sordid guest.

In the little country village
Where her aged parents live,
Though they drink champagne she sends them
Yet they never can forgive.

It's the same the whole world over;
It's the poor as gets the blame;
It's the rich as has the pleasure.
Ain't it all a bleeding shame.

THE EDDYSTONE LIGHT

My father was the keeper of the Eddystone light
And he slept with a mermaid one fine night.
From this union there came three—
A porpoise and a porgy, and the other was me.

One night while I was a-trimmin' of the glim,
A-singin' a verse of the evenin' hymn,
A voice from the starboard shouted, "Ahoy!"
And there was my mother a-settin' on a buoy.

"O what has become of my children three?"
My mother then she asked of me.
"One was exhibited as a talking fish,
And the other was served in a chafing dish."

Then the phosphorus flashed in her seaweed hair,
I looked again and my mother wasn't there.
A voice come a-echoin' out of the night—
"To hell with the keeper of the Eddystone light!"

VENEZUELA

I met her in Venezuela
With a basket on her head,
If she loved others, she didn't say,
But I knew she'd do to pass away,
To pass away the time in Venezuela.

I bought her a sash of blue,
A beautiful sash of blue,
Because I knew that she could do
With all the tricks I knew she knew
To pass away the time in Venezuela.

When the wind was out to sea,
The wind was out to sea,
And she was takin' leave of me
I said, "Cheer up, there'll always be
Sailors ashore in Venezuela."

Her lingo was strange but the thought of her smile,
The thought of her beautiful smile
Will haunt me and taunt me for many a mile,
For she was my girl, and she did the while
To pass away the time in Venezuela.

THE FOGGY, FOGGY DEW

When I was a bachelor, I lived all alone,
I worked at the weaver's trade;
And the only, only thing I did that was wrong,
Was to woo a fair young maid.

I wooed her in the wintertime
And in the summer too;
And the only, only thing I did that was wrong,
Was to keep her from the foggy, foggy dew.

One night she knelt close by my side,
When I was fast asleep.
She threw her arms around my neck,
And then began to weep.
She wept, she cried, she tore her hair,
Ah me, what could I do?
So all night long I held her in my arms,
Just to keep her from the foggy, foggy dew.

Again I am a bachelor, I live with my son,
We work at the weaver's trade;
And every single time I look into his eyes
He reminds me of the fair young maid.
He reminds me of the wintertime
And of the summer too;
And the many, many times that I held her in my arms,
Just to keep her from the foggy, foggy dew.

THE SAGA OF REX

A farmer's dog came into town,
    His Christian name was Rex;
A noble pedigree had he,
    Unusual was his text.
And as he trotted down the street
    'Twas beautiful to see
His work on every corner,
    His work on every tree.

He watered every gateway too,
    And never missed a post,
For piddling was his specialty
    And piddling was his boast.
The city curs looked on amazed
    With deep and jealous rage
To see a simple country dog
    The piddler of the age.

Then all the dogs from everywhere
    Were summoned with a yell,
To sniff the country stranger o'er
    And judge him by the smell.

Some thought that he a king might be,
  Beneath his tail a rose,
So every dog drew near to him
  And sniffed it up his nose.

They smelled him over one by one
  They smelled him two by two
And noble Rex, in high disdain,
  Stood still till they were through.
Then just to show the whole shebang
  He didn't give a damn,
He trotted in a grocery store
  And piddled on a ham.

He piddled in a mackerel keg
  He piddled on the floor,
And when the grocer kicked him out
  He piddled through the door.
Behind him all the city dogs
  Lined up with instinct true
To start a piddling carnival
  And see the stranger through.

They showed him every piddling post
  They had in all the town,
And started in with many a wink
  To pee the stranger down.
They sent for champion piddlers
  Who were always on the go,
Who sometimes did a piddling stunt
  Or gave a piddle show.

They sprung these on him suddenly,
  When midway of the town;
Rex only smiled and polished off
  The ablest, white or brown.
For Rex was with them every trick
  With vigor and with vim.
A thousand piddles, more or less,
  Were all the same to him.

So he was wetting merrily
  With hind leg kicking high,
When most were hoisting legs in bluff
  And piddling mighty dry.
On and on, Rex sought new grounds
  By piles and scraps and rust,

'Til every city dog went dry
    And piddled only dust.

But on and on went noble Rex
    As wet as any rill,
And all the champion city pups
    Were pee'd to a standstill.
Then Rex did free-hand piddling
    With fancy flirts and flits
Like "double dip" and "gimlet twist"
    And all those latest hits.

And all the time this country dog
    Did never wink or grin,
But piddled blithely out of town
    As he had piddled in.
The city dogs conventions held
    To ask, "What did defeat us?"
But no one ever put them wise
    That Rex had diabetes.

JO ANDERSON

HENRY FIELDING (1707–1754)

Henry Fielding was born in 1707 and was, by birth, background and edu-cation, especially suited to satirize the manners and morals of eighteenth-century English gentry. His father, an army officer, came of a titled family; his mother was the daughter of a peer who was a judge of the King's Bench. Henry's own career vacillated between literature and law. He had several years' success as a playwright, after which he earned his living at the bar. A lusty voracious fellow himself, he suffered from the gout, and the limitations of illness led to writing again. Fielding composed articles, dramatic works, political tracts, and stories intermittently, as his fortunes and health rose and fell. In 1749 Tom Jones, considered the forerunner of the modern novel, ap-peared. The book is a lively, fast-moving picaresque narrative, written in an entertaining and simple style. Its uniqueness, for its time, lies in the human-ness of its hero. Tom has the weaknesses of the ordinary man as well as his virtues. Although his love for the heroine, Sophia Western (modeled after Fielding's first wife) is genuine, he satisfies his sexual appetites quite casually with others and briefly (as we shall now see) lets a woman keep him.

At this point in the story, Tom, who is a foundling, has been turned out of his home by his foster father, Mr. Allworthy. All his money has been stolen,

*and though he has found a pocketbook containing a bank note, he will not in
honor spend it since it belongs to his beloved Sophia. With Partridge, his
manservant, he comes to Bath in search of Sophia who has vowed never to see
him again. He tries to find out her whereabouts from her cousins, Mrs. Fitzpatrick and Lady Bellaston. On the morning on which the following episode
begins Tom is having breakfast with his landlady, Mrs. Miller, her two
daughters, Nancy and Betty, and a fellow lodger, Mr. Nightingale.*

FROM: TOM JONES

THE AFFAIR WITH LADY BELLASTON

Their conversation was interrupted by the entrance of a maidservant, who
brought a bundle in her hand, which, she said, "was delivered by a porter for
Mr. Jones." She added, "That the man immediately went away, saying it required no answer."

Jones expressed some surprise on this occasion, and declared it must be
some mistake; but the maid persisting that she was certain of the name, all
the women were desirous of having the bundle immediately opened; which
operation was at length performed by little Betsy, with the consent of Mr.
Jones; and the contents were found to be a domino, a mask, and a masquerade
ticket.

Jones was now more positive than ever in asserting that these things must
have been delivered by mistake; and Mrs. Miller herself expressed some
doubt, and said, "She knew not what to think." But when Mr. Nightingale
was asked, he delivered a very different opinion. "All I can conclude from it,
sir," said he, "is that you are a very happy man; for I make no doubt but these
were sent you by some lady whom you will have the happiness of meeting at
the masquerade."

Jones had not a sufficient degree of vanity to entertain any such flattering
imagination; nor did Mrs. Miller herself give much assent to what Mr. Nightingale had said, till Miss Nancy having lifted up the domino, a card dropped
from the sleeve, in which was written as follows:

> TO MR. JONES
>
> *The queen of the fairies sends you this;*
> *Use her favors not amiss.*

Mrs. Miller and Miss Nancy now both agreed with Mr. Nightingale; nay,
Jones himself was almost persuaded to be of the same opinion. And as no
other lady but Mrs. Fitzpatrick, he thought, knew his lodging, he began to
flatter himself with some hopes that it came from her, and that he might possibly see his Sophia.

Mr. Jones having now determined to go to the masquerade that evening, Mr. Nightingale offered to conduct him thither . . . Mr. Nightingale, who grew every minute fonder of Jones, was very desirous of his company that day to dinner at the tavern, where he offered to introduce him to some of his acquaintances, but Jones begged to be excused, "as his clothes," he said, "were not yet come to town."

To confess the truth, Mr. Jones was now in a situation which sometimes happens to be the case of young gentlemen of much better figure than himself. In short, he had not one penny in his pocket. Notwithstanding, therefore, all the delicacies which love had set before him, namely, the hopes of seeing Sophia at the masquerade—on which, however ill-founded his imagination might be, he had voluptuously feasted during the whole day—the evening no sooner came than Mr. Jones began to languish for some food of a grosser kind. Partridge discovered this by intuition, and took the occasion to give some oblique hints concerning the bank-bill; and, when these were rejected with disdain, he collected courage enough once more to mention a return to Mr. Allworthy.

"Partridge," cries Jones, "you cannot see my fortune in a more desperate light than I see it myself; and I begin heartily to repent that I suffered you to leave a place where you was settled, and to follow me. However, I insist now on your returning home; and for the expense and trouble which you have so kindly put yourself to on my account, all the clothes I left behind in your care I desire you would take as your own. I am sorry I can make you no other acknowledgment."

He spoke these words with so pathetic an accent, that Partridge, among whose vices ill-nature or hardness of heart were not numbered, burst into tears; and, after swearing he would not quit him in his distress, he began with the most earnest entreaties to urge his return home.

"For Heaven's sake, sir," says he, "do but consider; what can your honor do?—how is it possible you can live in this town without money? Do what you will, sir, or go wherever you please, I am resolved not to desert you. But pray, sir, consider—do, pray, sir, for your own sake, take it into your consideration; and I'm sure," says he, "that your own good sense will bid you return home."

"How often shall I tell thee," answered Jones, "that I have no home to return to? Had I any hopes that Mr. Allworthy's doors would be open to receive me, I want no distress to urge me—but, alas! that I am forever banished from. His last words were—oh, Partridge, they still ring in my ears—his last words were, when he gave me a sum of money—what it was I know not, but considerable I'm sure it was—his last words were, 'I am resolved from this day forward on no account to converse with you any more.'"

Here passion stopped the mouth of Jones, as surprise for a moment did that of Partridge; but he soon recovered the use of speech, and after a short preface, in which he declared he had no inquisitiveness in his temper, inquired what Jones meant by a considerable sum—he knew not how much—and what was become of the money.

In both these points he now received full satisfaction; on which he was proceeding to comment, when he was interrupted by a message from Mr. Nightingale, who desired his master's company in his apartment.

When the two gentlemen were both attired for the masquerade, and Mr. Nightingale had given orders for chairs to be sent for, a circumstance of distress occurred to Jones, which will appear very ridiculous to many of my readers. This was how to procure a shilling; but if such readers will reflect a little on what they have themselves felt from the want of a thousand pounds, or, perhaps, of ten or twenty, to execute a favourite scheme, they will have a perfect idea of what Mr. Jones felt on this occasion. For this sum, therefore, he applied to Partridge, which was the first he had permitted him to advance, and was the last he intended that poor fellow should advance in his service. To say the truth, Partridge had lately made no offer of this kind. Whether it was that he desired to see the bank-bill broke in upon, or that distress should prevail on Jones to return home, or from what other motive it proceeded, I will not determine.

Our cavaliers now arrived at that temple where Heydegger, the great high-priest of pleasure, presides; and Mr. Nightingale, having taken a turn or two with his companion, soon left him, and walked off with a female, saying, "Now you are here, sir, you must beat about for your own game."

Jones now accosted every woman he saw whose stature, shape, or air bore any resemblance to his angel. Some of these answered by a question, in a squeaking voice, "Do you know me?" Much the greater number said, "I don't know you, sir," and nothing more. Some called him an impertinent fellow; some made him no answer at all; and many gave him as kind answers as he could wish, but not in the voice he desired to hear.

Whilst he was talking with one of these last (who was in the habit of a shepherdess) a lady in a domino came up to him, and slapping him on the shoulder, whispered to him, at the same time, in the ear, "If you talk any longer with that trollop I will acquaint Miss Western."

"Is she here, then, madam?" replied Jones, with some vehemence. Upon which the lady cried:

"Hush, sir, you will be observed. I promise you, upon my honour, Miss Western is not here."

Jones, now taking the mask by the hand, fell to entreating her in the most earnest manner to acquaint him where he might find Sophia; and when he could obtain no direct answer, he began to upbraid her gently for having disappointed him the day before; and concluded, saying, "Indeed, my good fairy queen, I know your majesty very well, notwithstanding the affected disguise of your voice. Indeed, Mrs. Fitzpatrick, it is a little cruel to divert yourself at the expense of my torments."

The mask answered, "Though you have so ingeniously discovered me, I must still speak in the same voice, lest I should be known by others. And do you think, good sir, that I have no greater regard for my cousin than to assist in carrying on an affair between you two which must end in her ruin as well as your own?"

Jones vowed he had no such design on Sophia, "That he would rather suffer the most violent of deaths than sacrifice her interest." He said, "He knew how unworthy he was of her, every way; that he had long ago resolved to quit all such aspiring thoughts, but that some strange accidents had made him desirous to see her once more, when he promised he would take leave of her forever. No, madam," concluded he, "my love is not of that base kind which seeks its own satisfaction at the expense of what is most dear to its object. I would sacrifice everything to the possession of my Sophia, but Sophia herself."

The lady now, after silence of a few moments, said, "She did not see his pretensions to Sophia in the light of presumption. Young fellows," says she, "can never have too aspiring thoughts. Perhaps you may succeed with those who are infinitely superior in fortune. Nay, I am convinced there are women —but don't you think me a strange creature, Mr. Jones, to be thus giving advice to a man with whom I am so little acquainted, and one with whose behaviour to me I have so little reason to be pleased?"

Here Jones began to apologize, and to hope he had not offended in anything he had said of her cousin. To which the mask answered, "And are you so little versed in the sex, to imagine you can well affront a lady more than by entertaining her with your passion for another woman? If the fairy queen had conceived no better opinion of your gallantry, she would scarce have appointed you to meet her at the masquerade."

Jones had never less inclination to an amour than at present; but gallantry to the ladies was among his principles of honour, and he held it as much incumbent on him to accept a challenge to love as if it had been a challenge to fight. He began, therefore, to make a very warm answer to her last speech.

While Jones and his mask were walking together about the room, he observed his lady speak to several masks with the same freedom of acquaintance as if they had been barefaced. He could not help expressing his surprise at this, to which the lady answered:

"You cannot conceive anything more insipid and childish than a masquerade to the people of fashion, who know one another as well here as when they meet in an assembly or a drawing room, and generally retire from hence more tired than from the longest sermon. If I have any faculty at guessing, you are not much better pleased. I protest it would be almost charity in me to go home for your sake."

"I know but one charity equal to it," cries Jones, "and that is to suffer me to wait on you home."

"Sure," answered the lady, "you have a strange opinion of me, to imagine that upon such an acquaintance I would let you into my doors at this time of night. Are you used, Mr. Jones, to make these sudden conquests?"

"I am not used, madam," said Jones, "to submit to such sudden conquests; but as you have taken my heart by surprise, the rest of my body hath a right to follow; so you must pardon me if I resolve to attend you wherever you go."

He accompanied these words with some proper actions; upon which the lady, after a gentle rebuke, and saying their familiarity would be observed, told him, "She was going to sup with an acquaintance, whither she hoped he would not follow her."

The lady, presently after, quitted the masquerade, and Jones, notwithstanding the severe prohibition he had received, presumed to attend her. He was now reduced to the same dilemma we have mentioned before, namely, the want of a shilling, and could not relieve it by borrowing as before. He therefore walked boldly on after the chair in which his lady rode, pursued by a grand huzza from all the chairmen present, who wisely take the best care they can to discountenance all walking afoot by their betters.

The lady was set down in a street not far from Hanover Square, where the door being presently opened, she was carried in, and the gentleman, without any ceremony, walked in after her.

Jones and his companion were now together in a very well-furnished and well-warmed room; when the female, still speaking in her masquerade voice, said she was surprised at her friend, who must absolutely have forgot her appointment; at which, after venting much resentment, she suddenly expressed some apprehension from Jones, and asked him what the world would think of their having been alone together in a house at that time of night? But instead of a direct answer to so important a question, Jones began to be very importunate with the lady to unmask; and at length having prevailed, there appeared not Mrs. Fitzpatrick, but the Lady Bellaston herself.

It would be tedious to give the particular conversation, which consisted of very common and ordinary occurrences, and which lasted from two till six o'clock in the morning. It is sufficient to mention all of it that is anywise material to this history. And this was a promise that the lady would endeavour to find out Sophia, and in a few days bring him to an interview with her, on condition that he would then take his leave of her. When this was thoroughly settled, and a second meeting in the evening appointed at the same place, they separated. The lady returned to her house, and Jones to his lodgings.

Jones, having refreshed himself with a few hours' sleep, summoned Partridge to his presence; and delivering him a bank-note of fifty pounds, ordered him to go and change it. Partridge received this with sparkling eyes, though the only way he could possibly find to account for the possession of this note was by robbery; and, to confess the truth, the reader, unless he should suspect it was owing to the generosity of Lady Bellaston, can hardly imagine any other.

To clear, therefore, the honour of Mr. Jones, and to do justice to the liberality of the lady, he had really received this present from her, who, though she did not give much into the hackney charities of the age, such as building hospitals, etc., was not, however, entirely void of that Christian virtue; and conceived (very rightly, I think) that a young fellow of merit without a shilling in the world, was no improper object of this virtue.

(Lady Bellaston immediately becomes possessive and importunate. Not seeing or hearing from Tom for a day, she pays a surprise visit to his rooms, only to find another woman there. This is the following morning.)

Mr. Jones, at his return home, found the following letters lying on his table, which he luckily opened in the order they were sent.

LETTER I: *Surely I am under some strange infatuation; I cannot keep my resolutions a moment, however strongly made or justly founded. Last night I resolved never to see you more; this morning I am willing to hear if you can, as you say, clear up this affair. And yet I know that to be impossible. I have said everything to myself which you can invent.—Perhaps not. Perhaps your invention is stronger. Come to me, therefore, the moment you receive this. If you can forge an excuse I almost promise you to believe it. Betrayed too—I will think no more—— Come to me directly—— This is the third letter I have writ, the two former are burnt—— I am almost inclined to burn this too—— I wish I may preserve my senses—— Come to me presently.*

LETTER II: *If you ever expect to be forgiven, or even suffered within my doors, come to me this instant.*

LETTER III: *I now find you was not at home when my notes came to your lodgings. The moment you receive this let me see you—— I shall not stir out; nor shall anybody be let in but yourself. Sure nothing can detain you long.*

Jones had just read over these three billets when Mr. Nightingale came into the room. "Well, Tom," said he, "any news from Lady Bellaston, after last night's adventure?"

"The Lady Bellaston?" answered Jones, very gravely.

"Nay, dear Tom," cries Nightingale, "don't be so reserved to your friends. Though I was too drunk to see her last night, I saw her at the masquerade. Do you think I am ignorant who the queen of the fairies is?"

"And did you really then know the lady at the masquerade?" said Jones.

"Yes, upon my soul, did I," said Nightingale, "and have given you twenty hints of it since, though you seemed always so tender on that point that I would not speak plainly. I fancy, my friend, by your extreme nicety in this matter, you are not so well acquainted with the character of the lady as with her person. Don't be angry, Tom, but upon my honour you are not the first young fellow she hath debauched. Her reputation is in no danger, believe me."

Jones, having very attentively heard all that Nightingale had to say, fetched a deep sigh; which the other, observing cried, "Heyday! Why, thou art not in love, I hope!"

"Oh, my dear friend!" cries Jones, "I am so entangled with this woman that I know not how to extricate myself. In love, indeed! No, my friend; but I am under obligations to her, and very great ones."

"Pooh!" answered the other, "you are not the first upon whom she hath conferred obligations of this kind. She is remarkably liberal where she likes; though, let me tell you, her favours are so prudently bestowed that they should rather raise a man's vanity than his gratitude."

Nightingale proceeded so far on his head, and told his friend so many stories of the lady, which he swore to the truth of, that he entirely removed all esteem for her from the breast of Jones; and his gratitude was lessened in proportion. Indeed he began to look on all the favours he had received rather as wages than benefits, which depreciated not only her, but himself too in his own conceit, and put him quite out of humour with both. The result of all was that he determined to quit her if he could but find a handsome pretence: which being communicated to his friend, Nightingale considered a little, and then said:

"I have it, my boy! I have found out a sure method: propose marriage to her, and I would venture hanging upon the success."

"Marriage?" cries Jones.

"Ay, propose marriage," answered Nightingale, "and she will declare off in a moment. I knew a young fellow whom she kept formerly, who made the offer to her in earnest, and was presently turned off for his pains."

Jones declared he could not venture the experiment. "Perhaps," said he, "she may be less shocked at this proposal from one man than from another. And if she should take me at my word, where am I then? Caught in my own trap, and undone for ever!"

"No," answered Nightingale, "not if I can give you an expedient by which you may at any time get out of the trap."

"What expedient can that be?" replied Jones.

"This," answered Nightingale. "The young fellow I mentioned, who is one of the most intimate acquaintances I have in the world, is so angry with her for some ill offices she hath since done him, that I am sure he would, without any difficulty, give you a sight of her letters; upon which you may decently break with her, and declare off before the knot is tied, if she should really be willing to tie it, which I am convinced she will not."

After some hesitation, Jones, upon the strength of this assurance, consented; but, as he swore he wanted the confidence to propose the matter to her face, he wrote the following letter, which Nightingale dictated:

MADAM—*I am extremely concerned that, by an unfortunate engagement abroad, I should have missed receiving the honour of your ladyship's commands the moment they came; and the delay which I must now suffer of vindicating myself to your ladyship greatly adds to this misfortune. Oh, Lady Bellaston! what a terror have I been in for fear your reputation should be exposed by these perverse accidents! There is one only way to secure it. I need not name what that is. Only permit me to say, that as your honour is as dear to me as my own, so my sole ambition is to have the glory of laying my liberty at your feet; and believe me when I assure you, I can never be made completely happy without you generously bestow on me a legal right of calling you mine forever.—I am, madam, with most profound respect, your ladyship's most obliged, obedient, humble servant,*

THOMAS JONES.

To this she presently returned the following answer:

SIR—*When I read over your serious epistle, I could, from its coldness and formality, have sworn that you already had the legal right you mention; nay, that we had for many years composed that monstrous animal a husband and wife. Do you really then imagine me a fool? Or do you fancy yourself capable of so entirely persuading me out of my senses, that I should deliver my whole fortune into your power, in order to enable you to support your pleasures at my expense? Are these the proofs of love which I expected? Is this the return for——? But I scorn to upbraid you, and am in great admiration of your profound respect.*

P.S.—I am prevented from revising:—Perhaps I have said more than I meant.—Come to me at eight this evening.

Jones, by the advice of his privy council, replied:

MADAM—*It is impossible to express how much I am shocked at the suspicion you entertain of me. Can Lady Bellaston have conferred favours on a man whom she could believe capable of so base a design? Or can she treat the most solemn tie of love with contempt? Can you imagine, madam, that if the violence of my passion, in an unguarded moment, overcame the tenderness which I have for your honour, I would think of indulging myself in the continuance of an intercourse which could not possibly escape long the notice of the world, and which, when discovered, must prove so fatal to your reputation? If such be your opinion of me, I must pray for a sudden opportunity of returning those pecuniary obligations which I have been so unfortunate to receive at your hands; and for those of a more tender kind, I shall ever remain, etc.*

And so concluded in the very words with which he had concluded the former letter. The lady answered as follows:

I see you are a villain! and I despise you from my soul. If you come here I shall not be at home!

LAURENCE STERNE (1713–1768)

To make sure posterity would not misunderstand him—and he was certain about posterity—Laurence Sterne underscored everything he wrote. Making it easy for his biographer, he was explicit when he came to put down the facts of his life. He tells us that he was born November 24, 1713, at Clonmel, in the South of Ireland; that his father was a lieutenant in the Army and that, as a consequence, the family moved from place to place. Fascinated by the continual peregrinations of military life (reflected in the later portraits of Uncle Toby and Corporal Trim), young Laurence would have been happy to live always in transit; but when he was eighteen his father was killed in a duel and the boy was sent to various schools by relatives. He won a scholarship at Cambridge, thanks largely to the fact that six such scholarships had been given to the university by the Archbishop of York, who happened to be his great-grandfather. A slightly tubercular priest at twenty-five, nicknamed "Pastor Yorick" because of his whimsical wit, two years later Sterne married the unattractive and excessively dignified Elizabeth Lumley. It is said that the Sunday after the wedding, Sterne prefaced his sermon with this text from Luke: "We have toiled all night and taken nothing."

Although married and a clergyman, Sterne had, as one biographer puts it, in a cliché of understatement, "a weakness for the ladies." His extramarital affairs were many and far from discreet—they included liaisons with a titled lady, a concert singer, and a young bride thirty years Sterne's junior. His wife suffered a breakdown eighteen years after the marriage—much of the time she declared she was Queen of Bohemia—but recovered and outlived him.

Practically unknown until he was forty-seven, Sterne became both famous and infamous with the publication of Tristram Shandy. *It was relished by countless readers for its sly suggestiveness, its naughty double-entendres and outright bawdiness; but Sterne was hurt by such literary mentors as Horace Walpole, Oliver Goldsmith, and Samuel Johnson, who attacked it not only for its immorality but its literary "formlessness." Actually Sterne was creating a new form, a digressive and even disjointed style similar to what was to become known as "stream of consciousness." As to his licentiousness, Sterne's was a peculiarly intellectual fooling; his ribaldry was, says Bergen Evans, more ludicrous than lewd.*

Sterne continued to enjoy the gaieties of life until, a sick man nearing fifty, he was forced to seek quiet in the countryside of France and Italy. The sojourn did not restore his health, but it produced the delightfully piquant A Sentimental Journey. *It also allowed him to add new episodes to* Tristram Shandy *which grew to nine volumes. Knowing that he was dying, Sterne returned to England and lived just long enough to see the first printed copy of*

A Sentimental Journey. *Three weeks after its appearance he died, March 18, 1768. Untroubled by condemnation, he was serene about his reputation. "If my enemies knew that, by their rage of abuse and ill will, they were effectively serving the interest both of myself and my works," he wrote, "they would be more quiet. But it has been the fate of my betters who have found that the way to fame is like the way to heaven: through much tribulation. And till I shall have the honour to be as much maltreated as Rabelais and Swift were, I must continue humble, for I have not filled up the measure of half their persecutions."*

FROM: A SENTIMENTAL JOURNEY

THE TEMPTATION

When I alighted at the hotel, the porter told me a young woman with a band-box had been that moment inquiring for me. I do not know, said the porter, whether she is gone away or not. I took the key of my chamber of him, and went upstairs; and, when I had got within ten steps of the top of the landing before my door, I met her coming easily down.

It was the fair *fille de chambre* I had walked along the Quai de Conti with: Madame de R—— had sent her upon some commission to a *marchande de modes* within a step or two of the Hotel de Modene; and, as I had failed in waiting upon her, had bid her inquire if I had left Paris; and, if so, whether I had not left a letter addressed to her.

As the fair *fille de chambre* was so near my door, she returned back, and went into the room with me for a moment or two, whilst I wrote a card.

It was a fine still evening in the latter end of the month of May—the crimson window-curtains (which were of the same colour as those of the bed) were drawn close—the sun was setting, and reflected through them so warm a tint in the fair *fille de chambre's* face, I thought she blushed; the idea of it made me blush myself; we were quite alone, and that superinduced a second blush before the first could get off.

There is a sort of a pleasing half-guilty blush, where the blood is more in fault than the man; 'tis sent impetuous from the heart, and virtue flies after it, not to call it back, but to make the sensation of it more delicious to the nerves; 'tis associated . . .

But I'll not describe it. I felt something at first within me which was not in strict unison with the lesson of virtue I had given her the night before; I sought five minutes for a card; I knew I had not one. I took up a pen; I laid it down again; my hand trembled: the devil was in me.

I know as well as anyone he is an adversary, whom, if we resist, he will fly from us; but I seldom resist him at all, from a terror that, though I may conquer, I may still get a hurt in the combat; so I give up the triumph for security; and, instead of thinking to make him fly, I generally fly myself.

The fair *fille de chambre* came close up to the bureau, where I was looking for a card, took up first the pen I cast down, then offered to hold the ink. She offered it so sweetly, I was going to accept it, but I durst not; I have nothing, my dear, said I, to write upon. Write it, said she simply, upon anything.

I was just going to cry out, Then I will write it, fair girl, upon thy lips!

If I do, said I, I shall perish; so I took her by the hand, and led her to the door, and begged she would not forget the lesson I had given her. She said indeed she would not, and, as she uttered it with some earnestness, she turned about, and gave me both her hands, closed together, into mine. It was impossible not to compress them in that situation; I wished to let them go; and all the time I held them, I kept arguing within myself against it. And still I held them on. In two minutes I found I had all the battle to fight over again; and I felt my legs and every limb about me tremble at the idea.

The foot of the bed was within a yard and a half of the place where we were standing. I had still hold of her hands (and how it happened, I can give no account); but I neither asked her, nor drew her, nor did I think of the bed; but so it did happen, we both sat down.

I'll just show you, said the fair *fille de chambre*, the little purse I have been making to-day to hold your crown. So she put her hand into her right pocket, which was next me, and felt for it some time; then into the left. She had lost it. I never bore expectation more quietly; it was in her right pocket at last; she pulled it out; it was of green taffeta, lined with a little bit of white quilted satin, and just big enough to hold the crown. She put it into my hand: it was pretty; and I held it ten minutes, with the back of my hand resting upon her lap, looking sometimes at the purse, sometimes on one side of it.

A stitch or two had broke out in the gathers of my stock; the fair *fille de chambre*, without saying a word, took out her little "housewife," threaded a small needle, and sewed it up. I foresaw it would hazard the glory of the day, and, as she passed her hand in silence across and across my neck in the manoeuvre, I felt the laurels shake which fancy had wreathed about my head.

A strap had given way in her walk, and the buckle of her shoe was just falling off. See, said the *fille de chambre*, holding up her foot. I could not, from my soul, but fasten the buckle in return; and, putting in the strap, and, lifting up the other foot with it, when I had done, to see both were right, in doing it so suddenly, it unavoidably threw the fair *fille de chambre* off her centre, and then——

THE CASE OF DELICACY

The peasants had been all day at work in removing an obstruction in the road; and, by the time my *voiturin* got to the place, it wanted full two hours of completing, before a passage could anyhow be gained. There was nothing but to wait with patience;—'twas a wet and tempestuous night; so that by the delay and that together, the *voiturin* found himself obliged to put up five miles short of his stage, at a little decent kind of an inn by the roadside.

I forthwith took possession of my bed-chamber, got a good fire, ordered supper, and was thanking Heaven it was no worse,—when a *voiturin* arrived with a lady in it, and her servant-maid.

As there was no other bed-chamber in the house, the hostess, without much nicety, led them into mine, telling them, as she ushered them in, that there was nobody in it but an English gentleman—that there were two good beds in it, and a closet within the room which held another. The accent in which she spoke of this third bed, did not say much for it—however, she said there were three beds, and but three people—and she durst say the gentleman would do anything to accommodate matters. I left the lady not a moment to make a conjecture about it, so instantly made a declaration that I would do anything in my power.

As this did not amount to an absolute surrender of my bed-chamber, I still felt myself so much the proprietor, as to have a right to do the honours of it;—so I desired the lady to sit down, pressed her into the warmest seat, called for more wood, desired the hostess to enlarge the plan of the supper, and to favour us with the very best wine.

The lady had scarce warmed herself five minutes at the fire before she began to turn her head back and to give a look at the beds: and the oftener she cast her eyes that way, the more they returned perplexed. I felt for her —and for myself; for in a few minutes, what by her looks, and the case itself, I found myself as much embarrassed as it was possible the lady could be herself.

That the beds we were to lie in were in one and the same room, was enough simply by itself to have excited all this;—but the position of them (for they stood parallel, and so very close to each other as only to allow a space for a small wicker-chair betwixt them) rendered the affair still more oppressive to us;—they were fixed up, moreover, near the fire, and the projection of the chimney on one side, and a large beam which crossed the room on the other, formed a kind of recess for them that was no way favourable to the nicety of our sensations:—if anything could have added to it, it was that the two beds were both of them so very small as to cut us off from every idea of the lady and the maid lying together, which, in either of them, could it have been feasible, my lying beside them, though a thing not to be wished, yet there was nothing in it so terrible which the imagination might not have passed over without torment.

As for the little room within, it offered little or no consolation to us. 'Twas a damp, cold closet, with a half-dismantled window-shutter, and with a window which had neither glass nor oil-paper in it to keep out the tempest of the night. I did not endeavour to stifle my cough when the lady gave a peep into it; so it reduced the case in course to this alternative,—that the lady should sacrifice her health to her feelings, and take up with the closet herself, and abandon the bed next mine to her maid,—or, that the girl should take the closet, etc.

The lady was a Piedmontese of about thirty, with a glow of health in her cheeks. The maid was a Lyonoise of twenty, and as brisk and lively a French girl as ever moved. There were difficulties every way,—and the obstacle of the stone in the road, which brought us into the distress, great as it appeared whilst the peasants were removing it, was but a pebble to what lay in our way now—I have only to add that it did not lessen the weight which hung upon our spirits, that we were both too delicate to communicate what we felt to each other upon the occasion.

We sat down to supper; and, had we not had more generous wine to it than a little inn in Savoy could have furnished, our tongues had been tied up till Necessity herself had set them at liberty. But the lady having a few bottles of Burgundy in her *voiture*, sent down her *fille de chambre* for a couple of them; so that by the time supper was over and we were left alone, we felt ourselves inspired with a strength of mind sufficient to talk, at least, without reserve, upon our situation. We turned it every way, and debated and considered it in all kinds of lights in the course of a two hours' negotiation; at the end of which the articles were settled finally betwixt us, and stipulated for in form and manner of a treaty of peace,—and, I believe, with as much religion and good faith on both sides, as in any treaty which has yet had the honour of being handed down to posterity.

They were as follows:

First. As the right of the bed-chamber is in Monsieur,—and he thinking the bed next to the fire to be the warmest, he insists upon the concession on the lady's side of taking up with it.

Granted on the part of Madame; with a proviso that, as the curtains of that bed are of a flimsy transparent cotton, and appear likewise too scanty to draw close, that the *fille de chambre* shall fasten up the opening, either by corking-pins or needle and thread, in such a manner as shall be deemed a sufficient barrier on the side of Monsieur.

Second. It is required on the part of Madame, that Monsieur shall lie the whole night through in his *robe de chambre*.

Rejected: inasmuch as Monsieur is not worth a *robe de chambre*; he having nothing in his portmanteau but six shirts and a black silk pair of breeches.

The mentioning the silk pair of breeches made an entire change of the article, for the breeches were accepted as an equivalent for the *robe de chambre*; and so it was stipulated and agreed upon that I should lie in my black silk breeches all night.

Third. It was insisted upon, and stipulated for, by the lady, that after Monsieur was got to bed, and the candle and fire extinguished, Monsieur should not speak one single word the whole night.

Granted, provided Monsieur's saying his prayers might not be deemed an infraction of the treaty.

There was but one point forgot in this treaty, and that was the manner

in which the lady and myself should be obliged to undress and get to bed;
—there was one way of doing it, and that I leave to the reader to devise,
protesting as I do it, that if it is not the most delicate in nature,—'tis the
fault of his own imagination,—against which this is not my first complaint.

Now when we were got to bed, whether it was the novelty of the situation,
or what it was, I know not; but so it was, I could not shut my eyes. I tried
this side and that, and turned and turned again, till a full hour after midnight, when Nature and Patience both wearing out,—O my God! said I.

—You have broken the treaty, Monsieur, said the lady, who had no more
slept than myself. I begged a thousand pardons; but insisted it was no more
than an ejaculation.—She maintained 'twas an entire infraction of the treaty.
—I maintained it was provided for in the clause of the third article.

The lady would by no means give up the point, though she weakened her
barrier by it; for, in the warmth of the dispute, I could hear two or three
corking-pins fall out of the curtain to the ground.

—Upon my word and honour, Madame, said I, stretching my arm out of
bed by way of asseveration——

(I was going to have added, that I would not have trespassed against the
remotest idea of decorum for the world)—

—But the *fille de chambre*, hearing there were words between us, and fearing that hostilities would ensue in course, had crept silently out of her closet;
and, it being totally dark, had stolen so close to our beds that she had got
herself into the narrow passage which separated them, and had advanced so
far up as to be in a line betwixt her mistress and me.

So that, when I stretched out my hand, I caught hold of the *fille de
chambre's*——

FROM: TRISTRAM SHANDY

HOW I WAS BEGOT

I wish either my father or my mother, or indeed both of them, as they
were in duty both equally bound to it, had minded what they were about
when they begot me; had they duly considered how much depended upon
what they were then doing;—that not only the production of a rational Being
was concerned in it, but that possibly the happy formation and temperature
of his body, perhaps his genius and the very cast of his mind;—and, for aught
they knew to the contrary, even the fortunes of his whole house might take
their turn from the humours and dispositions which were then uppermost;
—had they duly weighed and considered all this, and proceeded accordingly,
—I am verily persuaded I should have made a quite different figure in the
world, from that in which the reader is likely to see me.—Believe me, good
folks, this is not so inconsiderable a thing as many of you may think it;—
you have all, I dare say, heard of the animal spirits, as how they are trans-

fused from father to son, etc. etc.—and a great deal to that purpose:—Well, you may take my word, that nine parts in ten of a man's sense or his nonsense, his successes and miscarriages in this world depend upon their motions and activity, and the different tracts and trains you put them into, so that when they are once set a-going, whether right or wrong, 'tis not a halfpenny matter,—away they go cluttering like hey-go mad; and by treading the same steps over and over again, they presently make a road of it, as plain and as smooth as a garden-walk, which, when they are once used to, the devil himself sometimes shall not be able to drive them off it.

"Pray, my dear," quoth my mother, "have you not forgot to wind up the clock?"—"Good G——!" cried my father, making an exclamation, but taking care to moderate his voice at the same time. "Did ever woman, since the creation of the world, interrupt a man with such a silly question?" Pray, what was your father saying?—Nothing.

—Then, positively, there is nothing in the question that I can see, either good or bad.—Then, let me tell you, sir, it was a very unseasonable question at least,—because it scattered and dispersed the animal spirits, whose business it was to have escorted and gone hand in hand with the Homunculus, and conducted him safe to the place destined for his reception.

The Homunculus, sir, in however low and ludicrous a light he may appear, in this age of levity, to the eye of folly or prejudice;—to the eye of reason in scientific research, he stands confessed—a Being guarded and circumscribed with rights.—The minutest philosophers who, by the bye, have the most enlarged understandings, (their souls being inversely as their enquiries) shew us incontestably, that the Homunculus is created by the same hand,—engendered in the same course of nature,—endowed with the same locomotive powers and faculties with us:—That he consists as we do, of skin, hair, fat, flesh, veins, arteries, ligaments, nerves, cartilages, bones, marrow, brains, glands, genitals, humours, and articulations;—is a Being of as much activity, —and, in all senses of the word, as much and as truly our fellow-creature as my Lord Chancellor of England.—He may be benefited,—he may be injured, —he may obtain redress;—in a word, he has all the claims and rights of humanity, which Tully, Puffendorf, or the best ethic writers allow to arise out of that state and relation.

Now, dear sir, what if any accident had befallen him in his way alone!—or that, through terror of it, natural to so young a traveller, my little Gentleman had got to his journey's end miserably spent;—his muscular strength and virility worn down to a thread;—his own animal spirits ruffled beyond description,—and that in this sad disordered state of nerves, he had lain down a prey to sudden starts, or a series of melancholy dreams and fancies, for nine long, long months together.—I tremble to think what a foundation had been laid for a thousand weaknesses both of body and mind, which no skill of the physician or the philosopher could ever afterwards have set thoroughly to rights.

To my uncle Mr. Toby Shandy do I stand indebted for the preceding anecdote, to whom my father, who was an excellent natural philosopher, and much given to close reasoning upon the smallest matters, had oft, and heavily complained of the injury; but once more particularly, as my uncle Toby well remembered, upon his observing a most unaccountable obliquity, (as he called it) in my manner of setting up my top, and justifying the principles upon which I had done it,—the old gentleman shook his head, and in a tone more expressive by half of sorrow than reproach,—he said his heart all along foreboded, and he saw it verified in this, and from a thousand other observations he had made upon me, That I should neither think nor act like any other man's child:—"But alas!" continued he, shaking his head a second time, and wiping away a tear which was trickling down his cheeks, "My Tristram's misfortunes began nine months before ever he came into the world."

—My mother, who was sitting by, looked up,—but she knew no more than her backside what my father meant,—but my uncle, Mr. Toby Shandy, who had been often informed of the affair,—understood him very well.

I was begot in the night, betwixt the first Sunday and the first Monday in the month of March, in the year of our Lord one thousand seven hundred and eighteen. I am positive I was,—But how I came to be so very particular in my account of a thing which happened before I was born, is owing to another small anecdote known only in our own family, but now made public for the better clearing up this point.

My father, you must know, who was originally a Turkey merchant, but had left off business for some years, in order to retire to, and die upon, his paternal estate in the county of ———, was, I believe, one of the most regular men in everything he did, whether 'twas matter of business, or matter of amusement, that ever lived. As a small specimen of this extreme exactness of his, to which he was in truth a slave,—he had made it a rule for many years of his life—on the first Sunday-night of every month throughout the whole year,—as certain as ever the Sunday-night came,—to wind up a large house-clock, which we had standing on the backstairs head, with his own hands:—And being somewhere between fifty and sixty years of age at the time I have been speaking of,—he had likewise gradually brought some other little family concernments to the same period, in order, as he would often say to my uncle Toby, to get them all out of the way at one time, and be no more plagued and pestered with them the rest of the month.

It was attended with but one misfortune, which, in a great measure, fell upon myself, and the effects of which I fear I shall carry with me to my grave; namely, that from an unhappy association of ideas, which have no connection in nature, it so fell out at length, that my poor mother could never hear the said clock wound up,—but the thoughts of some other things unavoidably popped into her head—and *vice versâ*:—Which strange combination of ideas, the sagacious Locke, who certainly understood the nature of these things better than most men, affirms to have produced more wry actions than all other sources of prejudice whatsoever.

But this by the bye.

Now it appears by a memorandum in my father's pocketbook, which now lies upon the table, "That on Lady-day, which was on the 25th of the same month in which I date my geniture,—my father set out upon his journey to London, with my eldest brother Bobby, to fix him at Westminster school"; and, as it appears from the same authority, "That he did not get down to his wife and family till the second week in May following,"—it brings the thing almost to a certainty.

—But pray, sir, What was your father doing all December,—January, and February?—Why, madam,—he was all that time afflicted with a sciatica.

OLD EPITAPHS AND EPIGRAMS

EPITAPH ON HIS WIFE

> Here lies my wife: here let her lie.
> Now she's at rest. And so am I.

JOHN DRYDEN (1631–1700)

EPITAPH ON A POPULAR COURTESAN

> When she for whom the night was meant for sport,
> Pet of the king and mistress of the court,
> Died in her bed, they carved this on her stone:
> "At last she sleeps—at last she sleeps alone."

Seventeenth-century French, *translated by* L.U.

EPITAPH ON A SCOLD

> Here lies a woman, no man can deny it,
> Who now is at peace, though she lived most unquiet.
> Her husband beseeches, if near here you're walking,
> Speak soft, or she'll wake, and then she'll start talking.

TOWARD THE RESURRECTION

> Within this grave we both do lie,
> Back to back, my wife and I.
> When the last trump the air shall fill
> She will get up, and I'll lie still.

IN A SUFFOLK CHURCHYARD

Reader, pass on, nor waste your time
On bad biography and bitter rhyme;
For what I am this crumbling clay insures,
And what I was is no affair of yours.

ON A DENTIST

Stranger, approach this spot with gravity.
John Brown is filling his last cavity.

DR. I. LETSOME'S OWN EPITAPH

When people's ill they come to I;
   I physics, bleeds, and sweats 'em.
Sometimes they live; sometimes they die.
   What's that to I? I. Letsome.

A MAN NAMED MERIDETH

Still young, he said with his last breath:
"A short life and a Merideth."

THE RUDE RESPONSE

"No! No! Spare my virginity!
When I lose that," said Rose, "I'll die!"
"Behind the elms last night," cried Dick,
"Rose, were you not extremely sick?"

MATHEW PRIOR (1664–1721)

THE DIFFICULT CHOICE

"Come, come," said Tom's father, "at your time of life,
   There's no longer excuse for thus playing the rake.
It is time you should think, boy, of taking a wife."
   "Why, so it is, Father. Whose wife shall I take?"

THOMAS MOORE (1779–1852)

MEN AND WOMEN

1

Two things make women slow, we find,
    When going any place:
For first she must make up her mind
    And then her face.

KEITH PRESTON (1884–1927)

2

Women's faults are many,
    Men have only two:
Everything they say,
    And everything they do.

AUTHOR UNKNOWN

3

Breathes there a man with hide so tough
Who says two sexes aren't enough?

SAMUEL HOFFENSTEIN (1890–1947)

MY MOTHER

My mother's an apple-pie baker,
    My father he fiddles for gin,
My sister works nights for her living,
    O my, how the money rolls in!

ON LADY POLTAGRUE, A PUBLIC PERIL

The Devil, having nothing else to do,
Went off to tempt My Lady Poltagrue.
My Lady, tempted by a private whim,
To his extreme annoyance, tempted him.

HILAIRE BELLOC (1870–1953)

THE RABBIT

The rabbit has a charming face:
Its private life is a disgrace.
I really dare not name to you
The awful things that rabbits do;
Things that your paper never prints—

You only mention them in hints.
They have such low, degraded souls
No wonder they inhabit holes;
When such depravity is found
It only can live underground.

AUTHOR UNKNOWN

The bonds of wedlock are so heavy that it takes two to carry them—sometimes three.

ALEXANDRE DUMAS

Vanity, shame, and temperament account for most men's bravery and most women's chastity.

LA ROCHEFOUCAULD

It is not as hard to find a woman who has never been guilty of an indiscretion as to find a woman who has been guilty of only one.

LA ROCHEFOUCAULD

Women can control their passion, but not their desire to rouse it.

LA ROCHEFOUCAULD

Virtuous women, like prostitutes, often grow weary of their profession.

LA ROCHEFOUCAULD

Bigamy is having one wife too many. Monogamy is the same.

AUTHOR UNKNOWN

A reputation for chastity is advisable for a woman. Chastity itself is sometimes useful.

AUTHOR UNKNOWN

If the young only knew! If the old only could.

AUTHOR UNKNOWN

Women would rather be looked at than up to.

AUTHOR UNKNOWN

Women give themselves to God when the devil is through with them.

SOPHIE ARNOULD

Believe everything you hear said about the world—even the worst. Nothing is too bad to be impossible.

HONORÉ DE BALZAC

Women who have made a sheep of a man always tell him he has the strength of a lion.

HONORÉ DE BALZAC

Do not do unto others as you would that they should do unto you. Their tastes may not be the same . . . Remember that your morals are only your habits, and do not call other people immoral because they have other habits.

GEORGE BERNARD SHAW

A pessimist is a man who thinks all others as nasty as himself—and hates them for it.

GEORGE BERNARD SHAW

GIACOMO CASANOVA (1725–1798)

Giacomo Casanova, born in Venice in the year 1725, was one of the remarkable personalities of all time. Known to us merely as an irresistible lover—possibly because irresistible lovers are more of a rarity now than they were in the eighteenth century—he was known to his contemporaries as nearly everything else. Educated for a career in the Church, he was made an abbé at fifteen, a Doctor of Laws at sixteen, delivered his first and unique sermon, and shortly afterward renounced the cloth. Though an avowed "believer," he sacrificed chiefly on the altars of Comus, Bacchus, and Venus.

He became, in turn, violinist, soldier, prisoner of state, gentleman of

*leisure, adventurer, and author with overtones of poet, ambassador, business-
man, scholar, economist, sociologist, and magician. He consorted with the
aristocracy, both of birth and of spirit, and rendered service to a handful of
reigning sovereigns. He ran the state lottery for Louis XV of France; made
a report for the court of Madrid on the colonization of an Andalusian waste-
land by Swiss immigrants; advised the Polish King on the workings of an
industrial venture; refused a position offered him by Frederick of Prussia;
and talked tête-à-tête with Catherine the Great. He was expelled from
Vienna by order of the Empress; received one of Louis XV's famous lettres
de cachet, inviting him to leave Paris; fought and wounded the royal favorite
in Warsaw, being thus forced to quit the city in secrecy; made a hurried exit
from Spain under threat of assassination; and left England precipitously because of unpayable debts. He was generous to the point of prodigality with
what money he came by, lived—if any man ever did—by his wits, and died
poorer than he was born. More than thirty of his written works were published by 1797, among them a history of Poland, a history of the Venetian
Republic, and the Icosameron, a fantasy told in twenty days about a Utopia
at the center of the earth.*

*A fascinating rogue, Casanova was made much of by the women, most of
whom he loved with artistry and left with distinction. He delighted in their
robust appetite as well as their beauty, wit, and voluptuousness, and, by his
own statement, four fifths of the pleasure he took with them came from the
certainty of the pleasure he gave. His Memoirs, written in his late sixties and
published first in 1826, have been declared "perhaps the most precious document that we possess on the society of the eighteenth century," and French
scholars claim them as part of French literature—high praise for an Italian
with the temerity to write in bad French.*

*For the purpose of this anthology, the following passages from Casanova's
voluminous work have been chosen for their wide range from the carefully
delicate to the frankly gross. The original manuscript having already passed
through the hands of many editors, correctors and expurgators, it seemed best
to set down as clearly as possible the author's intention, with an eye to style
and story. The translation, never published before, is by Juliette Rypinski.*

FROM: THE MEMOIRS OF CASANOVA

I FORGET ANGELA AND DISCOVER HER PRETTY COUSINS (VENICE)

[*Casanova, a serious sixteen, is still a nominal virgin. He has been languishing after a certain Angela, toward his conquest of whom her young cousins,
Nanette and Marton, have been helpfully, if vainly, contriving. Casanova arrives at the secret nocturnal rendezvous they have arranged.*]

Three quarters of an hour later, I heard the door of the street open and Nanette and Marton appeared. They led me inside.

"Where is Angela?" I asked Nanette, as we tiptoed up to the third floor.

"She must not have been able to come, nor to let us know. She certainly knows you are here."

"Hah, she has merely played another trick on all of us. At least you know her now for what she is. She is simply making sport of me and she has triumphed. For if she had come, it is I who would have made sport of her."

"Oh, permit me to doubt that."

"Have no doubt, pretty Nanette. You will be convinced by the agreeable night we will spend without her."

"You mean that, being philosophical, you will be satisfied with us rather than nothing. Well, you may sleep here and we will go and sleep on the sofa in the next room."

"If you like," I said, "but that would be a very mean trick. Besides, I have no intention of sleeping."

"What!" she exclaimed. "You'd have the fortitude to spend seven hours alone with us? I'm sure that when you can't think of anything to say, you'll fall asleep."

"We shall see. Meanwhile, here are the provisions. You will surely not be so cruel as to let me sup alone. Do you have some bread?"

"Of course. And we won't be cruel; we'll have a second supper."

"I really ought to be in love with you," I said. "Tell me, lovely Nanette, if I *were* in love with you, as I was with Angela, would you make me suffer as she did?"

"How can you ask such a question? She is a fool. All I can say is, I really don't know anything about it."

They quickly set the table for three, brought bread, Parmesan cheese, and water, laughing merrily the while, and soon we were busy over our supper. The wine, to which they were not at all accustomed, went to their heads and they became deliciously gay. I was astonished, considering them, that I had never before noticed their merit.

After our little supper, which was excellent, I seated myself between them and, raising a hand of each to my lips, I asked them if they were really my friends and if they approved the shameful manner in which Angela had treated me. They replied both at once that I had moved them to tears.

"Allow me to love you as a brother," I went on, "and share my love as though you were my sisters. Let us exchange tokens in the innocence of our hearts and swear eternal loyalty."

The first kiss I gave them was neither the product of any sentiment of love nor an overture to seduction, and as for them, they assured me several days later that they only returned it to convince me that they shared my sincere fraternal sentiments. But these innocent kisses soon grew hot and sparked such flames in us that we must ourselves have been taken aback, for we stopped them suddenly and looked at each other in astonishment. They both rose simply and left me alone to reflect.

It was hardly surprising that the fire these kisses had lit in my being and which now circulated in my veins, and had made me suddenly fall hopelessly in love with these charming creatures. They were both prettier than Angela, and Nanette's wit, as Marton's sweet naïveté, were infinitely superior to hers. I was amazed at not having recognized this before. But these were noble respectable girls, and the accident that had put them in my hands must not be allowed to become a fatal one for them. I was not so fatuous as to believe they loved me; but I supposed that my kisses had had the same effect on them as theirs on me. Reasoning thus, I saw plainly that by employing seductive wiles, of whose force they were ignorant, it would not be difficult for me, during the course of the long night I was to spend with them, to elicit from their innocence concessions whose consequences might become decisive. This thought repelled me, and I made a firm resolve to respect them, never doubting that I would have the force necessary to keep it.

When they reappeared I saw on their faces an expression of security and contentment, and I immediately assumed the same aspect, determined not to expose myself again to the temptation of their kisses.

We passed an hour talking of Angela, and I told them that I was determined not to see her again, persuaded as I was that she did not love me.

"She does love you," said Marton earnestly, "I'm sure of that. But if you don't intend to marry her, you would do well to break with her entirely, because she has determined not to allow you even to kiss her as long as you are not a serious suitor. So you must make up your mind either to forget her or to be satisfied with nothing."

"You argue like an angel. But how do you know for sure that she loves me?"

"I am positive, and since we have promised each other fraternal friendship, I can tell you how I know. When Angela sleeps with us she always kisses me and calls me 'my dearest abbé.'"

At these words Nanette, bursting into laughter, put her hand over her sister's mouth. But this naïveté moved me so much that I was at some pains to contain myself.

Marton said that, being very intelligent, it was impossible that I should not know what went on between young girls when they slept together.

"Of course," I said, hastily, "everyone knows about that nonsense, and I do not think, my dear Nanette, that you should consider your sister's friendly confidence an indiscretion."

"Well, it's done—but these are things one simply doesn't say. If Angela knew . . . !"

"She would be in despair. But Marton has shown herself such a friend that I will be grateful to her all my life. Besides, I've had enough of Angela. I detest Angela and I shall never speak to her again. She is false and her only intention is to tantalize me."

"But if she loves you, she's perfectly right to want to marry you."

"Granted. But she only thinks of herself, for, knowing how I suffer, if she loved me for myself, would she behave this way? In the meanwhile her imagination furnishes her the means to appease her own desires with this charming Marton, who obliges by playing 'husband' to her."

At this, Nanette's laughter redoubled. But I remained serious and continued speaking to her sister in the same manner, making great case of her sincerity. Finally I said that no doubt, in fair exchange, Angela ought to play *her* husband; but she answered laughingly that she was only Nanette's husband, and Nanette had to agree.

"But I don't understand," I went on, "does Nanette call out her husband's name during her transports?"

"No one knows anything about him."

"You love someone then, Nanette?"

"Yes, but no one will ever know my secret."

This diffidence suggested to me that I might well be the secret and that Nanette was Angela's rival. Such seductive conversation made me little by little lose the desire to spend the night in idleness with these two charming girls, both made for love.

"I am very glad," I said, "that I have only friendly sentiments toward you, because otherwise I would be hard put to it to pass the night with you without being tempted to give you proofs of my affection and to receive yours. For you are both ravishingly pretty and have charms to turn the head of any man."

And continuing on this note, I pretended to become sleepy. Nanette, being the first to remark it, said:

"Don't be polite. Go to bed. We'll go in the other room and rest on the sofa."

"I would consider myself the most boorish of men if I did such a thing. Let us go on talking; I'll get over being sleepy. I'm only worried about you. You go to bed here and I, my charming friends, I will go in the other room. If you are afraid of me, lock the door. But you would be wrong, for I love you only as a brother."

"We would never do that," said Nanette. "But do allow yourself to be persuaded. Go to bed here."

"I couldn't sleep with my clothes on."

"Undress yourself. We won't look."

"I'm not afraid of that. But I could never sleep knowing that you were obliged to stay up on my account."

"We'll go to sleep too," said Marton, "but with our clothes on."

"That shows a distrust which offends my probity. Tell me, Nanette, do you believe me to be a man of honor?"

"Yes, of course."

"Very good. But you must both prove it to me. Get in the bed beside me, undressed, and count on my given word of honor that I will not touch you.

Besides, you are two against one. What could happen to you? Aren't you free to get out of bed if I cease to behave myself? Well, if you refuse me this mark of confidence—at least when you see that I am asleep—I will not go to bed at all."

Then, falling silent, I pretended to doze off. They conferred a moment in lowered voices, then Marton told me to go to bed, that they would follow me as soon as they were sure I was asleep. Nanette having confirmed this promise, I turned my back to them, undressed, and after wishing them a good night I got into bed. As soon as I lay down I pretended to fall asleep; but very soon, sleep actually did overcome me, and I awoke to find them slipping into bed on either side of me. I turned over drowsily and stayed immobile until I had reason to believe they were alseep; if they weren't they had their own reasons for pretending to be.

They had turned their backs to me and the light was out; I was thus obliged to act on hazard, and I proffered my first homages to the one on my right, not knowing whether it was Nanette or Marton. I found her lying with her knees drawn up, enveloped in the only garment she had kept on. Without disturbing anything, and with due regard for her modesty, I gradually made it impossible for her to do otherwise than to admit defeat, and persuade herself that the best thing she could do was to go on pretending to sleep and let me do what I wished. Soon, her own nature acting in concert with mine, I achieved my purpose, and my efforts, crowned with complete success, left me no doubt as to having obtained the first favors, to which prejudice makes us attach so much importance. Overjoyed at having savored a delight which I had just tasted completely for the first time, I quitted my beauty gently, to offer to the other a new tribute of my ardor.

I found her lying on her back, as one deep in tranquil slumber. Taking care with my approach, as though afraid to waken her, I began by titillating her senses, assuring myself that she was as much a novice as her sister, and as soon as a natural movement made it clear that love welcomed the offering, I set about consummating the sacrifice. Suddenly, giving in to the vivacity of the sentiments which moved her, and as though tired of the role she had adopted, she strained me tightly in her arms, covered me with kisses, exchanging transport for transport, and love confounded our beings in an equal voluptuousness.

By these signs I thought I recognized Nanette; I told her so.

"Yes, it's me," she said, "and I count myself fortunate, as well as my sister, if you are honorable and constant."

"Until death, my angels. And since all that we have done is the work of love, let there be no more question of Angela between us."

I asked her then to get up and light the candles, but Marton, eager to oblige, got up quickly and left us together. When I saw Nanette in my arms, animated by the fires of love, and Marton beside us, a candle in her hand, with an expression that seemed to accuse us of ingratitude for not recognizing that she, having been the first to give in, had encouraged her sister to imitate her, I realized the extent of my happiness.

"Let us get up, my dearest friends," I said, "and swear eternal fidelity."

As soon as we were up we made communal ablutions, which made them laugh heartily, and which renewed our ardor. Then, in the costume of the Golden Age, we finished what we had left of the supper. After having told each other a hundred things which, in the inebriation of the senses, only love can interpret, we went back to bed and the most delicious of nights was passed in reciprocal evidences of our tenderness. It was Nanette who received the last proof of my ardor, for Mme. Orio having gone out to mass, I was obliged to hasten my departure, assuring them that they had extinguished in my heart all my sentiments toward Angela.

Arrived at my house, I went to bed and slept the sweetest of sleeps until dinnertime.

MY PASSION FOR THE MISTRESS OF THE COUNT DE LA TOUR D'AUVERGNE AND HOW I WAS CURED OF IT (PARIS)

Camille, actress and dancer of the Comédie Italienne, whom I had first loved at Fontainebleau seven years before, was the one to whom I was most attached, because of the hospitality and agreeable company to be found at her pretty house at Barrière Blanche, where she was kept by the Count d'Aigreville, who was fond of me and enjoyed my society. He was the brother of the Marquis de Gamache and of the Countess de Rumain, handsome, gentle, and fairly rich. He was never so happy as when he found a gay company at his mistress', a rather singular taste, rarely encountered, but a very convenient one, marking a nature without jealousy or suspicion.

Camille loved only him, a rare quality in a courtesan-actress; but, being full of wit and *savoir-faire*, she never disappointed anyone who had a taste for her. She was neither stingy nor prodigal of her favors, and she had the secret of making everyone adore her, without risking the affliction of indiscretion or the mortification of being abandoned.

After her lover, the man to whom she was most devoted was the Count de la Tour d'Auvergne, a highborn lord who idolized her and who, not being rich enough to own her entirely, seemed content with the portion she allotted him. He had the reputation of being her sincere second choice.

Camille practically maintained for him a young girl who had been in her service, and of whom she had made him a gift as soon as she discovered he was in love with the child. La Tour d'Auvergne kept her in a furnished room in Paris, and said that he loved her as one loves a portrait, because he had got her from his dear Camille.

The Count often brought her to Camille's suppers. She was fifteen, naïve, simple, and without ambition. She told her lover that she would never forgive him an infidelity except with Camille, to whom she felt she must cede him, since it was to her that she owed her happiness.

I became so mad about this young person that I often went to Camille's suppers merely in the hope of finding her there and of enjoying the ingenuousness with which she enchanted everyone. I did my best to hide my passion, but I was so far gone that I often left feeling utterly miserable, since I saw no way of curing my desire in the ordinary way. I would, of course, have made myself ridiculous if I had let anyone guess, and Camille would have teased me unmercifully. Here, however, is the comic episode which cured me in a most unexpected manner.

One rainy evening, Camille's house being at some distance from Paris, I had sent for a fiacre to take me home. But it was one o'clock in the morning and there were none to be found in the square.

"My dear Casanova," said La Tour d'Auvergne, "I'll be delighted to drop you at your house. My carriage has only place for two," he added, "but my little one will sit on our knees."

I accepted, naturally, and there I am in the carriage, with the Count on my left and Babet seated on both our laps.

In love, burning with desire, I decide to seize the occasion and, without losing a moment, for the coachman drives fast, I take her hand and press it gently. I feel her own press mine discreetly. Oh, happiness! I raise it to my lips and cover it with mute but ardent kisses. Impatient to convince her of my ardor, and thinking that her dear hand would not refuse me a sweet service . . . but at the moment of the climax: "I'm obliged to you," says La Tour d'Auvergne, "for a courtesy of your country of which I thought myself no longer worthy. I *do* hope you haven't made a mistake."

At these terrible words, I extend my hand and feel the sleeve of his dress coat. There is no presence of mind that can rise to such an occasion, especially as these words were followed by a howl of laughter which would have confounded the most hardened of men. Needless to say, I could neither laugh, nor deny the fact, and the horrible situation was only modified by the blessed dark which hid my confusion.

Babet remained silent, waiting no doubt to ask the Count what he was laughing at; for when he tried to speak, his laughter only erupted more violently, and in my heart I was thankful. Finally, the carriage stopped at my door and, my domestic having opened the gate, I alighted rapidly, bidding them a goodnight which La Tour d'Auvergne returned, between explosions of laughter.

I went inside, in a state of near-imbecility, and it was fully half an hour before I began to see the humor and laugh myself at the singularity of the adventure. What deviled me most was the thought of the ribald jokes which awaited me, for I certainly had no right to expect discretion from the Count. I was wise enough, however, to make a resolution, if not to laugh with the laughers, at least to take no offense at the baiting of which I was certain to be the object. This was, and is, in Paris, the surest way of putting the laughers on one's own side.

I let three days go by without seeing the good Count. The fourth day, I decided, about nine o'clock, to go and ask if I might lunch with him, since Camille had sent to inquire after me. This affair need not keep me from continuing to see her, but I wanted to prepare myself by finding out the general opinion of it.

As soon as La Tour d'Auvergne saw me he burst into laughter. I did the same and we embraced affectionately. But he, bantering, began acting like a girl.

"My dear Count," I said, "forget this idiocy. You can get no satisfaction from attacking me, since I have no way of defending myself."

"My dear fellow, why think of defending yourself? We all love you and this comic adventure is our delight; we laugh about it every evening."

"Everyone knows about it, then?"

"You can imagine! But it's the most natural thing in the world. Camille simply chokes over it. Come this evening; I'll bring Babet and she'll make you laugh, for she maintains that you made no mistake."

"She's right."

"How, right? Tell that to someone else! You do me too much honor and I don't believe you. But that is to be your story?"

"I can't do better. But actually it was *not* to you that my delirious imagination offered such burning homage."

At table I joked with the others, pretending astonishment at the Count's indiscretion, and proclaimed proudly that I was cured of my passion. Babet, with a little pout, called me horrid, and insisted that I was *not* cured. But the fact is that I was, for this incident had disgusted me with her, and given me instead a sincere attachment for the Count, who had all the virtues to make him beloved by everyone.

THE MARTYRDOM OF DAMIENS AND ITS CONSEQUENCES (PARIS)

On Sunday we dined with Lambertini, the adventuress who posed as a Pope's niece, and with whom my friend and compatriot, the Count Tiretta, had formed such a close alliance that he was lodging in her house. The fat old bigot, Mme. ——, was there, and her lovely niece, with whom I had so compromised myself as to be half betrothed to her without having accomplished anything.

At an odd moment in the conversation I brought up the subject of the great crowds that would be at the Grève for the execution of Damiens and, finding them very curious to see this horrible spectacle, I offered them the use of my spacious window on the square. The ladies accepted eagerly, and I promised to take them.

I had no window, of course; but I knew that in Paris, as elsewhere, everything is to be had for money. After dinner, pleading a business affair, I went out and leaped into the first fiacre that I saw. Within a quarter of an hour, I was possessor of a beautiful window on a mezzanine which I had rented for three louis.

On the twenty-eighth of March, the day of Damiens' martyrdom, I left early to call for the ladies at Lambertini's and we proceeded to the Place de Grève. The ladies, huddling as close together as possible, took their places at the window, leaning on their arms so that we could see over their heads. There were two steps leading up to this window, and the ladies were perched on the second. Tiretta and I were obliged to stand behind them on the same step, since on the first step we should have been no taller than they. It is not without reason that I give these details to my readers, for without them, it would be difficult to imagine the details that I am obliged to withhold.

We had the constancy to stay four hours at this frightful spectacle. The torture of Damiens is too well known for me to dwell on it here, first because the telling would be too long, and also because such horrors outrage nature. Damiens was a fanatic who, believing that he was rendering a service and so meriting his place in Paradise, had attempted to assassinate Louis XV, and though, in fact, he merely succeeded in scratching the monarch, was martyrized as though the crime had been consummated.

During the torture of this victim of the Jesuits, I was obliged to turn away and stop my ears to his rending shrieks, when no more than half his body was left intact. But Lambertini and the fat aunt made not the slightest movement. Was it because of their heart's cruelty? I had to pretend to believe them when they said that the horror which overcame them at the thought of this monster's crime had kept them from feeling the pity that such unspeakable torture would otherwise have aroused in them. The fact is that Tiretta kept the devout aunt singularly occupied during the entire execution; and perhaps he was the reason why this virtuous lady dared not move, nor even turn her head.

Finding himself placed very close behind her, Tiretta had taken the precaution of raising her dress, so as not to step on it. This was natural no doubt, but soon, by an involuntary movement in their direction, I perceived that Tiretta had taken a bit too much precaution. Not wishing to interrupt my friend nor embarrass the lady, I turned the other way and placed myself so that my pretty friend would not see anything. I heard rustlings during two full hours and, finding it highly amusing, I forced myself to remain immobile the whole time. I had to admire Tiretta's good appetite as well as his intrepidity; but I admired even more the fine resignation of the pious aunt.

When, at the end of this long séance, I saw Mme. —— turn around, I looked straight at Tiretta and found him fresh, gay, and calm, as though nothing had happened. But the dear aunt seemed pensive and more serious than usual. We left and, having escorted the Pope's niece to her door, I asked her to loan me Tiretta for a few hours and then conducted Mme. —— to her home, where she asked me to come and see her the next day. I noticed as we left that she did not bid my friend good-by.

We went to dinner at Laudel's, where the food is excellent at six francs a head. I thought my mad friend must have great need to repair his energies. "What," I said, "were you doing in back of Mme.——?"

"I am sure you saw nothing, nor anyone else."

"No one else, perhaps. For I, having seen the beginning of your maneuvers and foreseeing what was to come, placed myself in such a way that neither Lambertini nor the pretty niece could see you. I can guess how far you went, and I admit I admire your robust appetite. But it appears that the poor victim is furious."

"Ah, my friend, merely the coquetry of middle age. She can pretend to be angry, but since she stayed perfectly quiet for two hours, I'm willing to bet she's ready to start all over."

"Well, actually I think so too. But she's bound to take the position that you were disrespectful to her, and not, I must say, without reason."

"Disrespectful? But don't we always have to be disrespectful to women when we want to do that? Besides, the act having been consummated four separate times, doesn't her entire consent go without saying?"

"Very good logic. But you see, she wants to speak to me tomorrow and you certainly will be put on the carpet."

"I hardly imagine she'll talk about this nonsense; she would be mad."

"Why not? You know what bigots are. Raised in the Jesuit school, where they often get good lessons on this subject, they are delighted to make such confessions to a third party, and these confessions, well-seasoned with crocodile tears, give them in their own eyes an aura of holiness."

"She may demand satisfaction," I continued, "and if so, I shall be delighted to act as intermediary."

"Really, you make me laugh. What satisfaction can she claim, unless she wants to prosecute me for violating her, which is hardly likely unless she is prepared to risk being exposed as an old offender? If the game was not to her taste, she had only to give me a kick which would have sent me flying over backwards."

"But that would have given away the attempt."

"Well, the least movement would have made it impossible. But no—quiet as a lamb, no opposition whatsoever, nothing could have been easier."

The next morning I presented myself at the home of the old prude, whom I found with her ravishing niece. We talked briefly about the weather, then she told the girl to leave us. I was prepared for the scene and I waited quietly for her to break the silence that any woman in her place would naturally observe for a few minutes.

At last: "You will be surprised, monsieur, at what I have to tell you, for the complaint that I have finally brought myself to make to you is of an unheard-of nature. It is a most delicate matter, and only the idea I conceived of you the first time I met you could have decided me. I believe you to be wise, discreet, and above all, a man of honor and good morals. Finally, I believe you to be filled with the true spirit of religion. If I am wrong, the consequences will be serious for, insulted as I am, and not lacking influence, I will know how to avenge myself. And you, being his friend, will suffer indirectly."

"Is it of Tiretta, madame, that you complain?"

"None other."

"And how has he been guilty of offending you? You can trust me."

"Monsieur, I simply cannot say it, it is impossible and utterly without precedent, but I hope you will be able to guess. Yesterday, at the execution of that wretched Damiens, he . . . for two hours . . . he took gross advantage of the position in which he found himself behind me."

"I understand! I can guess what he must have done and you need say no more. You have every reason to be angry and I join in condemning him. It was a dishonest trick. But permit me to say that the case is not without precedent; it is not, if I may say so, even very rare. I go so far as to think that one might even forgive him, attributing it to, possibly, love, the hazards of the situation, the too great proximity of the enemy temptress—above all when the sinner is young and hot-blooded. Besides, it is a crime that can be expiated in many ways, providing the parties can agree. Tiretta is a bachelor, he is a gentleman, good-looking and at bottom, very honorable. A marriage is perfectly feasible."

I waited for an answer, but seeing that the complainant kept silent, which seemed a good sign, I went on. "If marriage is not to your taste, he might atone for his fault by a constancy of friendship which would prove his repentance and merit your indulgence. Reflect, madame, that Tiretta is a man, and consequently subject to all the weaknesses of mankind. Remember, too, that you are not without fault."

"I, monsieur?"

"Yes, madame, but innocently; because, of course, you are not directly to blame if your charms caused him to lose his head. However, I feel sure that without them the thing would never have happened. And I think that this circumstance should help you to find it in your heart to pardon him."

"Pardon? You are a clever pleader, monsieur, but I do you the justice of recognizing that what you have said comes from a Christian spirit. However, all your reasoning is founded upon a false supposition. You don't know the facts. But then, how could anyone guess!"

Mme. ——, by now in tears, had me completely baffled. I didn't know what to think. "Could he have stolen her purse?" I said to myself. "He's not capable of such a thing or I'll put a bullet through his head."

Soon she dried her tears and went on thus: "You imagine a crime which, with an effort, one might consider reasonable and find for it, I agree, an acceptable reparation. But what the brute did to me is an infamy which I wish I were able to refrain from even thinking of, for it was enough to make me lose my reason."

"Good God! What do I hear! I tremble! Tell me, for the love of Heaven, if I am right?"

"I believe so, for I think no one could imagine anything worse. I see that you are shaken, but that is nevertheless the fact. Forgive my tears; you may find their source in my repugnance and the shame with which I feel myself covered."

"And in your religion."

"That, too, of course. That is really the principal thing. I only omitted it in the fear that you were not as attached to it as I."

"As much as I can be, God be praised, and nothing will ever detach me."

Comforted by this assurance, she began to speak of her desire for revenge, and I could not move her until suddenly I had the inspiration to tell her that Tiretta's life was in danger from the criminal gang at Lambertini's and that I was trying to rescue him from the precipice. This produced more tears.

"You astonish me! You edify me! I do not wish his death, monsieur. But you must agree that I should have some satisfaction."

"I agree. One does not treat a charming Frenchwoman in the Italian manner without making a magnificent reparation. But I can think of no satisfaction equivalent to the insult. I only know of one, and I will do my utmost to procure it for you if you are satisfied with it."

"And what is that?"

"I will deliver the guilty one by surprise into your hands and leave him alone with you, exposed to the full force of your anger. But on condition that, without his knowing, I am to be in the next room, for I must be satisfied that his life is not in danger."

"I consent," she said graciously. "But he must not suspect. Oh, when will you bring him to me? I can't wait to confound him. I will make him tremble. I'm curious to know what reasons he will manufacture to justify such conduct."

"It is possible that your presence will make him eloquent. I hope so, for I would be pleased to see you satisfied with each other."

She insisted that I dine with her and the Abbé Des Forges, who arrived at one o'clock. I spoke so well about "grace" during dinner, I cited St. Augustine so often that the abbé and the old bigot took me for a Jansenist fanatic. After dinner, which by the way was excellent, I promised to bring the guilty party, tied hands and feet, the next evening after the theater.

The reader does not need to be told that I gave Tiretta a faithful account of my interview with the good matron. If certain timorous souls accuse me of bad faith, I will tell them that I made the promises with a mental reservation.

The mad fellow merely laughed when I reproached him with a quasi-serious air for such a horrible action, and expressed astonishment that she should have told me everything.

"You don't deny it then?"

"I have no reason to doubt the lady's word," he said calmly. "Though, as you may understand, under the circumstances I would have no way of knowing for certain. Anyway, I will calm her."

I urged him to take as much time as possible, for my sake as well as his own, for I did not expect to be bored while he was transforming her anger into a sweeter sentiment. For the least the old prude owed me was not to leave me alone and without a fire. Above all, I counseled him to properly expiate the blackness of his fault.

"I can simply tell her the truth. I proceeded blindly."

"The reason is unique," I said, "and a Frenchwoman may well find it good."

Everything being well understood, we went to the opera the next evening, and from there walked to the house of the offended dame, who received us with great dignity but with a certain amenity of manner which boded well.

"I never have supper," she said, "but if I had known you were coming, messieurs, I would have had something prepared for you."

After having told her all the gossip we had heard at the theater, I pretended to have an appointment and asked her permission to leave her alone a few minutes with my friend. "If I am more than a quarter of an hour, my dear Count, don't wait for me. Take a fiacre home and we shall see each other tomorrow."

Instead of going downstairs I went into the next room off the corridor, and two minutes later my charming friend came in carrying a light and seemed agreeably surprised to see me.

"I don't know if I am dreaming," she said, "but my aunt told me not to leave you alone and to tell the maid not to come up until she rang. Your friend is with her and she cautioned me to speak low since he mustn't know that you are here. May I know the meaning of this singular affair?"

"You shall know all, my angel. But it's cold in here."

"My aunt ordered me to make a good fire. She has suddenly become generous, even prodigal. Look, candles!"

"Is that something new?"

"It is indeed."

As soon as we were installed in front of the fire I told her the whole story, but, I having felt it necessary to graze certain portions, she did not quite understand the nature of Tiretta's crime. I was not sorry to have to explain it more precisely and, to render the picture more expressive, I added the language of gesture, which made her laugh and blush at the same time. I then told her that, having to arrange a satisfaction for her aunt, I had managed the thing so that I was sure to find myself alone with her all the time that my friend should be with her aunt. Thereupon I began to cover her pretty face with kisses and, since I permitted myself no other liberties, she received my embraces as evidence of my love and the purity of my sentiments.

We passed an hour in agreeable conversation, touching briefly on the beastliness of men and ending with my conjecture as to the outcome of her aunt's interview with Tiretta. He was still with her, and I judged that the affair must have become serious. I said as much to my charming companion and suggested that she give me something to eat.

Quick as a doe, she set a small table for two and brought everything she could find. There was a delicious Roquefort cheese, two bottles of a Chambertin that I can still taste, and an excellent jellied ham, enough to satisfy ten hungry people. Ah, what perfect nourishment for bringing a budding love to prompt maturity are Chambertin and Roquefort cheese!

We found a little crevice where we could peep into the next room, but could see no one. "What did I tell you!" I exclaimed. "Give me a blanket and I will sleep on this sofa. And you, my dear, go along to bed. But first, show me your room."

She led me to a little room where I saw a pretty bed, a prayer stool, and a great crucifix. "Your bed is too small for you, my heart."

"Oh no, it is just right." And so saying, she extended herself gracefully upon it as though to prove her point.

"What a lovely wife I'll have! Ah, don't move, let me look at you that way. And let my hand just caress this dainty corset where two lovely globes seem to tremble in their captivity. Here, let me free them. . . ."

"My friend," she said piteously, "I cannot defend myself. But afterward you will love me no longer."

"All my life," I said unhesitatingly. For who can stop to reflect at such a moment? I pressed her in my arms and, my caresses inflaming her all the more since it was the first time that her charms had been exposed to the ardent lips of a man and the touch of a libertine hand, she responded fervently to my ardor and we plunged into a voluptuousness of pleasure until dawn.

We had passed four or five delicious hours together. She left me to make a good fire, then installed me with a blanket on the sofa, where I fell into a profound slumber. I was awakened by Mme. ——, who appeared about midday in a seductive dressing gown.

"Still sleeping, M. Casanova?"

"Ah, good morning, madame. Well, what has become of my friend?"

"He has become mine."

"Truly?"

"Truly. I have forgiven him."

"And what did he do to deserve such a generous pardon?"

"He has given me absolute proof that he was mistaken."

"I am simply delighted. But where is he?"

"You will find him at home. But don't tell him that you spent the night here. He will think you were with my niece. Ah, that dear young man is something above mortals. If you knew how he loves me! I'm infinitely obliged to you and I count on your indulgence and, above all, your discretion. I am taking him in pension for a year. He will be well lodged and fed and so on. We are leaving today for Villette where I have a dear little house; for you understand that in the beginning one must be careful to give wagging tongues the least possible cause for gossip. There my friend will have everything he desires, and you, monsieur, whenever you may deign to rejoice us with your presence, you will find a pretty room and a good bed. I'm sorry about only one thing, and that is that you will be bored, for my niece is so dreary."

"Your niece, madame, is very charming. She gave me a delicious supper last night and kept me company until three o'clock this morning, when she went to her room there, and I rested perfectly on this excellent sofa."

"I'm delighted that things worked out to your satisfaction as well as mine. I can't imagine what she gave you, for there was nothing, and I would never have thought my niece capable of so much intelligence."

"She has a great deal, madame, in my opinion at least."

"You are a connoisseur, monsieur. Let's go and see her. But she has locked her door. Open the door, child! Why did you lock your door, silly girl? What have you to be afraid of? Monsieur is a perfectly honorable man."

A DROLL ENCOUNTER ON MY WAY TO CONSTANTINOPLE. (ORSERA)

Strolling at Orsera while they loaded our vessel with ballast to give the necessary equilibrium for navigation, I saw a man of good appearance stop and consider me with close attention. Making certain that he was not a creditor, I decided that my good appearance must interest him and, finding nothing wrong with that, I was continuing on my way when he approached me.

"May I be so bold as to ask you, Captain, if this is your first visit to our city?"

"No, sir, it is my second."

"Were you not here last year?"

"Precisely."

"But you were not in uniform then?"

"No, I was not. But your questions begin to be a little indiscreet."

"You must pardon me, sir, for my curiosity is the child of my gratitude. You are the man to whom I have the greatest of obligations, and I would like to think that Providence has brought you here especially so that I may go on contracting them."

"Whatever have I done for you, and what can I do now? I can't imagine what you are talking about."

"Be good enough to come and lunch with me. Here is my house. I have some fine Refosco which you must try, and I will convince you in a few words that you are my true benefactor and that I have reason to hope you have come back to renew your good works."

I could not suppose the fellow to be mad, and, understanding nothing of what he said, I could only imagine that he would try to sell me his wine, so I accepted. We went up to his room where he left me a moment to go and order the luncheon. I noticed some surgical instruments, which made me conclude that he must be a doctor. On his return I asked him.

"Yes, Captain. For twenty years I have practiced that profession in this city, where I lived in poverty, for I had little but an occasional bloodletting, a few boils to cup, scratches to bandage or a sprain to set. What I earned was not enough to live on. But since last year, I can tell you that my position has changed! I have earned a great deal of money, which I have invested at a profit. And it is all to you, Captain, to you—may God bless you!—that I owe my present well-being."

"But how?"

"It's like this, Captain. Last year you became—er—acquainted with Don Jerome's housekeeper and, on parting, you left her an amorous souvenir which she communicated to a gentleman friend who, in good faith, made a present of it to his wife. The latter, not wishing to be stingy, gave it to a libertine who, in turn, was so generous with it that in less than a month I had fifty clients. The months that followed were no less fertile, and I gave my services gladly to all, assuring myself of a good fee, as was only right. I still have a few cases. But within a month I shall have none, for the malady has now been arrested. You can understand the joy I felt at seeing you again. It seemed like a good omen. May I express the lively hope that you will stay a few days and recharge the springs of my fortune?"

His tale made me laugh, but I had to give him the bad news that I was in perfect health! He assured me that I would not be able to say as much on my return, since the country to which I was going was full of doubtful merchandise, and that no one knew as well as he how to cure it. He enjoined me to come to him, and not on any account to put myself in the hands of the charlatans who would offer me their remedies.

I gave him my promise, thanked him, and returned to my ship.

THE QUESTION OF BUNDLING (CIRCA 1770)

According to Webster's dictionary, bundling is an intransitive verb meaning "to sleep on the same bed without undressing." Its origins are remote, but it was largely practiced in the New England colonies for two reasons: beds were few, and fuel was too scarce to waste. Thus bundling came into favor (a) for the accommodation of travelers who were permitted to bundle with the innkeeper's wife, daughter, and even husband; (b) for the better acquaintance of young couples who had to do their courting in houses that were cruelly cold. Henry Reed Stiles begins his Bundling: Its Origin, Progress, and Decline in America *with this explanation: "Bundling was practiced in two forms—first, between strangers, as a simple domestic makeshift arrangement, often arising from the necessities of a new country, although by no means peculiar to America; and, secondly, between lovers, who shared the same couch with the mutual understanding that innocent endearments should not be exceeded. It was, in either case, a custom of convenience."*

It is not surprising however, that in spite of "mutual understanding," lovers lying together, although fully clothed, exchanged endearments that ceased to be innocent. The prospect of marriage aided in the relaxation of strict observance of such courtship, and the institution of bundling was violently at-

tacked by some as a pernicious practice "which prevailed among the young to a degree which . . . sapped the fountain of morality and tarnished the escutcheons of thousands of families." At the same time, bundling was vigorously defended not only as an expedient but a necessity, a convenience so generally sanctioned that it was almost sanctified. In those primitive times, it was, says Washington Irving in his Knickerbocker's History of New York, "considered as an indispensable preliminary to marriage, their courtships commencing where ours usually finish—by which means they acquired that intimacy with each other's good qualities before marriage, which has been pronounced by philosophers the sure basis of a happy union. Thus early did this cunning and ingenious people display a shrewdness at making a bargain, which has ever since distinguished them, and a strict adherence to the good old vulgar maxim about 'buying a pig in a poke.' "

The opposed attitudes to bundling are reflected in the following two poems. The first exists in several forms. As "A New Song in Favor of Courting," printed and sold in eighteenth-century Boston, it has been preserved by the American Antiquarian Society; but the original version was (so Stiles tells us) transcribed from a volume of manuscript ballads in the handwriting of Israel Perkins of Connecticut, written in 1786.

THE WHORE ON THE SNOW CRUST

Adam at first was formed of dust,
　　As we find on record;
And did receive a wife call'd Eve,
　　By a creative word.

From Adam's side a crooked bride,
　　We find complete in form;
Ordained that they in bed might lay
　　And keep each other warm.

To court indeed they had no need,
　　She was his wife at first,
And she was made to be his aid,
　　Whose origin was dust.

This new made pair full happy were,
　　And happy might remained,
If his helpmeet had never eat
　　The fruit that was restrained.

Tho' Adam's wife destroyed his life
　　In manner that is awful;
Yet marriage now we all allow
　　To be both just and lawful.

And now-a-days there are two ways.
  Which of the two is right:
To lie between sheets sweet and clean
  Or sit up all the night?

But some suppose bundling in clothes
  The good and wise doth vex;
Then let me know which way to go
  To court the fairer sex.

Whether they must be hugg'd and buss'd
  When sitting up all night;
Or whether they in bed may lay,
  Which reason doth invite?

Nature's request is, give me rest,
  Our bodies seek repose;
Night is the time, and 'tis no crime
  To bundle in our clothes.

Since in a bed a man and maid
  May bundle and be chaste;
It doth no good to burn up wood;
  It is a needless waste.

Let coat and shift be turned adrift,
  And breeches take their flight,
An honest man and virgin can
  Lie quiet all the night.

But if there be dishonesty
  Implanted in the mind,
Breeches nor smocks, nor scarce padlocks
  The rage of lust can bind.

Kate, Nance, and Sue proved just and true,
  Tho' bundling did practise;
But Ruth beguil'd and proved with child,
  Who bundling did despise.

Whores will be whores, and on the floor
  Where many has been laid,
To sit and smoke and ashes poke,
  Won't keep awake a maid.

Bastards are not at all times got
  In feather beds we know;
The strumpet's oath convinces both
  Oft times it is not so.

One whorish dame, I fear to name
   Lest I should give offence,
But in this town she was took down
   Not more than eight months since.

She was the first that on snow crust,
   I ever knew to gender;
I'll hint no more about this whore
   For fear I should offend her.

'Twas on the snow when Sol was low,
   And was in Capricorn,
A child was got, and it will not
   Be long ere it is born.

Now unto those that do oppose
   The bundling trade, I say
Perhaps there's more got on the floor,
   Than any other way.

In ancient books no knowledge is
   Of these things to be got;
Whether young men did bundle then,
   Or whether they did not.

Since ancient books says wife they took,
   It don't say how they courted;
Whether young men did bundle then,
   Or by the fire sported.

(But some do hold in times of old,
   That those about to wed,
Spent not the night, nor yet the light,
   By fire, or in the bed.)

They only meant to say they sent
   A man to choose a bride;
Isaac was so, but let me know,
   If any one beside.

Men don't pretend to trust a friend
   To choose him sheep or cows;
Much more a wife whom all his life
   He does expect to house.

Since it doth stand each one in hand
   To happify his life;
I would advise each to be wise,
   And choose a prudent wife.

Since bundling is not a thing
   That judgment will procure;
Go on young men and bundle then,
   But keep your bodies pure.

Of the various poetic protests against bundling, the most often quoted was first issued as a broadside. This blast was published toward the decline of the custom and, according to the scholarly researches of Dr. Stiles, "perhaps no single thing tended so much to break up the practice as the publication of a song, or ballad, in an almanac about 1785. . . . It had a much larger circulation than could have been obtained in any other way, and the descriptions were so pat that each one who saw them was disposed to apply them in a joking way to any other who was known to practice bundling. The result was such a storm of banter and ridicule that no girl had the courage to stand against it and continue to admit her lovers to her bed."

A NEW BUNDLING SONG

OR A REPROOF TO THOSE YOUNG COUNTRY WOMEN,
WHO FOLLOW THAT REPROACHFUL PRACTICE,
AND TO THEIR MOTHERS FOR UPHOLDING THEM THEREIN.

Since bundling very much abounds,
In many parts in country towns,
No doubt but some will spurn my song,
And say I'd better hold my tongue;
But none I'm sure will take offence,
Or deem my song impertinence,
But only those who guilty be,
And plainly here their pictures see.
Some maidens say, if through the nation,
Bundling should quite go out of fashion,
Courtship would lose its sweets; and they
Could have no fun till wedding day.
It shant be so, they rage and storm,
And country girls in clusters swarm,
And fly and buz, like angry bees,
And vow they'll bundle when they please.
Some mothers too, will plead their cause,
And give their daughters great applause,
And tell them, 'tis no sin nor shame,
For we, your mothers, did the same;
We hope the custom ne'er will alter,
But wish its enemies a halter.
Dissatisfaction great appear'd,

In several places where they've heard
Their preachers bold, aloud disclaim
That bundling is a burning shame;
This too was cause of direful rout
And talk'd and told of, all about,
That ministers should disapprove
Sparks courting in a bed of love,
So justified the custom more,
Than e'er was heard or known before.
The pulpit then it seems must yield,
And female valor take the field,
In places where their custom long
Increasing strength has grown so strong;
When mothers herein bear a sway,
And daughters joyfully obey.
And young men highly pleased too,
Good Lord! what can't the devil do.
Can this vile practice ne'er be broke?
Is there no way to give a stroke,
To wound it or to strike it dead,
And girls with sparks not go to bed.
'Twill strike them more than preacher's tongue,
To let the world know what they've done,
And let it be in common fame,
Held up to view a noted shame.

Young miss if this your practice be,
I'll teach you now yourself to see:
You plead you're honest, modest too,
But such a plea will never do;
For how can modesty consist,
With shameful practice such as this?
I'll give your answer to the life:
"You don't undress, like man and wife."
That is your plea, I'll freely own,
But who's your bondsmen when alone,
That further rules you will not break,
And marriage liberties partake?
Some really do, as I suppose,
Upon design keep on some clothes,
And yet in truth I'm not afraid
For to describe a bundling maid;
She'll sometimes say when she lies down,
She can't be cumber'd with a gown,
And that the weather is so warm,

To take if off can be no harm:
The girl it seems had been at strift;
For widest bosom to her shift,
She gownless, when the bed they're in,
The spark, nought feels but naked skin.
But she is modest, also chaste,
While only bare from neck to waist,
And he of boasted freedom sings,
Of all above her apron strings.
And where such freedoms great are shar'd
And further freedoms feebly bar'd,
I leave for others to relate,
How long she'll keep her virgin state.
Another pretty lass we'll scan,
That loves to bundle with a man,
For many different ways they take,
Through modest rules they all will break.
Some clothes I'll keep on, she will say,
For that has always been my way,
Nor would I be quite naked found,
With spark in bed, for thousand pound.
But petticoats, I've always said,
Were never made to wear in bed,
I'll take them off, keep on my gown,
And then I dare defy the town,
To charge me with immodesty,
While I so ever cautious be.
The spark was pleased with his maid,
Of apprehension quick he said,
Her witty scheme was keen he swore,
Lying in gown open before.
Another maid when in the dark,
Going to bed with her dear spark,
She'll tell him that 'tis rather shocking,
To bundle in with shoes and stockings.
Nor scrupling but she's quite discreet,
Lying with naked legs and feet,
With petticoat so thin and short,
That she is scarce the better for't;
But you will say that I'm unfair,
That some who bundle take more care,
For some we may with truth suppose,
Bundle in bed with all their clothes.
But bundler's clothes are no defence;
Unruly horses push the fence.

A certain fact I'll now relate,
That's true indeed without debate.
A bundling couple went to bed,
With all their clothes from foot to head,
That the defence might seem complete,
Each one was wrapped in a sheet.
But O! this bundling's such a witch
The man of her did catch the itch,
And so provoked was the wretch,
That she of him a bastard catch'd.
Ye bundle-misses, don't you blush,
You hang your heads and bid me hush.
If you wont tell me how you feel,
I'll ask your sparks, they best can tell.
But it is custom you will say,
And custom always bears the sway,
If I wont take my sparks to bed,
A laughing stock I shall be made;
A vulgar custom 'tis, I own,
Admir'd by many a slut and clown,
But 'tis a method of proceeding,
As much abhorr'd by those of breeding.
You're welcome to the lines I've penn'd,
For they were written by a friend,
Who'll think himself quite well rewarded,
If this vile practice is discarded.

The Nineteenth Century

GEORGE GORDON, LORD BYRON (1788–1824)

It has been said that Byron's feeling for himself was the greatest love affair of the nineteenth century. He dramatized his aristocratic inheritance, his finely chiseled profile, his flashing gifts, and his petted sensuality to such an extent that he became his own flamboyant creation. He traveled sporadically, wrote continuously, and made love indiscriminately. Famous at twenty-four, he was followed by women wherever he went. Caroline Lamb disguised herself as a boy in order to visit him in his rooms without being discovered. His wife, the lovely Anne Milbanke, left him within a year, claiming that Byron was having incestuous relations with his half sister, Augusta. Byron excused himself by saying that the charge was unfounded and, besides, he had not seen Augusta for so long a time that he regarded her as he would any other woman. Claire Clairmont, Shelley's sister-in-law, succumbed to him (or, as Byron insisted, pursued him) and bore the poet a daughter. In Italy the Countess Guiccioli, married to a nobleman, went about with him as his acknowledged inamorata, but Byron made no pretense about being faithful to her. Unashamedly vain and promiscuous, he boasted he was "studious in the day, dissolute in the evening," particularly when he was in the South. He explained it in a couplet:

> What men call gallantry and gods adult'ry
> Is much more common where the climate's sultry.

Even his death was the result of romanticism run riot. In revolt against the conventions, he took part in a revolutionary movement in Italy and, when it failed, joined the Greek patriots. However, instead of dying on the battlefield, he succumbed to fever. The sultry climate and his previous excesses aggravated his condition; he went into delirium and died at the age of thirty-six.

Author of a great quantity of serious and sentimental poetry, Byron was at his best when writing jaunty and satirical verse. Don Juan in particular is a triumph of wit and craftsmanship. Obviously a semi-autobiographical glorification of Byron's wishful fantasies and swashbuckling realities, Don Juan is bold in manner, brisk in rhyme, and gay as a set of naughty episodes—which it is.

FROM: DON JUAN

'Twas midnight—Donna Julia was in bed,
  Sleeping, most probably,—when at her door
Arose a clatter might awake the dead,
  If they had never been awoke before,
And that they have been so we all have read,
  And are to be so, at the least, once more;—
The door was fasten'd, but with voice and fist
First knocks were heard, then "Madam—Madam—hist!

"For God's sake, Madam—Madam—here's my master,
  With more than half the city at his back—
Was ever heard of such a curst disaster!
  'Tis not my fault—I kept good watch—Alack!
Do pray undo the bolt a little faster—
  They're on the stair just now, and in a crack
Will all be here; perhaps he yet may fly—
Surely the window's not so *very* high!"

By this time Don Alfonso was arrived,
  With torches, friends, and servants in great number;
The major part of them had long been wived,
  And therefore paused not to disturb the slumber
Of any wicked woman, who contrived
  By stealth her husband's temples to encumber:
Examples of this kind are so contagious,
Were *one* not punish'd, *all* would be outrageous.

I can't tell how, or why, or what suspicion
  Could enter into Don Alfonso's head;
But for a cavalier of his condition
  It surely was exceedingly ill-bred,
Without a word of previous admonition,
  To hold a levee round his lady's bed,
And summon lackeys, armed with fire and sword,
To prove himself the thing he most abhorred!

Poor Donna Julia! starting as from sleep
  (Mind—that I do not say—she had not slept),
Began at once to scream, and yawn, and weep;
  Her maid, Antonia, who was an adept,
Contrived to fling the bed-clothes in a heap,
  As if she had just now from out them crept:
I can't tell why she should take all this trouble
To prove her mistress had been sleeping double.

But Julia, mistress, and Antonia, maid,
   Appear'd like two poor harmless women, who
Of goblins, but still more of men afraid,
   Had thought one man might be deterr'd by two,
And therefore side by side were gently laid,
   Until the hours of absence should run through,
And truant husband should return, and say,
"My dear, I was the first who came away."

Now Julia found at length a voice, and cried,
   "In heaven's name, Don Alfonso, what d'ye mean?
Has madness seized you? Would that I had died
   Ere such a monster's victim I had been!
What may this midnight violence betide,
   A sudden fit of drunkenness or spleen?
Dare you suspect me, whom the thought would kill?
Search, then, the room!"—Alfonso said, "I will."

He search'd, *they* search'd, and rummaged everywhere,
   Closet and clothes-press, chest and window-seat,
And found much linen, lace, and several pair
   Of stockings, slippers, brushes, combs, complete,
With other articles of ladies fair,
   To keep them beautiful, or leave them neat:
Arras they prick'd and curtains with their swords,
And wounded several shutters, and some boards.

Under the bed they search'd, and there they found—
   No matter what—it was not that they sought;
They open'd windows, gazing if the ground
   Had signs or footmarks, but the earth said nought;
And then they stared each other's faces round:
   'Tis odd, not one of all these seekers thought,
And seems to me almost a sort of blunder,
Of looking *in* the bed as well as under.

During this inquisition Julia's tongue
   Was not asleep—"Yes, search and search," she cried,
"Insult on insult heap, and wrong on wrong!
   It was for this that I became a bride!
For this in silence I have suffered long
   A husband like Alfonso at my side;
But now I'll bear no more, nor here remain,
If there be law or lawyers, in all Spain.
"Yes, Don Alfonso! husband now no more,
   If ever you indeed deserved the name,

Is't worthy of your years?—you have threescore—
　　Fifty, or sixty, it is all the same—
Is't wise or fitting, causeless to explore
　　For facts against a virtuous woman's fame?
Ungrateful, perjured, barbarous Don Alfonso,
How dare you think your lady would go on so? . . .

"There is the closet, there the toilet, there
　　The antechamber—search them under, over;
There is the sofa, there the great arm-chair,
　　The chimney—which would really hold a lover.
I wish to sleep, and beg you will take care
　　And make no further noise, till you discover
The secret cavern of this lurking treasure—
And when 'tis found, let me, too, have that pleasure.

"And now, Hidalgo! now that you have thrown
　　Doubt upon me, confusion over all,
Pray have the courtesy to make it known
　　Who is the man you search for? How d'ye call
Him? what's his lineage? let him but be shown—
　　I hope he's young and handsome—is he tall?
Tell me—and be assured, that since you stain
Mine honour thus, it shall not be in vain."

She ceased, and turn'd upon her pillow; pale
　　She lay, her dark eyes flashing through their tears,
Like skies that rain and lighten; as a veil,
　　Waved and o'ershading her wan cheek, appears
Her streaming hair; the black curls strive, but fail,
　　To hide the glossy shoulder, which uprears
Its snow through all;—her soft lips lie apart,
And louder than her breathing beats her heart.

But Don Alfonso stood with downcast looks,
　　And, truth to say, he made a foolish figure;
When, after searching in five hundred nooks,
　　And treating a young wife with so much rigour,
He gain'd no point, except some self-rebukes,
　　Added to those his lady with such vigour
Had pour'd upon him for the last half hour,
Quick, thick, and heavy—as a thunder-shower.

He stood in act to speak, or rather stammer,
　　But sage Antonia cut him short before
The anvil of his speech received the hammer,
　　With "Pray, sir, leave the room, and say no more,

Or madam dies."—Alfonso mutter'd, "D—n her."
    But nothing else; the time of words was o'er.
He cast a rueful look or two, and did,
He knew not wherefore, that which he was bid.

With him retired his *"posse comitatus,"*
    The attorney last, who linger'd near the door
Reluctantly, still tarrying there as late as
    Antonia let him—not a little sore
At this most strange and unexplain'd *"hiatus"*
    In Don Alfonso's facts, which just now wore
An awkward look; as he revolved the case,
The door was fasten'd in his legal face.

No sooner was it bolted, than—Oh shame!
    Oh sin! Oh sorrow! and Oh womankind!
How can you do such things and keep your fame,
    Unless this world, and t'other too, be blind?
Nothing so dear as an unfilch'd good name!
    But to proceed—for there is more behind:
With much heartfelt reluctance be it said,
Young Juan slipp'd, half-smother'd, from the bed.

He had been hid—I don't pretend to say
    How, nor can I indeed describe the where—
Young, slender, and pack'd easily, he lay,
    No doubt, in little compass, round or square;
But pity him I neither must nor may
    His suffocation by that pretty pair;
'Twere better, sure, to die so, than be shut
With maudlin Clarence in his Malmsey butt.

And, secondly, I pity not, because
    He had no business to commit a sin,
Forbid by heavenly, fined by human laws,
    At least 'twas rather early to begin;
But at sixteen the conscience rarely gnaws
    So much as when we call our old debts in
At sixty years, and draw the accompts of evil,
And find a deuced balance with the devil.

Of his position I can give no notion:
    'Tis written in the Hebrew Chronicle,
How the physicians, leaving pill and potion,
    Prescribed, by way of blister, a young belle,

When old King David's blood grew dull in motion,
  And that the medicine answer'd very well;
Perhaps 'twas in a different way applied,
For David lived, but Juan nearly died.

HEINRICH HEINE (1797–1856)

Born in Düsseldorf in 1797, Heinrich Heine was a creature of self-con-
tradictions. A German, he spent most of his creative life in France. A Jew,
he became (so he could be admitted to the bar) a Protestant and married
his mistress, a Catholic. Educated to be a businessman, he turned to the
study of law, obtained his degree, and never practiced the profession. The
most lyric of German poets, he was also the bitterest and bawdiest; a ro-
manticist at heart, he blasted the roots of Romanticism. An extraordinary
stylist, he used the simple language of the people rather than the diction
of traditional poetry. A humorist, he was also a political idealist; a hack
journalist, he attained the stature of a liberator.

Heine's personal life was an equal mixture of fulfillments and frustrations.
The exile never ceased to nurse the defeat of a youthful hope of marrying
his cousin, but this did not prevent him from having a long liaison with a
practically illiterate French girl whom he eventually married. Unfaithful to
his mistress-wife, he was happy only in her company and, even under the
utmost provocation, never left her; she, in turn, alternately fought with and
adored him. She was his constant attendant during the eight years he lay
on his "mattress grave," suffering from a "consumption of the spinal marrow"
(now believed to have been syphilis) which slowly killed him.

His work surprises the reader by its combination of delicacy and coarseness,
by its sudden descents from the ecstatic to the rudely ironic, most of all by
its peculiarly acrid volatility. His cynical wit asserts itself in epigrams like
the following:

A wedding march and a military march have this in common: both suggest
a call to battle.

I will not say that women have no character; I would rather say that they
have a new character every new day.

Offered a choice between a bad conscience and a toothache, I would always
choose the former.

We praise the poet, the preacher, and the actor who move us to tears—
a talent they share with the common onion.

Women have just one way to make us happy but thirty thousand ways to make us miserable.

My desires are simple—a decent bed, satisfactory food, a little milk and butter, and a few trees in front of my door. But if the Lord wanted to make me really happy he would do one thing for me. He would grant me the pleasure of seeing six or seven of my enemies swinging from those trees. Then, with a heart full of compassion, I would forgive the injuries they had done to me. Yes, we should learn to forgive our enemies—but not until they are hanged.

The heart of Heine, however, is in his poetry, a bittersweet verse which is alternately moving and mocking, tender and satiric, uplifting and brutal. Casual as common speech, Heine's colloquial idiom added a new vocabulary to poetry—his seemingly improvised lines are as nearly perfect as lyrics can be. The translations, which render the meaning without the music, are by the editor, originally published in his Heinrich Heine: Paradox and Poetry.

YOU LOVE ME NOT

You love me not—you love me not.
  Oh, that's a trivial thing.
For when I see your face, my lot
  Is that of any king.

You hate me, hate me—even this.
  Your red lips dare declare it!
Well, let me have those lips to kiss,
  And I, my child, can bear it.

LAOCOÖN

O come, love—now I resign me,
  I yield myself to your charms;
O come, that you may intertwine me
  With the tenderest, supplest of arms.

And winding thus and wounding,
  Embracing and crushing, is shown
The fairest of serpents surrounding
  The happiest Laocoön.

BODY AND SOUL

It will not die, but solely
    This thought comes to condole,
How once I had you wholly;
    Your body and your soul.

Your body still I crave for,
    Your body's lovely growth.
Your soul you may dig a grave for;
    I've soul enough for us both!

I'll cut my spirit in two, dear,
    And breathe in you half of the whole
And clasp you—thus forming anew, dear,
    One perfect body and soul.

PASSION

'Tis a heavenly pleasure indeed,
    Curbing passion's wild excess;
And when I do not succeed
    'Tis a pleasure none the less.

QUANDARY

Which of them shall I fall in love with?
    Both of them make my senses swirl.
The mother's still a lovely woman;
    The daughter's an enchanting girl.

In those young arms and virgin beauties
    My trembling heart is almost caught.
But thrilling too are genial glances
    That understand each casual thought.

My heart resembles our gray brother,
    Who stands, a jackass self-confessed,
Between two bundles of his fodder,
    Uncertain which may taste the best.

THE MORNING AFTER

The bottles are empty, the breakfast was good,
    The ladies are gay as at night;
They pull off their corsets (I knew that they would);
    I think they are just a bit tight.

The shoulders—how white! The young breasts—how neat!
  I stand, like the dumbest of lovers.
They throw themselves down on the bed's snowy sheet,
  And, giggling, dive under the covers.

They draw the bed-curtains; I watch them prepare
  To shed the last wisp of their clothing . . .
And there, like the fool of the world, I stare
  At the foot of the bed, and do nothing.

A WOMAN

They loved each other beyond belief—
She was a strumpet, he was a thief;
Whenever she thought of his tricks, thereafter
She'd throw herself on the bed with laughter.

The day was spent with a reckless zest;
All night she lay upon his breast.
So when they took him, a moment after,
She watched at the window, with laughter.

He sent word, pleading, "Oh, come to me,
I need you, need you bitterly,
Yes, here and in the hereafter."
Her little head shook with laughter.

At six in the morning they swung him high;
At seven the turf on his grave was dry;
At eight, however, she quaffed her
Red wine, and sang with laughter!

SURFEIT

It makes a man feel happy
  It drains him to the dregs,
When he has three fair sweethearts
  And just one pair of legs.

I visit the first in the morning;
  I seek the second at night;
The third does not wait, but comes to me
  At noon in a blaze of light.

Farewell, my three fair sweethearts,
  Two legs are all I've got!
I'll go and make love to Nature
  In some more quiet spot.

THE EFFICIENT HOUSEWIFE

Lovely and efficient lady,
　House and farm are well endowed;
And your cellar's well appointed,
　And your fields are all well plowed.

In your clean and shining garden
　Weeds can never raise their heads;
And the straw, when threshing's over,
　Will be used to stuff the beds.

But your heart and lips, fair lady,
　Fallow lie, as hard as stone;
And the bed is but half useful
　Where you lie, and sleep alone.

HONORÉ DE BALZAC (1799–1850)

Honoré de Balzac wrote the prodigious sequence of novels that is called The Human Comedy, *recording in them the changing French society of his time with exacting detail and in all its complexity. In between writing the extensive chronicles of the France in which he lived, he recreated in equally remarkable detail another world altogether, the France of three hundred years earlier, localizing his narratives in Touraine where he was born. Scholars and historians agree that in the twenty-odd Droll Tales—he intended to write one hundred—Balzac was completely faithful to the mores and morals of the time of Rabelais, picturing that earlier society as though he had seen it with his own eyes. Even the language of the stories is true to their period.*

In addition to their remarkableness as creative phenomena, the tales have the liveliest wit, the most agile imagination, and the brilliant if bawdy exuberance that raises them to the rank of enduring art. Balzac meant them to adorn the base of his monumental literary edifice as "a childlike and humorous decoration." The spirit which pervades the tales is one of continual mockery, a spirit which the author points up by polishing off the stories with teasing, tongue-in-cheek "lessons."

FROM: DROLL STORIES

THE REPROACH

The fair laundress of Portillon-les-Tours was a girl blessed with as much cunning as if she had stolen that of six priests and three women at least.

She did not want for sweethearts, and had so many that one would have compared them, seeing them around her, to bees swarming of an evening towards their hive. An old silk dyer, who lived in the Rue Montfumier, and there possessed a house of scandalous magnificence, coming from his place at La Grenadière, passed on horseback through Portillon in order to gain the Bridge of Tours. By reason of the warmth of the evening, he was seized with a wild desire on seeing the pretty washerwoman sitting upon her doorstep. Now as for a very long time he had dreamed of this merry maid, his resolution was taken to make her his wife, and in a short time she was transformed from a washerwoman into a dyer's wife, a good townswoman with laces, fine linen, and furniture to spare, and was happy in spite of the dyer, seeing that she knew very well how to manage him. The good dyer had for a crony a silk-machinery manufacturer, who was small in stature, deformed for life, and full of wickedness. So on the wedding-day he said to the dyer, "You have done well to marry, my friend, *we* shall have a pretty wife;" and a thousand sly jokes, such as it is usual to address to a bridegroom.

In fact, this said hunchback courted the dyer's wife, who from her nature caring little for badly built people, laughed to scorn the request of the mechanician, and joked him about the springs, engines, and spools of which his shop was full. However, this great love of the hunchback was rebuffed by nothing, and became so irksome to the dyer's wife that she resolved to cure it by a thousand practical jokes. One evening, after the sempiternal pursuit, she told her lover to come to the back door and toward midnight she would open everything to him. Now note, this was on a winter's night; the Rue Montfumier is close by the Loire, and in this corner there continually blow, in winter, winds sharp as a hundred needle points. The good hunchback, well muffled up in his mantle, failed not to come, and trotted up and down to keep himself warm while waiting for the appointed hour. Toward midnight he was half frozen, as fidgety as thirty-two devils caught in a stole, and was about to give up his happiness, when a feeble light passed by the cracks of the window and came toward the little door.

"Ah! it is she!" said he.

And this hope warmed him once more. Then he got close to the door, and heard a little voice.

"Are you there?" said the dyer's wife to him.

"Yes."

"Cough, that I may see."

The hunchback began to cough.

"It is not you."

Then the hunchback said aloud,

"How do you mean, it is not I? Do you not recognize my voice? Open the door!"

"Who's there?" said the dyer, opening the window.

"There, you have awakened my husband, who returned from Amboise unexpectedly this evening."

Thereupon the dyer, seeing by the light of the moon a man at his door, threw a good big pot of cold water over him, and cried out, "Thieves! thieves!" in such a manner that the hunchback was forced to run away; but in his fear he failed to clear the chain stretched across the bottom of the road, and fell into the common sewer, which the sheriff had not then replaced by a sluice to discharge the mud into the Loire. In this bath the mechanician expected every moment to breathe his last, and cursed the fair Tascherette, for her husband's name being Taschereau, so was she called by way of a little joke by the people of Tours.

Carandas—for so was named the manufacturer of machines to weave, to spin, to spool, and wind the silk—was not sufficiently smitten to believe in the innocence of the dyer's wife, and swore a devilish hate against her. But some days afterward, when he had recovered from his wetting in the dyer's drain, he came to sup with his old comrade. Then the dyer's wife reasoned with him so well, flavored her words with so much honey, and wheedled him with so many fair promises, that he dismissed his suspicions.

He asked for a fresh assignation, and the fair Tascherette, with the face of a woman whose mind is dwelling on the subject, said to him, "Come to-morrow evening; my husband will be staying some days at Chenonceaux. The queen wishes to have some of her old dresses dyed and would settle the colors with him. It will take some time."

Carandas put on his best clothes, failed not to keep the appointment, appeared at the time fixed, and found a good supper prepared, lampreys, wine of Vouvray, fine white napkins—for it was not necessary to remonstrate with the dyer's wife on the color of her linen—and everything so well prepared that it was quite pleasant to him to see the dishes of fresh eels, to smell the good odor of the meats, and to admire a thousand nameless little things about the room, and La Tascherette fresh and appetizing as an apple on a hot day. Now the mechanician, excited to excess by these warm preparations, was on the point of attacking the charms of the dyer's wife, when Master Taschereau gave a loud knock at the street door.

"Ha!" said madame, "what has happened? Put yourself in the clothes chest, for I have been much abused respecting you; and if my husband finds you, he may undo you; he is so violent in his temper."

And immediately she thrust the hunchback into the chest, and went quickly to her good husband, who she knew well would be back from Chenonceaux to supper. Then the dyer was kissed warmly on both his eyes and both his ears, and he caught his good wife to him and bestowed upon her two hearty smacks with his lips that sounded all over the room. Then the pair sat down to supper, talked together, and finished by going to bed; and the mechanician heard all, though obliged to remain crumpled up, and not to cough or to make a single movement. He was in with the linen, crushed up as close as a sardine in a box, and had about as much air as he would have had at the bottom of a river; but he had, to divert him, the music of love, the sighs of the dyer, and the little jokes of La Tascherette.

At last, when he fancied his old comrade was asleep, he made an attempt to get out of the chest.

"Who is there?" said the dyer.

"What is the matter, my little one?" said his wife, lifting her nose above the counterpane.

"I heard a scratching," said the good man.

"We shall have rain tomorrow; it's the cat," replied his wife.

The good husband put his head back upon the pillow after having been gently embraced by his spouse. "There, my dear, you are a light sleeper. It's no good trying to make a proper husband of you. There, be good. Oh! oh! my little papa, your nightcap is on one side. There, put it on the other way, for you must look pretty even when you are asleep. There! are you all right?"

"Yes."

"Are you asleep?" said she, giving him a kiss.

"Yes."

In the morning the dyer's wife came softly and let out the mechanician, who was whiter than a ghost.

"Give me air, give me air!" said he.

And away he ran, cured of his love, but with as much hate in his heart as a pocket could hold of black wheat. The said hunchback left Tours and went to live in the town of Bruges, where certain merchants had sent for him to arrange the machinery for making hauberks.

During his long absence, Carandas, who had Moorish blood in his veins, since he was descended from an ancient Saracen left half dead after the great battle which took place between the Moors and the French in the commune of Ballan, in which place are the Landes of Charlemagne, where nothing grows because of the cursed wretches and infidels there interred, and where the grass disagrees even with the cows—this Carandas never rose up or lay down in the foreign land without thinking of how he could give strength to his desires of vengeance; and he was dreaming always of it, and wished nothing less than the death of the fair washerwoman of Portillon, and often would cry out, "I will eat her flesh! I will cook one of her breasts, and swallow it without sauce!" It was a tremendous hate of good constitution —a cardinal hate—a hate of a wasp or old maid. It was all known hates molded into one single hate, which boiled itself, concocted itself, and resolved itself into an elixir of wicked and diabolical sentiments, warmed at the fire of the most flaming furnaces of hell—it was, in fact, a master hate!

Now one fine day, the said Carandas came back into Touraine with much wealth that he brought from the country of Flanders, where he had sold his mechanical secrets. He bought a splendid house in the Rue Montfumier, which is still to be seen, and is the astonishment of the passers-by, because it has certain very queer round humps fashioned upon the stones of the wall. Carandas, the hater, found many notable changes at the house of his friend the dyer, for the good man had two sweet children, who, by curious chance, presented no resemblance either to the mother or to the father. But as it is necessary that children bear a resemblance to some one, there are certain people who look for the features of their ancestors, when they are good-looking—the flatterers. So it was found by the good husband that his two boys were like one of his uncles, formerly a priest at Notre Dame de l'Egrinolles, but, according to certain jokers, these two children were the living portraits of a good-looking shaven crown officiating in the church of Notre Dame la Riche, a celebrated parish situated between Tours and Plessis. Now believe one thing, and inculcate it in your minds, and when in this book you shall only have gleaned, gathered, extracted and learned this one principle of truth, look upon yourself as a lucky man—namely, that a man can never dispense with his nose, *id est*, that a man will always be snotty—that is to say, he will remain a man, and thus will continue throughout all future centuries to laugh and drink, to find himself in his shirt without feeling either better or worse there, and will have the same occupations. But these preparatory ideas are to better fix in the understanding that this two-footed soul will always accept as true these things which flatter his passions, caress his hates, or serve his amours; from this comes logic. So it was that, the first day the above-mentioned Carandas saw his old comrade's children, saw the handsome priest, saw the beautiful wife of the dyer, saw Le Taschereau, all seated at the table, and saw to his detriment the best piece of lamprey given with a certain air by La Tascherette to her friend the priest, the mechanician said to himself, "My old friend is a cuckold, his wife intrigues with the little confessor, and the children have been begotten with his holy water. I'll show them that the hunchbacks have something more than other men."

And this was true—true as it is that Tours has always had its feet in the Loire, like a pretty girl who bathes herself and plays with the water, making a flick-flack, by beating the waves with her fair white hands; for this town is more smiling, merry, loving, fresh, flowery, and fragrant than all the other towns of the world, which are not worthy to comb her locks, or to buckle her waistband. And be sure if you go there you will find in the center of it, a sweet place, in which is a delicious street where every one promenades, where there is always a breeze, shade, sun, rain, and love. Ha! ha! laugh away, but go there. It is a street always new, always royal, always imperial—a patriotic street, a street with two paths, a street open at both ends, a wide street, a street so large that no one has ever cried, "Out of the way!" there. A street which does not wear out, a street which leads to the abbey of Grand-Mont, and to a trench, which works very well with the bridge, and at the end of which is a fine fair ground. A street well paved, well built, well washed, as clean as a glass, populous, silent at certain times, a coquette with a sweet nightcap on its pretty blue tiles—to be short, it is the street where I was born; it is the queen of streets, always between the earth and the sky; a street with a fountain; a street which lacks nothing to be celebrated among streets; and, in fact, it is the real street, the only street of Tours. If there are others, they are dark, muddy, narrow, and damp, and all come respectfully to salute this noble street, which commands them . . . Where am I? For once in this street no one cares to come out of it, so pleasant it is. But I owed this filial homage, this descriptive hymn sung from the heart, to my natal street, at the corners of which there are wanting only the brave figures of my good master, Rabelais, and of Monsieur Descartes, both unknown to the people of the country.

To resume: the said Carandas was, on his return from Flanders, entertained by his comrade and by all those by whom he was liked for his jokes, his drollery and quaint remarks. The hunchback appeared cured of his old love, embraced the children, and when he was alone with the dyer's wife recalled the night in the clothes chest, and the night in the sewer, to her memory, saying to her, "Ha! ha! What games you used to have with me."

"It was your own fault," she said, laughing. "If you had allowed yourself by reason of your great love to be ridiculed and bantered a few more times, you might have made an impression on me, like the others."

Thereupon Carandas began to laugh, though inwardly raging. Seeing the chest where he had nearly suffocated, his anger increased the more violently because the sweet creature had become still more beautiful, like all those who are permanently young from bathing in the waters of youth. The mechanician studied the proceedings in the way of cuckoldom at his neighbor's house in order to revenge himself, for as many houses as there are, so many varieties of manner are there in this business; and although all amours resemble each other in the same manner that all men resemble each other, it is proved to the abstractors of true things, that for the happiness of women, each love has its especial physiognomy, and if there is nothing that resembles a man so much as a man, there is also nothing differs from a man so much as a man. That it is which confuses all things, or explains the thousand fantasies of women, who seek the best men with a thousand pains and a thousand pleasures, perhaps more one than the other. But how can I blame them for their essays, changes, and contradictory aims? Why, Nature frisks and wriggles, twists and turns about, and you expect a woman to remain still! Do you know if ice is really cold? No. Well, then, neither do you know that cuckoldom is not a lucky chance, the produce of brains well furnished and better made than all others. . . . Do you understand? So in all languages does Nature belong to the feminine gender, being a thing essentially changeable and fruitful and fertile in tricks.

Now Carandas soon recognized the fact that among cuckoldoms the best understood and the most discreet is ecclesistical cuckoldom. This is how the good dyer's wife had laid her plans. She went always toward her cottage at Grenadière-les-St.-Cyr on the eve of the Sabbath, leaving her good husband to finish his work, to count up and check his books, and to pay his workmen; then Taschereau would join her there on the morrow, and always found a good breakfast ready and his good wife gay, and always brought the priest with him. The fact is, this damnable priest crossed the Loire the night before in a small boat, in order to keep the dyer's wife warm, and to calm her fancies, in order that she might sleep well during the night, a duty which young men understand very well. Then this fine curber of fantasies got back to his house in the morning by the time Taschereau came to invite him to spend the day at La Grenadière, and the cuckold always found the priest asleep in his bed. The boatman being well paid, no one knew anything of these goings on, for the lover journeyed the night before after nightfall, and on the Sunday in the early morning. As soon as Carandas had verified the arrangement and constant practice of these gallant diversions, he determined to wait for a day when the lovers would meet, hungry one for the other, after some accidental abstinence. This meeting took place very soon, and the curious hunchback saw the boatman waiting below the square, at the Canal St. Antoine, for the young priest, who was handsome, blond, slender, and well shaped. Then the mechanician went to find the old dyer, who always loved his wife and always believed himself the only man who had a finger in her pie.

"Ah! good evening, old friend," said Carandas to Taschereau; and Taschereau made him a bow.

Then the mechanician related to him all the secret festivals of love, vomited words of peculiar import, and pricked the dyer on all sides.

At length, seeing he was ready to kill both his wife and the priest, Carandas said to him, "My good neighbor, I have brought back from Flanders a poisoned sword, which will instantly kill anyone if it only make a scratch upon him. Now, directly you shall have merely touched your wench and her paramour, they will die."

"Let us go and fetch it," said the dyer.

Then the two merchants went in great haste to the house of the hunchback, to get the sword and rush off to the country.

"But shall we find them *in flagrante delicto?*" asked Taschereau.

"You will see," said the hunchback, jeering his friend. In fact, the cuckold had not long to wait to behold the joy of the two lovers.

The sweet wench and her well-beloved were busy trying to catch, in a certain lake that you probably know, the little bird that never stays in it, and they were laughing and trying, and still laughing.

"Ah, my darling!" said she, clasping him, as though she wished to take an outline of him on her chest, "I love thee so much I should like to eat thee! Nay, more than that, to have you in my skin, so that you might never quit me."

"I should like it too," replied the priest, "but as you can't have me altogether, you must try a little bit at a time."

It was at this moment that the husband entered, his sword unsheathed and flourished above him. The beautiful Tascherette, who knew her lord's face well, saw what would be the fate of her well-beloved, the priest. But suddenly she sprang towards the good man, half naked, her hair streaming over her, beautiful with shame but more beautiful with love, and cried to him, "Stay, unhappy man! Wouldst thou kill the father of thy children?" Thereupon the good dyer, staggered by the paternal majesty of cuckoldom, and perhaps also by the fire of his wife's eyes, let the sword fall upon the foot of the hunchback, who had followed him, and thus killed him.

This teaches us not to be spiteful.

HOW THE PRETTY MAID OF PORTILLON CONVINCED HER JUDGE

The maid of Portillon, who became, as every one knows, La Tascherette, was, before she became a dyer, a laundress at the said place of Portillon, from which she took her name. If any there be who do not know Tours, it may be well to state that Portillon is down the Loire, on the same side as St. Cyr, about as far from the bridge which leads to the cathedral of Tours as the said bridge is distant from Marmoutier, since the bridge is in the center of the embankment between Portillon and Marmoutier. Do you thoroughly understand?

Yes? Good! Now the maid had there her washhouse, from which she ran to the Loire with her washing in a second, and took the ferryboat to get to St. Martin, which was on the other side of the river, for she had to deliver the greater part of her work in Chateauneuf and other places. About Midsummer day, seven years before marrying old Taschereau, she had just reached the right age to be loved. As she was a merry girl she allowed herself to be loved, without making a choice from any of the lads who pursued her with their intentions. Although there used to come to the bench under her window the son of Rabelais, who had seven boats on the Loire, Jehan's eldest, Marchandeau the tailor, and Peccard the ecclesiastical goldsmith, she made fun of them all, because she wished to be taken to church before burthening herself with a man, which proves that she was an honest woman until she was wheedled out of her virtue. She was one of those girls who take great care not to be contaminated, but who, if by chance they get deceived, let things take their course, thinking that for one stain or for fifty a good polishing up is necessary. These characters demand our indulgence.

A young noble of the court perceived her one day when she was crossing the water in the glare of the noonday sun, which lit up her ample charms, and seeing her, asked who she was. An old man, who was working on the banks, told him she was called the Pretty Maid of Portillon, a laundress, celebrated for her merry ways and her virtue. This young lord, besides ruffles to starch, had many precious linen draperies and things; he resolved to give the custom of his house to this girl, whom he stopped on the road. He was thanked by her and heartily, because he was the Sire du Fou, the king's chamberlain. This encounter made her so joyful that her mouth was full of his name. She talked about it a great deal to the people of St. Martin, and when she got back to her washhouse was still full of it, and on the morrow at her work her tongue went nineteen to the dozen, and all on the same subject, so that as much was said concerning my Lord du Fou in Portillon as of God in a sermon; that is, a great deal too much.

"If she works like that in cold water, what will she do in warm?" said an old washerwoman. "She wants Du Fou; he'll give her Du Fou!"

The first time this giddy wench, with her head full of Monsieur du Fou, had to deliver the linen at his hotel, the chamberlain wished to see her, and was very profuse in praises and compliments concerning her charms, and wound up by telling her that she was not at all silly to be beautiful, and therefore he would give her more than she expected. The deed followed the word, for the moment his people were out of the room, he began to caress the maid, who thinking he was about to take out the money from his purse, dared not look at the purse, but said, like a girl ashamed to take her wages, "It will be for the first time."

"It will be soon," said he.

Some people say that he had great difficulty in forcing her to accept what he offered her, and hardly forced her at all; others that he forced her badly, because she came out, like an army flagging on the route, crying and groaning, and came to the judge. It happened that the judge was out. La Portillone awaited his return in his room, weeping and saying to the servant that she had been robbed, because Monseigneur du Fou had given her nothing but his mischief; whilst a canon of the chapter used to give her large sums for that which M. du Fou wanted for nothing. If she loved a man she would think it wise to do things for him for nothing, because it would be a pleasure to her; but the chamberlain had treated her roughly, and not kindly and gently, as he should have done, and that therefore he owed her the thousand crowns of the canon. The judge came in, saw the wench, and wished to kiss her, but she put herself on guard, and said she had come to make a complaint. The judge replied that certainly she could have the offender hanged if she liked, because he was most anxious to serve her. The injured maiden replied that she did not wish the death of her man, but that he should pay her a thousand gold crowns, because she had been robbed against her will.

"Ha! ha!" said the judge, "what he took was worth more than that."

"For the thousand crowns I'll cry quits, because I shall be able to live without washing."

"He who has robbed you, is he well off?"

"Oh, yes."

"Then he shall pay dearly for it. Who is it?"

"Monseigneur du Fou."

"Oh, that alters the case," said the judge.

"But justice?" said she.

"I said the case, not the justice of it," replied the judge. "I must know how the affair occurred."

Then the girl related naïvely how she was arranging the young lord's ruffles in his wardrobe, when he began to play with her skirts, and she turned round, saying:

"Go on with you!"

"You have no case," said the judge, "for by that speech he thought that you gave him leave to go on. Ha! ha!"

Then she declared that she had defended herself, weeping and crying out, and that that constitutes an assault.

"A wench's antics to incite him," said the judge.

Finally, La Portillone declared that against her will she had been taken around the waist and thrown, although she had kicked and cried and struggled, but that seeing no help at hand, she had lost courage.

"Good! good!" said the judge. "Did you take pleasure in the affair?"

"No," she said. "My anguish can only be paid for with a thousand crowns."

"My dear," said the judge, "I cannot receive your complaint, because I believe no girl can be thus treated against her will."

"Hi! hi! hi! Ask your servant," said the little laundress, sobbing, "and hear what she'll tell you."

The servant affirmed that there were pleasant assaults and unpleasant ones; that if La Portillone had received neither amusement nor money, either one or the other was due her. This wise counsel threw the judge into a state of great perplexity.

"Jacqueline," said he, "before I sup I'll get to the bottom of this. Now go and fetch my needle and the red thread that I sew legal paper bags with."

Jacqueline came back with a big needle, pierced with a pretty little hole, and a big red thread, such as the judges use. Then she remained standing to see the question decided, very much disturbed, as was also the complainant at these mysterious preparations.

"My dear," said the judge, "I am going to hold the bodkin, of which the eye is sufficiently large, to put this thread into it without trouble. If you do put it in, I will take up your case, and will make Monseigneur offer you a compromise."

"What's that?" said she. "I will not allow it."

"It is a word used in justice to signify an agreement."

"A compromise is then agreeable with justice?" said La Portillone.

"My dear, this violence has also opened your mind. Are you ready?"

"Yes," said she.

The waggish judge gave the poor nymph fair play, holding the eye steady for her; but when she wished to slip in the thread that she had twisted to make straight, he moved a little, and the thread went on the other side. She suspected the judge's argument, wetted the thread, stretched it, and came back again. The judge moved, twisted about, and wriggled like a bashful maid—and still the cursed thread would not enter. The girl kept trying at the eye, and the judge kept fidgeting. The union of the thread and the needle could not be consummated; the bodkin remained virgin, and the servant began to laugh, saying to La Portillone that she knew better how to endure than to perform. Then the roguish judge laughed too, and the fair Portillone cried for her golden crowns.

"If you don't keep still," cried she, losing patience; "if you keep moving about I shall never be able to put the thread in."

"Then, my dear, if you had done the same, Monseigneur would have been unsuccessful too. Think, too, how easy is the one affair, and how difficult the other."

The pretty wench, who declared she had been forced, remained thoughtful, and sought to find a means to convince the judge by showing how she had been compelled to yield, since the honor of all poor girls liable to violence was at stake.

"Monseigneur, in order that the bet may be fair, I must do exactly as the young lord did. If I had only had to move I should be moving still, but he went through other performances."

"Let us hear them," replied the judge.

Then La Portillone straightens the thread; and rubs it in the wax of the candle, to make it firm and straight; then she looks towards the eye of the bodkin, held by the judge, slipping always to the right or to the left. Then she began making endearing little speeches, such as, "Ah, the pretty little bodkin! what a pretty mark to aim at! Never did I see such a little jewel! What a pretty little eye! Let me put this little thread into it! Ah! you will hurt my poor thread, my nice little thread! Keep still! Come, my love of a judge, judge of my love! Won't the thread go nicely into this iron gate, which makes good use of the thread, for it comes out very much out of order?" Then she burst out laughing, for she was better up in this game than the judge, who laughed too, so saucy and comical and arch was she, pushing the thread backward and forward. She kept the poor judge with the case in his hand until seven o'clock, keeping on fidgeting and moving about like a schoolboy let loose; but as La Portillone kept on trying to put the thread in, he could not help it. As, however, his joint was burning, and his wrist was tired, he was obliged to rest himself for a minute on the side of the table. Then very dexterously the fair maid of Portillon slipped the thread in, saying:

"That's how the thing occurred."

"But my joint was burning."

"So was mine," said she.

The judge, convinced, told La Portillone that he would speak to Monseigneur du Fou, and would himself carry the affair through, since it was certain the young lord had embraced her against her will, but that for valid reasons he would keep the affair dark. On the morrow the judge went to the Court and saw the Monseigneur du Fou, to whom he recounted the young woman's complaint, and how she had set forth her case. This complaint lodged in Court tickled the king immensely. Young Du Fou having said that there was some truth in it, the king asked if he had much difficulty, and as he replied, innocently, "No," the king declared the girl was quite worth a hundred gold crowns, and the chamberlain gave them to the judge, in order not to be taxed with stinginess, and said that starch would be a good income to La Portillone. The judge came back to La Portillone, and said, smiling, that he had raised a hundred gold crowns for her. But if she desired the balance of the thousand, there were at that moment in the king's apartments certain lords who, knowing the case, had offered to make up the sum for her with her consent. The little hussy did not refuse this offer, saying, that in order to do no more washing in the future she did not mind doing a little hard work now. She gratefully acknowledged the trouble the good judge had taken, and gained her thousand crowns in a month.

From this came the falsehoods and jokes concerning her because out of these ten lords jealousy made a hundred, while, differently from young men, La Portillone settled down to a virtuous life directly she had her thousand crowns. Even a duke, who would have counted out five hundred crowns, would have found this girl rebellious, which proves she was niggardly with her property. It is true that the king caused her to be sent for to his retreat of Rue Quinquangrogne, on the mall of Chardonneret, found her extremely pretty, exceedingly affectionate, enjoyed her society, and forbade the sergeants to interfere with her in any way whatever. Seeing she was so beautiful, Nicole Beaupertuis, the king's mistress, gave her a hundred gold crowns to go to Orléans, in order to see if the color of the Loire was the same there as at Portillon. She went there, and the more willingly because she did not care very much for the king. When the good man came who confessed the king in his last hour, and was afterward canonized, La Portillone went to him to polish up her conscience, did penance, and founded a bed in the leper house of St. Lazare-les-Tours. Many ladies whom you know have been assaulted by more than two lords, and have founded no other beds than those of their own houses. It is well to relate this fact in order to cleanse the reputation of this honest girl, who herself once washed dirty things, and who afterward became famous for her clever tricks and her wit. She gave a proof of her merit in marrying Taschereau, whom she cuckolded right merrily, as has been related in the story of "The Reproach." This proves to us most satisfactorily that with strength and patience justice itself can be violated.

CONCERNING A POOR MAN WHO WAS CALLED LE VIEUX PAR-CHEMINS

The old chronicler who furnished the hemp to weave the present story, is said to have lived at the time when the affair occurred in the city of Rouen. In the environs of this fair town, where at that time dwelt Duke Richard, an old man used to beg, whose name was Tryballot, but to whom was given the nickname of *Le Vieux par-Chemins*, or Old Man of the Roads; not because he was yellow and dry as vellum, but because he was always in the highways and the byways—up hill and down dale—slept with the sky for his counterpane, and went about in rags and tatters. Notwithstanding this, he was very popular in the duchy, where every one had grown used to him, so much so that if the month went by without any one seeing his cup held toward them, people would say, "Where is the old man?" and the usual answer was, "On the roads."

This said man had had for a father a Tryballot, who was in his lifetime a skilled artisan, so economical and careful that he left considerable wealth to his son.

But the young lad soon frittered it away, for he was the very opposite of the old fellow, who, returning from the fields to his house, picked up, now here, now there, many a little stick of wood left right and left, saying, conscientiously, that one should never come home empty handed. Thus he warmed himself in winter at the expense of the careless; and he did well. Every one recognized what a good example this was for the country, since a year before his death no one left a morsel of wood on the road; he had compelled the most dissipated to be thrifty and orderly. But his son made ducks and drakes of everything, and did not follow his wise examples. The father had predicted the thing. From the boy's earliest youth, when the good Tryballot set him to watch the birds who came to eat the peas, the beans, and the grain, and to drive the thieves away, above all, the jays, who spoiled everything, he would study their habits, and took delight in watching with what grace they came and went, flew off loaded, and returned, watching with a quick eye the snares and nets; and he would laugh heartily at their cleverness in avoiding them. Tryballot senior went into a passion when he found his grain considerably less in measure. But although he pulled his son's ears whenever he caught him idling and trifling under a nut tree, the little rascal did not alter his conduct, but continued to study the habits of the blackbirds, sparrows, and other intelligent marauders. One day his father told him that he would be wise to model himself after them, for that if he continued this kind of life, he would be compelled in his old age, like them, to pilfer, and like them, would be pursued by justice. This came true; for, as has before been stated, he dissipated in a few days the crowns which his careful father had acquired in a lifetime. He dealt with men as he did with the sparrows, letting every one put a hand in his pocket, and contemplating the grace and polite demeanor of those who assisted to empty it. The end of his wealth was thus soon reached. When the devil had the empty money bag to himself, Tryballot did not appear at all cut up, saying that he "did not wish to damn himself for this world's goods, and that he had studied philosophy in the school of the birds."

After having thoroughly enjoyed himself, of all his goods there only remained to him a goblet bought at Landict, and three dice, quite sufficient furniture for drinking and gambling, so that he went about without being encumbered, as are the great, with chariots, carpets, dripping pans, and an infinite number of varlets. Tryballot wished to see his good friends, but they no longer knew him, which fact gave him leave no longer to recognize any one. Seeing this, he determined to choose a profession in which there was nothing to do and plenty to gain. Thinking this over, he remembered the indulgences of the blackbirds and the sparrows. Then the good Tryballot selected for his profession that of begging money at people's houses and pilfering. From the first day, charitable people gave him something, and Tryballot was content, finding the business good, without advance money or bad debts; on the contrary, full of accommodation. He went about it so heartily, that he was liked everywhere, and received a thousand consolations refused to rich people. The good man watched the peasants planting, sowing, reaping, and making harvest, and said to himself, that they worked a little for him as well. He who had a pig in his larder owed him a bit of it, without suspecting it. The man who baked a loaf in his oven often cooked it for Tryballot without knowing it. He took nothing by force; on the contrary, people said to him kindly, while making him a present, "Here, Vieux par-Chemins, cheer up, old fellow. How are you? Come, take this; the cat began it, you can finish it."

Vieux par-Chemins was at all the weddings, baptisms, and funerals, because he went everywhere where there was, openly or secretly, merriment and feasting. He religiously kept the statutes and canons of his order—namely, to do nothing, because if he had been able to do the smallest amount of work no one would ever give him anything again. After having refreshed himself, this wise man would lie at full length in a ditch, or against a church wall, and think over public affairs; and then he would philosophize, like his pretty tutors, the blackbirds, jays, and sparrows, and thought a good deal while mumping; for, because his apparel was poor, was that a reason his understanding should not be rich? His philosophy amused his clients, to whom he would repeat, by way of thanks, the finest aphorisms of his science. According to him, suppers produced gout in the rich; he boasted that he had nimble feet, because his shoemaker gave him boots that did not pinch his corns. There were aching heads beneath diadems, but his never ached, because it was touched neither by luxury nor any other chaplet. And again, that jeweled rings hindered the circulation of the blood. Although he covered himself with sores after the manner of cadgers, you may be sure he was as sound as a child at the baptismal font. The good man disported himself with other rogues, playing with his three dice, which he kept to remind him to spend his coppers, in order that he might always be poor. In spite of his vow, he was, like all the order of mendicants, so wealthy that one day at the Paschal feast, another beggar wishing to rent his profit from him, Vieux par-Chemins refused ten crowns for it; in fact, the same evening he spent fourteen crowns in drinking the healths of the almsgivers, because it is in the statutes of beggary that one should show one's gratitude to donors. Although he carefully got rid of that which had been a source of anxiety to others, who having too much wealth went in search of poverty, he was happier with nothing in the world than when he had his father's money.

At last Vieux par-Chemins reached the age of eighty-two years, having never been a single day without picking up money, and possessed the healthiest color and complexion imaginable. He believed that if he had persevered in the race for wealth he would have been spoiled and buried years before. It is possible he was right.

In his early youth Vieux par-Chemins had the illustrious virtue of being very partial to the ladies; and his abundance of love was, it is said, the result of his studies among the sparrows. Thus it was that he was always ready to give the ladies his assistance in counting the joists, and this generosity finds its physical cause in the fact that, having nothing to do, he was always ready to do something. His secret virtues brought about, it is said, that popularity which he enjoyed in the provinces. Certain people say that the lady of Caumont had him in her castle, to learn the truth about these qualities, and kept him there for a week, to prevent him begging. But the good man jumped over the hedges and fled in great terror of being rich. Advancing in age, this great quintessencer found himself disdained, although his notable faculties of loving were in no way impaired. This unjust turning away on the part of the female tribe caused the first trouble of Vieux par-Chemins, and the celebrated trial of Rouen, to which it is time I came.

In the eighty-second year of his age he was compelled to remain continent for about seven months, during which time he met no woman kindly disposed toward him; and he declared before the judge that that caused the greatest astonishment of his long and honorable life. In this most pitiable state he saw in the fields during the merry month of May a girl, who by chance was a maiden, and minding cows. The heat was so excessive that this cowherdess had stretched herself beneath the shadow of a beech tree, her face to the ground, after the custom of people who labor in the fields, in order to get a little nap while her animals were grazing. She was awakened by the deed of the old man, who had stolen from her that which a poor girl can only lose once. Finding herself ruined without receiving from the process either knowledge or pleasure, she cried out so loudly that the people working in the fields ran to her, and were called upon by her as witnesses, at the time when that destruction was visible in her which is appropriate only to a bridal night. She cried and groaned, saying that the old ape might just as well have played his tricks on her mother, who would have said nothing.

He made answer to the peasants, who had already raised their hoes to kill him, that he had been compelled to enjoy himself. These people objected that a man can enjoy himself very well without enjoying a maiden—a case for the provost, which would bring him straight to the gallows; and he was taken with a great clamor to the gaol at Rouen.

The girl, interrogated by the provost, declared that she was sleeping in order to do something, and that she thought she was dreaming of her lover, with whom she was then at loggerheads, because before marriage he wished to take certain liberties; and, jokingly, in this dream she let him reconnoiter to a certain extent, in order to avoid any dispute afterward, and that in spite of her prohibition he went further than she had given him leave to go, and finding more pain than pleasure in the affair, she had been awakened by Vieux par-Chemins, who had attacked her as a Gray Friar would a ham at the end of Lent.

This trial caused so great a commotion in the town of Rouen that the provost was sent for by the duke, who had an intense desire to know if the thing were true. Upon the affirmation of the provost, he ordered Vieux par-

Chemins to be brought to his palace, in order that he might hear what defense he had to make. The poor old fellow appeared before the prince, and informed him naïvely of the misfortune which his impulsive nature had brought upon him, declaring that he was like a young fellow impelled by imperious desires; that up to the present year he had sweethearts of his own, but for the last eight months he had been a total abstainer; that he was too poor to find favor with girls of the town; that honest women, who once were charitable to him, had taken a dislike to his hair, which had feloniously turned white in spite of the green love of his youth, and that he felt compelled to avail himself of the chance when he saw this maiden who, stretched out at full length underneath the beech tree, left visible the lining of her dress and two hemispheres white as snow, which had deprived him of reason; that the fault was the girl's and not his, because young maidens should be forbidden to entice passers-by by showing them that which caused Venus to be named *Callipyge*; finally, the prince ought to be aware what trouble a man has to control himself at the hour of noon, because it was at that time of day when King David was smitten with the charms of Uriah's wife; that where a Hebrew king, beloved of God, had succumbed, a poor man, deprived of all joy and reduced to begging for his bread, could not hope to escape; that, for the matter of that, he was quite willing to sing Psalms for the remainder of his days, and play upon the lute by way of penance, in imitation of the said king, who had had the misfortune to slay a husband, while he had only done a trifling injury to a peasant girl. The duke listened to the arguments of Vieux par-Chemins, and said that he was a man of good parts. Then he made this memorable decree, that if, as this beggar declared, he had need of such gratifications at his age, he gave permission to prove it at the foot of the ladder which he would have to mount to be hanged, according to the sentence already passed on him by the provost; that if then, the rope being round his neck, between the priest and the hangman, a like desire seized him, he should have a free pardon.

This decree becoming known, there was a tremendous crowd to see the old fellow led to the gallows. There was a line drawn up as if for a ducal entry, and in it a many more bonnets than hats. Vieux par-Chemins was saved by a lady curious to see how this precious violator would finish his career. She told the duke that religion demanded that he should have a fair chance. And she dressed herself out as if for a ball; she brought intentionally into evidence two hillocks of such snowy whiteness that the whitest linen neckerchief would have paled before them; indeed, these fruits of love stood out, without a wrinkle, over her corset, like two beautiful apples, and made one's mouth water, so exquisite were they. This noble lady, who was one of those who rouse one's manhood, had a smile ready on her lips for the old fellow. Vieux par-Chemins, dressed in garments of coarse cloth, more certain of being in the desired state after hanging than before it, came along between the officers of justice, with a sad countenance, glancing now here and there, and seeing nothing but headdresses; and he would, he declared, have given a hundred crowns for a girl tucked up as was the cowherdess, whose lovely plump white thighs, though they had been his ruin, he still remembered, and they might still have saved him; but, as he was old, the remembrance was not sufficiently recent. But when, at the foot of the ladder, he saw the twin charms of the lady, and the pretty delta that their confluent rotundities produced, his swelling codpiece revealed his excitement.

"Make haste and see that the required conditions are fulfilled," said he to the officers. "I have gained my pardon, but I cannot answer for my savior."

The lady was well pleased with this homage, which, she said, was greater than his offense. The guards, whose business it was to proceed to a verification, believed the culprit to be the devil, because never in their writs had they seen an I so perpendicular as was the old man. He was marched in triumph through the town to the palace of the duke, to whom the guards and others stated the facts. In that period of ignorance, this affair was thought so much of that the town voted the erection of a column on the spot where the old fellow gained his pardon, and he was portrayed thereon in stone in the attitude he assumed at the sight of that honest and virtuous lady. The statue was still to be seen when Rouen was taken by the English, and the writers of the period have included this history among the notable events of the reign.

As the town offered to supply the old man with all he required, and see to his sustenance, clothing, and amusements, the good duke arranged matters by giving the injured maiden a thousand crowns and marrying her to her seducer, who then lost his name of Vieux par-Chemins. He was named by the duke the Sieur de Bonne-C——. This wife was confined nine months afterward of a perfectly formed male child, alive and kicking, and born with two teeth. From this marriage came the House of Bonne-C——, who, from motives modest but wrong, besought out well-beloved king, Louis Eleventh, to grant them letters patent to change their name to that of Bonne-Chose. The king pointed out to the Sieur de Bonne-C—— that there was in the State of Venice an illustrious family named *Coglioni*, who wore three "C—— au naturel" on their coat of arms. The gentlemen of the House of Bonne-C—— stated to the king that their wives were ashamed to be thus called in public assemblies; the king answered that they would lose a good deal, because there is a good deal in a name. Nevertheless, he granted the letters. After that this race was known by this name, and founded families in many provinces. The first Sieur de Bonne-C—— lived another twenty-seven years, and had another son and two daughters. But he grieved much at becoming rich, and no longer being able to pick up a living in the streets.

From this you can obtain finer lessons and higher morals than from any story you will read all your life long—of course, excepting these hundred glorious *Droll Tales*—namely, that never could adventure of this sort have happened to the impaired and ruined constitutions of court rascals, rich people, and others who dig their graves with their teeth by overeating and drinking many wines that impair the implements of happiness; which said overfed people were lolling luxuriously in costly draperies and on feather beds, while the Sieur de Bonne-Chose was roughing it. In a similar situation, if they had eaten cabbage, it would have given them the diarrhea. This may incite many of those who read this story to change their mode of life, in order to imitate Vieux par-Chemins in his old age.

ODD SAYINGS OF THREE PILGRIMS

'When the Pope left his good town of Avignon to take up his residence in Rome, certain pilgrims were thrown out who had set out for this country, and would have to pass the high Alps, in order to gain this said town of Rome, where they were going to seek remittance of various sins. Then were to be seen on the roads, and in the hostelries, those who wore the collar of the order of Cain, otherwise the flower of the penitents, all wicked fellows, burthened with leprous souls, which thirsted to bathe in the papal piscina, and all carrying with them gold or precious things to purchase absolution, pay for their beds, and present to the saints. You may be sure that those who drank water going, on their return, if the landlords gave them water, wished it to be the holy water of the cellar.

At this time three pilgrims came to this said town of Avignon to their injury, seeing that it was widowed of the Pope. While they were passing the Rhodane, to reach the Mediterranean coast, one of the three pilgrims, who had with him a son about ten years of age, parted company with the others, and near the town of Milan suddenly appeared again, but without the boy. Now in the evening, at supper, they had a hearty feast in order to celebrate the return of the pilgrim, who they thought had become disgusted with penitence through the Pope not being in Avignon. Of these three roamers towards Rome, one had come from the city of Paris, the other from Germany, and the third, who doubtless wished to instruct his son on the journey, had his home in the duchy of Burgundy, in which he had certain fiefs, was a younger son of the house of Villers-la-Faye and was named La Vaugrenand. The German baron had met the citizen of Paris just past Lyons, and both had accosted the Sire de la Vaugrenand in sight of Avignon.

Now, in this hostelry the three pilgrims loosened their tongues, and agreed to journey to Rome together, in order the better to resist the footpads, night birds, and other malefactors, who made it their business to ease pilgrims of that which weighed upon their bodies before the Pope eased them of that which weighed upon their consciences. After drinking, the three companions commenced to talk together, for the bottle is the key of conversation, and each made his confession—that the cause of his pilgrimage was a woman. The servant who watched them drinking, told them that of a hundred pilgrims who stopped in the locality, ninety-nine were traveling from the same thing. These three wise men then began to consider how pernicious is woman to man. The baron showed the heavy gold chain that he had in his hauberk to present to St. Peter, and said his crime was such that he would not get rid of with the value of two such chains. The Parisian took off his glove and exposed a ring set with a white diamond, saying that he had a hundred like it for the Pope. The Burgundian took off his hat, and exhibited two wonderful pearls, that were beautiful ear pendants for Notre-Dame-de-Lorette, and candidly confessed that he would rather have left them round his wife's neck.

Thereupon the servant exclaimed that their sins must have been as great as those of Visconti.

Then the pilgrims replied that they were such that they had each made a solemn vow in their minds never to go astray again during the remainder of their days, however beautiful the woman might be, and this in addition to the penance which the Pope might impose upon them.

Then the servant expressed her astonishment that all had made the same vow. The Burgundian added that this vow had been the cause of his lagging behind, because he had been in extreme fear that his son, in spite of his age, might go astray, and that he had made a vow to prevent people and beasts alike gratifying their passions in his house or upon his estates. The baron having inquired the particulars of the adventure, the sire narrated the affair as follows:

"You know that the good Countess Jeanne d'Avignon made formerly a law for the harlots, whom she compelled to live in the outskirts of the town in houses with window shutters painted red and closed. Now passing in your company through this vile neighborhood, my lad remarked these houses with closed window shutters, painted red, and his curiosity being aroused—for these ten-year-old little devils have eyes for everything—he pulled me by the sleeve, and kept on pulling me until he had learned from me what these houses were. Then, to obtain peace, I told him that young lads had nothing to do with such places, and could only enter them at peril of their lives, because it was a place where men and women were manufactured, and the danger was such for any one unacquainted with the business that if a novice entered, flying chancres and other wild beasts would seize upon his face. Fear seized the lad, who then followed me to the hostelry in a state of agitation, and not daring to cast his eyes upon these said bordels. While I was in the stable, seeing to the putting up of the horses, my son went off like a robber, and the servant was unable to tell me what had become of him. Then I was in great fear of the wenches, but had confidence in the laws, which forbade them to admit such children. At suppertime the rascal came back to me looking no more ashamed of himself than did our divine Savior in the temple among the doctors. 'Whence come you?' said I to him. 'From the house with the red shutters,' he replied. 'Little blackguard!' said I. 'I'll give you a taste of the whip!' Then he began to moan and cry. I told him that if he would confess all that had happened to him I would let him off the beating. 'Ha,' said he, 'I took good care not to go in, because of the flying chancres and the other wild beasts. I only looked through the chinks of the windows, in order to see how men were manufactured.' 'And what did you see?' I asked. 'I saw,' said he, 'a fine woman just being finished, because she only needed one peg, which a young workman was fitting in with energy. Directly she was finished she turned round, spoke to, and kissed her manufacturer.'

" 'Have your supper,' said I; and the same night I returned into Burgundy and left him with his mother, being sorely afraid that at the first town he might want to fit a peg into some girl."

"These children often make these sort of answers," said the Parisian. "One of my neighbor's children revealed the cuckoldom of his father by a reply. One day I asked, to see if he were well instructed at school in religious matters, 'What is hope?' 'One of the king's big archers, who comes here when father goes out,' said he. Indeed, the sergeant of the archers was named Hope. My friend was dumfounded at this, and, although to keep his countenance he looked in the mirror, he could not see his horns there."

The baron observed that the boy's remark was good in this way: that Hope is a person who comes to bed with us when the realities of life are out of the way.

"Is a cuckold made in the image of God?" asked the Burgundian.

"No," said the Parisian, "because God was wise in this respect, that he took no wife; therefore is He happy through all eternity."

"But," said the maidservant, "cuckolds are made in the image of God before they are horned."

Then the three pilgrims began to curse the women, saying that they were the cause of all the evil in the world.

"Their heads are as empty as helmets," said the Burgundian.

"Their hearts as straight as billhooks," said the Parisian.

"Why are there so many men pilgrims and so few women pilgrims?" said the German baron.

"Their cursed member never sins," replied the Parisian. "It knows neither father nor mother, the commandments of God, nor those of the Church, neither laws divine nor human: their member knows no doctrine, understands no heresies, and cannot be blamed; it is innocent of all, and always on the laugh; its understanding is *nil*; and for this reason do I hold it in utter detestation."

"I also," said the Burgundian, "and I begin to understand the different reading by a learned man of the verses of the Bible, in which the account of the Creation is given. In this Commentary, which in my country we call a *Noël*, lies the reason of imperfection of this feature of women, of which, different to that of other female animals, no man can slake the thirst, because such diabolical heat exists there. In the *Noël* it is stated that the Lord God, having turned his head to look at a donkey who had brayed for the first time in Paradise, at the very moment he was manufacturing Eve, the devil seized this opportunity to put his finger into the divine creature, and made a warm wound which the Lord took care to close with a stitch, from which comes the maid. By means of this frenum, the woman should remain closed, and children be made in the same manner in which God made the angels, by a pleasure far above carnal pleasure as the heaven is above the earth. Observing this closing, the devil, wild at being cheated, pinched Adam, who was asleep, by the skin, and stretched a portion of it out in imitation of his diabolical tail; but as the father of man was on his back this appendage came out in front. Thus these two productions of the devil had a desire to reunite themselves, following the law of similarities which God had laid down for the conduct of the world. From this came the first sin and the sorrows of the human race, because God, noticing the devil's work, determined to see what would come of it."

The servant declared that they were quite correct in their statements, for that woman was a bad animal, and that she herself knew some who were better under the ground than on it. The pilgrims, noticing then how pretty the girl was, were afraid of breaking their vows, and went straight to bed. The girl went and told her mistress that she was harboring infidels, and told her what they had said about women.

"Ah!" said the landlady, "what matters it to me the thoughts my customers have in their brains, so long as their purses are well filled."

And when the servant had told of the jewels, she exclaimed:

"Ah, these are questions which concern all women. Let us go and reason with them. I'll take the nobles, you can have the citizen."

The landlady, who was the most shameless inhabitant of the duchy of Milan, went into the chamber where the Sire de la Vaugrenand and the German baron were sleeping, and congratulated them upon their vows, saying that the women would not lose much by them; but to accomplish these said vows it was necessary they should endeavor to withstand the strongest temptation. Then she offered to lie down beside them, so anxious was she to see if she would be left unmolested, a thing which had never happened to her yet in the company of a man.

On the morrow, at breakfast, the servant had the ring on her finger, her mistress had the gold chain and the pearl earrings. The three pilgrims stayed in the town about a month, spending there all the money they had in their purses, and agreed that if they had spoken so severely of women it was because they had not known those of Milan.

On his return to Germany the baron made this observation: that he was only guilty of one sin, that of being in his castle. The citizen of Paris came back full of stories for his wife, and found her full of Hope. The Burgundian saw Madame de la Vaugrenand so troubled that he nearly died of the consolations he administered to her, in spite of his former opinions. This teaches us to hold our tongues in hostelries.

ÉMILE ZOLA (1840–1902)

Émile Zola was a young man, just beginning to make a name for himself as an author, when he came under the influence of Flaubert, the great realist. He immediately resolved to outdo Flaubert in accuracy and impersonality, to achieve an expression unhampered by "good taste," undeterred by the genteel tradition and the need to conform. This was the basic tenet of what was to become known as "naturalism." Zola envisioned a series of books from which nothing could be excluded and a kind of writing which would shock the world by its power and range.

His early struggles, years of poverty and hunger in Paris, where he was born and spent most of his life, gave him a bitter sympathy for those whom he felt, along with himself, had been victimized by society. This point of view influenced the choice of subject matter when he conceived the large work he spent a quarter of a century writing. Known as the Rougon-Macquart novels, they encompass in twenty volumes the history of a family which the author analyzed in terms of the effect of background and heredity upon their actions.

Nana is perhaps not the best of this series, but is certainly the most sensational and the most popular. It tells the story of a girl raised in an environment of the most wretched squalor and degeneracy, whose physical appeal is so spectacular that she rises from prostitute to France's most devastating actress-courtesan. The following intense description of Nana's first public performance is condensed from the first chapter of the novel.

FROM: NANA

NANA'S DEBUT

At nine o'clock the Variety Theatre was still almost empty. In the balcony and orchestra stalls a few persons waited, lost amid the garnet-colored velvet seats, in the faint light of the half-extinguished gasalier. Two young men suddenly appeared in the stalls close to the orchestra. They remained standing, looking round about them.

"What did I tell you, Hector?" exclaimed the elder—a tall fellow, with a slight, black mustache. "We have come too early. You might just as well have allowed me to finish my cigar."

An attendant passed by at this moment. "Oh! M. Fauchery," she said familiarly, "it will not begin for half an hour."

"Did you succeed in securing a stage box for Lucy?" asked Hector.

"Yes," replied the other, "but not without a deal of trouble. Oh! there is no danger of Lucy's coming too early—not she!" He stifled a yawn, and then, after a brief silence, resumed; "You are lucky, you who have never yet been present at a first night. 'The Blond Venus' will be the success of the year. Everyone has been speaking of the piece for six months past. Ah! my boy, such music—such 'go'! Bordenave, who knows what's what, kept it purposely for the time of the Exhibition."

Hector listened religiously. At length he hazarded a question: "And Nana —the new star who is to play Venus—do you know her?"

"Oh, hang it! are you going to begin that too?" exclaimed Fauchery, gesticulating wildly. "Ever since this morning I have heard of nothing but Nana. I have met more than twenty fellows I know, and it has been Nana here and Nana there! Do you suppose I know every petticoat in Paris? Nana is one of Bordenave's inventions. She must be something choice!"

After this explosion he calmed down a little. But the emptiness of the house, the dim light that pervaded the whole, the opening and shutting of doors, and the hushed voice suggestive of a church, irritated him.

"Confound it!" he said suddenly. "I can't stand this, you know. I must go out. Perhaps we shall meet Bordenave below. He will give us some details."

In the marble-paved vestibule, where the box office was situated, they found the public beginning to arrive. Near the box office a thickset man, with a big, clean-shaven face, was roughly replying to some people who were in vain endeavoring to obtain seats.

"There's Bordenave!" said Fauchery, as he and Hector descended the stairs.

But the manager had caught sight of him. "You are a nice fellow," he called out. "That is the way you write me a notice, is it? I opened the 'Figaro' this morning—not a word."

"Wait a bit," replied Fauchery. "I must see your Nana before I can write about her. Besides, I made no promise!"

Then, to prevent further discussion, he presented his cousin, M. Hector de la Faloise, a young man who had come to complete his education in Paris. The manager weighed the young man at a glance; but Hector surveyed the manager with some little emotion. This then was Bordenave, the exhibitor of women, whom he treated in the style of a prison warder, and whose brain was ever hatching some fresh money-making scheme—a perfect cynic, always shouting or spitting or smacking his thighs, and possessing the coarse mind of a trooper! Hector was anxious to make a good impression on him.

"Your theater——" he began, in clear musical tones.

Bordenave interrupted him quietly and said, with the coolness of a man who prefers to call things by their right names: "Say my brothel, rather."

Fauchery laughed approvingly, but La Faloise was shocked to a degree, and his meditated compliment stuck in his throat as he endeavored to look as though he appreciated the joke.

"I have been told," he began, wishing at any rate to say something, "that Nana has a delicious voice."

"She!" cried the manager, shrugging his shoulders—"she has no more voice than a squirt."

The young man hastened to add: "Besides, she is an excellent actress."

"She!—a regular lump! She never knows where to put her hands or her feet."

La Faloise colored slightly. He was at a loss what to understand. He managed to stammer out: "On no account would I have missed this first night. I know that your theater——"

"Say my brothel," interrupted Bordenave again, with the cool obstinacy of a man thoroughly convinced.

Meanwhile Fauchery had been calmly examining the women as they entered. He now came to his cousin's assistance, when he saw him doubtful whether to laugh or be angry. "Gratify Bordenave; call his theater just what he desires, as it amuses him. And as for you, my dear fellow, you need not try to fool us. If your Nana can't sing and can't play, you will make a regular fiasco of it tonight. And that is just what I am expecting."

"A fiasco! a fiasco!" exclaimed the manager, whose face became purple with rage. "Is it necessary for a woman to know how to sing and act? Ah! my boy, you are much too stupid. Nana has something else, damn her! and something that will make up for anything she may lack. I scented it, and she has plenty of it, or I have the nose of a fool! You will see, you will see— she has only to appear and all the spectators will at once smack their lips." He raised his big hands, which trembled with enthusiasm, and then, lowering his voice, murmured to himself, "Yes, she will go far—ah! damn her! yes, she will go far. A skin—oh, such a skin!"

Then, in answer to Fauchery's questions, he condescended to give certain details, making use of such offensive language that he quite shocked Hector. He had become acquainted with Nana, and wished to bring her out; and it so happened that he was in want of a Venus. He never allowed a woman to hang on to him very long; he preferred to let the public have its share of her at once. But he had had a damnable time in his shop; the arrival of this great hulking girl had revolutionized everything. Rose Mignon, his star, a fine actress and an adorable singer, threatened daily to leave him in the lurch. Divining a rival in Nana, she was furious. And the playbills—deuce take it! what a row they had caused. However, he had decided to print the names of the two actresses in letters of equal size. They had better not badger him too much. When one of his little women, as he called them, Clarisse or Simone, did not do as she was told, he just kicked her behind. If he treated them differently they would never leave him any peace. He dealt in them, and he knew what they were worth, the hussies!

"Ah!" he exclaimed, interrupting himself. "There come Mignon and Steiner! They are always together. You know that Steiner begins to have had enough of Rose; so the husband sticks to him like a plaster lest he should escape."

The flaring gas jets running along the cornice of the theater threw a sheet of vivid light over the footpath. The crowd at the box office became more compact, the buzz of voices grew louder, and the name of Nana was repeated over and over again with a singsong enunciation of its two syllables. The men standing in front of the posters read it out loud; others, as they passed, uttered it interrogatively, while the women, smiling and uneasy, repeated it softly with an air of surprise. No one knew Nana. Where on earth had Nana come from? And little jokes were passed about from ear to ear, and little tales told. The very name sounded like a caress and fell familiarly from the lips of every one. Its constant repetition amused the crowd and kept it in a good humor. A fever of curiosity took possession of everybody—that Parisian curiosity which is sometimes as violent as an attack of brain fever. All were eager to see Nana. One lady had the train of her dress torn, and a gentleman lost his hat.

"Ah! you ask me too much," cried Bordenave, whom twenty men were besieging with questions. "You will see her presently. I must be off, they are waiting for me."

He disappeared, radiant at having inflamed his public.

"Hallo! there's Lucy, over there, getting out of her carriage," said La Faloise to Fauchery.

It was in fact Lucy Stewart—a little, ugly woman of about forty, with a neck too long, a thin, drawn face, and thick lips, but so lively, so graceful, that she charmed every one. She was accompanied by Caroline Héquet and her mother. Caroline with her frigid beauty, the mother very stately, and looking as if she were stuffed.

"You are coming with us, of course," she said to Fauchery; "I have kept a place for you."

"So that I shall see nothing!—not if I know it!" he answered. "I have an orchestra stall; I prefer to be there."

Lucy fired up at once. Was he afraid to be seen with her? Then suddenly calming down, she jumped to another subject.

"Why did you never tell me that you knew Nana?"

"Nana! I never saw her!"

"Is that really true? I have been assured that you once slept with her."

But Mignon, who was in front, put his finger to his lips to signal to them to be silent. And when Lucy asked why, he pointed to a young man who had just passed, murmuring, "Nana's sweetheart."

They all stared after him. He was certainly very good-looking. Fauchery recognized him: his name was Daguenet, and he had squandered a fortune of three hundred thousand francs on women, and now dabbled in stocks in order to make a little money with which he could treat them to an occasional bouquet and dinner. Lucy thought he had very handsome eyes.

"Ah! there's Blanche!" she exclaimed. "It was she who told me that you had slept with Nana."

Blanche de Sivry, a heavy blonde, whose pretty face was getting too fat, arrived, accompanied by a slender, well-dressed man with a most distinguished air.

"Count Xavier de Vandeuvres," whispered Fauchery to La Faloise.

The count shook hands with the journalist, while a lively discussion took place between Lucy and Blanche. They quite blocked up the entry with their skirts covered with flounces, one in pink and the other in blue, and Nana's name fell from their lips so frequently that the crowd lingered to listen. The count at length led Blanche away, but Nana's name did not cease to resound from the four corners of the vestibule in louder and more eager tones. Would they never begin? The men pulled out their watches, latecomers leaped from their carriages before they really drew up, and the groups left the pavement, while the passers-by, as they slowly crossed the stream of light, stretched their necks to see what was going on in the theater. A street urchin who came up whistling, stood for a moment before one of the posters at the door; then, in a drunken voice shouted out, "Oh, my! Nana!" and reeled on his way, dragging his old shoes along the asphalt. People laughed, and several well-dressed gentlemen repeated, "Nana! Oh, my! Nana!" The crush was tremendous. A quarrel broke out at the box office, the cries for Nana increased; one of those stupid fits of brutal excitement common to crowds had taken possession of this mass of people. Suddenly, above this uproar, the sound of a bell was heard. The rumor extended to the Boulevards that the curtain was about to rise, and there was more pushing and struggling; everyone wished to get in.

Fauchery and La Faloise stood in their places, examining the house, which was now very brilliant. The crystal gasalier blazed with prismatic hues, and the light was reflected from the ceiling on to the pit like a shower of gold. The seats were gradually filling; here and there appeared a bright-colored robe, and a head with a delicate profile displayed a chignon on which sparkled some valuable jewel.

At length the conductor of the orchestra gave the signal, the musicians struck the first note of the overture. People were still coming in and the noise and bustle increased. On special occasions like this there were different parts of the house where friends met with a smile; while the regular frequenters, thoroughly at their ease, exchanged bows right and left. All Paris was there—the Paris of letters, of finance, and of pleasure, many journalists, some few authors, and several speculators, more kept girls than respectable women—a company, in short, that was a most singular mixture, composed of every kind of genius, tainted with every description of vice, where the same weariness and the same fever seemed inscribed on every face. By degrees the noise subsided, with an occasional swell from time to time. And in the midst of this faint murmur, of these expiring whispers, the orchestra burst forth in the gay little notes of a waltz, the saucy rhythm of which suggested the laugh raised by some overfree piece of buffoonery. The audience, fairly tickled, already began to smile; but the claque, seated in the front row of the pit, commenced to applaud vociferously. The curtain rose.

The first act of "The Blonde Venus" was laid in Olympus—a cardboard Olympus, with clouds at the sides, and Jupiter's throne on the right. Iris and Ganymede first appeared, surrounded by a crowd of celestial assistants, who sang a chorus as they arranged the seats for the gods in council. Again the applause of the paid claque was heard, but the audience as yet was not inclined to respond. La Faloise, however, had applauded Clarisse Besnus, one of Bordenave's little women, who played the part of Iris, in pale blue, with a broad scarf of the seven colors fastened round her waist.

"You know she takes off her chemise to get into that costume," he said to Fauchery in a loud whisper. "We tried it on this morning, and the chemise showed under the arms and on the back."

But a slight tremor took possession of the audience on the appearance of Rose Mignon as Diana. Although she had neither the face nor the figure for the part, as she was thin and dark, with the adorable ugliness of a Parisian urchin, she seemed charming, intended as she might have been as a mockery of the character she personated. Her entrance song, consisting of words stupid enough to send you to sleep, and in which she complained of Mars, who was neglecting her for Venus, was sung in a bashful manner, but so full of smutty innuendoes, that the audience warmed up. Her husband and Steiner laughed aloud as they sat side by side. And the whole house burst into applause when Prullière, that especial favorite, appeared as Mars in the uniform of a general, adorned with a monstrous plume, and dragging a sword that reached to his shoulder. He had had enough of Diana; she expected too much. So she swore to watch him and be revenged. Their duo wound up with a ludicrous tyrolienne, which Prullière sang in his funniest style, and in the voice of an angry tabby. He possessed the amusing conceit of a young actor in high favor, and swaggered about as he rolled his eyes in a way that elicited the shrill laughter of the women in the boxes. After that, however, the audience became as cool as before; the scenes which followed were dull in the extreme. Old Bosc, as an imbecile Jupiter, his head crushed under an enormous crown, succeeded only in raising a smile, as he quarreled with Juno on account of their cook's wages. The procession of the gods Neptune, Pluto, Minerva, and all the others, almost spoiled everything. The spectators were becoming very impatient, an ominous murmur slowly arose, every one began to lose all interest in the piece, and looked about the house rather than upon the stage. But suddenly the applause of the claque burst forth with the regularity of a discharge of musketry, and every eye became riveted on the stage once more. Was it Nana at last—that Nana who had kept them waiting so long?

It was a deputation of mortals introduced by Ganymede and Iris, respectable citizens, all deceived husbands, come to lay before Jupiter a complaint against Venus, who inspired their wives with a great deal too much ardor. The chorus, which they sang in a simple and doleful manner, was now and again interrupted by the most significant pauses, and amused the audience immensely. A whisper went round the house: "The cuckolds' chorus, the cuckolds' chorus"; the name stuck to it, and it was encored. The getup of the singers was very comic, their faces were in accordance with the part they played; there was one especially, a stout fellow with a face as round as a moon. Vulcan, however, appeared on the scene in a state of furious indignation, seeking his wife, who had disappeared from home three days before. The chorus struck up again, imploring Vulcan, the god of cuckolds, to help them. The part of Vulcan was played by Fontan, a comic actor gifted with a talent as spicy as it was original, who waddled about in the most ludicrous manner imaginable, in the costume of a village blacksmith, with a flaring red wig on his head, and his arms bare and tattooed all over with hearts pierced by arrows. A woman's voice exclaimed aloud, "Oh! isn't he ugly!" and every one laughed as they applauded. The next scene seemed interminable. Would Jupiter never get all the gods together that he might submit to them the deceived husbands' petition? And still no Nana! Did they mean to keep back Nana until the curtain fell? This long suspense ended by irritating the spectators, and they recommenced their murmurs.

"It's going from bad to worse," said Mignon, delighted, to Steiner. "A regular fiasco. See if it isn't!"

At this moment the clouds parted at the back of the stage, and Venus appeared. Nana, very tall and very plump for her eighteen years, in the white tunic of a goddess, and with her beautiful golden hair floating over her shoulders, walked toward the footlights with calm self-possession, smiling at the crowd before her. Her lips parted, and she commenced her great song:

"When Venus takes an evening stroll——"

At the second line, people exchanged glances of wonder. Was this a jest on the part of Bordenave, or a wager? Never had so false a voice and so poor a method been heard. The manager had spoken truly when he said that she had no more voice than a squirt. Nor did she know how to stand or move on the stage. She threw her arms forward and wriggled her body about in a manner that was considered scarcely proper and very ungraceful. The pit was beginning to murmur, in fact a few hisses were heard, when suddenly from the orchestra stalls a voice, resembling that of a young cock molting, exclaimed aloud in a tone of intense conviction:

"She is stunning!"

The whole house looked to see who had uttered these words. It was the cherub, the youngster fresh from college, his lovely eyes strained wide open, his childish face all aglow with admiration of Nana. When he saw every one looking at him, he turned scarlet with shame at having unintentionally spoken so loud. Daguenet, who sat next him, looked at him with a smile, and the audience laughed aloud and thought no more of hissing, while the young gentlemen with white kid gloves also carried away by Nana's curves, applauded with vehemence.

"So she is!" they cried. "Bravo!"

Nana, seeing every one laughing, laughed also, and this redoubled the gaiety. She was funny, all the same, this beautiful girl; and as she laughed, a love of a dimple appeared on her chin. She waited, not in the least embarrassed, but on the contrary quite at her ease and thoroughly at home with the audience, looking as though she herself were saying with a wink of her eye that she didn't possess a penny's worth of talent, but it didn't matter, she had something better than that. And after making a sign to the conductor, which meant, "Off you go, old boy!" she commenced her second verse:

"At midnight, Venus passes by——"

It was still the same grating voice, but this time it tickled the hearers in the right place, and succeeded now and again in eliciting an approving murmur. Nana's smile was still on her red lips, and shone in her large light blue eyes. At certain lines, which were a trifle broad in meaning, her pink nostrils dilated and the color rose to her cheeks. She continued to wriggle her body about, not knowing what else to do; but it was no longer considered unbecoming; on the contrary, every opera glass was turned upon her. As she finished the verse her voice failed her entirely, and she saw that she could not go on. Without being in the least disturbed, she jerked her hip in a manner which indicated its plumpness beneath her scanty tunic, and, with her body bent forward, displaying her bare breast, she extended her arms. Applause burst forth from all parts of the house. She at once turned round, showing as she retired to the back of the stage the nape of a neck, the red hair on which looked like the fleece of an animal; and the applause became deafening.

The end of the act elicited less enthusiasm. Vulcan wished to slap his wife's face. The gods took council, and decided that they had best investigate matters on the earth, before deciding in favor of the deceived husbands. Diana, overhearing some tender passages between Venus and Mars, swore that she would not once let them out of her sight during the journey. There was also a scene in which Cupid, acted by a little girl of twelve, answered to every question, "Yes, mamma," "No, mamma," in tearful tones and with her fingers in her nose. Then Jupiter, with all the severity of an angry master, shut Cupid in a dark closet, and bade him conjugate twenty times the verb, "to love." The finale, a chorus very brilliantly rendered, met with more success. But, after the curtain had fallen, the claque in vain tried to obtain an encore; everybody rose and moved toward the doors. As the audience pushed their way through the rows of seats, they exchanged their impressions. One phrase was constantly heard: "It is simply idiotic!" A critic observed that the piece wanted a great deal of cutting down. But the piece, after all, mattered little. Nana was the chief topic of conversation. Fauchery and La Faloise, who were among the first to leave their seats, met Steiner and Mignon in the passage leading to the stalls.

"But I know her!" cried Steiner as soon as he saw Fauchery. "I have certainly seen her somewhere. At the Casino, I think; and she was so drunk that she got locked up."

"Well, I'm not quite sure," said the journalist. "I'm like you, I have certainly met her somewhere." He lowered his voice and added with a laugh. "At old Tricon's, I daresay."

"Of course, in some vile place!" exclaimed Mignon, who seemed exasperated. "It is disgusting to see the public welcome in such a way the first filthy wench that offers. Soon there will not be a respectable woman left on the stage. Yes, I shall have to forbid Rose playing any more."

Fauchery could not repress a smile. Meanwhile, the heavily shod crowd continued to pour down the stairs, and a little man in a cap said, in a drawling voice: "Oh, my! she is plump! You could eat her!"

In the lobby two young men with their hair exquisitely curled and looking very stylish with their stuck-up collars turned slightly down in front, were quarreling. One kept saying, "Vile! vile!" without giving any reason; while the other retaliated with, "Stunning! stunning!" equally disdaining to explain. La Faloise liked her immensely. He, however, only ventured to observe that she would be much better if she cultivated her voice. Then Steiner, who had left off listening, seemed to wake up with a start. They must wait, though. Perhaps in the next acts everything would come to grief.

The scenery of the second act was a surprise. It represented a low dancing establishment of the suburbs, called the "Boule Noire," on a Shrove Tuesday. Some masqueraders, dressed in grotesque costumes, sang a lively strain, the chorus of which they accompanied by stamping their heels. The words and gestures being not overdecorous and quite unexpected, amused the audience immensely, and secured the honors of an encore. And it was into this place that the troop of gods, led astray by Iris, who falsely claimed to know the earth, had come to pursue their investigations. They were disguised so as to preserve their incognito. Jupiter appeared as King Dagobert, with his breeches turned wrong side out, and a huge tin crown on his head, Phœbus masqueraded as the Postillion of Longjumeau, and Minerva as a Norman wet nurse. Shouts of laughter greeted Mars, who wore a preposterous costume, as a Swiss admiral; but the mirth became scandalous when Neptune, dressed in a blouse and tall cap, with little curls glued to his temples, dragged after him his slipshod shoes, and said in an unctuous tone of voice: "Well! what next? When a fellow's handsome, he must allow himself to be adored!" This elicited a few "Oh! ohs!" while the ladies slightly raised their fans. Lucy, in her stage box, laughed so noisily that Caroline Héquet entreated her to be quiet. From this moment the piece was saved, and was even a great success. This carnival of the gods, Olympus dragged through the mud, religion and poetry alike scoffed at, struck the public as extremely witty. A fever of irreverence took possession of this intellectual first-night audience; ancient legends were trodden underfoot, and antique images were broken. Jupiter had a fine head, Mars was highly successful. Royalty became a farce, and the Army a jest. When Jupiter, desperately smitten all of a sudden by the charms of a little laundress, broke into a wild cancan, and Simone who played the part of the laundress, raised her foot on a level with the nose of the master of the gods, calling him, in such a funny manner, "My fat old boy!" a peal of mad laughter shook the house. While the others danced, Phœbus treated Minerva to some hot wine, and Neptune sat surrounded by some seven or eight women, who stuffed him with cakes. The audience snatched at the faintest illusions, obscenities were discovered where none were intended, and the most inoffensive words were invested with a totally different meaning by the exclamations of the occupants of the stalls. It was long since the theater-going public had wallowed in such disgusting foolery, and it took its fill. The action of the piece, however, advanced in spite of all this byplay. Vulcan, dressed in the latest style, only all in yellow, and with yellow gloves and a monocle in his eye, was there in pursuit of Venus, who at last arrived, dressed as a fish woman, a handkerchief thrown over her head, her breasts protruding, and covered with huge gold ornaments. Nana was so white and so plump and so natural in this part of a person strong in the hips and the gift of the gab, that she at once gained the entire audience. Rose Mignon, a delicious baby, with a baby bonnet on her head, and in short muslin skirts, was quite forgotten, although she had just sung Diana's woes in a charming voice. The other, the big girl with her arms akimbo, who clucked like a hen, was so full of life and the power of woman that the audience became fairly intoxicated.

After this no exception was taken at anything that Nana did. She was allowed to pose badly, to move badly, to sing every note false, and forget her part. She had only to turn to the audience and smile, to be treated with wild applause. Each time she gave her peculiar movement of the hips the occupants of the stalls brightened up, and the enthusiasm rose from gallery to gallery up to the very roof, so that when she led the dance her triumph was complete. She was in her element as, with arms akimbo, she dragged Venus through the mire. The music, too, seemed written for her voice of the gutter—a music of reed pipes, a sort of reminiscence of a return from the fair of Saint Cloud, with the sneezes of the clarionets and the gambols of the flutes. Two concerted pieces were again encored. The waltz of the overture, that waltz with the saucy rhythm, returned and whirled the gods round and round. Juno, as a farmer's wife, caught Jupiter flirting with the washerwoman, and spanked him. Diana surprising Venus in the act of arranging a meeting with Mars, hastened to inform Vulcan of the time and place, when the latter exclaimed, "I have my plan." The remainder of the act did not seem very clear. The gods' inquiry terminated in a final gallopade, after which Jupiter, in a great perspiration, all out of breath, and having lost his crown, proclaimed that the little women of the earth were delicious, and that the men alone were in the wrong. The curtain fell, and above the applause rose some voices shouting loudly, "All! All!" Then the curtain rose again, and the actors and actresses reappeared hand in hand. In their midst were Nana and Rose Mignon, bowing side by side. The applause was repeated, the claque surpassed their former efforts, and then the house slowly became half empty.

Outside, in front of the theater, Fauchery and La Faloise lit their cigarettes. A small crowd blocked the pavement, formed of a part of the male portion of the audience, who had come down the steps to breath the fresh night air amid the growing stillness of the Boulevard.

In the meanwhile Mignon had dragged Steiner to the Café des Variétés. Seeing Nana's success, he spoke of her enthusiastically, all the time watching the banker from out of the corner of his eye. He knew him; twice had he assisted him in deceiving Rose, and when the caprice was over, had brought him back to her, faithful and penitent. Inside the café the too-numerous customers were squeezing round the marble tables, and some men, standing up, were drinking hastily; the large mirrors reflected this mass of heads *ad infinitum*, and increased inordinately the size of the narrow saloon with its three gasaliers, its moleskin-covered seats, and its winding staircase draped with red. Steiner seated himself at a table in the outer room, which was quite open onto the Boulevard, the frontage having been removed a little too early for the season. As Fauchery and his cousin passed, the banker stopped them.

"Come and take a glass of beer with us," he said.

He himself, however, was absorbed with an idea which had just occurred to him; he wanted to have a bouquet thrown to Nana. At length he called one of the waiters, whom he familiarly named Augustus. Mignon, who was listening to all he said, looked at him so straight in the eyes that he became quite disconcerted as he faltered, "Two bouquets, Augustus, and give them to one of the attendants. One for each of the ladies, at the right moment, you understand."

The two cousins, who had finished their beer, wished to return to the theater; they felt cold. Then, Mignon left alone with Steiner, leaned both elbows on the table, and, looking him full in the face, said, "Well then, it's quite understood, we will call on her and I will introduce you. You know, it's quite between ourselves; my wife need not know anything about it."

Back in their places, Fauchery and La Faloise noticed in the second tier of boxes a very pretty woman, very quietly dressed. She was accompanied by a solemn-looking gentleman, the head of a department at the Ministry of the Interior, whom La Faloise knew from having met him at the Muffats'. As for Fauchery, he said he believed she was called Madame Robert—a worthy woman who had a lover, but never more than one, and he was always a highly respectable person. As they turned round, Daguenet smiled at them. Now that Nana had proved a success, he no longer kept himself in the background; he had just returned from wandering about the house and enjoying her triumph. The youngster, fresh from college, beside him had not once quitted his seat, so overpowering was the state of admiration into which the sight of Nana had plunged him. So *that*, then, was woman, and he blushed deeply, and kept taking off and putting on his gloves mechanically. At last, as his neighbor had talked about Nana, he ventured to question him.

"Excuse me, sir," he said, "but this lady, who is playing—do you happen to know her?"

"Yes—a little——" murmured Daguenet in surprise, and with some hesitation.

"Then you know her address?"

The question came so abruptly and so strangely as addressed to him that Daguenet felt like slapping the lad's face.

"I do not," he answered coldly, and turned his back.

The youngster understood that he had been guilty of some impropriety; he blushed all the more and was mortified beyond expression.

The three knocks resounded throughout the house, and some of the attendants, their arms full of opera cloaks and overcoats, were obstinately endeavoring to restore the various garments to their owners, who were hastening back to their seats. The claque applauded the scenery, which represented a grotto in Mount Etna, hollowed out of a silver mine, with sides that glittered like newly coined crown pieces; at the back was Vulcan's forge, with all the tints of a sunset. In the second scene Diana arranged everything with the god, who was to pretend to go on a journey so as to leave the coast clear for Venus and Mars. Then scarcely was Diana left alone, than Venus arrived. A thrill ran through the audience. Nana was next to naked. She appeared in her nakedness with a calm audacity, confident in the all-powerfulness of her flesh. A slight gauze enveloped her; her round shoulders, her amazonian breasts, the rosy tips of which stood out straight and firm as lances, her broad hips swayed by the most voluptuous movements, her plump thighs, in fact, her whole body could be divined, nay, seen, white as the foam, beneath the transparent covering. It was Venus rising from the sea, with no other veil than her locks. And when Nana raised her arms, the glare of the footlights displayed to every gaze the golden hairs of her armpits. There was no applause. No one laughed now. The grave faces of the men were bent forward, their nostrils contracted, their mouths parched and irritated. A gentle breath, laden with an unknown menace, seemed to have passed over all. Out of this laughing girl there had suddenly emerged a woman, appalling all who beheld her, crowning all the follies of her sex, displaying to the world the hidden secrets of inordinate desire. Nana still preserved her smile, but it was the mocking one of a destroyer of men.

"The devil!" said Fauchery to La Faloise.

Mars, in the meantime, hurrying to the meeting, with his big hat and plume, found himself caught between the two goddesses. Then there ensued a scene in which Prullière played very ingeniously. Fondled by Diana, who wished to make a last attempt to bring him back into the right path before delivering him up to Vulcan's vengeance, cajoled by Venus, whom the presence of her rival stimulated, he abandoned himself to all these endearments with the happy expression of a donkey in a field of clover. The scene ended with a grand trio, and it was at this moment that an attendant entered Lucy Stewart's box, and threw two enormous bouquets of white lilac on to the stage. Everyone applauded, and Nana and Rose Mignon curtsied their acknowledgements, while Prullière picked up the flowers. Some of the occu-

pants of the stalls turned smilingly in the direction of the box occupied by
Steiner and Mignon. The banker, all inflamed, moved his chin convulsively
as though something had stuck in his throat. The acting which followed quite
took the house by storm. Diana having gone off furious, Venus, seated on a
bed of moss, at once called Mars to her side. Never before had so warm a
scene of seduction been risked upon the stage. Nana, her arms around
Prullière's neck, was slowly drawing him to her, when Fontan, grotesquely
imitating the most awful fury, exaggerating the looks of an outraged husband
who surprises his wife in the very act, appeared at the back of the grotto.
In his hands he held his famous iron net; for a moment he poised it like a
fisherman about to throw, then, by some ingenious device, Venus and Mars
were ensnared, the net covered them, and held them fast in their guilty
posture.

Then arose a murmur resembling one huge sigh. A few hands clapped,
and every opera glass was fixed on Venus. Little by little Nana had gained
possession of the audience and now every man succumbed to her. The lust
she inspired, similar to an animal in heat, had grown more and more till it
filled the house. Now, her slightest movements fanned the desire; the raising
of her little finger caused all the flesh beholding her to quiver. Backs were
arched, vibrating as though the muscles, like so many fiddlestrings, were being played on by some invisible hand; on the napes of the outstretched necks
the down fluttered beneath the warm and errant breath escaped from some
women's lips. Fauchery beheld in front of him the youngster fresh from college start from his seat in his agitation. He had the curiosity to look at Count
de Vandeuvres, who was very pale, with tightly pressed lips—the stout Steiner,
whose apoplectic face seemed bursting—Labordette examining through his
eyeglass with the astonished look of a jockey admiring a thoroughbred mare
—Daguenet, whose ears were flaming red, and trembling with enjoyment.

The heat was suffocating; even the hair weighed heavily on the perspiring
heads. During the three hours that the piece had lasted, the foul breath had
given the atmosphere an odor of human flesh. In the blaze of light the dust
now appeared thicker, and seemed suspended, motionless, beneath the big
crystal gasalier. The audience, tired and excited, seized with those drowsy,
midnight desires which murmur their wishes in the depths of alcoves, vacillated, and was gradually becoming dazed. And Nana, facing this half-swoon-
ing crowd, these fifteen hundred persons, packed one above the other, and
sinking with emotion and the nervous excitement of an approaching finale,
remained victorious with her marble flesh, her sex alone strong enough to
conquer them all and remain scatheless.

The play was rapidly drawing to an end. In answer to Vulcan's triumphant
calls, all Olympus defiled before the lovers, uttering cries of stupefaction or
indulging in broad remarks. Jupiter said, "My son, I consider you are very
foolish to call us to see this." Then there was a sudden change of feeling in
favor of Venus. The deputation of cuckolds, again introduced by Iris, be-
seeched the master of the gods not to give heed to their petition, for since

their wives passed their evenings at home they made their lives unbearable, so they preferred to be deceived and happy, which was the moral of the piece. Venus, therefore is set free. Vulcan obtained a judicial separation. Mars made it up again with Diana. Jupiter, for the sake of peace and quietness at home, sent the little washerwoman into a constellation; and Cupid was at last released from his prison, where he had been making paper fowls, instead of conjugating the verb "to love." The curtain fell on an apotheosis, the deputation of cuckolds kneeling and singing a hymn of gratitude to Venus, smiling and exalted in her sovereign nudity.

The spectators had already risen from their seats, and were hastily making for the doors. The authors were named, and there was a double call in the midst of a thunder of applause. The cry, "Nana! Nana!" re-echoed again and again. Then, before the house was fairly empty, it became quite dark. The footlights were turned out, the lights of the gasalier were lowered, and long gray coverings were drawn over the gilding of the balconies; and the heat and the noise suddenly gave place to a deathlike stillness, and an odor of dust and mildew.

Fauchery and La Faloise had hurried to see the people come out. In the vestibule several gentlemen were waiting in a row, while down the double staircase descended two interminable and compact processions. At that moment Bordenave, opening a little door, appeared, and obtained from Fauchery a distinct promise of a notice. He was covered with perspiration, his face as red as though he had had a sunstroke, and looking intoxicated with success.

"Your piece will run for two hundred nights at least," said La Faloise, obligingly. "All Paris will visit your theater."

But Bordenave, indicated with a rapid movement of his chin the crowd that filled the vestibule—that mob of men with parched mouths and sparkling eyes, still inflamed with their passionate longing for Nana—and violently exclaimed:

"Say my brothel, can't you? you pig-headed animal!"

ANATOLE FRANCE (1844–1924)

An avowed critic of humanity's weaknesses, especially man's willingness to be controlled by a few dominating institutions and individual dictators, Anatole France got used to being called a sceptic. Although the critics meant the word as an insult, for France it was the finest praise. "That is what all the masters of French thought have been—Rabelais, Montaigne, Voltaire— all sceptics. . . . The word is made synonymous with negation and impotence; yet our great sceptics were often the most affirmative and courageous of men. They attacked everything that fetters the mind and the will. They struggled against ignorance that stupefies, against error that oppresses, against intolerance that tyrannizes, against cruelty that tortures, and against hatred that kills."

He was born Jacques Anatole Thibault but, like Voltaire, his intellectual ancestor, adopted a pseudonym for his work which, in common with Voltaire's, is rooted in irony. On the surface France's novels are easygoing and diverting, but the author is primarily concerned with mankind's delusions about civilization, religion, patriotism, and the whole conception of progress. In Penguin Island, for example, progress reaches such a peak that everything is destroyed by a radium bomb; barbarism takes over; the survivors go back to primitive agrarianism; and once more society begins at the bottom. When the primitive Penguins assault each other and beat their brains out, the author-commentator solemnly tells the reader that they are performing the most important of functions; "They are creating law; they are founding property; they are establishing the principles of civilization, the foundations of society, and the bases of the state. . . . Their work will be consecrated through the centuries by jurists, protected and confirmed by magistrates."

All this and much more is said with an air of utmost innocence; France's subtle ingenuities are surpassed only by his bland ingenuousness. However, even when France exposes the pitiful frailties and heartless carelessness of mankind, he does it with a pitying smile. Allying himself with Zola in the defense of Dreyfus, making himself a target of abuse and rotten vegetables, France was always ready to fight for the people who were unwilling to fight for him.

FROM: PENGUIN ISLAND

THE FIRST CLOTHES

One day St. Maël was sitting by the seashore on a warm stone that he found. He thought it had been warmed by the sun and he gave thanks to God for it, not knowing that the Devil had been resting on it. The apostle was waiting for the monks of Yvern who had been commissioned to bring a freight of skins and fabrics to clothe the inhabitants of the island of Alca.

Soon he saw a monk called Magis coming ashore and carrying a chest upon his back. This monk enjoyed a great reputation for holiness.

When he had drawn near to the old man he laid the chest on the ground and wiping his forehead with the back of his sleeve, he said:

"Well, father, you wish then to clothe these penguins?"

"Nothing is more needful, my son," said the old man. "Since they have been incorporated into the family of Abraham these penguins share the curse of Eve, and they know that they are naked, a thing of which they were ignorant before. And it is high time to clothe them, for they are losing the down that remained on them after their metamorphosis."

"It is true," said Magis as he cast his eyes over the coast where the penguins were to be seen looking for shrimps, gathering mussels, singing, or sleeping. "They are naked. But do you not think, father, that it would be better to leave them naked? Why clothe them? When they wear clothes and are under the moral law they will assume an immense pride, a vile hypocrisy, and an excessive cruelty."

"Is it possible, my son," sighed the old man, "that you understand so badly the effects of the moral law to which even the heathen submit?"

"The moral law," answered Magis, "forces men who are beasts to live otherwise than beasts, a thing that doubtless puts a constraint upon them, but that also flatters and reassures them; and as they are proud, cowardly, and covetous of pleasure, they willingly submit to restraints that tickle their vanity and on which they found both their present security and the hope of their future happiness. That is the principle of all morality . . . but let us not mislead ourselves. My companions are unloading their cargo of stuffs and skins on the island. Think, father, while there is still time! To clothe the penguins is a very serious business. At present when a penguin desires a penguin he knows precisely what he desires and his lust is limited by an exact knowledge of its object. At this moment two or three couples of penguins are making love on the beach. See with what simplicity! No one pays any attention and the actors themselves do not seem to be greatly preoccupied. But when the female penguins are clothed, the male penguin will not form so exact a notion of what it is that attracts him to them. His indeterminate desires will fly out into all sorts of dreams and illusions; in short, father, he will know love and its mad torments. And all the time the female penguins will cast down their eyes and bite their lips, and take on airs as if they kept a treasure under their clothes . . . what a pity!

"The evil will be endurable as long as these people remain rude and poor; but only wait for a thousand years and you will see, father, with what powerful weapons you have endowed the daughters of Alca. If you will allow me, I can give you some idea of it beforehand. I have some old clothes in this chest. Let us take at hazard one of these female penguins to whom the male penguins give such little thought, and let us dress her as well as we can.

"Here is one coming toward us. She is neither more beautiful nor uglier than the others; she is young. No one looks at her. She strolls indolently along the shore, scratching her back and with her finger at her nose as she walks. You cannot help seeing, father, that she has narrow shoulders, clumsy breasts, a stout figure, and short legs. Her reddish knees pucker at every step she takes, and there is, at each of her joints, what looks like a little monkey's head. Her broad and sinewy feet cling to the rock with their four crooked toes, while the great toes stick up like the heads of two cunning serpents. She begins to walk, all her muscles are engaged in the task, and, when we see them working, we think of her as a machine intended for walking rather than as a machine intended for making love, although visibly she is both, and contains within herself several other pieces of machinery besides. Well, venerable apostle, you will see what I am going to make of her."

With these words the monk, Magis, reached the female penguin in three bounds, lifted her up, carried her in his arms with her hair trailing behind her, and threw her, overcome with fright, at the feet of the holy Maël.

And while she wept and begged them to do her no harm, he took a pair of sandals out of his chest and commanded her to put them on.

"Her feet," observed the old man, "will appear smaller when squeezed in by the woollen cords. The soles, being two fingers high, will give an elegant length to her legs and the weight they bear will seem magnified."

As the penguin tied on her sandals she threw a curious look toward the open coffer, and seeing that it was full of jewels and finery, she smiled through her tears.

The monk twisted her hair on the back of her head and covered it with a chaplet of flowers. He encircled her wrist with golden bracelets and, making her stand upright, he passed a large linen band beneath her breasts, alleging that her bosom would thereby derive a new dignity and that her sides would be compressed to the greater glory of her hips.

He fixed this band with pins, taking them one by one out of his mouth.

"You can tighten it still more," said the penguin.

When he had, with much care and study, enclosed the soft parts of her bust in this way, he covered her whole body with a rose-colored tunic which gently followed the lines of her figure.

"Does it hang well?" asked the penguin.

And bending forward with her head on one side and her chin on her shoulder, she kept looking attentively at the appearance of her toilet.

Magis asked her if she did not think the dress a little long, but she answered with assurance that it was not—she would hold it up.

Immediately, taking the back of her skirt in her left hand, she drew it obliquely across her hips, taking care to disclose a glimpse of her heels. Then she went away, walking with short steps and swinging her hips.

She did not turn her head, but as she passed near a stream she glanced out of the corner of her eye at her own reflection.

A male penguin, who met her by chance, stopped in surprise, and retracing his steps began to follow her. As she went along the shore, others coming back from fishing went up to her, and after looking at her, walked behind her. Those who were lying on the sand got up and joined the rest.

Unceasingly, as she advanced, fresh penguins, descending from the paths of the mountain, coming out of clefts of the rocks, and emerging from the water, added to the size of her retinue.

And all of them, men of ripe age with vigorous shoulders and hairy breasts, agile youths, old men shaking the multitudinous wrinkles of their rosy and white-haired skins, or dragging their legs thinner and drier than the juniper staff that served them as a third leg, hurried on, panting and emitting an acrid odor and hoarse gasps. Yet she went on peacefully and seemed to see nothing.

"Father," cried Magis, "notice how each one advances with his nose pointed towards the center of gravity of that young damsel now that the center is covered by a garment. The sphere inspires the meditations of geometers by the number of its properties. When it proceeds from a physical and living nature it acquires new qualities, and in order that the interest of that figure might be fully revealed to the penguins it was necessary that, ceasing to see it distinctly with their eyes, they should be led to represent it to themselves in their minds. I myself feel at this moment irresistibly attracted toward that penguin. Whether it be because her skirt gives more importance to her hips, and that in its simple magnificence it invests them with a synthetic and general character and allows only the pure idea, the divine principle, of them to be seen—whether this be the cause I cannot say. But I feel that if I embraced her I would hold in my hands the heaven of human pleasure. It is certain that modesty communicates an invincible attraction to women. My uneasiness is so great that it would be vain for me to try to conceal it."

He spoke, and, gathering up his habit, he rushed among the crowd of penguins, pushing, jostling, trampling, and crushing, until he reached the daughter of Alca, whom he seized and suddenly carried in his arms into a cave that had been hollowed out by the sea.

Then the penguins felt as if the sun had gone out. And the holy Maël knew that the Devil had taken the features of the monk, Magis, in order that he might give clothes to the daughter of Alca. He was troubled in spirit and his soul was sad. As with slow steps he went toward his hermitage he saw the little penguins of six and seven years of age tightening their waists with belts made of seaweed and walking along the shore to see if anybody would follow them.

GUY DE MAUPASSANT (1850–1893)

Guy de Maupassant understood life but failed to live it. One of the most prolific of storytellers—he produced about three hundred stories, six novels, plays, articles, and many newspaper pieces within the space of ten years— he died at forty-three in an insane asylum. His mother was an intellectual woman who was separated from his father; through her, when he was only twenty-one, Guy became a protégé of Flaubert. For seven years he literally learned his craft from the father of the French naturalistic school; week after week, while he earned his living as a government clerk, he brought his stories to Flaubert for criticism. When Flaubert finally let him publish he was an immediate success.

For the rest of his active life, Maupassant's work was in great demand, earning him a consistently handsome income. Despite this, he was a morose man. He never married; his relations with women were spasmodic and on a low plane; his love of sports was hampered by agonizing headaches. It is thought that his insanity was the result of syphilis; completely paralyzed, he died in an asylum. He attributed his spiritual malaise to his vocation. Writing of himself in the third person, he complained: "All that he sees, his joys, his pleasures, his suffering, his despair, all instantaneously become subjects of observation. In spite of all, in spite of himself, he analyzes everything—hearts, faces, gestures, intonations . . . he lives condemned to be the mere reflection of himself and others."

Maupassant's stories have been criticized as being confined to typically French points of view, but they show a basic appreciation of the oddities of human behavior. Their echoes are heard in the skillfully constructed tales of W. Somerset Maugham and O. Henry, in whose hands the surprise ending often degenerated into a formula. Maupassant's unexpected denouements, however, are a natural outcome of his study of peasants and prostitutes as well as of members of Parisian society, all of whom are treated with a half-sympathetic, half-cynical understanding.

THE SIGNAL

The little Marchioness de Rennedon was still asleep in her dark and perfumed bedroom.

In her soft low bed, between sheets of delicate cambric, fine as lace and caressing as a kiss, she was sleeping alone and tranquil, the happy and profound sleep of divorced women.

She was awakened by loud noises in the little blue drawing room, and she recognized her dear friend, the little Baroness de Grangerie, who was disputing with the lady's maid, because the latter would not allow her to go into the Marchioness's room. So the little Marchioness got up, opened the door, drew back the door hangings and showed her head, nothing but her fair head, hidden under a cloud of hair.

"What is the matter with you, that you have come so early?" she asked. "It is not nine o'clock yet."

The little Baroness, who was very pale, nervous, and feverish, replied: "I must speak to you. Something horrible has happened to me."

"Come in, my dear."

She went in, they kissed each other and the little Marchioness got back into her bed, while the lady's maid opened the windows to let in light and air. Then when she had left the room, Madame de Rennedon went on: "Well, tell me what it is."

Madame de Grangerie began to cry, shedding those pretty bright tears which make women more charming. She sobbed out, without wiping her eyes, so as not to make them red: "Oh, my dear, what has happened to me is abominable, abominable. I have not slept all night, not a minute; do you hear, not a minute. Here, just feel my heart, how it is beating."

And taking her friend's hand, she put it on her breast, on that firm, round covering of women's hearts which often suffices men, and prevents them from seeking beneath. But her heart was really beating violently.

She continued: "It happened to me yesterday during the day, at about four o'clock—or half past four; I cannot say exactly. You know my apartments, and you know that my little drawing room, where I always sit, looks on to the Rue Saint-Lazare, and that I have a mania for sitting at the window to look at the people passing. The neighborhood of the railway station is very gay; so full of motion and lively—just what I like! So, yesterday, I was sitting in the low chair which I have placed in my window recess; the window was open and I was not thinking of anything, simply breathing the fresh air. You remember how fine it was yesterday!

"Suddenly, I remarked a woman sitting at the window opposite—a woman in red. I was in mauve, you know, my pretty mauve costume. I did not know the woman, a new lodger, who had been there a month, and as it has been raining for a month, I had not yet seen her, but I saw immediately that she was a bad girl. At first I was very much shocked and disgusted that she should be at the window just as I was; and then by degrees, it amused me to watch her. She was resting her elbows on the window ledge and looking at the men, and the men looked at her also, all or nearly all. One might have said that they knew of her presence by some means as they got near the house, that they scented her, as dogs scent game, for they suddenly raised their heads, and exchanged a swift look with her, a sort of freemason's look. Hers said: 'Will you?' Theirs replied: 'I have no time,' or else: 'Another day'; or else: 'I have not got a sou'; or else: 'Hide yourself, you wretch!'

"You cannot imagine how funny it was to see her carrying on such a piece of work, though after all it is her regular business.

"Occasionally she shut the window suddenly, and I saw a gentleman go in. She had caught him like a fisherman hooks a gudgeon. Then I looked at my watch, and I found that they never stopped longer than from twelve to twenty minutes. In the end she really infatuated me, the spider! And then the creature is so ugly.

"I asked myself: 'How does she manage to make herself understood so quickly, so well and so completely? Does she add a sign of the head or a motion of the hands to her looks?' And I took my opera glasses to watch her proceedings. Oh! they were very simple: first of all a glance, then a smile, then a slight sign with the head which meant: 'Are you coming up?' But it was so slight, so vague, so discreet, that it required a great deal of knack to succeed as she did. And I asked myself: 'I wonder if I could do that little movement, from below upward, which was at the same time bold and pretty, as well as she does,' for her gesture was very pretty.

"I went and tried it before the looking glass, and my dear, I did it better than she, a great deal better! I was enchanted, and resumed my place at the window.

"She caught nobody more then, poor girl, nobody. She certainly had no luck. It must really be very terrible to earn one's bread in that way, terrible and amusing occasionally, for really some of these men one meets in the street are rather nice.

"After that they all came on my side of the road and none on hers; the sun had turned. They came one after the other, young, old, dark, fair, gray, white. I saw some who looked very nice, really very nice, my dear, far better than my husband or than yours—I mean than your late husband, as you have got a divorce. Now you can choose.

"I said to myself: 'If I give them the sign, will they understand me, who am a respectable woman?' And I was seized with a mad longing to make that sign to them. I had a longing, a terrible longing; you know, one of those longings which one cannot resist! I have some like that occasionally. How silly such things are, don't you think so? I believe that we women have the souls of monkeys. I have been told (and it was a physician who told me) that the brain of a monkey is very like ours. Of course we must imitate someone or other. We imitate our husbands when we love them, during the first months after our marriage, and then our lovers, our female friends, our confessors when they are nice. We assume their ways of thought, their manners of speech, their words, their gestures, everything. It is very foolish.

"However, as for me, when I am much tempted to do a thing I always do it, and so I said to myself: 'I will try it once, on one man only, just to see. What can happen to me? Nothing whatever! We shall exchange a smile and that will be all and I shall deny it, most certainly.'

"So I began to make my choice, I wanted someone nice, very nice, and suddenly I saw a tall, fair, very good-looking fellow coming alone. I like fair men, as you know. I looked at him, he looked at me; I smiled, he smiled, I made the movement, oh! so faintly; he replied *yes* with his head, and there he was, my dear! He came in at the large door of the house.

"You cannot imagine what passed through my mind then! I thought I should go mad. Oh! how frightened I was. Just think, he will speak to the servants! To Joseph, who is devoted to my husband! Joseph would certainly think that I had known that gentleman for a long time.

"What could I do, just tell me? And he would ring in a moment. What could I do, tell me? I thought I would go and meet him, and tell him he had made a mistake, and beg him to go away. He would have pity on a woman, on a poor woman. So I rushed to the door and opened it, just at the moment when he was going to ring the bell, and I stammered out, quite stupidly: 'Go away, monsieur, go away; you have made a mistake, a terrible mistake; I took you for one of my friends whom you are very like. Have pity on me, monsieur.'

"But he only began to laugh, my dear, and replied: 'Good morning, my dear, I know all about your little story, you may be sure. You are married, and so you want forty francs instead of twenty, and you shall have them, so just show the way.'

"And he pushed me in, closed the door, and as I remained standing before him, horror-struck, he kissed me, put his arm round my waist and made me go back into the drawing room, the door of which had remained open. Then he began to look at everything like an auctioneer, and continued: 'By Jove, it is very nice in your rooms, very nice. You must be very down on your luck just now, to do the window business!'

"Then I began to beg him again. 'Oh! monsieur, go away, please go away! My husband will be coming in soon, it is just his time. I swear that you have made a mistake!' But he answered quite coolly: 'Come, my beauty, I have had enough of this nonsense, and if your husband comes in, I will give him five francs to go and have a drink at the *café* opposite.' And then seeing Raoul's photograph on the chimney piece, he asked me: 'Is that your—your husband?'

" 'Yes, that is he.'

" 'He looks like a nice, disagreeable sort of fellow. And who is this? One of your friends?'

"It was your photograph, my dear, you know, the one in ball dress. I did not know any longer what I was saying and I stammered: 'Yes, it is one of my friends.'

" 'She is very nice; you shall introduce me to her.'

"Just then the clock struck five, and Raoul comes home every day at half past! Suppose he were to come home before the other had gone, just fancy what would have happened! Then—then—I completely lost my head—altogether—I thought—I thought—that—that—the best thing would be—to get rid —of—of this man—as quickly as possible—— The sooner it was over—you understand."

*   *   *

The little Marchioness de Rennedon had begun to laugh, to laugh madly, with her head buried in her pillow, so that the whole bed shook, and when she was a little calmer she asked:

"And—and—was he good-looking?"

"Yes."

"And yet you complain?"

"But—but—don't you see, my dear, he said—he said—he should come again tomorrow—at the same time—and I—I am terribly frightened—— You have no idea how tenacious he is and obstinate—— What can I do—tell me—what can I do?"

The little Marchioness sat up in bed to reflect, and then she suddenly said: "Have him arrested!"

The little Baroness looked stupefied, and stammered out: "What do you say? What are you thinking of? Have him arrested? Under what pretext?"

"That is very simple. Go to the Commissary of Police and say that a gentle-

man has been following you about for three months; that he had the insolence to go up to your apartments yesterday; that he has threatened you with
another visit tomorrow, and that you demand the protection of the law, and
they will give you two police officers who will arrest him."

"But, my dear, suppose he tells——"

"They will not believe him, you silly thing, if you have told your tale cleverly to the Commissary, but they will believe you, who are an irreproachable
woman, and in society."

"Oh! I shall never dare to do it."

"You must dare, my dear, or you are lost."

"But think that he will—he will insult me if he is arrested."

"Very well, you will have witnesses, and he will be sentenced."

"Sentenced to what?"

"To pay damages. In such cases, one must be pitiless!"

"Ah! speaking of damages—there is one thing that worries me very much
—very much indeed. He left me two twenty-franc pieces on the mantelpiece."

"Two twenty-franc pieces?"

"Yes."

"No more?"

"No."

"That is very little. It would have humiliated me. Well?"

"Well! What am I to do with that money?"

The little Marchioness hesitated for a few seconds, and then she replied
in a serious voice:

"My dear—you must make—you must make your husband a little present
with it. That will be only fair!"

ROSE

The two young women have the appearance of being buried in a bed of
flowers. They are alone in an immense landau filled with bouquets like a
giant basket. Upon the seat before them are two small hampers full of Nice
violets, and upon the bearskin which covers their knees is a heap of roses,
gillyflowers, marguerites, tuberoses, and orange flowers, bound together with
silk ribbons, which seem to crush the two delicate bodies, only allowing to
appear above the spread-out, perfumed bed the shoulders, arms, and a little
of their bodices, one of which is blue and the other lilac.

The coachman's whip bears a sheath of anemones, the horses' heads are
decorated with wallflowers, the spokes of the wheels are clothed in mignon-
ette, and in place of lanterns, there are two round, enormous bouquets, which
seem like the two eyes of this strange, rolling, flowery beast.

The landau goes along Antibes street at a brisk trot, preceded, followed,
and accompanied by a crowd of other garlanded carriages full of women concealed under a billow of violets. For it is the Flower Festival at Cannes.

They arrived at the Boulevard Foncière where the battle takes place. The whole length of the immense avenue, a double line of bedecked equipages was going and coming, like a ribbon without end. They threw flowers from one to the other. Flowers passed in the air like balls, hit the fair faces, hovered and fell in the dust where an army of street urchins gathered them.

A compact crowd, clamorous but orderly, looked on, standing in rows upon the sidewalks, and held in place by policemen on horseback who passed along, pushing back the curious brutally with their feet, in order that the villains might not mingle with the rich.

Now, the people in the carriages recognize each other, call to each other, and bombard one another with roses. A chariot full of pretty young women, clothed in red like devils, attracts and holds all eyes. One gentleman, who resembles the portraits of Henri IV, throws repeatedly, with joyous ardor, a huge bouquet retained by an elastic. At the threat of the blow the women lower their heads and hide their eyes, but the gracious projectile only describes a curve and again returns to its master, who immediately throws it again to a new face.

The two young women empty their arsenal with full hands and receive a shower of bouquets; then, after an hour of battle, a little wearied at the last, they order the coachman to take the road to the Juan Gulf, which skirts the sea.

The sun disappeared behind the Esterel, outlining in black, upon a background of fire, the lacy silhouette of the stretched-out mountain. The calm sea was spread out blue and clear as far as the horizon, where it mingled with the sky and with the squadron anchored in the middle of the gulf, having the appearance of a troop of monstrous beasts, immovable upon the water, apocalyptic animals, humpbacked and clothed in coats of mail, capped with thin masts like plumes, and with eyes that lighted up when night came on.

The young women, stretched out under the fur robe, looked upon it languidly. Finally one of them said:

"How delicious these evenings are! Everything seems good. Is it not so, Margot?"

The other replied: "Yes, it is good. But there is always something lacking."

"What is it? For my part, I am completely happy. I have need of nothing."

"Yes? You think so, perhaps. But whatever well-being surrounds our bodies, we always desire something more—for the heart."

Said the other, smiling: "A little love?"

"Yes."

They were silent, looking straight before them; then the one called Marguerite said: "Life does not seem supportable to me without that. I need to be loved, if only by a dog. And we are all so, whatever you may say, Simone."

"No, no, my dear. I prefer not to be loved at all than to be loved by no one of importance. Do you think, for example, that it would be agreeable to me to be loved by—by——"

She looked for someone by whom she could possibly be loved, casting her eyes over the neighboring country. Her eyes, after having made the tour of the whole horizon, fell upon the two metal buttons shining on the coachman's back, and she continued, laughing, "By my coachman?"

Mademoiselle Marguerite scarcely smiled as she replied:

"I can assure you it is very amusing to be loved by a domestic. This has happened to me two or three times. They roll their eyes so queerly that one is dying to laugh. Naturally, the more one is loved, the more severe she becomes, since otherwise one puts herself in the way of being made ridiculous for some very slight cause, if anyone happened to observe it."

Mademoiselle Simone listened, her look fixed straight before her; then she declared:

"No, decidedly, the heart of my valet at my feet would not appear to me sufficient. But tell me how you perceived that you were loved."

"I perceived it in them as I do in other men, they become so stupid!"

"But others do not appear so stupid to me when they are in love."

"Idiots, my dear, incapable of chatting, of answering, of comprehending anything."

"And you? What effect did it have on you to be loved by a domestic? Were you moved—flattered?"

"Moved? No. Flattered? Yes, a little. One is always flattered by the love of a man, whoever he may be."

"Oh! now, Margot!"

"Yes, my dear. Wait! I will tell you a singular adventure that happened to me. You will see what curious things take place among us in such cases.

"It was four years ago in the autumn, when I found myself without a maid. I had tried five or six, one after the other, all of them incompetent, and almost despaired of finding one, when I read in the advertisements of a newspaper of a young girl, knowing how to sew, embroider, and dress hair, who was seeking a place and could furnish the best of references. She could also speak English.

"I wrote to the address given and the next day the person in question presented herself. She was rather tall, thin, a little pale, with a very timid air. She had beautiful black eyes, a charming color, and she pleased me at once. I asked for her references; she gave me one written in English, because she had come, she said, from the house of Lady Ryswell, where she had been for ten years.

"The certificate attested that the girl was returning to France of her own will, and that she had nothing to reproach her for during her long service with her, except a little of the *French coquettishness*.

"The modest turn of the English phrase made me smile a little and I engaged the maid immediately. She came to my house the same day; she called herself Rose.

"At the end of a month I adored her. She was a treasure, a pearl, a phenomenon.

"She could dress my hair with exquisite taste; she could flute the lace of a cap better than the best of the professionals, and she could make frocks. I was amazed at her ability. Never had I been so well served.

"She dressed me rapidly with an astonishing lightness of hand. I never felt her fingers upon my skin, and nothing is more disagreeable to me than contact with a maid's hand. I immediately got into excessively idle habits, so pleasant was it to let her dress me from head to foot, from chemise to gloves —this tall, timid girl, always blushing a little and never speaking. After my bath, she would rub me and massage me while I slept a little while on my divan; indeed, I came to look upon her more as a friend in poorer circumstances than a servant.

"One morning the *concierge*, with some show of mystery, said he wished to speak to me. I was surprised but let him enter. He was an old soldier, once orderly for my husband.

"He appeared to hesitate at what he was going to say. Finally, he said stammeringly: 'Madame, the police captain for this district is downstairs.'

"I asked: 'What does he want?'

" 'He wants to search the house.'

"Certainly the police are necessary, but I do detest them. I never can make it seem a noble profession. And I answered, irritated as well as wounded:

" 'Why search here? For what purpose? There has been no burglary.'

"He answered:

" 'He thinks that a criminal is concealed somewhere here.'

"I began to be a little afraid and ordered the police captain to be brought that I might have some explanation. He was a man rather well brought up and decorated with the Legion of Honor. He excused himself, asked my pardon, then asserted that I had among my servants a convict!

"I was thunderstruck, and answered that I could vouch for every one of them and that I would make a review of them for his satisfaction.

" 'There is Peter Courtin, an old soldier.'

"It was not he.

" 'The coachman, Francis Pingau, a peasant, son of my father's farmer.'

"It was not he.

" 'A stable boy, also from Champagne, and also a son of peasants I had known, and no more except the footman whom you have seen.'

"It was not any of them.

" 'Then, sir, you see that you have been deceived.'

" 'Pardon me, Madame, but I am sure I am not deceived. As he has not at all the appearance of a criminal, will you have the goodness to have all your servants appear here before you and me, all of them?'

"I hesitated at first, then I yielded, summoning all my people, men and women.

"He looked at them all for an instant, then declared:

" 'This is not all.'

" 'Your pardon, sir,' I replied, 'this is all except my own maid who could not possibly be confounded with a convict.'

"He asked: 'Could I see her too?'

"'Certainly.'

"I rang and Rose appeared immediately. Scarcely had she entered when he gave a signal and two men, whom I had not seen, concealed behind the door, threw themselves upon her, seized her hands, and bound them with cords.

"I uttered a cry of fury and was going to try and defend her. The captain stopped me:

"'This girl, Madame, is a man who calls himself John Nicholas Lecapet, condemned to death in 1879 for assassination preceded by violation. His sentence was changed to life imprisonment. He escaped four months ago. We have been on the search for him ever since.'

"I was dismayed, struck dumb. I could not believe it. The policeman continued, laughing:

"'I can only give you one proof. His right arm is tattooed.'

"His sleeve was rolled up. It was true. The policeman added, certainly in bad taste:

"'Doubtless you will be satisfied without the other proofs.'

"And he led away my maid!

"Well, if you will believe it, the feeling which was uppermost in me was that of anger at having been played with in this way, deceived and made ridiculous. It was not shame at having been dressed, undressed, handled, and touched by this man, but—a—profound humiliation—the humiliation of a woman. Do you understand?"

"No, not exactly."

"Let us see. Think a minute. He had been condemned—for violation, this young man—and that—that humiliated me—there! Now do you understand?"

And Mademoiselle Simone did not reply. She looked straight before her, with her eyes singularly fixed upon the two shining buttons of the livery, and with that sphinx's smile that women have sometimes.

THAT PIG OF A MORIN

"There, my friend," I said to Labarbe, "you have just repeated those five words, 'That pig of a Morin.' Why on earth do I never hear Morin's name mentioned without his being called a *pig?*"

Labarbe, who is a deputy, looked at me with eyes like an owl's, and said: "Do you mean to say that you do not know Morin's story, and yet come from La Rochelle?" I was obliged to declare that I did not know Morin's story, and then Labarbe rubbed his hands and began his recital.

"You knew Morin, did you not, and you remember his large linen-draper's shop on the Quai de la Rochelle?"

"Yes, perfectly."

"All right, then. You must know that in 1862 or '63 Morin went to spend a fortnight in Paris for pleasure, or for his pleasures, but under the pretext of renewing his stock, and you also know what a fortnight in Paris means for a country shopkeeper. It makes his blood grow hot. The theater every evening, women's dresses rustling up against you, and continual excitement. One goes almost mad with it. One sees nothing but dancers in tights, actresses in very low dresses, round legs, fat shoulders, all nearly within reach of one's hands, without daring or being able to touch, and one scarcely ever tastes an inferior dish. And one leaves it with heart still all in a flutter and a mind still exhilarated by a sort of longing for kisses which tickle one's lips.

"Morin was in that state when he took his ticket for La Rochelle by the 8:40 night express. And he was walking up and down the waiting room at the station, when he stopped suddenly in front of a young lady who was kissing an old one. She had her veil up and Morin murmured with delight: 'By Jove, what a pretty woman!'

"When she had said good-by to the old lady, she went into the waiting room and Morin followed her; then she went onto the platform and Morin still followed her; then she got into an empty carriage and he again followed her. There were very few travelers by the express, the engine whistled, and the train started. They were alone. Morin devoured her with his eyes. She appeared to be about nineteen or twenty, and was fair, tall, and with demure looks. She wrapped a railway rug round her legs and stretched herself on the seat to sleep.

"Morin asked himself: 'I wonder who she is?' And a thousand conjectures, a thousand projects went through his head. He said to himself: 'So many adventures are told as happening on railway journeys, that this may be one that is going to present itself to me. Who knows? A piece of good luck like that happens very quickly, and perhaps I need only be a little venturesome. Was it not Danton who said: 'Audacity, more audacity, and always audacity'? If it was not Danton it was Mirabeau, but that does not matter. But then, I have no audacity and that is the difficulty. Oh! If one only knew, if one could only read people's minds! I will bet that every day one passes by magnificent opportunities without knowing it, though a gesture would be enough to let me know that she did not ask for anything better.

"Then he imagined to himself combinations which led him to triumph. He pictured some chivalrous deed, or merely some slight service which he rendered her, a lively, gallant conversation which ended in a declaration, which ended in—in what you think.

"But he could find no opening; had no pretext, and he waited for some fortunate circumstance, with his heart ravaged and his mind topsy-turvy. The night passed and the pretty girl still slept, while Morin was meditating his own fall. The day broke and soon the first ray of sunlight appeared in the sky, a long, clear ray which shone on the face of the sleeping girl and woke her, so she sat up, looked at the country, then at Morin and smiled. She smiled like a happy woman, with an engaging and bright look, and Morin trembled. Certainly that smile was intended for him, it was a discreet invitation, the signal which he was waiting for. That smile meant to say: 'How stupid, what a ninny, what a dolt, what a donkey you are, to have sat there on your seat like a post all night.

" 'Just look at me, am I not charming? And you have sat like that for the whole night, when you have been alone with a pretty woman, you great simpleton!'

"She was still smiling as she looked at him. She even began to laugh; and he lost his head trying to find something suitable to say, no matter what. But he could think of nothing, nothing, and then, seized with a coward's courage, he said to himself: 'So much the worse, I will risk everything,' and suddenly, without the slightest warning, he went toward her, his arms extended, his lips protruding and seizing her in his arms kissed her.

"She sprang up with a bound, crying out: 'Help! help!' and screaming with terror; then she opened the carriage door, and waved her arm outside; then mad with terror she was trying to jump out, while Morin, who was almost distracted, and feeling sure that she would throw herself out, held her by her skirt and stammered: 'Oh! Madame! Oh! Madame!'

"The train slackened speed, and then stopped. Two guards rushed up at the young woman's frantic signals, and she threw herself into their arms, stammering: 'That man wanted—wanted—to—to——' And then she fainted.

"They were at Mauzé station, and the gendarme on duty arrested Morin. When the victim of his brutality had regained her consciousness she made her charge against him, and the police drew it up. The poor linen draper did not reach home till night, with a prosecution hanging over him for an outrage on morals in a public place.

II

"At that time I was editor of the 'Fanal des Charentes' and I used to meet Morin every day at the Café du Commerce. The day after his adventure he came to see me, as he did not know what to do. I did not hide my opinion from him, but said to him: 'You are no better than a pig. No decent man behaves like that.'

"He cried. His wife had given him a beating and he foresaw his trade ruined, his name dragged through the mire and dishonored, his friends outraged and taking no more notice of him. In the end he excited my pity and I sent for my colleague Rivet, a bantering, but very sensible little man, to give us advice.

"He advised me to see the public prosecutor, who was a friend of mine, and so I sent Morin home, and went to call on the magistrate. He told me that the woman who had been insulted was a young lady, Mademoiselle Henriette Bonnel, who had just received her certificate as governess in Paris, and spent her holidays with her uncle and aunt, who were very respectable tradespeople in Mauzé, and what made Morin's case all the more serious was that the uncle had lodged a complaint. But the public official had consented to let the matter drop if this complaint were withdrawn, so that we must try and get him to do this.

"I went back to Morin's and found him in bed, ill with excitement and distress. His wife, a tall, rawboned woman with a beard, was abusing him continually, and she showed me into the room, shouting at me: 'So you have come to see that pig of a Morin. Well, there he is, the darling!' And she planted herself in front of the bed, with her hands on her hips. I told him how matters stood and he begged me to go and see her uncle and aunt. It was a delicate mission, but I undertook it, and the poor devil never ceased repeating: 'I assure you I did not even kiss her, no, not even that. I will take my oath to it!'

"I replied: 'It is all the same; you are nothing but a pig.' And I took a thousand francs which he gave me, to employ them as I thought best, but as I did not care venturing to her uncle's house alone, I begged Rivet to go with me, which he agreed to do on the condition that we went immediately, for he had some urgent business at La Rochelle that afternoon. So two hours later we rang at the door of a nice country house. A pretty girl came and opened the door to us, who was assuredly the young lady in question, and I said to Rivet in a low voice: 'Confound it! I begin to understand Morin!'

"The uncle, Monsieur Tonnelet, subscribed to 'The Fanal,' and was a fervent political coreligionist of ours. He received us with open arms and congratulated us and wished us joy; he was delighted at having the two editors in his house, and Rivet whispered to me: 'I think we shall be able to arrange the matter of that pig of a Morin for him.'

"The niece had left the room, and I introduced the delicate subject. I waved the specter of scandal before his eyes; I accentuated the inevitable depreciation which the young lady would suffer if such an affair got known, for nobody would believe in a simple kiss. The good man seemed undecided, but could not make up his mind about anything without his wife, who would not be in until late that evening. But suddenly he uttered an exclamation of triumph: 'Look here, I have an excellent idea. I will keep you here to dine and sleep, and when my wife comes home I hope we shall be able to arrange matters.'

"Rivet resisted at first, but the wish to extricate that pig of a Morin decided him, and we accepted the invitation. So the uncle got up radiant, called his niece, and proposed that we should take a stroll in his grounds, saying: 'We will leave serious matters until the morning.' Rivet and he began to talk politics, while I soon found myself lagging a little behind with the girl, who was really charming! charming! And with the greatest precaution I began to speak to her about her adventure and try to make her my ally. She did not, however, appear the least confused, and listened to me like a person who was enjoying the whole thing very much.

"I said to her: 'Just think, mademoiselle, how unpleasant it will be for you. You will have to appear in court, to encounter malicious looks, to speak before everybody, and to recount that unfortunate occurrence in the railway carriage, in public. Do you not think, between ourselves, that it would have been much better for you to have put that dirty scoundrel back into his place without calling for assistance and merely to have changed your carriage?' She began to laugh and replied: 'What you say is quite true! But what could I do? I was frightened, and when one is frightened, one does not stop to reason with oneself. As soon as I realized the situation I was very sorry that I had called out, but then it was too late. You must also remember that the idiot threw himself upon me like a madman, without saying a word and looking like a lunatic. I did not even know what he wanted of me.'

"She looked me full in the face without being nervous or intimidated and I said to myself: 'She is a funny sort of girl, that: I can quite see how that pig Morin came to make a mistake,' and I went on jokingly: 'Come, mademoiselle, confess that he was excusable, for after all, a man cannot find himself opposite such a pretty girl as you are without feeling a legitimate desire to kiss her.'

"She laughed more than ever and showed her teeth and said: 'Between the desire and the act, monsieur, there is room for respect.' It was a funny expression to use although it was not very clear, and I asked abruptly: 'Well now, supposing I were to kiss you now, what would you do?' She stopped to look at me from head to foot, and then said calmly: 'Oh! You? That is quite another matter.'

"I knew perfectly well, by Jove, that it was not the same thing at all, as everybody in the neighborhood called me 'Handsome Labarbe.' I was thirty years old in those days, but I asked her: 'And why, pray?'

"She shrugged her shoulders, and replied: 'Well, because you are not so stupid as he is.' And then she added, looking at me slyly: 'Nor so ugly, either.'

"Before she could make a movement to avoid me, I had implanted a hearty kiss on her cheek. She sprang aside but it was too late, and then she said: 'Well, you are not very bashful, either! But don't do that sort of thing again.'

"I put on a humble look and said in a low voice: 'Oh! Mademoiselle, as for me, if I long for one thing more than another, it is to be summoned before a magistrate on the same charge as Morin.'

" 'Why?' she asked.

"Looking steadily at her, I replied: 'Because you are one of the most beautiful creatures living; because it would be an honor and a glory for me to have offered you violence, and because people would have said, after seeing you: 'Well, Labarbe has richly deserved what he has got, but he is a lucky fellow, all the same.'

"She began to laugh heartily again, and said: 'How funny you are!' And she had not finished the word *funny* before I had her in my arms and was kissing her ardently wherever I could find a place, on her forehead, on her eyes, on her lips occasionally, on her cheeks, in fact, all over her head, some part of which she was obliged to leave exposed, in spite of herself, in order to defend the others. At last she managed to release herself, blushing and angry. 'You are very unmannerly, monsieur,' she said, 'and I am sorry I listened to you.'

"I took her hand in some confusion and stammered out: 'I beg your pardon, mademoiselle. I have offended you; I have acted like a brute! Do not be angry with me for what I have done. If you knew——'

"I vainly sought for some excuse, and in a few moments she said: 'There is nothing for me to know, monsieur.' But I had found something to say and I cried: 'Mademoiselle, I love you!'

"She was really surprised and raised her eyes to look at me, and I went on: 'Yes, mademoiselle, and pray listen to me. I do not know Morin and I do not care anything about him. It does not matter to me the least if he is committed for trial and locked up meanwhile. I saw you here last year and I was so taken with you that the thought of you has never left me since, and it does not matter to me whether you believe me or not. I thought you adorable, and the remembrance of you took such a hold on me that I longed to see you again and so I made use of that fool Morin as a pretext, and here I am. Circumstances have made me exceed the due limits of respect and I can only beg you to pardon me.'

"She read the truth in my looks and was ready to smile again; then she murmured: 'You humbug!' But I raised my hand and said in a sincere voice (and I really believe that I was sincere): 'I swear to you that I am speaking the truth.' She replied quite simply: 'Really?'

"We were alone, quite alone, as Rivet and her uncle had disappeared in a side walk, and I made her a real declaration of love, while I squeezed and kissed her hands, and she listened to it as to something new and agreeable, without exactly knowing how much of it she was to believe, while in the end I felt agitated, and at last really myself believed what I said. I was pale, anxious, and trembling, and I gently put my arm round her waist, and spoke to her softly, whispering into the little curls over her ears. She seemed dead, so absorbed in thought was she.

"Then her hand touched mine and she pressed it, and I gently circled her waist with a trembling, and gradually a firmer, grasp. She did not move now and I touched her cheeks with my lips, and suddenly, without seeking them mine met hers. It was a long, long kiss, and it would have lasted longer still, if I had not heard a *Hum! Hum!* just behind me. She made her escape through the bushes, and I turning round saw Rivet coming toward me and walking in the middle of the path. He said without even smiling: 'So that is the way in which you settle the affair of that pig Morin.'

"I replied conceitedly: 'One does what one can, my dear fellow. But what about the uncle? How have you got on with him? I will answer for the niece.'

"'I have not been so fortunate with him,' he replied. Whereupon I took his arm, and we went indoors.

III

"Dinner made me lose my head altogether. I sat beside her and my hand continually met hers under the table cloth, my foot touched hers, and our looks encounted each other.

"After dinner we took a walk by moonlight and I whispered all the tender things I could think of to her. I held her close to me, kissed her every moment, moistening my lips against hers, while her uncle and Rivet were disputing as they walked in front of us. We went in, and soon a messenger brought a telegram from her aunt, saying that she would return by the first train the next morning at seven o'clock.

" 'Very well, Henriette,' her uncle said, 'go and show the gentlemen their rooms.' She showed Rivet his first and he whispered to me: 'There was no danger of her taking us into yours first.' Then she took me to my room, and as soon as she was alone with me I took her in my arms again and tried to excite her senses and overcome her resistance, but when she felt that she was near succumbing, she escaped out of the room and I got between the sheets, very much put out and excited and feeling rather foolish, for I knew that I should not sleep much. I was wondering how I could have committed such a mistake, when there was a gentle knock at my door, and on my asking who was there, a low voice replied: 'I.'

"I dressed myself quickly and opened the door and she came in: 'I forgot to ask you what you take in the morning,' she said, 'chocolate, tea, or coffee?' I put my arms around her impetuously and said, devouring her with kisses: 'I will take—I will take——' But she freed herself from my arms, blew out my candle, and disappeared, and left me alone in the dark, furious, trying to find some matches and not able to do so. At last I got some and I went into the passage, feeling half mad, with my candlestick in my hand.

"What was I going to do? I did not stop to reason, I only wanted to find her, and I would. I went a few steps without reflecting, but then I suddenly thought to myself: 'Suppose I should go into the uncle's room, what should I say?' And I stood still, with my head a void and my heart beating.

"But in a few moments I thought of an answer: 'Of course, I shall say that I was looking for Rivet's room, to speak to him about an important matter,' and I began to inspect all the doors, trying to find hers, and at last I took hold of a handle at a venture, turned it and went in. There was Henriette, sitting on her bed and looking at me in tears. So I gently turned the key, and going up to her on tiptoe, I said: 'I forgot to ask you for something to read, mademoiselle.' I will not tell you the book I read, but it is the most wonderful of romances, the most divine of poems. And when once I had turned the first page, she let me turn over as many leaves as I liked, and I got through so many chapters that our candles were quite burned out.

"Then, after thanking her, I was stealthily returning to my room, when a rough hand seized me, and a voice—it was Rivet's—whispered in my ear: 'So you have not yet quite settled that affair of Morin's?'

"At seven o'clock the next morning she herself brought me a cup of chocolate. I have never drunk anything like it, soft, velvety, perfumed, delicious. I could scarcely take away my lips from the cup, and she had hardly left the room when Rivet came in. He seemed nervous and irritable like a man who had not slept, and he said to me crossly: 'If you go on like this, you will end by spoiling the affair of that pig of a Morin!'

"At eight o'clock the aunt arrived. Our discussion was very short, for they withdrew their complaint, and I left five hundred francs for the poor of the town. They wanted to keep us for the day and they arranged an excursion to go and see some ruins. Henriette made signs to me to stay, behind her uncle's back, and I accepted, but Rivet was determined to go, and though I took him aside, and begged and prayed him to do this for me he appeared quite exasperated and kept saying to me: 'I have had enough of that pig of a Morin's affair, do you hear?'

"Of course I was obliged to go also, and it was one of the hardest moments of my life. I could have gone on arranging that business as long as I lived, and when we were in the railway carriage, after shaking hands with her in silence, I said to Rivet: 'You are a mere brute!' And he replied: 'My dear fellow, you were beginning to excite me confoundedly.'

"On getting to the 'Fanal' office, I saw a crowd waiting for us, and as soon as they saw us they all exclaimed: 'Well, have you settled the affair of that pig of a Morin?' All La Rochelle was excited about it, and Rivet, who had got over his ill-humor on the journey, had great difficulty in keeping himself from laughing as he said: 'Yes, we have managed it, thanks to Labarbe.' And we went to Morin's.

"He was sitting in an easy chair, with mustard plasters on his legs and cold bandages on his head, nearly dead with misery. He was coughing with the short cough of a dying man, without anyone knowing how he had caught it, and his wife seemed like a tigress ready to eat him. As soon as he saw us he trembled violently as to make his hands and knees shake, so I said to him immediately: 'It is all settled, you dirty scamp, but don't do such a thing again.'

"He got up choking, took my hands and kissed them as if they had belonged to a prince, cried, nearly fainted, embraced Rivet, and even kissed Madame Morin, who gave him such a push as to send him staggering back into his chair. But he never got over the blow; his mind had been too much upset. In all the country round, moreover, he was called nothing but 'that pig of a Morin,' and the epithet went through him like a sword thrust every time he heard it. When a street boy called after him: 'Pig!' he turned his head instinctively. His friends also overwhelmed him with horrible jokes and used to chaff him, whenever they were eating ham, by saying: 'It's a bit of you!' He died two years later.

"As for myself, when I was a candidate for the Chamber of Deputies in 1875, I called on the new notary of Foncerre, Monsieur Belloncle, to solicit his vote, and a tall, handsome, and evidently wealthy lady received me. 'You do not know me again?' she said.

"I stammered out: 'But—no, madame.'

"'Henriette Bonnel?'

"'Ah!' And I felt myself turning pale, while she seemed perfectly at her ease and looked at me with a smile.

"As soon as she had left me alone with her husband, he took both my hands, and squeezing them as if he meant to crush them, he said: 'I have been intending to go and see you for a long time, my dear sir, for my wife has very often talked to me about you. I know under what painful circumstances you made her acquaintance and I know also how perfectly you behaved, how full of delicacy, tact, and devotion you showed yourself in the affair——' He hesitated and then said in a lower tone as if he had been saying something low and coarse: 'in the affair of that pig of a Morin.'"

A SALE

The defendants, Césaire-Isidore Brument and Prosper-Napoléon Cornu, appeared before the court of assizes of the Seine-Inférieure, on a charge of attempted murder by drowning, of Madame Brument, lawful wife of the first of the aforenamed.

The two prisoners sat side by side on the traditional bench. They were two peasants; the first was small and stout with short arms, short legs, and a round head with a red pimply face, planted directly on his trunk, which was also round and short, and with apparently no neck. He was a raiser of pigs and lived at Cacheville-la-Goupil in the district of Criquetot.

Cornu (Prosper-Napoléon) was thin, of medium height, with enormously long arms. His head was on crooked, his jaw awry, and he squinted. A blue blouse as long as a shirt hung down to his knees, and his yellow hair, which was scanty and plastered down on his head, gave his face a worn-out dirty look, a dilapidated look that was frightful. He had been nicknamed "the curé" because he could imitate to perfection the chanting in church, and even the sound of the serpent. This talent attracted to his café—for he was a saloonkeeper at Criquetot—a great many customers who preferred the "Mass at Cornu" to the Mass in church.

Madame Brument, seated on the witness bench, was a thin peasant woman who seemed to be always asleep. She sat there motionless, her hands crossed on her knees, gazing fixedly before her with a stupid expression.

The judge continued his interrogation.

"Well, then, Madame Brument, they came into your house and threw you into a barrel full of water. Tell us the details. Stand up."

She rose. She looked as tall as a flagpole with her cap which looked like a white skullcap. She said in a drawling tone:

"I was shelling beans. Just then they came in. I said to myself, 'What is the matter with them? They do not seem natural, they seem up to some mischief.' They watched me sideways, like this, especially Cornu, because he squints. I do not like to see them together, for they are two good-for-nothings when they are in company. I said: 'What do you want with me?' They did not answer. I had a sort of mistrust——"

The defendant Brument interrupted the witness hastily, saying:

"I was full."

Then Cornu, turning toward his accomplice, said in the deep tones of an organ:

"Say that we were both full and you will be telling no lie."

The judge, severely:

"You mean by that that you were both drunk?"

Brument: "There can be no question about it."

Cornu: "That might happen to anyone."

The judge to the victim: "Continue your testimony, Woman Brument."

"Well, Brument said to me, 'Do you wish to earn a hundred sous?' 'Yes,' I replied, seeing that a hundred sous are not picked up in a horse's tracks. Then he said: 'Open your eyes and do as I do,' and he went to fetch the large empty barrel which is under the rain pipe in the corner, and he turned it over and brought it into my kitchen and stuck it down in the middle of the floor, and then he said to me: 'Go and fetch water until it is full.'

"So I went to the pond with two pails and carried water and still more water for an hour, seeing that the barrel was as large as a vat, saving your presence, M'sieu' le Président.

"All this time Brument and Cornu were drinking a glass and then another glass and then another. They were finishing their drinks when I said to them: 'You are full, fuller than this barrel.' And Brument answered me: 'Do not worry; go on with your work; your turn will come; each one has his share.' I paid no attention to what he said as he was full.

"When the barrel was full to the brim I said: 'There, that's done.'

"And then Cornu gave me a hundred sous, not Brument, Cornu; it was Cornu gave them to me. And Brument said: 'Do you wish to earn a hundred sous more?' 'Yes,' I said, for I am not accustomed to presents like that. Then he said: 'Take off your clothes.'

" 'Take off my clothes?'

" 'Yes,' he said.

" 'How many shall I take off?'

" 'If it worries you at all, keep on your chemise, that won't bother us.'

"A hundred sous is a hundred sous, and I have to undress myself; but I did not fancy undressing before those two good-for-nothings. I took off my cap and then my jacket and then my skirt and then my sabots. Brument said, 'Keep on your stockings also; we are good fellows.'

"And Cornu said, too, 'We are good fellows.'

"So there I was, almost like mother Eve. And they got up from their chairs, but could not stand straight, they were so full, saving your presence, M'sieu' le Président.

"I said to myself: 'What are they up to?'

"And Brument said: 'Are you ready?'

"And Cornu said: 'I'm ready!'

"And then they took me, Brument by the head, and Cornu by the feet, as one might take, for instance, a sheet that has been washed. Then I began to bawl.

"And Brument said: 'Keep still, wretched creature!'

"And they lifted me up in the air and put me into the barrel, which was full of water, so that I had a check of the circulation, a chill to my very insides.

"And Brument said: 'Is that all?'

"Cornu said: 'That is all.'

"Brument said: 'The head is not in. That will make a difference in the measure.'

"Cornu said: 'Put in her head.'

"And then Brument pushed down my head as if to drown me, so that the water ran into my nose, so that I could already see Paradise. And he pushed it down and I disappeared.

"And then he must have been frightened. He pulled me out and said: 'Go and get dry, carcass.'

"As for me, I took to my heels and ran as far as Monsieur le Curé's. He lent me a skirt belonging to his servant, for I was almost in a state of nature, and he went to fetch Maître Chicot, the country watchman who went to Criquetot to fetch the police who came to my house with me.

"Then we found Brument and Cornu fighting each other like two rams.

"Brument was bawling: 'It isn't true, I tell you that there is at least a cubic meter in it. It is the method that was no good.'

"Cornu bawled: 'Four pails, that is almost half a cubic meter. You need not reply, that's what it is.'

"The police captain put them both under arrest. I have no more to tell."

She sat down. The audience in the courtroom laughed. The jurors looked at one another in astonishment. The judge said:

"Defendant Cornu, you seem to have been the instigator of this infamous plot. What have you to say?"

And Cornu rose in his turn.

"Judge," he replied, "I was full."

The judge answered gravely:

"I know it. Proceed."

"I will. Well, Brument came to my place about nine o'clock, and ordered two drinks, and said: 'There's one for you, Cornu.' I sat down opposite him and drank and, out of politeness, I offered him a glass. Then he returned the compliment and so did I, and so it went on from glass to glass until noon, when we were full.

"Then Brument began to cry. That touched me. I asked him what was the matter. He said: 'I must have a thousand francs by Thursday.' That cooled me off a little, you understand. Then he said to me all at once: 'I will sell you my wife.'

"I was full and I was a widower. You understand, that stirred me up. I did not know his wife, but she was a woman, wasn't she? I asked him: 'How much would you sell her for?'

"He reflected, or pretended to reflect. When one is full one is not very clearheaded, and he replied: 'I will sell her by the cubic meter.'

"That did not surprise me, for I was as drunk as he was, and I knew what a cubic meter is in my business. It is a thousand liters, that suited me.

"But the price remained to be settled. All depends on the quality. I said: 'How much do you want a cubic meter?'

"He answered: 'Two thousand francs.'

"I gave a bound like a rabbit, and then I reflected that a woman ought not to measure more than three hundred liters. So I said: 'That's too dear.'

"He answered: 'I cannot do it for less. I should lose by it.'

"You understand, one is not a dealer in hogs for nothing. One understands one's business. But, if he is smart, the seller of bacon, I am smarter, seeing that I sell them also. Ha, Ha, Ha! So I said to him: 'If she were new I would not say anything, but she has been married to you for some time, so she is not as fresh as she was. I will give you fifteen hundred francs a cubic meter, not a sou more. Will that suit you?'

"He answered: 'That will do. That's a bargain!'

"I agreed and we started out, arm in arm. We must help each other in this world.

"But a fear came to me: 'How could you measure her unless you put her into the liquid?'

"Then he explained his idea, not without difficulty, for he was full. He said to me: 'I take a barrel and fill it with water to the brim. I put her in it. All the water that comes out we will measure, that is the way to fix it.'

"I said: 'I see, I understand. But this water that overflows will run away; how are you going to gather it up?'

"Then he began stuffing me and explained to me that all we should have to do would be to refill the barrel with the water his wife had displaced as soon as she should have left. All the water we should pour in would be the measure. I supposed about ten pails; that would be a cubic meter. He isn't a fool, all the same, when he is drunk, that old horse.

"To be brief, we reached his house and I took a look at its mistress. A beautiful woman she certainly was not. Anyone can see her, for there she is. I said to myself: 'I am disappointed, but never mind, she will be of value; handsome or ugly, it is all the same, is it not, Monsieur le Président?' And then I saw that she was as thin as a rail. I said to myself: 'She will not measure four hundred liters.' I understand the matter, it being in liquids.

"She told you about the proceeding. I even let her keep on her chemise and stockings, to my own disadvantage.

"When that was done she ran away. I said: 'Look out, Brument! she is escaping.'

"He replied: 'Do not be afraid. I will catch her all right. She will have to come back to sleep. I will measure the deficit.'

"We measured. Not four pailfuls. Ha, Ha, Ha!"

The witness began to laugh so persistently that a gendarme was obliged to punch him in the back. Having quieted down, he resumed:

"In short, Brument exclaimed: 'Nothing doing, that is not enough.' I bawled and bawled and bawled again, he punched me, I hit back. That would have kept on till the Day of Judgment, seeing we were both drunk.

"Then came the gendarmes! They swore at us, they took us off to prison. I want damages."

He sat down.

Brument confirmed in every particular the statements of his accomplice. The jury, in consternation, retired to deliberate.

At the end of an hour they returned a verdict of acquittal for the defendants, with some severe strictures on the dignity of marriage, and establishing the precise limitations of business transactions.

Brument went home to the domestic roof accompanied by his wife.

Cornu went back to his business.

THE FALSE GEMS

Monsieur Lantin had met the young woman at a soiree at the home of the assistant chief of his bureau and at first sight had fallen madly in love with her.

She was the daughter of a country physician who had died some months previously. She had come to live in Paris with her mother, who visited much among her acquaintances in the hope of making a favorable marriage for her daughter. They were poor and honest, quiet and unaffected.

The young girl was a perfect type of the virtuous woman whom every sensible young man dreams of one day winning for wife. Her simple beauty had the charm of angelic modesty, and the imperceptible smile which constantly hovered about her lips seemed to be the reflection of a pure and lovely soul. Her praises resounded on every side. People were never tired of saying: "Happy the man who wins her love! He could not find a better wife."

Now Monsieur Lantin enjoyed a snug little income of seven hundred dollars and, thinking he could safely assume the responsibilities of matrimony, proposed to this model young girl and was accepted.

He was unspeakably happy with her; she governed his household so cleverly and economically that they seemed to live in luxury. She lavished the most delicate attentions on her husband, coaxed and fondled him, and the charm of her presence was so great that six years after their marriage Monsieur Lantin discovered that he loved his wife even more than during the first days of their honeymoon.

He only felt inclined to blame her for two things: her love of the theater, and a taste for false jewelry. Her friends (she was acquainted with some officers' wives) frequently procured for her a box at the theater, often for the first representations of the new plays; and her husband was obliged to accompany her, whether he willed or not, to these amusements, though they bored him excessively after a day's labor at the office.

After a time Monsieur Lantin begged his wife to get some lady of her acquaintance to accompany her. She was at first opposed to such an arrangement; but after much persuasion on his part, she finally consented—to the infinite delight of her husband.

Now with her love for the theater came also the desire to adorn her person. True, her costumes remained as before, simple, and in the most correct taste; but she soon began to ornament her ears with huge rhinestones which glittered and sparkled like real diamonds. Around her neck she wore strings of false pearls and on her arms bracelets of imitation gold.

Her husband frequently remonstrated with her, saying:

"My dear, as you cannot afford to buy real diamonds, you ought to appear adorned with your beauty and modesty alone, which are the rarest ornaments of your sex."

But she would smile sweetly and say:

"What can I do? I am so fond of jewelry. It is my only weakness. We cannot change our natures."

Then she would roll the pearl necklaces around her fingers and hold up the bright gems for her husband's admiration, gently coaxing him:

"Look! are they not lovely? One would swear they were real."

Monsieur Lantin would then answer smilingly:

"You have Bohemian tastes, my dear."

Often of an evening, when they were enjoying a tête-à-tête by the fireside, she would place on the tea table the leather box containing the "trash," as Monsieur Lantin called it. She would examine the false gems with a passionate attention as though they were in some way connected with a deep and secret joy; and she often insisted on passing a necklace around her husband's neck and, laughing heartily, would exclaim: "How droll you look!" Then she would throw herself into his arms and kiss him affectionately.

One evening in winter she attended the opera and on her return was chilled through and through. The next morning she coughed and eight days later she died of inflammation of the lungs.

Monsieur Lantin's despair was so great that his hair became white in one month. He wept unceasingly; his heart was torn with grief and his mind was haunted by the remembrance, the smile, the voice—by every charm of his beautiful dead wife.

Time, the healer, did not assuage his grief. Often during office hours, while his colleagues were discussing the topics of the day, his eyes would suddenly fill with tears, and he would give vent to his grief in heart-rending sobs. Everything in his wife's room remained as before her decease; and here he was wont to seclude himself daily and think of her who had been his treasure—the joy of his existence.

But life soon became a struggle. His income, which in the hands of his wife had covered all household expenses, was now no longer sufficient for his own immediate wants; and he wondered how she could have managed to buy such excellent wines and such rare delicacies, things which he could no longer procure with his modest resources.

He incurred some debts and was soon reduced to absolute poverty. One morning, finding himself without a cent in his pocket, he resolved to sell something, and immediately the thought occurred to him of disposing of his wife's paste jewels. He cherished in his heart a sort of rancor against the false gems. They had always irritated him in the past and the very sight of them spoiled somewhat the memory of his lost darling.

To the last days of her life she had continued to make purchases; bringing home new gems almost every evening. He decided to sell the heavy necklace which she seemed to prefer, and which, he thought, ought to be worth about six or seven francs: for although paste it was nevertheless of very fine workmanship.

He put it in his pocket and started out in search of a jeweler's shop. He entered the first one he saw, feeling a little ashamed to expose his misery and also to offer such a worthless article for sale.

"Sir," said he to the merchant, "I would like to know what this is worth."

The man took his necklace, examined it, called his clerk and made some remarks in an undertone; then he put the ornament back on the counter and looked at it from a distance to judge of the effect.

Monsieur Lantin was annoyed by all this detail and was on the point of saying: "Oh! I know well enough it is not worth anything," when the jeweler said: "Sir, that necklace is worth from twelve to fifteen thousand francs; but I could not buy it unless you tell me now whence it comes."

The widower opened his eyes wide and remained gaping, not comprehending the merchant's meaning. Finally he stammered: "You say—are you sure?" The other replied dryly: "You can search elsewhere and see if anyone will offer you more. I consider it worth fifteen thousand at the most. Come back here if you cannot do better."

Monsieur Lantin, beside himself with astonishment, took up the necklace and left the store. He wished time for reflection.

Once outside, he felt inclined to laugh, and said to himself: "The fool! Had I only taken him at his word! That jeweler cannot distinguish real diamonds from paste."

A few minutes after, he entered another store in the Rue de la Paix. As soon as the proprietor glanced at the necklace, he cried out:

"Ah, *parbleu!* I know it well; it was bought here."

Monsieur Lantin was disturbed and asked:

"How much is it worth?"

"Well, I sold it for twenty thousand francs. I am willing to take it back for eighteen thousand when you inform me, according to our legal formality, how it comes to be in your possession."

This time Monsieur Lantin was dumfounded. He replied:

"But—but—examine it well. Until this moment I was under the impression that it was paste."

Said the jeweler:

"What is your name, sir?"

"Lantin—I am in the employ of the Minister of the Interior. I live at No. 16, Rue des Martyrs."

The merchant looked through his books, found the entry, and said: "That necklace was sent to Madame Lantin's address, 16 Rue des Martyrs, July 20, 1876."

The two men looked into each other's eyes—the widower speechless with astonishment, the jeweler scenting a thief. The latter broke the silence by saying:

"Will you leave this necklace here for twenty-four hours? I will give you a receipt."

"Certainly," answered Monsieur Lantin hastily. Then, putting the ticket in his pocket, he left the store.

He wandered aimlessly through the streets, his mind in a state of dreadful confusion. He tried to reason, to understand. He could not afford to purchase such a costly ornament. Certainly not. But, then it must have been a present!—a present!—a present from whom? Why was it given her?

He stopped and remained standing in the middle of the street. A horrible doubt entered his mind—she? Then all the other gems must have been presents too! The earth seemed to tremble beneath him—the tree before him was falling—throwing up his arms, he fell to the ground, unconscious. He recovered his senses in a pharmacy into which the passers-by had taken him, and was then taken to his home. When he arrived he shut himself up in his room and wept until nightfall. Finally, overcome with fatigue, he threw himself on the bed, where he passed an uneasy restless night.

The following morning he arose and prepared to go to the office. It was hard to work after such a shock. He sent a letter to his employer requesting to be excused. Then he remembered that he had to return to the jeweler's. He did not like the idea; but he could not leave the necklace with that man. So he dressed and went out.

It was a lovely day; a clear blue sky smiled on the busy city below, and men of leisure were strolling about with their hands in their pockets.

Observing them, Monsieur Lantin said to himself: "The rich, indeed, are happy. With money it is possible to forget even the deepest sorrow. One can go where one pleases and in travel find that distraction which is the surest cure for grief. Oh! If I were only rich!"

He began to feel hungry but his pocket was empty. He again remembered the necklace. Eighteen thousand francs! Eighteen thousand francs! What a sum!

He soon arrived in the Rue de la Paix, opposite the jeweler's. Eighteen thousand francs! Twenty times he resolved to go in, but shame kept him back. He was hungry, however—very hungry—and had not a cent in his pocket. He decided quickly, ran across the street in order not to have time for reflection, and entered the store.

The proprietor immediately came forward and politely offered him a chair; the clerks glanced at him knowingly.

"I have made inquiries, Monsieur Lantin," said the jeweler, "and if you are still resolved to dispose of the gems, I am ready to pay you the price I offered."

"Certainly, sir," stammered Monsieur Lantin.

Whereupon the proprietor took from a drawer eighteen large bills, counted and handed them to Monsieur Lantin, who signed a receipt and with a trembling hand put the money into his pocket.

As he was about to leave the store he turned toward the merchant, who still wore the same knowing smile and, lowering his eyes, said:

"I have—I have other gems which I have received from the same source. Will you buy them also?"

The merchant bowed: "Certainly, sir."

Monsieur Lantin said gravely: "I will bring them to you." An hour later he returned with the gems.

The large diamond earrings were worth twenty thousand francs; the bracelets thirty-five thousand; the rings, sixteen thousand; a set of emeralds and sapphires, fourteen thousand; a gold chain with solitaire pendant, forty thousand—making the sum of one hundred and forty-three thousand francs.

The jeweler remarked jokingly:

"There was a person who invested all her earnings in precious stones."

Monsieur Lantin replied seriously:

"It is only another way of investing one's money."

That day he lunched at Voisin's and drank wine worth twenty francs a bottle. Then he hired a carriage and made a tour of the Bois and, as he scanned the various turnouts with a contemptuous air, he could hardly refrain from crying out to the occupants:

"I, too, am rich! I am worth two hundred thousand francs."

Suddenly he thought of his employer. He drove up to the office and entered gaily, saying:

"Sir, I have come to resign my position. I have just inherited three hundred thousand francs."

He shook hands with his former colleagues and confided to them some of his projects for the future; then he went off to dine at the Café Anglais.

He seated himself beside a gentleman of aristocratic bearing, and during the meal informed the latter confidentially that he had just inherited a fortune of four hundred thousand francs.

For the first time in his life he was not bored at the theater and spent the remainder of the night in a gay frolic.

Six months afterward he married again. His second wife was a very virtuous woman with a violent temper. She caused him much sorrow.

THE SPICE OF LIFE

Paul and Henrietta had loved each other with the utmost chastity before they were married. They met at the seashore. He found her delightful, a sweet young girl who went by with her gay umbrella and bright costume against a background of the ocean. He fell in love with this frail blonde creature in a setting of blue waves and immense skies.

She loved him because he paid her attention, because he was young and rich, genteel and sensitive. She loved him because it is natural for young ladies to love young men who say tender words to them.

They dreamed of each other as soon as they were asleep, thought of each other as soon as they awoke, and, without yet saying so, called for and desired each other with their whole souls and bodies.

After marriage they adored each other above everything on earth. It was at first a kind of sensual indefatigable rage; then an exalted tenderness made of caresses already refined and of inventions both genteel and ungenteel. All their looks signified lasciviousness and all their gestures recalled to them the ardent intimacy of the bed.

Then, without confessing it, without even realizing it, they commenced to weary of one another. They loved each other, it is true; but there was nothing more to reveal, nothing more to do that had not often been done, nothing more to learn from each other, not even a new word of love, an unforeseen motion or an intonation, which sometimes is more expressive than a known word too often repeated.

They forced themselves, however, to relight the flame, enfeebled from the first embraces. They invented some new and tender artifice each day, some simple or complicated ruse, in the vain attempt to renew in their hearts the unappeasable ardor of the first days and in their veins the flame of the nuptial month.

From time to time, by working up their desire, they again found an hour of excitement which was immediately followed by a disappointing lassitude.

They tried moonlight walks under the leaves in the sweetness of the night, the poesy of the cliffs bathed in mist, the excitement of public festivals. Then one morning Henrietta said to Paul:

"Will you take me to dine at an inn?"

"Why, yes, if you wish."

"In a well-known inn?"

"Certainly."

He looked at her, questioning with his eye, understanding well that she had something in mind which she had not spoken.

She continued. "You know, an inn—how shall I explain it?—a sophisticated inn, where people make appointments to meet each other?"

He smiled. "Yes. I understand. A private room in a large café?"

"That is it. But in a large café where you are known, where you have already taken supper—no, dinner—that is—I mean—I want—no, I do not dare say it!"

"Speak out, *chérie*; between us what can it matter? We have no secrets from each other."

"No, I dare not."

"Oh! Come, now! Don't be coy. Say it."

"Well—I wish—I wish to be taken for your mistress—I wish the waiters, who do not know that you are married, may look upon me as your mistress, and you, too—that for an hour you believe me your mistress in that very place where you have remembrances of—— That's all! I myself will believe that I am your mistress. I want to commit a great sin—to deceive you—with yourself— there, I have said it! It is very bad, but that is what I want to do."

He laughed, very much amused, and responded:

"All right, we will go this evening to a very chic place where I am known."

.   .   .

It was almost seven o'clock when they mounted the staircase of a large café on the boulevard, he smiling, with the air of a conqueror, she timid, veiled, but delighted. When they were in a little room furnished with four armchairs and a large sofa covered with red velvet, the steward in black clothes entered and presented the bill of fare. Paul passed it to his wife.

"What do you wish to eat?" he said.

"I don't know; what do they have that is good here?"

"Allow me to order." He smiled and, turning to the waiter, he said:

"Serve this menu: Bisque soup, deviled chicken, sides of hare, duck, American style, vegetable salad and dessert. We will drink champagne—very dry."

The steward smiled and looked at the young lady. He took the card, murmuring: "Thank you, Monsieur Paul."

Henrietta was happy to find that this man knew her husband's name. They sat down side by side upon the sofa and began to eat.

Henrietta drank glass after glass to animate her, although she felt giddy from the first one. Paul, excited by certain memories, kissed his wife's hand repeatedly. Her eyes were brilliant.

She felt strangely moved by this suspicious situation; she was excited and happy, although she felt a little wicked. Two grave waiters who never spoke, accustomed to seeing everything and forgetting all, entered only when it was necessary, going and coming quickly and softly.

Toward the middle of the dinner Henrietta was drunk, charmingly drunk, and Paul, in his gaiety, pressed her knee with his hand. She prattled now, boldly, her cheeks red, her look lively and dizzy.

"Oh, come, Paul," she said, "confess now, won't you? I want to know all."

"What do you mean, *chérie?*"

"I dare not say it."

"Nonsense!"

"Have you had mistresses—many of them—before me?"

He hesitated, a little perplexed, not knowing whether he ought to conceal his good fortunes or boast of them.

She continued: "Oh! I beg you to tell me; have you had many?"

"Why, some."

"How many?"

"I don't know. How can one know such things?"

"You did not count them?"

"Of course not!"

"How many, do you suppose? Somewhere near——"

"I don't know at all, my dear. Some years I had many and some years only a few."

"How many a year, would you say?"

"Sometimes twenty or thirty, sometimes only four or five."

"Oh! That makes more than a hundred women in all."

"Yes, something like that."

"How disgusting!"

"Disgusting? Why?"

"Because it *is* disgusting—when one thinks of all those women—naked—and always—always the same thing. Oh! It is truly disgusting—more than a hundred women!"

He was shocked that she thought it disgusting and responded with that superior air which men assume to make women understand that they have said something foolish:

"Well, that is curious! If it is disgusting to have a hundred women, it is equally disgusting to have one."

"Oh no, not at all!"

"Why not?"

"Because with one woman there is intrigue, there is love, while with a hundred women there is only lewdness. I cannot understand how a man can meddle with all those girls who are so filthy."

"Filthy? They are immaculate."

"What? In a trade like that?"

"It is *because* of their trade that they are immaculate."

"Ridiculous! When one thinks of the nights they pass with others! It is ignoble!"

"It is no more ignoble than drinking from a glass from which I know not who drank this morning, and that has been—er—less thoroughly washed—I assure you."

"Oh, be still; you are revolting."

"But why ask me then if I have had mistresses?"

For a moment there was silence. Then Henrietta said:

"Tell me, were your mistresses all young girls, all of them—the whole hundred?"

"Why, no—no. Some were actresses—some little working girls—and some were, that is to say, women of the world."

"Which do you prefer, young girls or women of the world?"

"Women of the world."

"Oh, how depraved! Why?"

"Because I do not care much for amateur talent."

"Oh! You are abominable, do you know that? But tell me, is it very amusing to pass from one to another like that?"

"Yes, rather."

"What is there amusing about it? Is it because they do not resemble each other?"

"I suppose."

"Ah! The women do not resemble each other?"

"Not at all."

"In nothing?"

"In nothing."

"That is strange! In what respect do they differ?"

"In every respect."

"In body?"

"Yes, in body."

"In the whole body?"

"Yes, in the whole body."

"And in what else?"

"Why, in the manner of—embracing, of speaking—of doing the least thing."

"Ah! And it is very amusing, this changing?"

"Yes."

A pensive glaze came over her eyes, and in a moment she said, with a voice that seemed to come from far away:

"And are men different too?"

"That I do not know."

"You do not know?"

"No."

"They must be different."

"Perhaps."

She remained pensive, her glass of champagne in her hand. It was full and she drank it all at once without stopping for a breath. Her eyes were bright.

When the waiter again appeared, bringing in the fruits for the dessert, she was holding another glassful between her fingers. Looking to the bottom of the yellow transparent liquid, as if to see there things unknown, she murmured with a thoughtful voice:

"Different . . . in every respect . . . over a hundred . . . yes, I think I understand perfectly now. . . ."

Paul felt strangely uncomfortable to see the enigmatic smile upon her lips.

OSCAR WILDE (1856–1900)

Son of a profligate Irish surgeon and an eccentric poetess, Oscar Wilde far surpassed his parents in both profligacy and eccentricity. His peculiar characteristics involved him in one of the most sensational scandals of the century, and the trial which followed brought out evidence of such sexual abnormality that Wilde's career was totally ruined. The career had reached its peak with a series of brilliant successes: coruscating comedies that are still performed throughout the world, cleverly cynical essays, macabre novels, sensual poems, charming and even moral fairy tales—all of which, emphasized by his carefully publicized "aesthetic" postures, made him the most talked of figure of his day.

His witticisms centered about the surprisingly manipulated turn of phrase and twist of paradox. His plays, and to a great extent his other writings, read like a detonating chain of epigrams, a few of which follow.

TWENTY APHORISMS

Men marry because they are tired; women because they are curious. Both are disappointed.

The only way to get rid of a temptation is to yield to it.

The advantage of the emotions is that they lead us astray.

Moderation is a fatal thing. Nothing succeeds like excess.

Women's styles may change, but their designs remain the same.

Man argues that woman may not be trusted too far; woman feels that man cannot be trusted too near.

All women desire to be valued. They care much less about being respected.

Virtuous women are like hidden treasures—secure because no one is seeking them.

One can always recognize women who trust their husbands; they look so thoroughly unhappy.

The Bible says that woman is the last thing made by God. He must have made it Saturday night—it shows fatigue.

There is nothing in the world like the devotion of a married woman. It is a thing no married man knows anything about.

Young men want to be faithful and are not. Old men want to be faithless and cannot.

Twenty years of romance make a woman look like a ruin; but twenty years of marriage make her something like a public building.

No civilized man ever regrets a pleasure, and no uncivilized man knows what a pleasure is.

The only difference between the saint and the sinner is that every saint has a past and every sinner has a future.

What is the difference between scandal and gossip? Gossip is charming—history itself is merely gossip—but scandal is gossip made tedious by morality.

The one charm of marriage is that it makes a life of deception absolutely necessary for both parties.

I love scandals about other people, but scandals about myself do not interest me—they lack the charm of novelty.

Married men are horribly tedious when they are good husbands and abominably conceited when they are not.

The English public, as a mass, takes no interest in a work of art until it is told that the work in question is immoral.

The Moderns

W. SOMERSET MAUGHAM (1874–   )

"Tolerant, tranquil, and detached," "accomplished, class-conscious and slightly contemptuous," "a bland disregard of the milk of human kindness unless it is half soured"—these are a few of the phrases leveled at W(illiam) Somerset Maugham, born in Paris, where his father was connected with the British Embassy. He was, it seems, born to be a cosmopolitan, an inveterate traveler, a voracious reader, and a precocious writer. His first novel, Liza of Lambeth, *written before he was twenty-three and while he was a medical student, is a clinical report of slum conditions which the critics found sordid, even revolting, but unquestionably powerful. From that time on, practically everything that Maugham wrote—twenty plays, fifteen novels, many collections of short stories, essays, travel books—was subjected to a peculiarly mixed reception. The more successful the works were—and most of them, from* Of Human Bondage *to* The Moon and Sixpence, *were phenomenally successful— the more patronizing grew the critics. On his seventy-fifth birthday Maugham summed up their appraisal of his career: "In my twenties the critics said I was brutal; in my thirties they said I was flippant; in my forties they said I was cynical; in my fifties they said I was competent; and in my sixties they concluded I was superficial." By the time he was seventy-five he had written and edited about as many books as his years.*

Compared favorably to Maupassant and considered unfavorably as a skilled manufacturer of machine-made fiction, Maugham is a dispassionate observer and an uncanny recorder of the vagaries of human conduct. Whatever his final status as an artist may be, he is in the direct line of those who entertained at countless crowded courtyards and campfires: the traditional, old-fashioned and ever-popular teller of tales.

WINTER CRUISE

Captain Erdmann knew Miss Reid very little till the *Friedrich Weber* reached Haiti. She came on board at Plymouth, but by then he had taken on a number of passengers, French, Belgian and Haitian, many of whom had travelled with him before, and she was placed at the chief engineer's table. The *Friedrich Weber* was a freighter sailing regularly from Hamburg to Cartagena on the Colombian coast and on the way touching at a number of islands in the West Indies. She carried phosphates and cement from Germany and took back coffee and timber; but her owners, the Brothers Weber, were always willing to send her out of her route if a cargo of any sort made it worth their while. The *Friedrich Weber* was prepared to take cattle, mules, potatoes or anything else that offered the chance of earning an honest penny. She carried passengers. There were six cabins on the upper deck and six below. The accommodation was not luxurious, but the food was good, plain and abundant, and the fares were cheap. The round trip took nine weeks and was not costing Miss Reid more than forty-five pounds. She looked forward not only to seeing many interesting places, with historical associations, but also to acquiring a great deal of information that would enrich her mind.

The agent had warned her that till the ship reached Port-au-Prince in Haiti she would have to share a cabin with another woman. Miss Reid did not mind that, she liked company, and when the steward told her that her companion was a Madame Bollin she thought at once that it would be a very good opportunity to rub up her French. She was only very slightly disconcerted when she found that Madame Bollin was coal black. She told herself that one had to accept the rough with the smooth and that it takes all sorts to make a world. Miss Reid was a good sailor, as indeed was only to be expected since her grandfather had been a naval officer, but after a couple of roughish days the weather was fine and in a very short while she knew all her fellow passengers. She was a good mixer. That was one of the reasons why she had made a success of her business; she owned a tearoom at a celebrated beauty spot in the west of England and she always had a smile and a pleasant word for every customer who came in; she closed down in the winter and for the last four years had taken a cruise. You met such interesting people, she said, and you always learnt something. It was true that the passengers on the *Friedrich Weber* weren't of quite so good a class as those she had met the year before on her Mediterranean cruise, but Miss Reid was not a snob, and though the table manners of some of them shocked her somewhat, determined to look upon the bright side of things she decided to make the best of them. She was a great reader and she was glad, on looking at the ship's library, to find that there were a lot of books by Phillips Oppenheim, Edgar Wallace and Agatha Christie; but with so many people to talk to she had no time for reading and she made up her mind to leave them till the ship emptied herself at Haiti.

"After all," she said, "human nature is more important than literature."

Miss Reid had always had the reputation of being a good talker and she flattered herself that not once during the many days they were at sea she allowed the conversation at table to languish. She knew how to draw people out and whenever a topic seemed to be exhausted she had a remark ready to revive it or another topic waiting on the tip of her tongue to set the conversation off again. Her friend Miss Price, daughter of the late Vicar of Campden, who had come to see her off at Plymouth, for she lived there, had often said to her:

"You know, Venetia, you have a mind like a man. You're never at a loss for something to say."

"Well, I think if you're interested in everyone, everyone will be interested in you," Miss Reid answered modestly. "Practice makes perfect and I have the infinite capacity for taking pains which Dickens said was genius."

Miss Reid was not really called Venetia, her name was Alice, but, disliking it, she had, when still a girl, adopted the poetic name which she felt so much better suited to her personality.

Miss Reid had a great many interesting talks with her fellow passengers and she was really sorry when the ship at length reached Port-au-Prince and the last of them disembarked. The *Friedrich Weber* stopped two days there, during which she visited the town and the neighbourhood. When they sailed she was the only passenger. The ship was skirting the coast of the island stopping off at a variety of ports to discharge or to take on cargo.

"I hope you will not feel embarrassed alone with so many men, Miss Reid," said the captain heartily as they sat down to midday dinner.

She was placed on his right hand and at table besides sat the first mate, the chief engineer and the doctor.

"I'm a woman of the world, Captain. I always think if a lady is a lady, gentlemen will be gentlemen."

"We're only rough sailormen, madam, you mustn't expect too much."

"Kind hearts are more than coronets and simple faith than Norman blood, Captain," answered Miss Reid.

He was a short, thickset man, with a clean-shaven head and a red, clean-shaven face. He wore a white stingah-shifter, but except at mealtimes unbuttoned at the neck and showing his hairy chest. He was a jovial fellow. He could not speak without bellowing. Miss Reid thought him quite an eccentric, but she had a keen sense of humour and was prepared to make allowances for that. She took the conversation in hand. She had learnt a great deal about Haiti on the voyage out and more during the two days she had spent there, but she knew that men liked to talk rather than to listen, so she put them a number of questions of which she already knew the answers; oddly enough they didn't. In the end she found herself obliged to give quite a little lecture and before lunch was over, *Mittag Essen* they called it in their funny way, she had imparted to them a great deal of interesting information about the history and economic situation of the republic, the problems that confronted it and its prospects for the future. She talked rather slowly, in a refined voice, and her vocabulary was extensive.

At nightfall they put in at a small port where they were to load three hundred bags of coffee and the agent came on board. The captain asked him to stay to supper and ordered cocktails. As the steward brought them Miss Reid swam into the saloon. Her movements were deliberate, elegant and self-assured. She always said that you could tell at once by the way she walked if a woman was a lady. The captain introduced the agent to her and she sat down.

"What is that you men are drinking?" she asked.

"A cocktail. Will you have one, Miss Reid?"

"I don't mind if I do."

She drank it and the captain somewhat doubtfully asked her if she would have another.

"Another? Well, just to be matey."

The agent, much whiter than some, but a good deal darker than many, was the son of a former minister of Haiti to the German court and having lived for many years in Berlin spoke good German. It was indeed on this account that he had got a job with a German shipping firm. On the strength of this Miss Reid, during supper, told them all about a trip down the Rhine that she had once taken. Afterwards she and the agent, the skipper, the doctor and the mate, sat round a table and drank beer. Miss Reid made it her business to draw the agent out. The fact that they were loading coffee suggested to her that he would be interested in learning how they grew tea in Ceylon, yes, she had been to Ceylon on a cruise, and the fact that his father was a diplomat made it certain that he would be interested in the royal family of England. She had a very pleasant evening. When she at last retired to rest, for she would never have thought of saying she was going to bed, she said to herself:

"There's no doubt that travel is a great education."

It was really an experience to find herself alone with all those men. How they would laugh when she told them all about it when she got home! They would say that things like that only happened to Venetia. She smiled when she heard the captain on deck singing with that great booming voice of his. Germans were so musical. He had a funny way of strutting up and down on his short legs singing Wagner tunes to words of his own invention. It was *Tannhäuser* he was singing now (that lovely thing about the evening star) but knowing no German, Miss Reid could only wonder what absurd words he was putting to it. It was as well.

"Oh, what a bore that woman is. I shall certainly kill her if she goes on much longer." Then he broke into Siegfried's martial strain. "She's a bore, she's a bore, she's a bore. I shall throw her into the sea."

And that of course is what Miss Reid was. She was a crashing, she was a stupendous, she was an excruciating bore. She talked in a steady monotone and it was no use to interrupt her because then she started again from the beginning. She had an insatiable thirst for information and no casual remark could be thrown across the table without her asking innumerable questions about it. She was a great dreamer and she narrated her dreams at intolerable length. There was no subject upon which she had not something prosy to say. She had a truism for every occasion. She hit on the commonplace like a hammer driving a nail into the wall. She plunged into the obvious like a clown in a circus jumping through a hoop. Silence did not abash her. Those poor men far away from their homes and the patter of little feet, and with Christmas coming on, no wonder they felt low; she redoubled her efforts to interest and amuse them. She was determined to bring a little gaiety into their dull lives. For that was the awful part of it. Miss Reid meant well. She was not only having a good time herself, but she was trying to give all of them a good time. She was convinced that they liked her as much as she liked them. She felt that she was doing her bit to make the party a success and she was naïvely happy to think that she was succeeding. She told them

all about her friend Miss Price and how often she had said to her, Venetia,
no one ever has a dull moment in your company. It was the captain's duty
to be polite to a passenger and however much he would have liked to tell
her to hold her silly tongue he could not, but even if he had been free
to say what he liked, he knew that he could not have brought himself to
hurt her feelings. Nothing stemmed the torrent of her loquacity. It was as
irresistible as a force of nature. Once in desperation they began talking German, but Miss Reid stopped this at once.

"Now I won't have you saying things I don't understand. You ought all
to make the most of your good luck in having me all to yourselves and
practise your English."

"We were talking of technical matters that would only bore you, Miss
Reid," said the captain.

"I'm never bored. That's why, if you won't think me a wee bit conceited
to say so, I'm never boring. You see, I like to know things. Everything interests me and you never know when a bit of information won't come in
useful."

The doctor smiled drily.

"The captain was only saying that because he was embarrassed. In point
of fact he was telling a story that was not fit for the ears of a maiden lady."

"I may be a maiden lady but I'm also a woman of the world, I don't
expect sailors to be saints. You need never be afraid of what you say before
me, Captain, I shan't be shocked. I should love to hear your story."

The doctor was a man of sixty with thin gray hair, a gray moustache and
small bright blue eyes. He was a silent, bitter man, and however hard Miss
Reid tried to bring him into the conversation it was almost impossible to
get a word out of him. But she wasn't a woman who would give in without
a struggle and one morning when they were at sea, seeing him sitting on
deck with a book, she brought her chair next to his and sat down beside
him.

"Are you fond of reading, Doctor?" she said brightly.

"Yes."

"So am I. And I suppose like all Germans you're musical."

"I'm fond of music."

"So am I. The moment I saw you I thought you looked clever."

He gave her a brief look and pursing his lips went on reading. Miss Reid
was not disconcerted.

"But of course one can always read. I always prefer a good talk to a good
book. Don't you?"

"No."

"How very interesting. Now do tell me why?"

"I can't give you a reason."

"That's very strange, isn't it? But then I always think human nature is
strange. I'm terribly interested in people, you know. I always like doctors,
they know so much about human nature, but I could tell you some things

that would surprise even you. You learn a great deal about people if you run a teashop like I do, that's to say if you keep your eyes open."

The doctor got up.

"I must ask you to excuse me, Miss Reid. I have to go and see a patient."

"Anyhow I've broken the ice now," she thought as he walked away. "I think he was only shy."

But a day or two later the doctor was not feeling at all well. He had an internal malady that troubled him now and then, but he was used to it and disinclined to talk about it. When he had one of his attacks he only wanted to be left alone. His cabin was small and stuffy, so he settled himself on a long chair on deck and lay with his eyes closed. Miss Reid was walking up and down to get the half hour's exercise she took morning and evening. He thought that if he pretended to be asleep she would not disturb him. But when she had passed him half a dozen times she stopped in front of him and stood quite still. Though he kept his eyes closed he knew that she was looking at him.

"Is there anything I can do, Doctor?" she said.

He started.

"Why, what should there be?"

He gave her a glance and saw that her eyes were deeply troubled.

"You look dreadfully ill," she said.

"I'm in great pain."

"I know. I can see that. Can't something be done?"

"No, it'll pass off presently."

She hesitated for a moment then went away. Presently she returned.

"You look so uncomfortable with no cushions or anything. I've brought you my own pillow that I always travel with. Do let me put it behind your head."

He felt at that moment too ill to remonstrate. She lifted his head gently and put the soft pillow behind it. It really did make him feel more comfortable. She passed her hand across his forehead and it was cool and soft.

"Poor dear," she said. "I know what doctors are. They haven't the first idea how to take care of themselves."

She left him, but in a minute or two returned with a chair and a bag. The doctor when he saw her gave a twitch of anguish.

"Now I'm not going to let you talk, I'm just going to sit beside you and knit. I always think it's a comfort when one isn't feeling very well to have someone near."

She sat down and taking an unfinished muffler out of her bag began busily to ply her needles. She never said a word. And strangely enough the doctor found her company a solace. No one else on board had even noticed that he was ill, he had felt lonely, and the sympathy of that crashing bore was grateful to him. It soothed him to see her silently working and presently he fell asleep. When he awoke she was still working. She gave him a little smile, but did not speak. His pain had left him and he felt much better.

He did not go into the saloon till late in the afternoon. He found the captain and Hans Krause, the mate, having a glass of beer together.

"Sit down, Doctor," said the captain. "We're holding a council of war. You know that the day after tomorrow is *Sylvester Abend*."

"Of course."

Sylvester Abend, New Year's Eve, is an occasion that means a great deal to a German and they had all been looking forward to it. They had brought a Christmas tree all the way from Germany with them.

"At dinner today Miss Reid was more talkative than ever. Hans and I have decided that something must be done about it."

"She sat with me for two hours this morning in silence. I suppose she was making up for lost time."

"It's bad enough to be away from one's home and family just now anyway and all we can do is to make the best of a bad job. We want to enjoy our *Sylvester Abend* and unless something is done about Miss Reid we haven't a chance."

"We can't have a good time if she's with us," said the mate. "She'll spoil it as sure as eggs is eggs."

"How do you propose to get rid of her short of throwing her overboard?" smiled the doctor. "She's not a bad old soul; all she wants is a lover."

"At her age?" cried Hans Krause.

"Especially at her age. That inordinate loquacity, that passion for information, the innumerable questions she asks, her prosiness, the way she goes on and on—it is all a sign of her clamouring virginity. A lover would bring her peace. Those jangled nerves of hers would relax. At least for an hour she would have lived. The deep satisfaction which her being demands would travel through those exacerbated centres of speech and we should have quiet."

It was always a little difficult to know how much the doctor meant what he said and when he was having a joke at your expense. The captain's blue eyes, however, twinkled mischievously.

"Well, Doctor, I have great confidence in your powers of diagnosis. The remedy you suggest is evidently worth trying and since you are a bachelor it is clear that it is up to you to apply it."

"Pardon me, Captain, it is my professional duty to prescribe remedies for the patients under my charge in this ship but not to administer them personally. Besides, I am sixty."

"I am a married man with grown-up children," said the captain. "I am old and fat and asthmatic, it is obvious that I cannot be expected to undertake a task of this kind. Nature cut me out for the role of a husband or a father, not for that of a lover."

"Youth in these matters is essential and good looks are advantageous," said the doctor gravely.

The captain gave a great bang on the table with his fist.

"You are thinking of Hans. You're quite right. Hans must do it."

The mate sprang to his feet.

"Me? Never."

"Hans, you are tall, handsome, strong as a lion, brave and young. We have twenty-three days more at sea before we reach Hamburg, you wouldn't desert your trusted old captain in an emergency or let down your good friend the doctor?"

"No, Captain, it's asking too much of me. I have been married less than a year and I love my wife. I can hardly wait to get back to Hamburg. She is yearning for me as I am yearning for her. I will not be unfaithful to her, especially with Miss Reid."

"Miss Reid's not so bad," said the doctor.

"Some people might call her even nice looking," said the captain.

And indeed when you took Miss Reid feature by feature she was not in fact a plain woman. True, that she had a long, stupid face, but her brown eyes were large and she had very thick lashes; her brown hair was cut short and curled rather prettily over her neck; she hadn't a bad skin, and she was neither too fat nor too thin. She was not old as people go nowadays and if she had told you that she was forty you would have been quite willing to believe it. The only thing against her was that she was drab and dull.

"Must I then for twenty-three mortal days endure the prolixity of that tedious woman? Must I for twenty-three mortal days answer her inane questions and listen to her fatuous remarks? Must I, an old man, have my *Sylvester Abend*, the jolly evening I was looking forward to, ruined by the unwelcome company of that intolerable virgin? And all because no one can be found to show a little gallantry, a little human kindness, a spark of charity to a lonely woman. I shall wreck the ship."

"There's always the radio operator," said Hans.

The captain gave a great shout.

"Hans, let the ten thousand virgins of Cologne arise and call you blessed. Steward," he bellowed, "tell the radio operator that I want him."

The radio operator came into the saloon and smartly clicked his heels together. The three men looked at him in silence. He wondered uneasily whether he had done something for which he was to be hauled over the coals. He was above the middle height, with square shoulders and narrow hips, erect and slender, his tanned, smooth skin looked as though a razor had never touched it, he had large eyes of a startling blue and a mane of curling golden hair. He was a perfect specimen of young Teutonic manhood. He was so healthy, so vigorous, so much alive that even when he stood some way from you, you felt the glow of his vitality.

"Aryan, all right," said the captain. "No doubt about that. How old are you, my boy?"

"Twenty-one, sir."

"Married?"

"No, sir."

"Engaged?"

The radio operator chuckled. There was an engaging boyishness in his laugh.

"No, sir."

"You know that we have a female passenger on board?"

"Yes, sir."

"Do you know her?"

"I've said good morning to her when I've seen her on deck."

The captain assumed his most official manner. His eyes, which generally twinkled with fun, were stern and he got a sort of bark into his rich, fruity voice.

"Although this is a cargo boat and we carry valuable freight, we also take such passengers as we can get, and this is a branch of our business that the company is anxious to encourage. My instructions are to do everything possible to promote the happiness and comfort of the passengers. Miss Reid needs a lover. The doctor and I have come to the conclusion that you are well suited to satisfy Miss Reid's requirements."

"Me, sir?"

The radio operator blushed scarlet and then began to giggle, but quickly composed himself when he saw the set faces of the three men who confronted him.

"But she's old enough to be my mother."

"That at your age is a matter of no consequence. She is a woman of the highest distinction and allied to all the great families of England. If she were German she would be at least a countess. That you should have been chosen for this responsible position is an honour that you should greatly appreciate. Furthermore, your English is halting and this will give you an excellent opportunity to improve it."

"That of course is something to be thought of," said the radio operator. "I know that I want practice."

"It is not often in this life that it is possible to combine pleasure with intellectual improvement and you must congratulate yourself on your good fortune."

"But if I may be allowed to put the question, sir, why does Miss Reid want a lover?"

"It appears to be an old English custom for unmarried women of exalted rank to submit themselves to the embraces of a lover at this time of year. The company is anxious that Miss Reid should be treated exactly as she would be on an English ship and we trust that if she is satisfied, with her aristocratic connections she will be able to persuade many of her friends to take cruises in the line's ships."

"Sir, I must ask to be excused."

"It is not a request that I am making, it is an order. You will present yourself to Miss Reid, in her cabin, at eleven o'clock tonight."

"What shall I do when I get there?"

"Do?" thundered the captain. "Do? Act naturally."

With a wave of the hand he dismissed him. The radio operator clicked his heels, saluted and went out.

"Now let us have another glass of beer," said the captain.

At supper that evening Miss Reid was at her best. She was verbose. She was playful. She was refined. There was not a truism that she failed to utter. There was not a commonplace that she forebore to express. She bombarded them with foolish questions. The captain's face grew redder and redder as he sought to contain his fury; he felt that he could not go on being polite to her any longer and if the doctor's remedy did not help, one day he would forget himself and give her, not a piece, but the whole of his mind.

"I shall lose my job," he thought, "but I'm not sure that it wouldn't be worth it."

Next day they were already sitting at table when she came in to dinner.

"*Sylvester Abend* tomorrow," she said brightly. That was the sort of thing she would say. She went on: "Well, what have you all been up to this morning?"

Since they did exactly the same thing every day, and she knew very well what that was, the question was infuriating. The captain's heart sank. He briefly told the doctor what he thought of him.

"Now, no German, please," said Miss Reid archly. "You know I don't allow that, and why, Captain, did you give the poor doctor that sour look? It's Christmas time, you know; peace and goodwill to all men. I'm so excited about tomorrow evening and will there be candles on the Christmas tree?"

"Naturally."

"How thrilling! I always think a Christmas tree without candles isn't a Christmas tree. Oh, d'you know, I had such a funny experience last night. I can't understand it at all."

A startled pause. They all looked intently at Miss Reid. For once they hung on her lips.

"Yes," she went on in that monotonous, rather finicking way of hers, "I was just getting into bed last night when there was a knock at my door. 'Who is it?' I said. 'It's the radio operator,' was the answer. 'What is it?' I said. 'Can I speak to you?' he said."

They listened with rapt attention.

"'Well, I'll just pop on a dressing gown,' I said, 'and open the door.' So I popped on a dressing gown and opened the door. The radio operator said, 'Excuse me, miss, but do you want to send a radio?' Well, I did think it was funny his coming at that hour to ask me if I wanted to send a radio, I just laughed in his face, it appealed to my sense of humour if you understand what I mean, but I didn't want to hurt his feelings so I said, 'Thank you so much, but I don't think I want to send a radio.' He stood there, looking so funny, as if he was quite embarrassed, so I said, 'Thank you all the same for asking me,' and then I said 'Good night, pleasant dreams' and shut the door."

"The damned fool," cried the captain.

"He's young, Miss Reid," the doctor put in. "It was excess of zeal. I suppose he thought you would want to send a New Year's greeting to your friends and he wished you to get the advantage of the special rate."

"Oh, I didn't mind at all. I like these queer little things that happen to one when one's travelling. I just get a good laugh out of them."

As soon as dinner was over and Miss Reid had left them the captain sent for the radio operator.

"You idiot, what in heaven's name made you ask Miss Reid last night whether she wanted to send a radio?"

"Sir, you told me to act naturally. I am a radio operator. I thought it natural to ask her if she wanted to send a radio. I didn't know what else to say."

"God in heaven," shouted the captain, "when Siegfried saw Brünhilde lying on her rock and cried: *Das ist kein mann*," the captain sang the words and being pleased with the sound of his voice, repeated the phrase two or three times before he continued, "did Siegfried when she awoke ask her if she wished to send a radio, to announce to her papa, I suppose, that she was sitting up after her long sleep and taking notice?"

"I beg most respectfully to draw your attention to the fact that Brünhilde was Siegfried's aunt. Miss Reid is a total stranger to me."

"He did not reflect that she was his aunt. He knew only that she was a beautiful and defenceless woman of obviously good family and he acted as any gentleman would have done. You are young, handsome, Aryan to the tips of your fingers, the honour of Germany is in your hands."

"Very good, sir. I will do my best."

That night there was another knock on Miss Reid's door.

"Who is it?"

"The radio operator. I have a radio for you, Miss Reid."

"For me?" She was surprised, but it at once occurred to her that one of her fellow passengers who had got off at Haiti had sent her New Year's greetings. "How very kind people are," she thought. "I'm in bed. Leave it outside the door."

"It needs an answer. Ten words prepaid."

Then it couldn't be a New Year's greeting. Her heart stopped beating. It could only mean one thing; her shop had been burned to the ground. She jumped out of bed.

"Slip it under the door and I'll write the answer and slip it back to you."

The envelope was pushed under the door and as it appeared on the carpet it had really a sinister look. Miss Reid snatched it up and tore the envelope open. The words swam before her eyes and she couldn't for a moment find her spectacles. This is what she read:

"Happy New Year. Stop. Peace and goodwill to all men. Stop. You are very beautiful. Stop. I love you. Stop. I must speak to you. Stop. Signed: Radio Operator."

Miss Reid read this through twice. Then she slowly took off her spectacles and hid them under a scarf. She opened the door.

"Come in," she said.

Next day was New Year's Eve. The officers were cheerful and a little sentimental when they sat down to dinner. (*Mittag Essen* as they called it in their funny way.) The stewards had decorated the saloon with tropical creepers to make up for holly and mistletoe, and the Christmas tree stood on a table with the candles ready to be lit at suppertime. Miss Reid did not come in till the officers were seated and when they bade her good morning she did not speak but merely bowed. They looked at her curiously. She ate a good dinner, but uttered never a word. Her silence was uncanny. At last the captain could stand it no longer, and he said:

"You're very quiet today, Miss Reid."

"I'm thinking," she remarked.

"And will you not tell us your thoughts, Miss Reid?" the doctor asked playfully.

She gave him a cool, you might almost have called it a supercilious, look.

"I prefer to keep them to myself, Doctor. I will have a little more of that hash, I've got a very good appetite."

They finished the meal in a blessed silence. The captain heaved a sigh of relief. That was what mealtime was for, to eat, not to chatter. When they had finished he went up to the doctor and wrung his hand.

"Something has happened, Doctor."

"It has happened. She's a changed woman."

"But will it last?"

"One can only hope for the best."

Miss Reid put on an evening dress for the evening's celebration, a very quiet black dress, with artificial roses at her bosom and a long string of imitation jade round her neck. The lights were dimmed and the candles on the Christmas tree were lit. It felt a little like being in church. The junior officers were supping in the saloon that evening and they looked very smart in their white uniforms. Champagne was served at the company's expense and after supper they had a *maibowle*. They pulled crackers. They sang songs to the gramophone, *Deutschland, Deutschland über Alles, Alt Heidelberg* and *Auld Lang Syne*. They shouted out the tunes lustily, the captain's voice rising loud above the others, and Miss Reid joining in with a pleasing contralto. The doctor noticed that Miss Reid's eyes from time to time rested on the radio operator and in them he read an expression of some bewilderment.

"He's a good-looking fellow, isn't he?" said the doctor.

Miss Reid turned round and looked at the doctor coolly.

"Who?"

"The radio operator. I thought you were looking at him."

"Which is he?"

"The duplicity of women," the doctor muttered, but with a smile he answered: "He's sitting next to the chief engineer."

"Oh, of course, I recognize him now. You know, I never think it matters what a man looks like. I'm so much more interested in a man's brain than in his looks."

"Ah," said the doctor.

They all got a little tight, including Miss Reid, but she did not lose her dignity and when she bade them good night it was in her best manner.

"I've had a very delightful evening. I shall never forget my New Year's Eve on a German boat. It's been very interesting. Quite an experience."

She walked steadily to the door and this was something of a triumph, for she had drunk drink for drink with the rest of them through the evening.

They were all somewhat jaded next day. When the captain, the mate, the doctor and the chief engineer came down to dinner they found Miss Reid already seated. Before each place was a small parcel tied up in pink ribbon. On each was written: "Happy New Year." They gave Miss Reid a questioning glance.

"You've all been so very kind to me I thought I'd like to give each of you a little present. There wasn't much choice at Port-au-Prince, so you mustn't expect too much."

There was a pair of briar pipes for the captain, half a dozen silk handkerchiefs for the doctor, a cigar case for the mate and a couple of ties for the chief engineer. They had dinner and Miss Reid retired to her cabin to rest. The officers looked at one another uncomfortably. The mate fiddled with the cigar case she had given him.

"I'm a little ashamed of myself," he said at last.

The captain was pensive and it was plain that he too was a trifle uneasy.

"I wonder if we ought to have played that trick on Miss Reid," he said. "She's a good old soul and she's not rich; she's a woman who earns her own living. She must have spent the best part of a hundred marks on these presents. I almost wish we'd left her alone."

The doctor shrugged his shoulders.

"You wanted her silenced and I've silenced her."

"When all's said and done it wouldn't have hurt us to listen to her chatter for three weeks more," said the mate.

"I'm not happy about her," added the captain. "I feel there's something ominous in her quietness."

She had spoken hardly a word during the meal they had just shared with her. She seemed scarcely to listen to what they said.

"Don't you think you ought to ask her if she's feeling quite well, Doctor?" suggested the captain.

"Of course she's feeling quite well. She's eating like a wolf. If you want enquiries made you'd much better make them of the radio operator."

"You may not be aware of it, Doctor, but I am a man of great delicacy."

"I am a man of heart myself," said the doctor.

For the rest of the journey those men spoilt Miss Reid outrageously. They treated her with the consideration they would have shown to someone who was convalescent after a long and dangerous illness. Though her appetite was excellent they sought to tempt her with new dishes. The doctor ordered wine and insisted on her sharing his bottle with him. They played dominoes with her. They played chess with her. They played bridge with her. They engaged her in conversation. But there was no doubt about it, though she responded to their advances with politeness, she kept herself to herself. She seemed to regard them with something very like disdain; you might almost have thought that she looked upon those men and their efforts to be amiable as pleasantly ridiculous. She seldom spoke unless spoken to. She read detective stories and at night sat on deck looking at the stars. She lived a life of her own.

At last the journey drew to its close. They sailed up the English Channel on a still gray day; they sighted land. Miss Reid packed her trunk. At two o'clock in the afternoon they docked at Plymouth. The captain, the mate and the doctor came along to say good-bye to her.

"Well, Miss Reid," said the captain in his jovial way, "we're sorry to lose you, but I suppose you're glad to be getting home."

"You've been very kind to me, you've all been very kind to me, I don't know what I've done to deserve it. I've been very happy with you. I shall never forget you."

She spoke rather shakily, she tried to smile, but her lips quivered, and tears ran down her cheeks. The captain got very red. He smiled awkwardly.

"May I kiss you, Miss Reid?"

She was taller than he by half a head. She bent down and he planted a fat kiss on one wet cheek and a fat kiss on the other. She turned to the mate and the doctor. They both kissed her.

"What an old fool I am," she said. "Everybody's so good."

She dried her eyes and slowly, in her graceful, rather absurd way, walked down the companion. The captain's eyes were wet. When she reached the quay she looked up and waved to someone on the boat deck.

"Who's she waving to?" asked the captain.

"The radio operator."

Miss Price was waiting on the quay to welcome her. When they had passed the customs and got rid of Miss Reid's heavy luggage they went to Miss Price's house and had an early cup of tea. Miss Reid's train did not start till five. Miss Price had much to tell Miss Reid.

"But it's too bad of me to go on like this when you've just come home. I've been looking forward to hearing all about your journey."

"I'm afraid there's not very much to tell."

"I can't believe that. Your trip was a success, wasn't it?"

"A distinct success. It was very nice."

"And you didn't mind being with all those Germans?"

"Of course they're not like English people. One has to get used to their ways. They sometimes do things that—well, that English people wouldn't do, you know. But I always think that one has to take things as they come."

"What sort of things do you mean?"

Miss Reid looked at her friend calmly. Her long, stupid face had a placid look and Miss Price never noticed that in the eyes was a strangely mischievous twinkle.

"Things of no importance really. Just funny, unexpected, rather nice things. There's no doubt that travel is a wonderful education."

APPEARANCE AND REALITY

I do not vouch for the truth of this story, but it was told me by a professor of French literature at a celebrated university and he was a man of too high a character, I think, to have told it to me unless it were true. His practice was to draw the attention of his pupils to three French writers who in his opinion combined the qualities that are the mainsprings of the French character. By reading them, he said, you could learn so much about the French people that, if he had the power, he would not trust such of our rulers as have to deal with the French nation to enter upon their offices till they had passed a pretty stiff examination on their works. They are Rabelais, with his *gauloiserie*, which may be described as the ribaldry that likes to call a spade something more than a bloody shovel; La Fontaine, with his *bon sens*, which is just horse sense; and finally Corneille with his *panache*. This is translated in the dictionaries as the plume, the plume the knight at arms wore on his helmet, but metaphorically it seems to signify dignity and bravado, display and heroism, vainglory and pride. It was *le panache* that made the French gentlemen at Fontenoy say to the officers of King George II, fire first, gentlemen; it was *le panache* that wrung from Cambronne's bawdy lips at Waterloo the phrase: the guard dies but never surrenders; and it is *le panache* that urges an indigent French poet, awarded the Nobel prize, with a splendid gesture to give it all away. My professor was not a frivolous man and to his mind the story I am about to tell brought out so distinctly the three master qualities of the French that it had a high educational value.

I have called it "Appearance and Reality." This is the title of what I suppose may be looked upon as the most important philosophical work that my country (right or wrong) produced in the nineteenth century. It is stiff but stimulating reading. It is written in excellent English, with considerable humour, and even though the lay reader is unlikely to follow with understanding some of its very subtle arguments he has nevertheless the thrilling sensation of walking a spiritual tightrope over a metaphysical abyss, and he ends the book with a comfortable feeling that nothing matters a hang anyway. There is no excuse for my making use of the title of so celebrated a book except that it so admirably suits my story. Though Lisette was a philosopher only in the sense in which we are all philosophers that she exercised thought in dealing with the problems of existence, her feeling for reality was so strong and her sympathy for appearance so genuine that she might almost claim to have established that reconciliation of irreconcilables at which the philosophers have for so many centuries been aiming. Lisette was French and she passed several hours of every working day dressing and undressing herself at one of the most expensive and fashionable establishments in Paris. A pleasant occupation for a young woman who was well aware that she had a lovely figure. She was in short a mannequin. She was tall enough to be able to wear a train with elegance and her hips were so slim that in sports clothes she could bring the scent of heather to your nostrils. Her long legs enabled her to wear pyjamas with distinction and her slim waist, her little breasts, made the simplest bathing dress a ravishment. She could wear anything. She had a way of huddling herself in a chinchilla coat that made the most sensible persons admit that chinchilla was worth all the money it cost. Fat women, gross women, stumpy women, bony women, shapeless women, old women, plain women, sat in the comfortable armchairs and because Lisette looked so sweet bought the clothes that so admirably suited her. She had large brown eyes, a large red mouth and a very clear but slightly freckled skin. It was difficult for her to preserve that haughty, sullen and coldly indifferent demeanour that appears to be essential to the mannequin as she sails in with deliberate steps, turns round slowly and with an air of contempt for the universe equalled only by the camel's sails out. There was the suspicion of a twinkle in Lisette's large brown eyes and her red lips seemed to tremble as though on the smallest provocation they would break into a smile. It was the twinkle that attracted the attention of Monsieur Raymond Le Sueur.

He was sitting in a spurious Louis XVI chair by the side of his wife (in another) who had induced him to come with her to see the private view of the spring fashions. This was a proof of Monsieur Le Sueur's amiable disposition, for he was an extremely busy man who, one would have thought, had many more important things to do than to sit for an hour and watch a dozen beautiful young women parade themselves in a bewildering variety of costumes. He could not have thought that any of them could possibly make his wife other than she was, and she was a tall, angular woman of fifty, with features considerably larger than life size. He had not indeed married her for her looks and she had never, even in the first delirious days of their honeymoon, imagined that he had. He had married her in order to combine the flourishing steelworks of which she was the heiress with his equally flourishing manufactory of locomotives. The marriage had been a success. She had provided him with a son who could play tennis nearly as well as a professional, dance as well as a gigolo and hold his own at bridge with any of the experts; and a daughter whom he had been able to dower sufficiently to marry to a very nearly authentic prince. He had reason to be proud of his children. By perseverance and a reasonable integrity he had prospered sufficiently to gain the controlling interest in a sugar refinery, a manufactory of motorcars and a newspaper; and finally he had been able to spend enough money to persuade the free and independent electorate of a certain district to send him to the Senate. He was a man of a dignified presence, a pleasing corpulence and a sanguine complexion, with a neat gray beard cut square, a bald head and a roll of fat at the back of his neck. You had no need to look at the red button that adorned his black coat to surmise that he was a person of consequence. He was a man who made up his mind quickly and when his wife left the dressmaker's to go and play bridge he parted from her saying that for the sake of exercise he would walk to the Senate where his duty to his country called him. He did not however go as far as this, but contented himself with taking his exercise up and down a back street into which he rightly surmised the young ladies of the dressmaker's establishment would emerge at the close of business hours. He had barely walked for twenty minutes when the appearance of a number of women in groups, some young and pretty, some not so young and far from pretty, apprised him that the moment for which he had been waiting was come, and in two or three minutes Lisette tripped into the street. The Senator was well aware that his appearance and his age made it unlikely that young women would find him attractive at first sight, but he had found that his wealth and his position counterbalanced these disadvantages. Lisette had a companion with her, which would possibly have embarrassed a man of less importance, but did not cause the Senator to hesitate for an instant. He went up to her, raising his hat politely but not so much as to show how bald he was, and bade her good evening.

"*Bon soir, Mademoiselle,*" he said with an ingratiating smile.

She gave him the shortest possible look and, her full red lips just trembling with a smile, stiffened; she turned her head away and breaking into conversation with her friend, walked on with a very good assumption of supreme indifference. Far from disconcerted the Senator turned round and followed the two girls at a distance of a few yards. They walked along the little back street, turned into the boulevard and at the Place de la Madeleine took a bus. The Senator was well satisfied. He had drawn a number of correct conclusions. The fact that she was obviously going home with a girl friend proved that she had no accredited admirer. The fact that she had turned away when he had accosted her showed that she was discreet and modest and well-behaved, which he liked young women to be when they were pretty; and her coat and skirt, the plain black hat and the rayon stockings proclaimed that she was poor and therefore virtuous. In those clothes she looked just as attractive as in the splendid garments he had seen her wearing before. He had a funny little feeling in his heart. He had not had that peculiar sensation, pleasurable and yet oddly painful, for several years, but he recognized it at once.

"It's love, by blue," he muttered.

He had never expected to feel it again and squaring his shoulders he walked on with a confident step. He walked to the offices of a private detective and there left instructions that enquiries should be made about a young person called Lisette, who worked as a mannequin at such and such an address; and then, remembering that at the Senate they were discussing the American Debt, took a cab to the impressive building, entered the library where there was an armchair he very much liked and had a pleasant nap. The information he had asked for reached him three days later. It was cheap at the price. Mademoiselle Lisette Larion lived with a widowed aunt in a two-room apartment in the district of Paris known as the Batignolles. Her father, a wounded hero of the Great War, had a *bureau de tabac* in a small country town in the Southwest of France. The rent of the flat was two thousand francs. She led a regular life, but was fond of going to the pictures, was not known to have a lover and was nineteen years old. She was well spoken of by the concierge of the apartments and well liked by her companions at the shop. Obviously she was a very respectable young woman and the Senator could not but think that she was eminently suited to solace the leisure moments of a man who wanted relaxation from the cares of state and the exacting pressure of Big Business.

It is unnecessary to relate in detail the steps that Monsieur Le Sueur took to achieve the end he had in view. He was too important and too busy to occupy himself with the matter personally, but he had a confidential secretary who was very clever at dealing with electors who had not made up their minds how to vote, and who certainly knew how to put before a young woman who was honest but poor the advantages that might ensue if she were lucky enough to secure the friendship of such a man as his employer. The confidential secretary paid the widowed aunt, Madame Saladin by name, a visit and told her that Monsieur Le Sueur, always abreast of the times, had lately begun to take an interest in films and was indeed about to engage in the production of a picture. (This shows how much a clever brain can make use of a fact that an ordinary person would have passed over as insignificant.) Monsieur Le Sueur had been struck by the appearance of Mademoiselle Lisette at the dressmaker's and the brilliant way she wore her clothes and it had occurred to him that she might very well suit a part he had it in mind for her to play. (Like all intelligent people the Senator always stuck as close to the truth as he could.) The confidential secretary then invited Madame Saladin and her niece to a dinner where they could make one another's further acquaintance and the Senator could judge whether Mademoiselle Lisette had the aptitude for the screen that he suspected. Madame Saladin said she would ask her niece, but for her part seemed to think the suggestion quite reasonable.

When Madame Saladin put the proposition before Lisette and explained the rank, dignity and importance of their generous host, that young person shrugged her pretty shoulders disdainfully.

"*Cette vielle carpe,*" she said, of which the not quite literal translation is: that old trout.

"What does it matter if he's an old trout if he gives you a part?" said Madame Saladin.

"*Et ta soeur,*" said Lisette.

This phrase, which of course means: and your sister, and sounds harmless enough, and even pointless, is a trifle vulgar and is used by well-brought-up young women, I think, only if they want to shock. It expresses the most forcible unbelief and the only correct translation into the vernacular is too coarse for my chaste pen.

"Anyhow we should get a slap-up dinner," said Madame Saladin. "After all you're not a child any more."

"Where did he say we should dine?"

"The Château de Madrid. Everyone knows it's the most expensive restaurant in the world."

There is no reason why it should not be. The food is very good, the cellar is famous, and its situation makes it on a fine evening of early summer an enchanting place to eat at. A very pretty dimple appeared on Lisette's cheek and a smile on her large red mouth. She had perfect teeth.

"I can borrow a dress from the shop," she murmured.

A few days later the Senator's confidential secretary fetched them in a taxi and drove Madame Saladin and her engaging niece to the Bois de Boulogne. Lisette looked ravishing in one of the firm's most successful models and Madame Saladin extremely respectable in her own black satin and a hat that Lisette had made her for the occasion. The secretary introduced the ladies to Monsieur Le Sueur who greeted them with the benign dignity of the politician who is behaving graciously to the wife and daughter of a valued constituent; and this is exactly what in his astute way he thought people at adjacent tables who knew him would imagine his guests were. The dinner passed off very agreeably, and less than a month later Lisette moved into a charming little flat at a convenient distance both from her place of business and from the Senate. It was decorated in the modern style by a fashionable upholsterer. Monsieur Le Sueur wished Lisette to continue to work. It suited him very well that she should have something to do during the hours that he was obliged to devote to affairs, for it would keep her out of mischief, and he very well knew that a woman who has nothing to do all day spends much more money than one who has an occupation. An intelligent man thinks of these things.

But extravagance was a vice to which Lisette was strange. The Senator was fond and generous. It was a source of satisfaction to him that Lisette began very soon to save money. She ran her apartment with thrift and bought her clothes at trade prices, and every month sent a certain sum home to her heroic father who purchased little plots of land with it. She continued to lead a quiet and modest life and Monsieur Le Sueur was pleased to learn from the concierge, who had a son she wanted to place in a government office, that Lisette's only visitors were her aunt and one or two girls from the shop.

The Senator had never been happier in his life. It was very satisfactory to him to think that even in this world a good action had its reward, for was it not from pure kindness that he had accompanied his wife to the dressmaker's on that afternoon when they were discussing the American Debt at the Senate and thus seen for the first time the charming Lisette? The more he knew her the more he doted on her. She was a delightful companion. She was gay and debonair. Her intelligence was respectable and she could listen cleverly when he discussed business matters or affairs of state with her. She rested him when he was weary and cheered him when he was depressed. She was glad to see him when he came, and he came frequently, generally from five till seven, and sorry when he went away. She gave him the impression that he was not only her lover but her friend. Sometimes they dined together in her apartment, and the well-appointed meal, the genial comfort, gave him a keen appreciation of the charm of domesticity. His friends told the Senator he looked twenty years younger. He felt it. He was conscious of his good fortune. He could not but feel, however, that after a life of honest toil and public service it was only his due.

It was thus a shock to him, after things had been proceeding so happily for nearly two years, on coming back to Paris early one Sunday morning unexpectedly after a visit to his constituency which was to last over the weekend, when he let himself into the apartment with his latchkey, thinking since it was the day of rest to find Lisette in bed, to discover her having breakfast in her bedroom tête-à-tête with a young gentleman he had never seen before who was wearing his (the Senator's) brand-new pyjamas. Lisette was surprised to see him. Indeed she gave a distinct start.

"*Tiens*," she said. "Where have you sprung from? I didn't expect you till tomorrow."

"The Ministry has fallen," he answered mechanically. "I have been sent for. I am to be offered the Ministry of the Interior." But that was not what he wanted to say at all. He gave the gentleman who was wearing his pyjamas a furious look. "Who is that young man?" he cried.

Lisette's large red mouth broke into a most alluring smile.

"My lover," she answered.

"Do you think I'm a fool?" shouted the Senator. "I know he's your lover."

"Why do you ask then?"

Monsieur Le Sueur was a man of action. He went straight up to Lisette and smacked her hard on her right cheek with his left hand and then smacked her hard on the left cheek with his right hand.

"Brute," screamed Lisette.

He turned to the young man who had watched this scene of violence with some embarrassment and, drawing himself to his full height, flung out his arm and with a dramatic finger pointed to the door.

"Get out," he cried. "Get out."

One would have thought, such was the commanding aspect of a man who was accustomed to sway a crowd of angry taxpayers and who could dominate with his frown an annual meeting of disappointed shareholders, that the young man would have made a bolt for the door; but he stood his ground, irresolutely it is true, but he stood his ground; he gave Lisette an appealing look and slightly shrugged his shoulders.

"What are you waiting for?" shouted the Senator. "Do you want me to use force?"

"He can't go out in his pyjamas," said Lisette.

"They're not his pyjamas, they're my pyjamas."

"He's waiting for his clothes."

Monsieur Le Sueur looked round and on the chair behind him, flung down in a disorderly fashion, was a variety of masculine garments. The Senator gave the young man a look of contempt.

"You may take your clothes, Monsieur," he said with cold disdain.

The young man picked them up in his arms, gathered up the shoes that were lying about the floor, and quickly left the room. Monsieur Le Sueur had a considerable gift of oratory. Never had he made better use of it than now. He told Lisette what he thought of her. It was not flattering. He painted her ingratitude in the blackest colours. He ransacked an extensive vocabulary in order to find opprobrious names to call her. He called all the powers of heaven to witness that never had a woman repaid with such gross deception an honest man's belief in her. In short he said everything that anger, wounded vanity and disappointment suggested to him. Lisette did not seek to defend herself. She listened in silence, looking down and mechanically crumbling the roll which the Senator's appearance had prevented her from finishing. He flung an irritated glance at her plate.

"I was so anxious that you should be the first to hear my great news that I came straight here from the station. I was expecting to have my *petit déjeuner* with you, sitting at the end of your bed."

"My poor dear, haven't you had your breakfast? I'll order some for you at once."

"I don't want any."

"Nonsense. With the great responsibility you are about to assume you must keep up your strength."

She rang and when the maid came told her to bring in some hot coffee and another roll. It was brought and Lisette poured him out coffee and milk. He would not touch it. She buttered a roll for him. He shrugged his shoulders and began to eat. Meanwhile he uttered a few remarks on the perfidy of women. She remained silent.

"At all events it is something," he said, "that you have not the effrontery to attempt to excuse yourself. You know that I am not a man who can be ill-used with impunity. The soul of generosity when people behave well to me, I am pitiless when they behave badly. The very moment I have drunk my coffee I shall leave this apartment forever."

Lisette shrugged her shoulders.

"I will tell you now that I had prepared a surprise for you. I had made up my mind to celebrate the second anniversary of our union by settling a sum of money on you sufficient to give you a modest independence if anything happened to me."

"How much?" asked Lisette sombrely.

"A million francs."

She sighed a little. Suddenly something soft hit the Senator on the back of the head and he gave a start.

"What is that?" he cried.

"He's returning your pyjamas."

The young man had opened the door, flung the pyjamas at the Senator's head, and quickly closed it again. The Senator disengaged himself from the silk trousers that clung round his neck.

"What a way to return them! It is obvious that your friend has no education."

"Of course he has not got your distinction," murmured Lisette.

"And has he my intelligence?"

"Oh no."

"Is he rich?"

"Penniless."

"Then, name of a name, what is it you see in him?"

"He's young," smiled Lisette.

The Senator looked down at his plate and a tear rose in his eye and rolled down his cheek into the coffee. Lisette gave him a kindly look.

"My poor friend, one can't have everything in this life," she said.

"I knew I was not young. But my situation, my fortune, my vitality. I thought it made up. There are women who only like men of a certain age. There are celebrated actresses who look upon it as an honour to be the little friend of a Minister. I am too well brought up to throw your origins in your face, but the fact remains that you are a mannequin and I took you out of an apartment of which the rent is only two thousand francs a year. It was a step up for you."

"The daughter of poor but honest parents, I have no reason to be ashamed of my origins and it is not because I have earned my living in a humble sphere that you have the right to reproach me."

"Do you love this boy?"

"Yes."

"And not me?"

"You too. I love you both, but I love you differently. I love you because you are so distinguished and your conversation is instructive and interesting. I love you because you are kind and generous. I love him because his eyes are so big and his hair waves and he dances divinely. It's very natural."

"You know that in my position I cannot take you to places where they dance and I daresay when he's as old as I am he'll have no more hair than I have."

"That may well be true," Lisette agreed, but she did not think it much mattered.

"What will your aunt, the respectable Madame Saladin, say to you when she hears what you have done?"

"It will not be exactly a surprise to her."

"Do you mean to say that worthy woman countenances your conduct? *O tempora! O mores!* How long then has this been going on?"

"Since I first went to the shop. He travels for a big silk firm in Lyons. He came in one day with his samples. We liked the look of one another."

"But your aunt was there to defend you from the temptations to which a young girl is exposed in Paris. She should never have allowed you to have anything to do with this young man."

"I did not ask her permission."

"It is enough to bring the gray hairs of your poor father to the grave. Had you no thought of that wounded hero whose services to his country have been rewarded with a licence to sell tobacco? Do not forget that as Minister of the Interior the department is under my control. I should be within my rights if I revoked the licence on account of your flagrant immorality."

"I know you are too great a gentleman to do a dastardly thing like that." He sighed.

"Don't be afraid, I will never stoop so low as to revenge myself on one who has deserved well of his country for the misdeeds of a creature my sense of dignity forces me to despise."

He went on with his interrupted breakfast. Lisette did not speak and there was silence between them. But his appetite satisfied, his mood changed; he began to feel sorry for himself rather than angry with her, and with a strange ignorance of woman's heart he thought to arouse Lisette's remorse by exhibiting himself as an object of pity.

"It is hard to break a habit to which one has grown accustomed. It was a relief and a solace to me to come here when I could snatch a moment from my many occupations. Will you regret me a little, Lisette?"

"Of course."

He gave a deep sigh.

"I would never have thought you capable of so much deception."

"It is the deception that rankles," she murmured thoughtfully. "Men are funny in that way. They cannot forgive being made fools of. It is because they are so vain. They attach importance to things that are of no consequence."

"Do you call it a matter of no consequence that I should find you having breakfast with a young man wearing my pyjamas?"

"If he were my husband and you were my lover you would think it perfectly natural."

"Obviously. For then I should be deceiving him and my honour would be secure."

"In short I have only to marry him to make the situation perfectly regular."

For a moment he did not understand. Then her meaning flashed across his clever brain and he gave her a quick look. Her lovely eyes had the twinkle he always found so alluring and on her large red mouth was the suspicion of a roguish smile.

"Do not forget that as a member of the Senate I am by all the traditions of the Republic the authorized mainstay of morality and good behaviour."

"Does that weigh very heavily with you?"

He stroked his handsome square beard with a composed and dignified gesture.

"Not a row of beans," he replied, but the expression he used had a Gallic breadth that would perhaps have given his more conservative supporters something of a shock.

"Would he marry you?" he asked.

"He adores me. Of course he would marry me. If I told him I had a *dot* of a million francs he would ask nothing better."

Monsieur Le Sueur gave her another look. When in a moment of anger he told her that it had been his intention to settle a million francs on her he had exaggerated a good deal in the desire to make her see how much her treachery was costing her. But he was not the man to draw back when his dignity was concerned.

"It is much more than a young man in his position of life could aspire to. But if he adores you he would be always at your side."

"Didn't I tell you that he was a commercial traveller? He can only come to Paris for the weekend."

"That of course is a horse of another colour," said the Senator. "It would naturally be a satisfaction to him to know that during his absence I should be there to keep an eye on you."

"A considerable satisfaction," said Lisette.

To facilitate the conversation she rose from her seat and made herself comfortable on the Senator's knees. He pressed her hand tenderly.

"I am very fond of you, Lisette," he said. "I should not like you to make a mistake. Are you sure he will make you happy?"

"I think so."

"I will have proper enquiries made. I would never consent to your marrying anyone not of exemplary character and unimpeachable morality. For all our sakes we must make quite sure about this young man whom we are preparing to bring into our lives."

Lisette raised no objection. She was aware that the Senator liked to do things with order and method. He now prepared to leave her. He wanted to break his important news to Madame Le Sueur and he had to get in touch with various persons in the parliamentary group to which he belonged.

"There is only one more thing," he said, as he bade Lisette an affectionate farewell, "if you marry I must insist on your giving up your work. The place of a wife is the home and it is against all my principles that a married woman should take the bread out of a man's mouth."

Lisette reflected that a strapping young man would look rather funny walking round the room, with his hips swaying, to show off the latest models, but she respected the Senator's principles.

"It shall be as you wish, darling," she said.

The enquiries he made were satisfactory and the marriage took place on a

Saturday morning as soon as the legal formalities were completed. Monsieur Le Sueur, Minister of the Interior, and Madame Saladin were the witnesses. The bridegroom was a slim young man with a straight nose, fine eyes and black waving hair brushed straight back from his forehead. He looked more like a tennis player than a traveller in silk. The Mayor, impressed by the august presence of the Minister of the Interior, made according to French practice a speech which he sought to render eloquent. He began by telling the married couple what presumably they knew already. He informed the bridegroom that he was the son of worthy parents and was engaged in an honourable profession. He congratulated him on entering the bonds of matrimony at an age when many young men thought only of their pleasures. He reminded the bride that her father was a hero of the Great War, whose glorious wounds had been rewarded by a concession to sell tobacco, and he told her that she had earned a decent living since her arrival in Paris in an establishment that was one of the glories of French taste and luxury. The Mayor was of a literary turn and he briefly mentioned various celebrated lovers of fiction, Romeo and Juliet whose short but legitimate union had been interrupted by a regrettable misunderstanding, Paul's Virginia who had met her death at sea rather than sacrifice her modesty by taking off her clothes, and finally Daphnis and Chloë who had not consummated their marriage till it was sanctioned by the legitimate authority. He was so moving that Lisette shed a few tears. He paid a compliment to Madame Saladin whose example and precept had preserved her young and beautiful niece from the dangers that are likely to befall a young girl alone in a great city and finally he congratulated the happy pair on the honour that the Minister of the Interior had done them in consenting to be a witness at the ceremony. It was a testimony to their own probity that this captain of industry and eminent statesman should find time to perform a humble office to persons in their modest sphere and it proved not only the excellence of his heart but his lively sense of duty. His action showed that he appreciated the importance of early marriage, affirmed the security of the family and emphasized the desirability of producing offspring to increase the power, influence and consequence of the fair land of France. A very good speech indeed.

The wedding breakfast was held at the Château de Madrid which had sentimental associations for Monsieur Le Sueur. It has been mentioned already that among his many interests the Minister (as we must now call him) was interested in a firm of motorcars. His wedding present to the bridegroom had been a very nice two-seater of his own manufacture and in this, when lunch was over, the young couple started off for their honeymoon. This could only last over the weekend since the young man had to get back to his work and this was to take him to Marseilles, Toulon and Nice. Lisette kissed her aunt and she kissed Monsieur Le Sueur.

"I shall expect you at five on Monday," she whispered to him.

"I shall be there," he answered.

They drove away and for a moment Monsieur Le Sueur and Madame Saladin looked at the smart yellow roadster.

"As long as he makes her happy," sighed Madame Saladin, who was not used to champagne at lunch and felt unreasonably melancholy.

"If he does not make her happy he will have me to count with," said Monsieur Le Sueur impressively.

His car drove up.

"*Au revoir, chère Madame.* You will get a bus at the Avenue de Neuilly."

He stepped into his car and as he thought of the affairs of state that awaited his attention he sighed with content. It was evidently much more fitting to his situation that his mistress should be, not just a little mannequin in a dressmaker's shop, but a respectable married woman.

A HANDFUL OF LIMERICKS

The limerick is an odd kind of verse which, limited in length and small in scope, has covered a good deal of ground. Its origins are remote, although it has been asserted that it began in the Irish town of Limerick long before Edward Lear popularized it with such standard openings as "There was an old man of Cape Horn." Everyone, it seems, has tried his hand at fashioning the little five-line form, and the lure of the limerick is as potent today as it was a hundred years ago when it first came into favor.

It has been said that in spite of the great variety, there are just three sorts of limericks: the old, the new, and the unprintable. The following include some examples from the first and second categories, as well as a few somewhat expurgated versions from the third.

> The poor benighted Hindoo,
> He does the best he kindo.
> He sticks to caste
> From first to last.
> For pants he makes his skindo.

> There was a young lady of Twickenham,
> Whose boots were too tight to walk quickenham.
> She wore them in style,
> But after a while
> She pulled them both off and was sickenham.

There was an old man of Blackheath,
Who sat down on his set of false teeth.
 He jumped up with a start
 And cried, "Bless my heart!
I have bitten myself underneath!"

There was a young maiden of Siam
Who said to her lover, young Kiam,
 "If you kiss me, of course
 You will have to use force—
But God knows you are stronger than I am."

There was a young fellow of Lyme
Who lived with three wives at a time.
 When asked, "Why the third?"
 He said, "One's absurd,
And bigamy, sir, is a crime."

On the breast of a woman named Gail
Was tattooed the price of her tail.
 And on her behind,
 For the sake of the blind,
Was the same information in Braille.

When the First Selectman took advantage
Of a lovely young lady of Wantage,
 The County Surveyor
 Said, "You'll have to pay her,
For you've altered the line of her frontage."

There was a young lady of Louth,
Who returned from a trip to the South.
 Her father said, "Nelly,
 There's more in your belly
Than ever went in through your mouth."

There was a young fellow named Sydney,
Who drank till he ruined his kidney.
 It shriveled and shrank,
 As he sat there and drank . . .
But he had a good time at it, didn'he.

There was a young student at Johns
Who attempted to fondle the swans.
    Whereupon said the porter,
    "Oh, pray take my daughter.
The birds are reserved for the dons."

There was a fool gard'ner of Leeds
Who swallowed six packets of seeds.
    In a month the poor ass
    Was all covered with grass
And he could not sit down for the weeds.

A niece of the late Queen of Sheba
Was promiscuous with an amoeba.
    This queer blob of jelly
    Would lie on her belly
And, quivering, murmur: *"Ich liebe!"*

There was a young lady of Kent
Who said that she knew what it meant
    When men asked her to dine
    Upon lobster and wine.
She knew. Oh, she knew! But she went.

There was a pert lass from Madras
Who had a remarkable ass—
    Not rounded and pink,
    As you probably think.
It was gray, had long ears, and ate grass.

There was a young lady named Hopper
Who came a society cropper.
    She determined to go
    To Bordeaux with her beau . . .
The rest of the story's improper.

There once was a rake known as Baker
Who tried to seduce a fair Quaker.
    And when he had done it,
    She straightened her bonnet,
And said, "I give thanks to my Maker."

There was a young lady of York
Who was shortly expecting the stork,
     When the doctor walked in
     With a businesslike grin,
A pickax, a spade, and a fork.

There was a young actress named Ransom
Who was raped seven times in a hansom.
     When she clamored for more
     Came a voice from the floor,
"The name, ma'am, is Simpson—not Samson."

Have you heard about Madam Lupescu,
Who came to Rumania's rescue?
     It's a wonderful thing
     To be under a king.
Is democracy better? I eskyou!

Then there are the tricky and strangely fashioned ones—the ones that depend for their point on a trick of spelling, or abbreviation, or pronunciation, or just a pun. Here are a few freakish but often quoted examples.

There was a young lady named Banker,
Who slept while her ship lay at anchor.
     She awoke in dismay
     When she heard the mate say:
"Hi! Hoist up the top-sheet and spanker!"

A girl who weighed many an oz.
Used words that I dare not pronoz.
     For a fellow unkind
     Pulled her chair out behind
Just to see (so he said) if she'd boz.

She frowned and called him Mr.
Because he never kr.
     And so in spite
     That very nite
This Mr. kr. sr.

While Titian was mixing rose madder
His model was posed on a ladder.
  Her position to Titian
  Suggested fruition;
So he mounted the ladder and hadder.

The young things who attend picture palaces
Have no use for this psychoanalysis;
  And although Doctor Freud
  Is distinctly annoyed,
They cling to their long-standing fallacies.

LIMBERICK

It's time to make love. Douse the glim.
The fireflies twinkle and dim.
  The stars lean together
  Like birds of a feather
And the loin lies down with the limb.

CONRAD AIKEN

SHERWOOD ANDERSON (1876–1941)

Sherwood Anderson, a product of Midwest American puritanism, devoted himself to exposing the harmful effects of small-town morality. He broke through everything that was hypocritical and even conventional. Differing from the writers who dealt freely with sex, Anderson delved into the repressive conflict between instinct and convention. Like the Reverend Davidson in Somerset Maugham's Rain, *Anderson's Reverend Curtis Hartman is beset with the problem of sin. Unlike Maugham's unhappy preacher, Anderson's Winesburg minister is a "peeper," but his voyeurism tortures him into self-discovery. "The Strength of God" is that rare thing: a sexual story which, in its very horror of hedonism, is, ironically, a moral story.*

THE STRENGTH OF GOD

The Reverend Curtis Hartman was pastor of the Presbyterian Church of Winesburg, and had been in that position ten years. He was forty years old, and by his nature very silent and reticent. To preach, standing in the pulpit before the people, was always a hardship for him and from Wednesday morning until Saturday evening he thought of nothing but the two sermons that must be preached on Sunday. Early on Sunday morning he went into a little room called a study in the bell tower of the church and prayed. In his prayers there was one note that always predominated. "Give me strength and courage for Thy work, O Lord!" he pleaded, kneeling on the bare floor and bowing his head in the presence of the task that lay before him.

The Reverend Hartman was a tall man with a brown beard. His wife, a stout, nervous woman, was the daughter of a manufacturer of underwear at Cleveland, Ohio. The minister himself was rather a favorite in the town. The elders of the church liked him because he was quiet and unpretentious and Mrs. White, the banker's wife, thought him scholarly and refined.

The Presbyterian Church held itself somewhat aloof from the other churches of Winesburg. It was larger and more imposing and its minister was better paid. He even had a carriage of his own and on summer evenings sometimes drove about town with his wife. Through Main Street and up and down Buckeye Street he went, bowing gravely to the people, while his wife, afire with secret pride, looked at him out of the corners of her eyes and worried lest the horse become frightened and run away.

For a good many years after he came to Winesburg things went well with Curtis Hartman. He was not one to arouse keen enthusiasm among the worshipers in his church but on the other hand he made no enemies. In reality he was much in earnest and sometimes suffered prolonged periods of remorse because he could not go crying the word of God in the highways and byways of the town. He wondered if the flame of the spirit really burned in him and dreamed of a day when a strong sweet new current of power would come like a great wind into his voice and his soul and the people would tremble before the spirit of God made manifest in him. "I am a poor stick and that will never really happen to me," he mused dejectedly and then a patient smile lit up his features. "Oh well, I suppose I'm doing well enough," he added philosophically.

The room in the bell tower of the church, where on Sunday mornings the minister prayed for an increase in him of the power of God, had but one window. It was long and narrow and swung outward on a hinge like a door. On the window, made of little leaded panes, was a design showing the Christ laying his hand upon the head of a child. One Sunday morning in the summer as he sat by his desk in the room with a large Bible opened before him, and the sheets of his sermon scattered about, the minister was shocked to see, in the upper room of the house next door, a woman lying in her bed and smoking a cigarette while she read a book. Curtis Hartman went on tiptoe to the window and closed it softly. He was horror-stricken at the thought of a woman smoking and trembled also to think that his eyes, just raised from the pages of the book of God, had looked upon the bare shoulders and white throat of a woman. With his brain in a whirl he went down into the pulpit and preached a long sermon without once thinking of his gestures or his voice. The sermon attracted unusual attention because of its power and clearness. "I wonder if she is listening, if my voice is carrying a message into her soul," he thought and began to hope that on future Sunday mornings he might be able to say words that would touch and awaken the woman apparently far gone in secret sin.

The house next door to the Presbyterian Church, through the windows of which the minister had seen the sight that had so upset him, was occupied by two women. Aunt Elizabeth Swift, a gray competent-looking widow with money in the Winesburg National Bank, lived there with her daughter Kate Swift, a schoolteacher. The schoolteacher was thirty years old and had a neat trim-looking figure. She had few friends and bore a reputation of having a sharp tongue. When he began to think about her, Curtis Hartman remembered that she had been to Europe and had lived for two years in New York City. "Perhaps after all her smoking means nothing," he thought. He began to remember that when he was a student in college and occasionally read novels, good, although somewhat worldly women, had smoked through the pages of a book that had once fallen into his hands. With a rush of new determination he worked on his sermons all through the week and forgot, in his zeal to reach the ears and the soul of this new listener, both his embarrassment in the pulpit and the necessity of prayer in the study on Sunday mornings.

Reverend Hartman's experience with women had been somewhat limited. He was the son of a wagon maker from Muncie, Indiana, and had worked his way through college. The daughter of the underwear manufacturer had boarded in a house where he lived during his school days and he had married her after a formal and prolonged courtship, carried on for the most part by the girl herself. On his marriage day the underwear manufacturer had given his daughter five thousand dollars and he promised to leave her at least twice that amount in his will. The minister had thought himself fortunate in marriage and had never permitted himself to think of other women. He did not want to think of other women. What he wanted was to do the work of God quietly and earnestly.

In the soul of the minister a struggle awoke. From wanting to reach the ears of Kate Swift, and through his sermons to delve into her soul, he began to want also to look again at the figure lying white and quiet in the bed. On a Sunday morning when he could not sleep because of his thoughts he arose and went to walk in the streets. When he had gone along Main Street almost to the old Richmond place he stopped and, picking up a stone, rushed off to the room in the bell tower. With the stone he broke out a corner of the window and then locked the door and sat down at the desk before the open Bible to wait. When the shade of the window to Kate Swift's room was raised he could see, through the hole, directly into her bed, but she was not there. She also had arisen and had gone for a walk and the hand that raised the shade was the hand of Aunt Elizabeth Swift.

The minister almost wept with joy at this deliverance from the carnal desire to "peep" and went back to his own house praising God. In an ill moment he forgot, however, to stop the hole in the window. The piece of glass broken out at the corner of the window just nipped off the bare heel of the boy standing motionless and looking with rapt eyes into the face of the Christ.

Curtis Hartman forgot his sermon on that Sunday morning. He talked to his congregation and in his talk said that it was a mistake for people to think of their minister as a man set aside and intended by nature to lead a blameless life. "Out of my own experience I know that we, who are the ministers of God's word, are beset by the same temptations that assail you," he declared. "I have been tempted and have surrendered to temptation. It is only the hand of God, placed beneath my head, that has raised me up. As he has raised me so also will he raise you. Do not despair. In your hour of sin raise your eyes to the skies and you will be again and again saved."

Resolutely the minister put the thoughts of the woman in the bed out of his mind and began to be something like a lover in the presence of his wife. One evening when they drove out together he turned the horse out of Buckeye Street and in the darkness on Gospel Hill, above Waterworks Pond, put his arm about Sarah Hartman's waist. When he had eaten breakfast in the morning and was ready to retire to his study at the back of his house he went around the table and kissed his wife on the cheek. When thoughts of Kate Swift came into his head, he smiled and raised his eyes to the skies. "Intercede for me, Master," he muttered, "keep me in the narrow path intent on Thy work."

And now began the real struggle in the soul of the brown-bearded minister. By chance he discovered that Kate Swift was in the habit of lying in her bed in the evenings and reading a book. A lamp stood on a table by the side of the bed and the light streamed down upon her white shoulders and bare throat. On the evening when he made the discovery the minister sat at the desk in the study from nine until after eleven and when her light was put out stumbled out of the church to spend two more hours walking and praying in the streets. He did not want to kiss the shoulders and the throat of Kate Swift and had not allowed his mind to dwell on such thoughts. He did not know what he wanted. "I am God's child and He must save me from myself," he cried, in the darkness under the trees as he wandered in the streets. By a tree he stood and looked at the sky that was covered with hurrying clouds. He began to talk to God intimately and closely. "Please, Father, do not forget me. Give me power to go tomorrow and repair the hole in the window. Lift my eyes again to the skies. Stay with me, Thy servant, in his hour of need."

Up and down through the silent streets walked the minister and for days and weeks his soul was troubled. He could not understand the temptation that had come to him nor could he fathom the reason for its coming. In a way he began to blame God, saying to himself that he had tried to keep his feet in the true path and had not run about seeking sin. "Through my days as a young man and all through my life here I have gone quietly about my work," he declared. "Why now should I be tempted? What have I done that this burden should be laid on me?"

Three times during the early fall and winter of that year Curtis Hartman crept out of his house to the room in the bell tower to sit in the darkness looking at the figure of Kate Swift lying in her bed and later went to walk and pray in the streets. He could not understand himself. For weeks he would go along scarcely thinking of the schoolteacher and telling himself that he had conquered the carnal desire to look at her body. And then something would happen. As he sat in the study of his own house, hard at work on a sermon, he would become nervous and begin to walk up and down the room. "I will go out into the streets," he told himself and even as he let himself in at the church door he persistently denied to himself the cause of his being there. "I will not repair the hole in the window and I will train myself to come here at night and sit in the presence of this woman without raising my eyes. I will not be defeated in this thing. The Lord has devised this temptation as a test of my soul and I will grope my way out of darkness into the light of righteousness."

One night in January when it was bitter cold and snow lay deep on the streets of Winesburg, Curtis Hartman paid his last visit to the room in the bell tower of the church. It was past nine o'clock when he left his own house and he set out so hurriedly that he forgot to put on his overshoes. In Main Street no one was abroad but Hop Higgins the night watchman and in the whole town no one was awake but the watchman and young George Willard, who sat in the office of the *Winesburg Eagle* trying to write a story. Along the street to the church went the minister, plowing through the drifts and thinking that this time he would utterly give way to sin. "I want to look at the woman and to think of kissing her shoulders and I am going to let myself think what I choose," he declared bitterly and tears came into his eyes. He began to think that he would get out of the ministry and try some other way of life. "I shall go to some city and get into business," he declared. "If my nature is such that I cannot resist sin, I shall give myself over to sin. At least I shall not be a hypocrite, preaching the word of God with my mind thinking of the shoulders and neck of a woman who does not belong to me."

It was cold in the room of the bell tower of the church on that January night and almost as soon as he came into the room Curtis Hartman knew that if he stayed he would be ill. His feet were wet from tramping in the snow and there was no fire. In the room in the house next door Kate Swift had not yet appeared. With grim determination the man sat down to wait. Sitting in the chair and gripping the edge of the desk on which lay the Bible, he stared into the darkness. He thought of his wife, and for the moment he almost hated her. "She has always been ashamed of passion and she has cheated me," he thought. "Man has a right to expect living passion and beauty in a woman. He has no right to forget that he is an animal, and in me there is something that is Greek. I will throw off the woman of my bosom and seek other women. I will besiege this schoolteacher. I will fly in the face of all men, and if I am a creature of carnal lusts, then I will live for my lusts."

The distracted man trembled from head to foot, partly from cold, partly from the struggle in which he was engaged. Hours passed and a fever assailed his body. His throat began to hurt and his teeth chattered. His feet on the study floor felt like two cakes of ice. Still he would not give up. "I will see this woman and will think the thoughts I have never dared to think," he told himself, gripping the edge of the desk and waiting.

Curtis Hartman came near dying from the effects of that night of waiting in the church, and also he found in the thing that happened what he took to be the way of life for him. On other evenings when he had waited he had not been able to see, through the little hole in the glass, any part of the schoolteacher's room except that occupied by her bed. In the darkness he had waited until the woman suddenly appeared sitting in the bed in her white night robe. When the light was turned up she propped herself up among the pillows and read a book. Sometimes she smoked one of the cigarettes. Only her bare shoulders and throat were visible.

On the January night, after he had come near dying with cold and after his mind had two or three times actually slipped away into an odd land of fantasy so that he had by an exercise of will power to force himself back into consciousness, Kate Swift appeared. In the room next door a lamp was lighted and the waiting man stared into an empty bed. Then upon the bed before his eyes a naked woman threw herself. Lying face downward she wept and beat with her fists upon the pillow. With a final outburst of weeping she half arose, and in the presence of the man who had waited to look and to think thoughts the woman of sin began to pray. In the lamplight her figure, slim and strong, looked like the figure of the boy in the presence of the Christ on the leaded window.

Curtis Hartman never remembered how he got out of the church. With a cry he arose, dragging the heavy desk along the floor. The Bible fell, making a great clatter in the silence. When the light in the house next door went out he stumbled down the stairway and into the street. Along the street he went and ran in at the door of the *Winesburg Eagle*. To George Willard, who was tramping up and down in the office undergoing a struggle of his own, he began to talk half incoherently. "The ways of God are beyond human understanding," he cried, running in quickly and closing the door. He began to advance upon the young man, his eyes glowing and his voice ringing with fervor. "I have found the light," he cried. "After ten years in this town, God has manifested himself to me in the body of a woman." His voice dropped and he began to whisper. "I did not understand," he said. "What I took to be a trial of my soul was only a preparation for a new and more beautiful fervor of the spirit. God has appeared to me in the person of Kate Swift, the schoolteacher, kneeling naked on a bed. Do you know Kate Swift? Although she may not be aware of it, she is an instrument of God, bearing the message of truth."

Reverend Curtis Hartman turned and ran out of the office. At the door he stopped, and after looking up and down the deserted street, turned again to George Willard. "I am delivered. Have no fear." He held up a bleeding fist for the young man to see. "I smashed the glass of the window," he cried. "Now it will have to be wholly replaced. The strength of God was in me and I broke it with my fist."

JAMES BRANCH CABELL (1879–)

Jurgen, published in 1919, was by no means James Branch Cabell's first work—it was preceded by almost a dozen dexterous and delicately ironic volumes—but it was the first to cause a nationwide controversy which culminated in its temporary suppression. Its author, born in Richmond, Virginia, in 1879, called it A Comedy of Justice, *but it is actually a satire on the lush historical romances of the period and also on the platitudes and shibboleths of our own day.*

Jurgen takes place in Poictesme, a kingdom which is a composite of myths, magic, and metaphorical symbols. If the story is, as some have contended, escapist and out of touch with ordinary living, it is a nostalgic fantasy that is also a rowdy romp in the poet's ivory tower. The tale concerns a man in search of his lost dreams. As a courtesy to Jurgen, a middle-aged pawnbroker, the devil, a realist, has spirited away the dreamer's shrewish wife, but the harassed husband nevertheless feels it is his duty to go after her. His quest leads to the recovery of his youth and, as the transformed Duke of Logreus, the discovery of many lovely and generous ladies, including Guinevere, Helen of Troy, the Lady of the Lake, and other fabulous creatures. A "monstrous clever fellow," Jurgen has a wild year of glorious adventure which ends in a series of disillusionments and a resigned return to his nagging Dame Lisa. In spite of the prosaic ending, the author agrees with the inciting Anaïtis, one of his favorite characters, who maintains that "a man possesses nothing certainly save a brief loan of his body: and yet the body of man is capable of much curious pleasure."

FROM: JURGEN

ABOUT A COCK THAT CROWED TOO SOON

Next the tale tells of how Jurgen and the ghost of Queen Sylvia Tereu came into the White Turret. Anaïtis, the Lady of the Lake, was in bed. She slept unaccompanied, as Jurgen noted with approval, for he wished to intrude upon no more tête-à-têtes. And Dame Anaïtis did not at first awake . . .

The two of them paused in the winding stairway; and in the darkness, after he had restored her comb, the Queen was telling Jurgen how sorry she was to part with him.

"For it is back to the cold grave I must be going now, Messire Jurgen, and to the tall flames of Purgatory: and it may be that I shall not ever see you any more."

"I shall regret the circumstance, madame," said Jurgen, "for you are the loveliest person I have ever seen."

The Queen was pleased. "That is a delightfully boyish speech, and one can see it comes from the heart. I only wish that I could meet such unsophisticated persons in my present abode. Instead, I am herded with battered sinners who have no heart, who are not frank and outspoken about anything, and I detest their affectations."

"Ah, then you are not happy with your husband, Sylvia? I suspected as much."

"I see very little of Smoit. It is true he has eight other wives all resident in the same flame, and cannot well show any partiality. Two of his queens, though, went straight to Heaven: and his eighth wife, Gudrun, we are compelled to fear, must have been an unrepentant sinner, for she has never reached Purgatory. But I always distrusted Gudrun, myself: otherwise I would never have suggested to Smoit that he have her strangled in order to make me his Queen. You see, I thought it a fine thing to be a queen, in those days, Jurgen, when I was an artless slip of a girl. And Smoit was all honey and perfume and velvet, in those days, Jurgen, and little did I suspect the cruel fate that was to befall me."

"Indeed, it is a sad thing, Sylvia, to be murdered by the hand which, so to speak, is sworn to keep an eye on your welfare, and which rightfully should serve you on its knees."

"It was not that I minded. Smoit killed me in a fit of jealousy, and jealousy is in its blundering way a compliment. No, a worse thing than that befell me, Jurgen, and embittered all my life in the flesh." And Sylvia began to weep.

"And what was that thing, Sylvia?"

Queen Sylvia whispered the terrible truth. "My husband did not understand me."

"Now, by Heaven," said Jurgen, "when a woman tells me that, even though the woman be dead, I know what it is she expects of me."

So Jurgen put his arm about the ghost of Queen Sylvia Tereu and comforted her. Then, finding her quite willing to be comforted, Jurgen sat for a while upon the dark steps, with one arm still about Queen Sylvia. The effect of the potion had evidently worn off, because Jurgen found himself to be composed no longer of cool imponderable vapor, but of the warmest and hardest sort of flesh everywhere. But probably the effect of the wine which Jurgen had drunk earlier in the evening had not worn off: for now Jurgen began to talk wildishly in the dark about the necessity of his, in some way, avenging the injury inflicted upon his nominal grandfather, Ludwig, and Jurgen drew his sword, charmed Caliburn.

"For, as you perceive," said Jurgen, "I carry such weapons as are sufficient for all ordinary encounters. And am I not to use them, to requite King Smoit for the injustice he did poor Ludwig? Why, certainly I must. It is my duty."

"Ah, but Smoit by this time is back in Purgatory," Queen Sylvia protested. "And to draw your sword against a woman is cowardly."

"The avenging sword of Jurgen, my charming Sylvia, is the terror of envious men, but it is the comfort of all pretty women."

"It is undoubtedly a very large sword," said she. "Oh, a magnificent sword, as I can perceive even in the dark. But Smoit, I repeat, is not here to measure weapons with you."

"Now your arguments irritate me, whereas an honest woman would see to it that all the legacies of her dead husband were duly satisfied——"

"Oh, oh! and what do you mean?"

"Well, but certainly a grandson is—at one remove, I grant you—a sort of legacy."

"There is something in what you advance——"

"There is a great deal in what I advance, I can assure you. It is the most natural and most penetrating kind of logic; and I wish merely to discharge a duty——"

"But you upset me, with that big sword of yours, you make me nervous, and I cannot argue so long as you are flourishing it about. Come now, put up your sword! Oh, what is anybody to do with you! Here is the sheath for your sword," said she.

At this point they were interrupted.

"Duke of Logreus," said the voice of Dame Anaïtis, "do you not think it would be better to retire, before such antics at the door of my bedroom give rise to a scandal?"

For Anaïtis had half opened the door of her bedroom, and, with a lamp in her hand, was peering out into the narrow stairway. Jurgen was a little embarrassed, for his apparent intimacy with a lady who had been dead for sixty-three years would be, he felt, a matter difficult to explain. So Jurgen rose to his feet, and hastily put up the weapon he had exhibited to Queen Sylvia, and decided to pass airily over the whole affair. And outside, a cock crowed, for it was now dawn.

"I bid you a good morning, Dame Anaïtis," said Jurgen. "But the stairways hereabouts are confusing, and I must have lost my way. I was going for a stroll. This is my distant relative Queen Sylvia Tereu, who kindly offered to accompany me. We were going out to gather mushrooms and to watch the sunrise, you conceive."

"Messire de Logreus, I think you had far better go back to bed."

"To the contrary, madame, it is my manifest duty to serve as Queen Sylvia's escort——"

"For all that, messire, I do not see any Queen Sylvia."

Jurgen looked about him. And certainly his grandfather's ninth wife was no longer visible. "Yes, she has vanished. But that was to be expected at cockcrow. Still, that cock crew just at the wrong moment," said Jurgen ruefully. "It was not fair."

And Dame Anaïtis said: "Gogyrvan's cellar is well stocked: and you sat late with Urien and Aribert: and doubtless they also were lucky enough to discover a queen or two in Gogyrvan's cellar. No less, I think you are still a little drunk."

"Now answer me this, Dame Anaïtis: were you not visited by two ghosts tonight?"

"Why, that is as it may be," she replied, "but the White Turret is notoriously haunted, and it is few quiet nights I have passed there, for Gogyrvan's people were a bad lot."

"Upon my word," wondered Jurgen, "what manner of person is this Dame Anaïtis, who remains unstirred by such a brutal murder as I have committed, and makes no more of ghosts than I would of moths? I have heard she is an enchantress; I am sure she is a fine figure of a woman; and in short, here is a matter which would repay looking into, were not young Guinevere the mistress of my heart."

Aloud he said: "Perhaps then I am drunk, madame. None the less, I still think the cock crew just at the wrong moment."

"Someday you must explain the meaning of that," said she. "Meanwhile I am going back to bed, and I again advise you to do the same."

Then the door closed, the bolt fell, and Jurgen went away, still in considerable excitement.

"This Dame Anaïtis is an interesting personality," he reflected, "and it would be a pleasure, now, to demonstrate to her my grievance against the cock, did occasion serve. Well, things less likely than that have happened. Then, too, she came upon me when my sword was out, and in consequence knows I wield a respectable weapon. She may feel the need of a good swordsman someday, this handsome Lady of the Lake who has no husband. So let us cultivate patience. Meanwhile, it appears that I am of royal blood. Well, I fancy there is something in the scandal, for I detect in me a deal in common with this King Smoit. Twelve wives, though! No, that is too many. I would limit no man's liaisons, but twelve wives in lawful matrimony bespeaks an optimism unknown to me. No, I do not think I am drunk; but it is unquestionable that I am not walking very straight. Certainly, too, we did drink a great deal. So I had best go quietly back to bed and say nothing more about tonight's doings."

H. L. MENCKEN (1880-1956)

A *belligerent* non-conformer, harangued but never howled down by the enemies he delighted to make, Henry Louis Mencken fought pretension, challenged every platitude, and disputed all the shibboleths in the credo of puritanism. Born in Baltimore, Maryland, in 1880, Mencken began his career as a boy reporter and, although he became an editor, essayist, critic, and lexicographer of the monumental The American Language, a newspaperman he remained the rest of his life. Attacked as a destructive cynic, Mencken replied that he never pretended to be a reformer, that he hated all forms of "uplift," and that his chief aim was "to stir up the animals."

Stir them up he did with a series of prodding exposures, each a little more savage than its predecessor. A reckless iconoclast and a careful scholar, stubborn, arbitrary, often wrong, but never dull, Mencken abhorred academic smugness, fake sentiment, and intellectual lethargy. He was, in the most creative sense, a "disturber of the peace"; but if his ideas disturbed his countrymen, they never failed to amuse even when they irritated. When his impudences were most boisterous they were most calculated to make readers soberly reappraise their prejudices.

All Mencken's books—and there were more than a score of them—reveal the writer whose irreverences are not those of a mischief-maker (the role assigned him by his detractors) but a controversialist who attacked the genteel tradition and sanctimonious cant with equal zeal. Whether broad and outrageous, as in In Defense of Women—a defense for which no woman would give thanks—or nostalgically winning, as in the biographical Happy Days, the spirit which animates the writing is not only gay but galvanic.

In 1948 Mencken suffered an intense stroke that affected all his activities except his power to think. Two years later another coronary occlusion made it impossible for him to write or even read. For six years he sank into aphasia and total inaction, a horrible ending for one of the lustiest and most actively provocative men of his times. He was in his seventy-sixth year when he died on January 29, 1956.

Mencken was a hearty forty when he wrote his own premature epitaph. Quoted as a key sentence in the obituaries, it is in the manner of the wry epigrams in The Greek Anthology, and it is also pure Menckenese: "If, after I depart this vale, you ever remember me and have thought to please my ghost, forgive some sinner and wink your eye at some homely girl."

TWENTY SENTENTIOUS MAXIMS

Conscience is the inner voice which warns us that someone may be looking.

Evil is that which one believes of others. It is a sin to believe evil of others, but it is seldom a mistake.

The difference between a moral man and a man of honor is that the latter regrets a discreditable act, even when it has worked and he has not been caught.

Truth is something somehow discreditable to someone.

A gentleman is one who never strikes a woman without provocation.

When women kiss it always reminds one of prize fighters shaking hands.

Happiness is peace after strife, the overcoming of difficulties, the feeling of security and well-being. The only really happy folk are married women and single men.

No matter how much a woman loves a man, it would still give her a glow to see him commit suicide for her.

The first kiss is stolen by the man; the last is begged by the woman.

Temptation is woman's weapon and man's excuse.

Men have a much better time of it than women. For one thing they marry later. For another thing, they die earlier.

Women do not like timid men. Cats do not like prudent mice.

No matter how happily a woman may be married, it always pleases her to discover that there is a nice man who wishes she were not.

Clergyman: A ticket-speculator outside the gates of heaven.

Sunday: A day given over by Americans to wishing that they were dead and in heaven, and that their neighbors were dead and in hell.

Theology: An effort to explain the unknowable by putting it into terms of the not worth knowing.

Judge: A law student who marks his own examination papers.

The atheist confesses: Let us thank God there is no God.

Adultery is the application of democracy to love.

Love is the delusion that one woman differs from another.

FROM: IN DEFENSE OF WOMEN

THE LIBERTINE

The average man of our time and race is far more virtuous than his wife's imaginings make him out—far less schooled in sin, far less enterprising in amour. I do not say, of course, that he is pure in heart, for the chances are that he isn't; what I do say is that, in the overwhelming majority of cases, he is pure in act, even in the face of temptation. And why? For several main reasons, not to go into minor ones. One is that he lacks the courage. Another is that he lacks the money. Another is that he is fundamentally moral, and has a conscience. It takes more sinful initiative than he has to plunge into any affair save the most casual and sordid; it takes more ingenuity and intrepidity than he has to carry if off; it takes more money than he can conceal from his consort to finance it. A man may force his actual wife to share the direst poverty, but even the least vampirish woman of the third part demands to be courted in what, considering his station in life, is the grand manner, and the expenses of that grand manner scare off all save a small minority of specialists in deception. So long, indeed, as a wife knows her husband's income accurately, she has a sure means of holding him to his oaths.

Even more effective than the fiscal barrier is the barrier of poltroonery. The one character that distinguishes man from the other higher Vertebrata is his excessive timorousness, his easy yielding to alarms, his incapacity for adventure without a crowd behind him. In his normal incarnation he is no more capable of initiating an extralegal affair—at all events, above the mawkish harmlessness of a flirting match with a cigar girl in a cafe—than he is of scaling the battlements of hell. He likes to think of himself doing it, just as he likes to think of himself leading a cavalry charge or climbing the Matterhorn. Often, indeed, his vanity leads him to imagine the thing done, and he admits by winks and blushes that he is a bad one. But at the bottom of all that tawdry pretense there is usually nothing more material than a scraping of shins under the table. Let any woman who is disquieted by reports of her husband's derelictions figure to herself how long it would have taken him to propose to her if left to his own enterprise, and then let her ask herself if so pusillanimous a creature could be imagined in the role of Don Giovanni!

Finally, there is his conscience—the accumulated sediment of ancestral faintheartedness in countless generations, with vague religious fears and superstitions to leaven and mellow it. What! a conscience? Yes, dear friends, a conscience. That conscience may be imperfect, inept, unintelligent, brummagem. It may be indistinguishable, at times, from the mere fear that someone may be looking. It may be shot through with hypocrisy, stupidity, play acting. But nevertheless, as consciences go in Christendom, it is genuinely entitled to the name—and it is always in action. A man, remember, is not a being *in vacuo*; he is the fruit and slave of the environment that bathes him. One cannot enter a state legislature or a prison for felons without becoming, in some measure, a dubious character. One cannot fall overboard without shipping water. And by the same token one cannot live and have one's being in a modern democratic state, year in and year out, without falling, to some extent at least, under that moral obsession which is the hallmark of the mobman set free.

The moment a concrete Temptress rises before him, her nose talcked, her lips scarlet, her eyelashes dropping provokingly—the moment such an abandoned wench has at him, and his lack of ready funds begins to conspire with his lack of courage to assault and wobble him—at that precise moment his conscience flares into function, and so finishes his business. First he sees difficulty, then he says danger, then he sees wrong. The result? The result is that he slinks off in trepidation, and another vampire is baffled of her prey. It is, indeed, the secret scandal of Christendom, at least in the Protestant regions, that most men are faithful to their wives. You will travel a long way before you find a married man who will admit that *he* is, but the facts are the facts. For one American husband who maintains a chorus girl in Levantine luxury around the corner, there are hundreds who are as true to their oaths, year in and year out, as so many convicts in the death house, and would be no more capable of any such loathsome malpractice, even in the face of free opportunity, than they would be of cutting off the ears of their young.[1]

THE LURE OF BEAUTY

Save on the stage, the handsome fellow has no appreciable advantage in amour over his more Gothic brother. In real life, indeed, he is viewed with the utmost suspicion by all women save the most stupid. A ten-cent-store girl, perhaps, may plausibly fall in love with a movie actor, and a half idiotic old widow may succumb to a gigolo with shoulders like the Parthenon, but no woman of poise and self-respect, even supposing her to be transiently flustered by a lovely buck, would yield to that madness for an instant, or confess it to her dearest friend.

This disdain of the pretty fellow is often accounted for by amateur psychologists on the ground that women are anesthetic to beauty—that they lack the quick and delicate responsiveness of man. Nothing could be more absurd. Women, in point of fact, commonly have a far keener esthetic sense than men. Beauty is more important to them; they give more thought to it; they crave more of it in their immediate surroundings. The average man, at least in England and America, takes a bovine pride in his indifference to the arts; he can think of them only as sources of somewhat discreditable amusement; one seldom hears of him showing half the enthusiasm for any beautiful thing that his wife displays in the presence of a fine fabric, an effective color, or a graceful form. Women are resistant to so-called beauty in men for the simple and sufficient reason that such beauty is chiefly imaginary. A truly beautiful man, indeed, is as rare as a truly beautiful piece of jewelry.

What men mistake for beauty in themselves is usually nothing save a certain hollow gaudiness, a revolting flashiness, the superficial splendor of a prancing animal. The most lovely movie actor, considered in the light of genuine esthetic values, is no more than a study in vulgarity; his like is to be

[1] I see nothing in the Kinsey Report to change my conclusions here. All that humorless document really proves is (a) that all men lie when they are asked about their adventures in amour, and (b) that pedagogues are singularly naïve and credulous creatures.

found, not in the Uffizi Gallery or among the harmonies of Brahms, but among the plush sofas, rococo clocks, and hand-painted oil paintings of a third-rate auction room. All women, save the least intelligent, penetrate this imposture with sharp eyes. They know that the human body, except for a brief time in childhood, is not a beautiful thing, but a hideous thing. Their own bodies give them no delight; it is their constant effort to disguise and conceal them; they never expose them esthetically, but only as an act of the grossest sexual provocation. If it were advertised that a troupe of men of easy virtue were to do a strip-tease act upon a public stage, the only women who would go to the entertainment would be a few delayed adolescents, a psychopathic old maid or two, and a guard of indignant members of the parish Ladies' Aid Society.

Men show no such sagacious apprehension of the relatively feeble loveliness of the human frame. The most effective lure that a woman can hold out to a man is the lure of what he fatuously conceives to be her beauty. This so-called beauty, of course, is almost always a pure illusion. The female body, even at its best, is very defective in form; it has harsh curves and very clumsily distributed masses; compared to it the average milk jug, or even cuspidor, is a thing of intelligent and gratifying design—in brief, an *objet d'art*. Below the neck by the bow and below the waist astern there are two masses that simply refuse to fit into a balanced composition. Viewed from the side, a woman presents an exaggerated S bisected by an imperfect straight line, and so she inevitably suggests a drunken dollar mark.

Moreover, it is extremely rare to find a woman who shows even the modest sightliness that her sex is theoretically capable of; it is only the rare beauty who is even tolerable. The average woman, until art comes to her aid, is ungraceful, misshapen, badly calved and crudely articulated, even for a woman. If she has a good torso, she is almost sure to be bowlegged. If she has good legs, she is almost sure to have bad hair. If she has good hair, she is almost sure to have scrawny hands, or muddy eyes, or no chin. A woman who meets fair tests all round is so uncommon that she becomes a sort of marvel, and usually gains a livelihood by exhibiting herself as such, either on the stage, in the half-world, or as the private jewel of some wealthy connoisseur.

But this lack of genuine beauty in women lays on them no practical disadvantage in the primary business of their sex, for its effects are more than overborne by the emotional suggestibility, the herculean capacity for illusion, the almost total absence of critical sense in men. Men do not demand genuine beauty, even in the most modest doses; they are quite content with the mere appearance of beauty. That is to say, they show no talent whatever for differentiating between the artificial and the real. A film of face powder, skillfully applied, is as satisfying to them as an epidermis of damask. The hair of a dead Chinaman, artfully dressed and dyed, gives them as much delight as the authentic tresses of Venus. False bosoms intrigue them as effectively as the soundest of living fascia. A pretty frock fetches them quite as surely and securely as lovely legs, shoulders, hands, or eyes.

In brief, they estimate women, and hence acquire their wives, by reckoning up purely superficial aspects, which is just as intelligent as estimating an egg by purely superficial aspects. They never go behind the returns; it never occurs to them to analyze the impressions they receive. The result is that many a man, deceived by such paltry sophistications, never really sees his wife—that is, as our Heavenly Father is supposed to see her, and as the embalmer will see her—until they have been married for years. All the tricks may be infantile and obvious, but in the face of so naïve a spectator the temptation to continue practicing them is irresistible. A trained nurse tells me that even when undergoing the extreme discomfort of parturition the great majority of women continue to modify their complexions with pulverized magnesium silicate, and to give thought to the arrangement of their hair. Such transparent devices reduce the psychologist to a sour sort of mirth, yet it must be plain that they suffice to entrap and make fools of men, even the most discreet.

And what esthetic deafness, dumbness and blindness thus open the way for, vanity instantly reinforces. That is to say, once a normal man has succumbed to the meretricious charms of a definite fair one (or, more accurately, once a definite fair one has marked him out and grabbed him by the nose), he defends his choice with all the heat and steadfastness appertaining to the defense of a point of honor. To tell a man flatly that his wife is not beautiful is so harsh and intolerable an insult that even an enemy seldom ventures upon it. One would offend him far less by arguing that his wife is an idiot. One would, relatively speaking, almost caress him by spitting into his eye. The ego of the male is simply unable to stomach such an affront. It is a weapon as discreditable as the poison of the Borgias.

Thus, on humane grounds, a conspiracy of silence surrounds the delusion of female beauty, and its victim is permitted to get quite as much delight out of it as if it were sound. The baits he swallows most are not edible and nourishing ones, but simply bright and gaudy ones. He succumbs to a pair of well-managed eyes, a graceful twist of the body, a synthetic complexion, or a skillful display of legs without giving the slightest thought to the fact that a whole woman is there, and that within the cranial cavity of the woman lies a brain, and that the idiosyncrasies of that brain are of vastly more importance than all imaginable physical stigmata combined. But not many men, lost in the emotional maze preceding, are capable of any very clear examination of such facts. They dodge those facts, even when they are favorable, and lay all stress upon the surrounding and concealing superficialities. The average stupid and sentimental man, if he has a noticeably sensible wife, is almost apologetic about it. The ideal of his sex is always a pretty wife, and the vanity and coquetry that so often go with prettiness are erected into charms.

FRANKIE AND JOHNNY

The most famous of American offbeat ballads, "Frankie and Johnny," originated about 1850. Although much research has been spent upon its history, no one has been able to discover its author or place of birth. Some claim that the scene of the affair was Natchez-under-the-Hill, while others maintain that the locale was St. Louis and that the real "heroine" was an actual Frankie Baker who shot her "mack," or pimp, in a jealous brawl. In any case the song took such a hold on the popular imagination that by 1935 two plays, a motion picture, and several ballets (serious and burlesque) had been built around the story, as well as dozens of versions of the ballad itself, some of which are unprintable. The version which follows is a composite of several of the most frequently printed texts.

Frankie and Johnny were sweethearts, O Lordy, how they could love!
Swore to be true to each other, true as the stars above.
    He was her man, but he done her wrong.

Frankie she was a good woman, just like everybody knows;
She gave her man a hundred dollars to buy himself a suit of clothes.
    He was her man, but he done her wrong.

Frankie and Johnny went walking, Johnny in his brand new suit.
"Oh, good Lord," says Frankie, "don't my Johnny look cute?"
    He was her man, but he done her wrong.

Frankie went down to Memphis, she went on the evening train.
She paid one hundred dollars for Johnny a watch and chain.
    He was her man, but he done her wrong.

Frankie lived in the crib-house, crib-house had only two doors;
Gave all her money to Johnny, who spent it on those parlor whores.
    He was her man, but he done her wrong.

Frankie went down to the corner to buy a glass of beer,
Says to the fat bartender, "Has my lovingest man been here?
    He was my man, but he's doing me wrong."

"Ain't going to tell you no story; ain't going to tell you no lie;
I seen your man 'bout an hour ago with a girl named Nellie Bly.
    If he's your man, he's doing you wrong."

Frankie went down to the pawnshop, she didn't go there for fun;
She hocked all of her jewelry, bought a pearl-handled forty-four gun
    For to get her man, who was doing her wrong.

Frankie went down to the hotel, she rang that hotel bell.
"Stand back, all you chippies, or I'll blow you straight to hell.
    I want my man, who's doing me wrong."

Frankie went up to the parlor, looked over the transom so high;
There on the bed was her Johnny a-lovin' up Nellie Bly.
    He was her man, but he was doing her wrong.

Frankie threw back her kimono, she took out her forty-four,
Root-a-toot three times she shot right through that hotel door
    She was after her man, who was doing her wrong.

Johnny grabbed off his Stetson, "Oh, good Lord, Frankie, don't shoot!"
But Frankie pulled the trigger and the gun went root-a-toot-toot.
    He was her man, but she shot him down.

"Roll me over easy; roll me over slow;
Roll me over on my left side, for the bullet is hurting me so.
    I was her man, but I done her wrong."

Oh, bring on your rubber-tired hearses; bring on your rubber-tired hacks;
They're taking Johnny to the cemetery, and they ain't a-bringing him back.
    He was her man, but he done her wrong.

Now it was not murder in the second degree, it was not murder in the third.
The woman simply dropped her man, like a hunter drops his bird.
    He was her man, and he done her wrong.

"Oh, put me in that dungeon. Oh, put me in that cell.
Put me where the northeast wind blows from the southwest corner of hell.
    I shot my man, 'cause he done me wrong."

Frankie walked up the scaffold, as calm as a girl can be,
And turning her eyes to heaven she said, "Good Lord, I'm coming to Thee.
    He was my man, and I done him wrong."

This story has got no moral; this story has got no end.
This story only goes to show that there ain't no good in men.
    He was her man, but he done her wrong.

DAMON RUNYON (1884–1946)

Charles Dickens and Mark Twain were two of the most illustrious literary figures who began as hardworking newspapermen, and Damon Runyon is of their company. All three were humorists who were also humanists. Their characters were people, not fiction's stock figures. Runyon's bookies, babes, crap-

shooters, horse players, gangsters, actors waiting to act, and an assortment of extraordinary guys and dolls immediately convince you that they are alive. Theirs is a small world and an even smaller country; its capital is Broadway and it centers about Times Square. They answer to such weird names as Harry the Horse, Big Butch, Nicely-Nicely Jones, Madame La Gimp, Izzy Cheesecake, Waldo Winchester (not too remotely related to Walter Winchell), Hymie Banjo Eyes, Sorrowful, Cold Cuts, and the Lemon Drop Kid. All of them speak a language which is pure and authentic American. Runyon knew every one of their inflections because, as sportswriter, he had lived among them.

A Kansan born in 1880, by an odd coincidence his midwestern birthplace and the metropolitan borough he later adopted bore the same name: Manhattan. As a minor he convinced a recruiting officer that he was eighteen and joined the Army at the age of fourteen. Then he became a roving reporter for years. When the sportswriter became the laureate of the big town, wearing O. Henry's mantle with ease, his understanding of New Yorkers and New Yorkese was profound and was praised by the most critical. What's more he caught, and eternally preserved, the tough boys' swagger, their pride, and their hard-boiled humor.

SENSE OF HUMOR

One night I am standing in front of Mindy's restaurant on Broadway, thinking of practically nothing whatever, when all of a sudden I feel a very terrible pain in my left foot. In fact, this pain is so very terrible that it causes me to leap up and down like a bullfrog, and to let out loud cries of agony, and to speak some very profane language, which is by no means my custom, although of course I recognize the pain as coming from a hot foot, because I often experience this pain before.

Furthermore, I know Joe the Joker must be in the neighborhood, as Joe the Joker has the most wonderful sense of humor of anybody in this town, and is always around giving people the hot foot, and gives it to me more times than I can remember. In fact, I hear Joe the Joker invents the hot foot, and it finally becomes a very popular idea all over the country. The way you give a hot foot is to sneak up behind some guy who is standing around thinking of not much, and stick a paper match in his shoe between the sole and the upper along about where his little toe ought to be, and then light the match. By and by the guy will fell a terrible pain in his foot, and will start stamping around, and hollering, and carrying on generally, and it is always a most comical sight and a wonderful laugh to one and all to see him suffer.

No one in the world can give a hot foot as good as Joe the Joker, because it takes a guy who can sneak up very quiet on the guy who is to get the hot foot, and Joe can sneak up so quiet many guys on Broadway are willing to lay odds that he can give a mouse a hot foot if you can find a mouse that wears shoes. Furthermore, Joe the Joker can take plenty of care of himself in case the guy who gets the hot foot feels like taking the matter up, which sometimes happens, especially with guys who get their shoes made to order at forty bucks per copy and do not care to have holes burned in these shoes.

But Joe does not care what kind of shoes the guys are wearing when he feels like giving out hot foots, and furthermore, he does not care who the guys are, although many citizens think he makes a mistake the time he gives a hot foot to Frankie Ferocious. In fact, many citizens are greatly horrified by this action, and go around saying no good will come of it.

This Frankie Ferocious comes from over in Brooklyn, where he is considered a rising citizen in many respects, and by no means a guy to give hot foots to, especially as Frankie Ferocious has no sense of humor whatever. In fact, he is always very solemn, and nobody ever sees him laugh, and he certainly does not laugh when Joe the Joker gives him a hot foot one day on Broadway when Frankie Ferocious is standing talking over a business matter with some guys from the Bronx.

He only scowls at Joe, and says something in Italian, and while I do not understand Italian, it sounds so unpleasant that I guarantee I will leave town inside of the next two hours if he says it to me.

Of course Frankie Ferocious' name is not really Ferocious, but something in Italian like Feroccio, and I hear he originally comes from Sicily, although he lives in Brooklyn for quite some years, and from a modest beginning he builds himself up until he is a very large operator in merchandise of one kind and another, especially alcohol. He is a big guy of maybe thirty-odd, and he has hair blacker than a yard up a chimney, and black eyes, and black eyebrows, and a slow way of looking at people.

Nobody knows a whole lot about Frankie Ferocious, because he never has much to say, and he takes his time saying it, but everybody gives him plenty of room when he comes around, as there are rumors that Frankie never likes to be crowded. As far as I am concerned, I do not care for any part of Frankie Ferocious, because his slow way of looking at people always makes me nervous, and I am always sorry Joe the Joker gives him a hot foot, because I figure Frankie Ferocious is bound to consider it a most disrespectful action, and hold it against everybody that lives on the island of Manhattan.

But Joe the Joker only laughs when anybody tells him he is out of line in giving Frankie the hot foot, and says it is not his fault if Frankie has no sense of humor. Furthermore, Joe says he will not only give Frankie another hot foot if he gets a chance, but that he will give hot foots to the Prince of Wales or Mussolini, if he catches them in the right spot, although Regret, the horse player, states that Joe can have twenty to one any time that he will not give Mussolini any hot foots and get away with it.

Anyway, just as I suspect, there is Joe the Joker watching me when I feel the hot foot, and he is laughing very heartily, and furthermore, a large number of other citizens are also laughing heartily, because Joe the Joker never sees any fun in giving people the hot foot unless others are present to enjoy the joke. Well, naturally when I see who it is gives me the hot foot I join in the laughter, and go over and shake hands with Joe, and when I shake hands with him there is more laughter, because it seems Joe has a hunk of Limburger cheese in his duke, and what I shake hands with is this Limburger. Furthermore, it is some of Mindy's Limburger cheese, and everybody knows Mindy's Limburger is very squashy, and also very loud.

Of course I laugh at this, too, although to tell the truth I will laugh much more heartily if Joe the Joker drops dead in front of me, because I do not like to be made the subject of laughter on Broadway. But my laugh is really quite hearty when Joe takes the rest of the cheese that is not on my fingers and smears it on the steering wheels of some automobiles parked in front of Mindy's, because I get to thinking of what the drivers will say when they start steering their cars.

Then I get to talking to Joe the Joker, and I ask him how things are up in Harlem, where Joe and his younger brother, Freddy, and several other guys have a small organization operating in beer, and Joe says things are as good as can be expected considering business conditions. Then I ask him how Rosa is getting along, this Rosa being Joe the Joker's ever-loving wife, and a personal friend of mine, as I know her when she is Rosa Midnight and is singing in the old Hot Box before Joe hauls off and marries her.

Well, at this question Joe the Joker starts laughing, and I can see that something appeals to his sense of humor, and finally he speaks as follows:

"Why," he says, "do you not hear the news about Rosa? She takes the wind on me a couple of months ago for my friend Frankie Ferocious, and is living in an apartment over in Brooklyn, right near his house, although," Joe says, "of course you understand I am telling you this only to answer your question, and not to holler copper on Rosa."

Then he lets out another large ha-ha, and in fact Joe the Joker keeps laughing until I am afraid he will injure himself internally. Personally, I do not see anything comical in a guy's ever-loving wife taking the wind on him for a guy like Frankie Ferocious, so when Joe the Joker quiets down a bit I ask him what is funny about the proposition.

"Why," Joe says, "I have to laugh every time I think of how the big grease-ball is going to feel when he finds out how expensive Rosa is. I do not know how many things Frankie Ferocious has running for him in Brooklyn," Joe says, "but he better try to move himself in on the mint if he wishes to keep Rosa going." Then he laughs again, and I consider it wonderful the way Joe is able to keep his sense of humor even in such a situation as this, although up to this time I always think Joe is very daffy indeed about Rosa, who is a little doll, weighing maybe ninety pounds with her hat on and quite cute.

Now I judge from what Joe the Joker tells me that Frankie Ferocious knows Rosa before Joe marries her and is always pitching to her when she is singing in the Hot Box, and even after she is Joe's ever-loving wife, Frankie occasionally calls her up, especially when he commences to be a rising citizen of Brooklyn, although of course Joe does not learn about these calls until later. And about the time Frankie Ferocious commences to be a rising citizen of Brooklyn, things begin breaking a little tough for Joe the Joker, what with the depression and all, and he has to economize on Rosa in spots, and if there is one thing Rosa cannot stand it is being economized on.

Along about now, Joe the Joker gives Frankie Ferocious the hot foot, and just as many citizens state at the time, it is a mistake, for Frankie starts calling Rosa up more than somewhat, and speaking of what a nice place Brooklyn is to live in—which it is, at that—and between these boosts for Brooklyn and Joe the Joker's economy, Rosa hauls off and takes the subway to Borough Hall, leaving Joe a note telling him that if he does not like it he knows what he can do.

"Well, Joe," I say, after listening to his story, "I always hate to hear of these little domestic difficulties among my friends, but maybe this is all for the best. Still, I feel sorry for you, if it will do you any good," I say.

"Do not feel sorry for me," Joe says. "If you wish to feel sorry for anybody, feel sorry for Frankie Ferocious, and," he says, "if you can spare a little more sorrow, give it to Rosa."

And Joe the Joker laughs very hearty again and starts telling me about a little scatter that he has up in Harlem where he keeps a chair fixed up with electric wires so he can give anybody that sits down in it a nice jolt, which sounds very humorous to me, at that, especially when Joe tells me how they turn on too much juice one night and almost kill Commodore Jake.

Finally Joe says he has to get back to Harlem, but first he goes to the telephone in the corner cigar store and calls up Mindy's and imitates a doll's voice, and tells Mindy he is Peggy Joyce, or somebody, and orders fifty dozen sandwiches sent up at once to an apartment in West Seventy-second Street for a birthday party, although of course there is no such number as he gives, and nobody there will wish fifty dozen sandwiches if there is such a number.

Then Joe gets in his car and starts off, and while he is waiting for the traffic lights at Fiftieth Street, I see citizens on the sidewalks making sudden leaps, and looking around very fierce, and I know Joe the Joker is plugging them with pellets made out of tin foil, which he fires from a rubber band hooked between his thumb and forefinger.

Joe the Joker is very expert with this proposition, and it is very funny to see the citizens jump, although once or twice in his life Joe makes a miscue and knocks out somebody's eye. But it is all in fun, and shows you what a wonderful sense of humor Joe has.

Well, a few days later I see by the papers where a couple of Harlem guys Joe the Joker is mobbed up with are found done up in sacks over in Brooklyn, very dead indeed, and the coppers say it is because they are trying to move in on certain business enterprises that belong to nobody but Frankie Ferocious. But of course the coppers do not say Frankie Ferocious puts these guys in the sacks, because in the first place Frankie will report them to Headquarters if the coppers say such a thing about him, and in the second place putting guys in sacks is strictly a St. Louis idea and to have a guy put in a sack properly you have to send to St. Louis for experts in this matter.

Now, putting a guy in a sack is not as easy as it sounds, and in fact it takes quite a lot of practice and experience. To put a guy in a sack properly, you first have to put him to sleep, because naturally no guy is going to walk into a sack wide awake unless he is a plumb sucker. Some people claim the best way to put a guy to sleep is to give him a sleeping powder of some kind in a drink but the real experts just tap the guy on the noggin with a blackjack, which saves the expense of buying the drink. Anyway, after the guy is asleep, you double him up like a pocketknife, and tie a cord or a wire around his neck and under his knees. Then you put him in a gunny sack, and leave him some place, and by and by when the guy wakes up and finds himself in the sack, naturally he wants to get out and the first thing he does is to try to straighten out his knees. This pulls the cord around his neck up so tight that after a while the guy is all out of breath. So then when somebody comes along and opens the sack they find the guy dead, and nobody is responsible for this unfortunate situation, because after all the guy really commits suicide, because if he does not try to straighten out his knees he may live to a ripe old age, if he recovers from the tap on the noggin.

Well, a couple of days later I see by the papers where three Brooklyn citizens are scragged as they are walking peaceably along Clinton Street, the scragging being done by some parties in an automobile who seem to have a machine gun, and the papers state that the citizens are friends of Frankie Ferocious, and that it is rumored the parties with the machine gun are from Harlem.

I judge by this that there is some trouble in Brooklyn, especially as about a week after the citizens are scragged in Clinton Street, another Harlem guy is found done up in a sack like a Virginia ham near Prospect Park, and now who is it but Joe the Joker's brother, Freddy, and I know Joe is going to be greatly displeased by this.

By and by it gets so nobody in Brooklyn will open as much as a sack of potatoes without first calling in the gendarmes, for fear a pair of No. 8 shoes will jump out at them.

Now one night I see Joe the Joker, and this time he is all alone, and I wish to say I am willing to leave him all alone, because something tells me he is hotter than a stove. But he grabs me as I am going past, so naturally I stop to talk to him, and the first thing I say is how sorry I am about his brother.

"Well," Joe the Joker says, "Freddy is always a kind of a sap. Rosa calls him up and asks him to come over to Brooklyn to see her. She wishes to talk to Freddy about getting me to give her a divorce," Joe says, "so she can marry Frankie Ferocious, I suppose. Anyway," he says, "Freddy tells Commodore Jake why he is going to see her. Freddy always likes Rosa, and thinks maybe he can patch it up between us. So," Joe says, "he winds up in a sack. They get him after he leaves her apartment. I do not claim Rosa will ask him to come over if she has any idea he will be sacked," Joe says, "but," he says, "she is responsible. She is a bad-luck doll."

Then he starts to laugh, and at first I am greatly horrified, thinking it is because something about Freddy being sacked strikes his sense of humor, when he says to me like this:

"Say," he says, "I am going to play a wonderful joke on Frankie Ferocious."

"Well, Joe," I say, "you are not asking me for advice, but I am going to give you some free gratis, and for nothing. Do not play any jokes on Frankie Ferocious, as I hear he has no more sense of humor than a nanny goat. I hear Frankie Ferocious will not laugh if you have Al Jolson, Eddie Cantor, Ed Wynn, and Joe Cook telling him jokes all at once. In fact," I say, "I hear he is a tough audience."

"Oh," Joe the Joker says, "he must have some sense of humor somewhere to stand for Rosa. I hear he is daffy about her. In fact, I understand she is the only person in the world he really likes, and trusts. But I must play a joke on him. I am going to have myself delivered to Frankie Ferocious in a sack."

Well, of course I have to laugh at this myself, and Joe the Joker laughs with me. Personally, I am laughing just at the idea of anybody having themselves delivered to Frankie Ferocious in a sack, and especially Joe the Joker, but of course I have no idea Joe really means what he says.

"Listen," Joe says, finally. "A guy from St. Louis who is a friend of mine is doing most of the sacking for Frankie Ferocious. His name is Ropes McGonnigle. In fact," Joe says, "he is a very dear old pal of mine, and he has a wonderful sense of humor like me. Ropes McGonnigle has nothing whatever to do with sacking Freddy," Joe says, "and he is very indignant about it since he finds out Freddy is my brother, so he is anxious to help me play a joke on Frankie. Only last night," Joe says, "Frankie Ferocious sends for Ropes and tells him he will appreciate it as a special favor if Ropes will bring me to him in a sack. I suppose," Joe says, "that Frankie Ferocious hears from Rosa what Freddy is bound to tell her about my ideas on divorce. I have very strict ideas on divorce," Joe says, "especially where Rosa is concerned. I will see her in what's-this before I ever do her and Frankie Ferocious such a favor as giving her a divorce.

"Anyway," Joe the Joker says, "Ropes tells me about Frankie Ferocious propositioning him, so I send Ropes back to Frankie Ferocious to tell him he knows I am to be in Brooklyn tomorrow night, and furthermore, Ropes tells Frankie that he will have me in a sack in no time. And so he will," Joe says.

"Well," I say, "personally, I see no percentage in being delivered to Frankie Ferocious in a sack, because as near as I can make out from what I read in the papers, there is no future for a guy in a sack that goes to Frankie Ferocious. What I cannot figure out," I say, "is where the joke on Frankie comes in."

"Why," Joe the Joker says, "the joke is, I will not be asleep in the sack, and my hands will not be tied, and in each of my hands I will have a John Roscoe, so when the sack is delivered to Frankie Ferocious and I pop out blasting away, can you not imagine his astonishment?"

Well, I can imagine this, all right. In fact, when I get to thinking of the look of surprise that is bound to come to Frankie Ferocious' face when Joe the Joker comes out of the sack I have to laugh, and Joe the Joker laughs right along with me.

"Of course," Joe says, "Ropes McGonnigle will be there to start blasting with me, in case Frankie Ferocious happens to have any company."

Then Joe the Joker goes on up the street, leaving me still laughing from thinking of how amazed Frankie Ferocious will be when Joe bounces out of the sack and starts throwing slugs around and about. I do not hear of Joe from that time to this, but I hear the rest of the story from very reliable parties.

It seems that Ropes McGonnigle does not deliver the sack himself, after all, but sends it by an expressman to Frankie Ferocious' home. Frankie Ferocious receives many sacks such as this in his time, because it seems that it is a sort of passion with him to personally view the contents of the sacks and check up on them before they are distributed about the city, and of course Ropes McGonnigle knows about this passion from doing so much sacking for Frankie.

When the expressman takes the sack into Frankie's house, Frankie personally lugs it down into his basement, and there he outs with a big John Roscoe and fires six shots into the sack, because it seems Ropes McGonnigle tips him off to Joe the Joker's plan to pop out of the sack and start blasting.

I hear Frankie Ferocious has a very strange expression on his pan and is laughing the only laugh anybody ever hears from him when the gendarmes break in and put the arm on him for murder, because it seems that when Ropes McGonnigle tells Frankie of Joe the Joker's plan, Frankie tells Ropes what he is going to do with his own hands before opening the sack. Naturally, Ropes speaks to Joe the Joker of Frankie's idea about filling the sack full of slugs, and Joe's sense of humor comes right out again.

So, bound and gagged, but otherwise as right as rain in the sack that is delivered to Frankie Ferocious, is by no means Joe the Joker, but Rosa.

A SAMPLER OF MODERN RIBALD VERSE

The fashioning of ribald verse was a pronounced vogue in the seventeenth and eighteenth centuries, but it did not end there. Although the moderns may not always have achieved the adroit twists and sharply turned thrusts of the Restoration wits, they do not lack nimbleness of mind and manner. That their work had appeal as well as a kind of permanence is proved by a dozen or more compilations bearing such titles as An Uncensored Anthology, Stag Lines, Loose Lyrics, Rowdy Rhymes, Virile Verse, *et cetera. Robustious rhymes also insinuated themselves into countless songbooks and readers, including such estimable collections as The Nonesuch Press's perennial* Weekend Book *and Sigmund Spaeth's documentary* Read 'Em and Weep.

Poets of unquestionable respectability, moreover, allowed themselves an occasional fling. The austere Thomas Hardy and the restrained A. E. Housman occasionally forsook dignity for a few divertissements. That corn-fed, homespun laureate of childhood, James Whitcomb Riley, wrote about the vanishing outhouse in his most tender and nostalgic vein. Eugene Field, another all-American poet of the people, also let his muse wander through the years to linger on a moist but memorable episode. Rudyard Kipling's The Ladies *is a classic that has been countlessly quoted for its general philosophy and particularly for the last two famous lines. Modern poetry is indebted to E. E. Cummings not only for his unique lyricism but for his many-levelled mockery, to Dorothy Parker for her wry (and soda) flippancies, and to Ogden Nash for a new approach to light verse as well as (in* Four Prominent So-and-So's*) ironic echoes of the depression era. Bawdiness and burlesque mingle uproariously in* The Ballad of Yukon Jake, *Edward Paramore's wicked parody of Robert W. Service's red-blooded ballads which were so popular in the early nineteen hundreds.*

A passing tribute must also be paid to the unknown versifiers and lyricists whose identities have been lost and whose writings are continually reprinted, credited only to that fabulous and favorite author, "Anonymous."

THE RUINED MAID

"O 'Melia, my dear, this does everything crown!
Who could have supposed I should meet you in town?
And whence such fair garments, such prosperi-ty?"—
"O didn't you know I'd been ruined?" said she.

—"You left us in tatters, without shoes or socks,
Tired of digging potatoes, and spudding up docks;
And now you've gay bracelets and bright feathers three!"—
"Yes: that's how we dress when we're ruined," said she.

—"At home in the barton[1] you said 'thee' and 'thou,'
And 'thik oon,' and 'theas oon!' and 't'other'; but now
Your talking quite fits 'ee for high compa-ny!"—
"Some polish is gained with one's ruin," said she.

[1] On the farm.

—"Your hands were like paws then, your face blue and bleak,
But now I'm bewitched by your delicate cheek,
And your little gloves fit as on any la-dy!"—
"We never do work when we're ruined," said she.

—"You used to call home life a hag-ridden dream,
And you'd sigh, and you'd sock; but at present you seem
To know not of megrims or melanchol-ly!"
"True. There's an advantage in ruin," said she.

—"I wish I had feathers, a fine sweeping gown,
And a delicate face, and could strut about town!"—
"My dear—a raw country girl, such as you be,
Isn't equal to that. You ain't ruined!" said she.

THOMAS HARDY (1840–1928)

THE DARK-EYED GENTLEMAN

I pitched my day's leazings[1] in Crimmercrock Lane,
To tie up my garter and jog on again,
When a dear dark-eyed gentleman passed there and said,
In a way that made all o' me color rose-red,
　　"What do I see—
　　O pretty knee!"
And he came and he tied up my garter for me.

'Twixt sunset and moonrise it was, I can mind:
Ah, 'tis easy to lose what we nevermore find!—
Of the dear stranger's home, of his name, I knew nought,
But I soon knew his nature and all that it brought.
　　Then bitterly
　　Sobbed I that he
Should ever have tied up my garter for me!

Yet now I've beside me a fine lissom lad,
And my slip's nigh forgot, and my days are not sad;
My own dearest joy is he, comrade, and friend,
He it is who safeguards me, on him I depend;
　　No sorrow brings he,
　　And thankful I be
That his daddy once tied up my garter for me!

THOMAS HARDY (1840–1928)

---

[1] Leazings: bundles of gleaned corn.

OH, SEE HOW THICK THE GOLDCUP FLOWERS

Oh, see how thick the goldcup flowers
    Are lying in field and lane,
With dandelions to tell the hours
    That never are told again,
Oh, may I squire you round the meads
    And pick you posies gay?
—'Twill do no harm to take my arm.
    "You may, young man, you may."

Ah, spring was sent for lass and lad,
    'Tis now the blood runs gold,
And man and maid had best be glad
    Before the world is old.
What flowers today may flower tomorrow,
    But never as good as new.
—Suppose I wound my arm right round.
    " 'Tis true, young man, 'tis true."

Some lads there are, 'tis shame to say,
    That only court to thieve,
And once they bear the bloom away
    'Tis little enough they leave.
Then keep your heart for men like me
    And safe from trustless chaps.
My love is true and all for you.
    "Perhaps, young man, perhaps."

Oh, look in my eyes then, can you doubt?
    —Why, 'tis a mile from town.
How green the grass is all about!
    We might as well sit down.
—Ah, life, what is it but a flower?
    Why must true lovers sigh?
Be kind, have pity, my own, my pretty
    "Good-by, young man, good-by."

A. E. HOUSMAN (1859–1936)

OH, WHEN I WAS IN LOVE WITH YOU

Oh, when I was in love with you,
    Then I was clean and brave,
And miles around the wonder grew
    How well did I behave.

And now the fancy passes by,
    And nothing will remain,
And miles around they'll say that I
    Am quite myself again.

A. E. HOUSMAN (1859–1936)

ADAM AND EVE

When Adam day by day
    Woke up in Paradise,
He always used to say
    "Oh, this is very nice."

But Eve from scenes of bliss
    Transported him for life . . .
The more I think of this,
    The more I beat my wife.

A. E. HOUSMAN (1859–1936)

THE LADIES

I've taken my fun where I've found it;
    I've rogued an' I've ranged in my time;
I've 'ad my pickin' o' sweethearts,
    An' four o' the lot was prime.
One was an 'arf-caste widow,
    One was a woman at Prome,
One was the wife of a *jemadar-sais*,[1]
    An' one is a girl at 'ome.

Now I aren't no 'and with the ladies,
    For, takin' 'em all along,
You never can say till you've tried 'em,
    An' then you are like to be wrong.
There's times when you'll think that you mightn't,
    There's times when you'll know that you might;
But the things you will learn from the Yellow an' Brown,
    They'll 'elp you a lot with the White!

I was a young un at 'Oogli,
    Shy as a girl to begin;
Aggie de Castrer she made me,
    An' Aggie was clever as sin;

---

[1] Head-groom.

Older than me, but my first un—
More like a mother she were—
Showed me the way to promotion an' pay,
An' I learned about women from 'er!

Then I was ordered to Burma,
Actin' in charge o' Bazar,
An' I got me a tidy live 'eathen
Through buyin' supplies off 'er pa.
Funny an' yellow an' faithful—
Doll in a teacup she were—
But we lived on the square, like a true-married pair,
An' I learned about women from 'er!

Then we was shifted to Neemuch
(Or I might ha' been keepin' 'er now),
An' I took with a shiny she-devil,
The wife of a nigger at Mhow;
'Taught me the gipsy-folks' *bolee;*[1]
Kind o' volcano she were,
For she knifed me one night 'cause I wished she was white,
And I learned about women from 'er!

Then I come 'ome in a trooper,
'Long of a kid o' sixteen—
'Girl from a convent at Meerut,
The straightest I ever 'ave seen.
Love at first sight was 'er trouble,
She didn't know what it were;
An' I wouldn't do such, 'cause I liked 'er too much,
But—I learned about women from 'er!

I've taken my fun where I've found it,
An' now I must pay for my fun,
For the more you 'ave known o' the others
The less will you settle to one;
An' the end of it's sittin' and thinkin',
An' dreamin' hell-fires to see;
So be warned by my lot (which I know you will not),
An' learn about women from me!

What did the colonel's lady think?
  Nobody ever knew.
Somebody asked the sergeant's wife,
  An' she told 'em true.

[1] Slang.

When you get to a man in the case
   They're like as a row of pins—
For the colonel's lady an' Judy O'Grady
   Are sisters under the skins!

RUDYARD KIPLING (1865–1936)

SEE-SAW

She was a harlot, and I was a thief:
But we loved each other beyond belief:
She lived in the garret, and I in the kitchen,
And love was all that we both were rich in.

When they sent her at last to the hospital,
Both day and night my tears did fall.
They fell so fast that, to dry their grief,
I borrowed my neighbor's handkerchief.

The world, which, as it is brutally taught,
Still judges the act in lieu of the thought,
Found my hand in my neighbor's pocket,
And clapped me, at once, under chain and locket.

When they asked me about it, I told them plain,
Love it was that had turned my brain:
How should I heed where my hand had been,
When my heart was dreaming of Celestine?

Twelve friends were so struck by my woful air,
That they sent me abroad for change of air:
And, to prove me the kindness of their intent,
They sent me at charge of the government.

When I came back again—whom, think you, I meet
But Celestine, here, in Regent Street?
In a carriage adorned with a coronet,
And a dress, all flounces, and lace, and jet:

For her carriage drew up to the bookseller's door,
Where they publish those nice little books for the poor:
I took off my hat: and my face she knew,
And gave me—a sermon by Mr. Belew.

But she gave me (God bless her!) along with the book,
Such a sweet sort of smile, such a heavenly look,
That, as long as I live, I shall never forget
Celestine, in her coach with the earl's coronet.

There's a game that men play at in great London-town:
Whereby some must go up, sir, and some must go down:
And, since the mud sticks to your coat if you fall,
Why, the strongest among us keep close to the wall.

But someday, soon or late, in my shoes I shall stand,
More exalted than any great duke in the land;
A clean shirt on my back, and a rose in my coat,
And a collar conferred by the Queen round my throat.

And I know that my Celestine will not forget
To be there, in her coach with my lord's coronet:
She will smile to me then, as she smiled to me now:
I shall nod to her gayly, and make her my bow—

Before I rejoin all those famous old thieves
Whose deeds have immortalized Rome, sir, and Greece:
Whose names are inscribed upon history's leaves,
Like my own on the books of the city police:

Alexander, and Caesar, and other great robbers,
Who once tried to pocket the whole universe:
Not to speak of our own parliamentary jobbers,
With their hands, bless them all, in the popular purse!

OWEN MEREDITH (EARL OF LYTTON) (1831–1891)

THE REHEARSAL

Famous for more than half a century, "The Rehearsal" is the out-growth (or reverse of) puritan New England. Much of its popularity, as well as its humor, is due to the way in which scraps of hymn tunes have been woven into the far from solemn verses.

I sit here thinking, Will, of you,
    Of happy days gone by—
The old church, where oft we sang
    Together you and I;
But thoughts of one rehearsal night
    Will constantly arise,
Till I can hear my title clear
    To mansions in the skies.

I'm thinking of the rainy night—
    The rest had hurried home—
And we, in Deacon Foster's pew,
    Were sitting all alone;

You were a *seeker* then, dear Will,
   But not of *things above—*
The length, the depth, the breadth, the height
   Of everlasting love.

And I was on the "anxious" seat,
   Uncertain how to move,
Within thine arms of love embraced,
   Thy constancy to prove!
And oh! the promises you made—
   You were my own dear Will—
What peaceful hours I once enjoyed,
   How sweet their memory still.

Oh! what sweet words of love you spoke,
   And kissed away the tear;
And how I trembled at the thought
   Lest someone should appear;
But when you turned the lights all out,
   To guard against surprise,
I bade farewell to every fear,
   And wiped my weeping eyes.

I thought, could I these doubts remove,
   These gloomy doubts that rise,
And see the Canaan that we love
   With unbeclouded eyes!
And as you climbed the pulpit stairs,
   And viewed the landscape o'er,
Not Jordan's stream, not death's cold flood
   Could fright us from the floor.

And when you fixed the cushions up,
   And I reclined at ease,
The pulpit pillow 'neath my head,
   And you on bended knees;
With your warm kisses on my lips,
   How could I stay your hand;
The veil was lifted, and by faith,
   You viewed the promised land.

And oh! what rapturous feelings
   Thrilled every nerve, and when
I cried, *Oh Lord! my heart is touched,*
   You shouted out *Amen!*
My very soul was all ablaze;
   I thought that I could see

The land of rest, the saints' delight,
  The heaven prepared for me.

But that was many years ago,
  And I've no doubt that you
Remember still the rainy night
  In Deacon Foster's pew.
But oh, my first experience
  Will ne'er forgotten be,
While down the stream of life we glide
  To our eternity.

I'm married now; the good man thinks
  In me he has a prize.
Ah me! *Where ignorance is bliss*
  'Tis folly to be wise.
Of you, dear Will, he nothing knows
  And so my heart's at rest,
And not a wave of trouble rolls
  Across my peaceful breast.

AUTHOR UNKNOWN

A RONDEAU OF DIFFERENCE

"I can't conceive," she archly cried,
"What makes the male swell up with pride.
    Now that we've won our liberty
    Women at last have grown to be
Your peers in every human stride.

"This is a truth that none can hide;
    Yet why you men will not agree
    To recognize the new decree
        I can't conceive.

"Between ourselves, won't you confide
And tell me truly—jokes aside—
    What difference anyone can see
    Between your manly self and me."
"To tell you truly," he replied,
        "I can't conceive."

AUTHOR UNKNOWN

THE OLD BACKHOUSE

When memory keeps me company and moves to smiles or tears,
A weather-beaten object looms through the mist of years.
Behind the house and barn it stood, a hundred yards or more,
And hurrying feet a path had made, straight to its swinging door.
Its architecture was a type of simple classic art,
But in the tragedy of life it played a leading part.
And oft the passing traveler drove slow, and heaved a sigh,
To see the modest hired girl slip out with glances shy.

We had our posey garden that the women loved so well,
I loved it, too, but better still I loved the stronger smell
That filled the evening breezes so full of homely cheer,
And told the night-o'ertaken tramp that human life was near.
On lazy August afternoons, it made a little bower
Delightful, where my grandsire sat and whiled away an hour.
For there the morning-glory its very eaves entwined,
And berry bushes reddened in the steaming soil behind.

All day fat spiders spun their webs to catch the buzzing flies
That flitted to and from the house, where Ma was baking pies.
And once a swarm of hornets bold, had built a palace there,
And stung my unsuspecting aunt—I must not tell you where.
Then Father took a flaming pole—that was a happy day—
He nearly burned the building up, but the hornets left to stay.
When summer bloom began to fade and winter to carouse
We banked the little building with a heap of hemlock boughs.

But when the crust was on the snow and the sullen skies were gray,
In sooth the building was no place where one could wish to stay.
We did our duties promptly, there one purpose swayed the mind;
We tarried not, nor lingered long on what we left behind.
The torture of that icy seat would make a Spartan sob,
For needs must scrape the goose flesh with a lacerating cob,
That from a frost-encrusted nail, was suspended by a string—
For Father was a frugal man and wasted not a thing.

When Grandpa had to "go out back" and make his morning call,
We'd bundle up the dear old man with a muffler and a shawl,
I knew the hole on which he sat—'twas padded all around,
And once I dared to sit there—'twas all too wide I found.
My loins were all too little, and I jackknifed there to stay,
They had to come and get me out, or I'd have passed away.
Then Father said ambition was a thing that boys should shun,
And I just used the children's hole 'till childhood days were done.

And still I marvel at the craft that cut those holes so true,
The baby hole, and the slender hole that fitted Sister Sue;
That dear old country landmark! I've tramped around a bit,
And in the lap of luxury my lot has been to sit,
But ere I die I'll eat the fruit of trees I robbed of yore,
Then seek the shanty where my name is carved upon the door.
I ween the old familiar smell will soothe my jaded soul,
I'm now a man, but none the less, I'll try the children's hole.

JAMES WHITCOMB RILEY (1849–1916)

LITTLE WILLIE

When Willie was a little boy,
    Not more than five or six,
Right constantly he did annoy
    His mother with his tricks.
Yet not a picayune cared I
    For what he did or said
Unless, as happened frequently,
    The rascal wet the bed.

Closely he cuddled up to me
    And put his hand in mine,
Till all at once I seemed to be
    Afloat in seas of brine.
Sabean odors clogged the air,
    And filled my soul with dread,
Yet I could only grin and bear
    When Willie wet the bed.

'Tis many times that rascal has
    Soaked all the bedclothes through,
Whereat I'd feebly light the gas
    And wonder what to do.
Yet there he lay, so peaceful-like,
    God bless his curly head!
I quite forgave the little tyke
    For wetting of the bed.

Ah, me! those happy days have flown,
    My boy's a father too,
And little Willies of his own
    Do what he used to do.

And I, ah! all that's left for me
  Are dreams of pleasure fled;
My life's not what it used to be
  When Willie wet the bed!

EUGENE FIELD (1850–1895)

KING DAVID AND KING SOLOMON

King David and King Solomon
  Led merry, merry lives
With many, many lady friends
  And many, many wives.
But when old age crept onward
  With all its heavy qualms,
King Solomon wrote the Proverbs
  And King David wrote the Psalms.

JAMES BALL NAYLOR (1860–1945)

ALMOST

My sweetheart has beneficent arms
  So full of tenderness and fire,
They almost cheat her other charms
  The way they rouse and still desire.

My sweetheart has the kindest breast,
  Two heavens with each a single star;
They give me everything but rest,
  So strange these rosy pillows are.

My sweetheart has the hungriest lips
  That seek and press unsparingly;
They probe until she almost slips
  Among her kisses into me.

My sweetheart's body is a cry,
  A poignant and resistless call;
It almost makes me wonder why
  She hasn't any mind at all.

LOUIS UNTERMEYER (1885–   )

EQUALS

Dear child, how can you dare complain
  That you and I may be mismated
Because, you say, you lack a brain
  And I'm so highly educated.

The body is the greater thing;
  And you are doubly gifted when
You have such hands and breasts that bring
  More peace than all the words of men.

Take pride in this, your beauty; drink
  The wine it offers for our love.
Be glad you do not have to think.
  One thoughtful lover is enough!

We're equal partners, that is plain;
  Our life cannot grow dull or shoddy,
While I have such a lovely brain
  And you have such a lively body.

LOUIS UNTERMEYER (1885–   )

THE LITTLE OLD LADY IN LAVENDER SILK

I was seventy-seven, come August,
  I shall shortly be losing my bloom;
I've experienced zephyr and raw gust
  And (symbolical) flood and simoom.

When you come to this time of abatement,
  To this passing from Summer to Fall,
It is manners to issue a statement
  As to what you got out of it all.

So I'll say, though reflection unnerves me
  And pronouncements I dodge as I can,
That I think (if my memory serves me)
  There was nothing more fun than a man!

In my youth, when the crescent was *too* wan
  To embarrass with beams from above,
By the aid of some local Don Juan
  I fell into the habit of love.

And I learned how to kiss and be merry, an
  Education left better unsung.

My neglect of the waters Pierian
   Was a scandal, when Grandma was young.

Though the shabby unbalanced the splendid,
   And the bitter outmeasured the sweet,
I should certainly do as I then did,
   Were I given the chance to repeat.

For contrition is hollow and wraithful,
   And regret is no part of my plan,
And I think (if my memory's faithful)
   There was nothing more fun than a man!

DOROTHY PARKER (1893–   )

INDIAN SUMMER

In youth, it was a way I had
   To do my best to please,
And change, with every passing lad,
   To suit his theories.

But now I know the things I know,
   And do the things I do;
And if you do not like me so,
   To hell, my love, with you!

DOROTHY PARKER (1893–   )

SHE BEING BRAND

she being Brand

-new;and you
know consequently a
little stiff i was
careful of her and(having

thoroughly oiled the universal
joint tested my gas felt of
her radiator made sure her springs were O.

K.)i went right to it flooded-the-carburetor cranked her

up,slipped the
clutch(and then somehow got into reverse she
kicked what
the hell)next
minute i was back in neutral tried and

again slo-wly;bare,ly nudg.   ing(my

lev-er Right-
oh and her gears being in
A 1 shape passed
from low through
second-in-to-high like
greasedlightning just as we turned the corner of Divinity

avenue i touched the accelerator and give

her the juice,good

                              (it
was the first ride and believe i we was
happy to see how nice she acted right up to
the last minute coming back down by the Public
Gardens i slammed on
the

internalexpanding
&
externalcontracting
brakes Bothatonce and

brought allofher tremB
-ling
to a:dead.

stand-
;Still)

                                        e. e. cummings (1894–   )

FOUR PROMINENT SO-AND-SO'S

I'm an autocratic figure in these democratic states,
I'm a dandy demonstration of hereditary traits.
As the children of the baker bake the most delicious breads,
As the sons of Casanova fill the most exclusive beds,
As the Barrymores, the Roosevelts, and others I could name
Inherited the talents that perpetuate their fame,
My position in the structure of society I owe
To the qualities my parents bequeathed me long ago.
My pappy was a gentleman, and musical, to boot,
He used to play piano in a house of ill repute.
The madam was a lady, and a credit to her cult,
She enjoyed my pappy's playing, and I was the result!

So my mammy and my pappy are the ones I have to thank
That I'm Chairman of the Board of the National Country Bank!

Chorus:

Oh, our parents forgot to get married,
Oh, our parents forgot to get wed,
Did a wedding bell chime? It was always a time
When our parents were somewhere in bed,
Tra la la la, they were somewhere in bed.
Oh, thanks to our kind loving parents,
We are kings in the land of the free—
Your banker, your broker, your Washington joker—
Four prominent bastards are we, tra la la la
Four prominent bastards are we.

2.

In a cozy little farmhouse in a cozy little dell
A dear old-fashioned farmer and his daughter used to dwell.
She was pretty, she was charming, she was tender, she was mild,
And her sympathy was such that she was frequently with child.
The year her hospitality attained a record high
She became the happy mammy of an infant, which was I.
Whenever she was gloomy I could always make her grin
By childishly inquiring who my pappy could have been.
The hired man was favored by the girls in Mammy's set
And a trav'ling man from Scranton was an even money bet.
But such were Mammy's motives, and such was her allure,
That even Roger Babson wasn't altogether sure.
Well, I took my mammy's morals and I took my pappy's crust
And I grew to be the founder of a big Investment Trust.

Chorus:

Oh, our parents forgot to get married,
Oh, our parents forgot to get wed.
Did a wedding bell chime? It was always a time
When our parents were somewhere in bed,
Tra la la la, they were somewhere in bed.
Oh, thanks to our kind loving parents,
We are kings in the land of the free—
Your banker, your broker, your Washington joker—
Four prominent bastards are we, tra la la la
Four prominent bastards are we.

3.

On a cozy little chain gang on a dusty southern road
My late lamented daddy had his permanent abode.
Now some were there for stealing, but Daddy's only fault
Was an overwhelming weakness for criminal assault.
His philosophy was simple, and free of moral tape:
Seduction is for sissies, but a he-man wants his rape.
Daddy's total list of victims was embarrassingly rich,
And though one of them was Mammy, he couldn't tell me which.
Well, I didn't go to college, but I got me a degree;
I reckon I'm the model of a perfect S.O.B.;
I'm a debit to my country but a credit to my dad,
The most expensive senator the nation ever had;
I remember Daddy's warning that raping is a crime
Unless you rape the voters a million at a time.

Chorus:

Oh, our parents forgot to get married,
Oh, our parents forgot to get wed.
Did a wedding bell chime? It was always a time
When our parents were somewhere in bed,
Tra la la la, they were somewhere in bed.
Oh, thanks to our kind loving parents,
We are kings in the land of the free—
Your banker, your broker, your Washington joker—
Four prominent bastards are we, tra la la la
Four prominent bastards are we.

4.

I'm an ordinary figure in these democratic states,
A pathetic demonstration of hereditary traits.
As the children of the cops possess the flattest kind of feet,
As the daughter of the floozie has a waggle to her seat,
My position at the bottom of society I owe
To the qualities my parents bequeathed me long ago.
My father was a married man, and what is even more,
He was married to my mother, a fact which I deplore,
I was born in holy wedlock, consequently, by and by,
I was rooked by every bastard with plunder in his eye.
I invested, I deposited, I voted every fall,
And if I saved a penny, the bastards took it all.
At last I've learned my lesson and I'm on the proper track:
I'm a self-appointed bastard and I'm goin' to get it back.

Chorus:

Oh, our parents forgot to get married,
Oh, our parents forgot to get wed.
Did a wedding bell chime? It was always a time
When our parents were somewhere in bed,
Tra la la la, they were somewhere in bed.
Oh, thanks to our kind loving parents,
We are kings in the land of the free—
Your banker, your broker, your Washington joker—
Four prominent bastards are we, tra la la la
Four prominent bastards are we.

OGDEN NASH (1902–   )

A BALLAD OF THE GOOD LORD NELSON

The good Lord Nelson had a swollen gland,
Little of the scripture did he understand
Till a woman led him to the promised land
    Aboard the Victory, Victory O.

Adam and Evil and a bushel of figs
Meant nothing to Nelson who was keeping pigs,
Till a woman showed him the various rigs
    Aboard the Victory, Victory O.

His heart was softer than a new-laid egg,
Too poor for loving and ashamed to beg,
Till Nelson was taken by the Dancing Leg
    Aboard the Victory, Victory O.

Now he up and did up his little tin trunk
And he took to the ocean on his English junk,
Turning like the hourglass in his lonely bunk
    Aboard the Victory, Victory O.

The Frenchman saw him a-coming there
With the one-piece eye and the valentine hair,
With the safety-pin sleeve and occupied air
    Aboard the Victory, Victory O.

Now you all remember the message he sent
As an answer to Hamilton's discontent—
There were questions asked about it in the Parliament
    Aboard the Victory, Victory O.

Now the blacker the berry, the thicker the juice.
Think of good Lord Nelson and avoid self-abuse,
For the empty sleeve was no mere excuse
    Aboard the Victory, Victory O.

"England Expects" was the motto he gave
When he thought of little Emma out on Biscay's wave,
And remembered working on her like a galley slave
    Aboard the Victory, Victory O.

The first great lord in our English land
To honor the Freudian command,
For a cast in the bush is worth two in the hand
    Aboard the Victory, Victory O.

Now the Frenchman shot him there as he stood
In the rage of battle in a silk-lined hood
And he heard the whistle of his own hot blood
    Aboard the Victory, Victory O.

Now stiff on a pillar with a phallic air
Nelson stylites in Trafalgar Square
Reminds the British what once they were
    Aboard the Victory, Victory O.

If they'd treat their woman in the Nelson way
There'd be fewer frigid husbands every day,
And many more heroes on the Bay of Biscay
    Aboard the Victory, Victory O.

LAWRENCE DURRELL (1912–   )

THE BALLAD OF YUKON JAKE

THE HERMIT OF SHARK TOOTH SHOAL

Oh the North Countree is a hard countree
    That mothers a bloody brood;
And its icy arms hold hidden charms
    For the greedy, the sinful and lewd.

And strong men rust, from the gold and lust
    That sear the Northland soul,
But the wickedest born, from the Pole to the Horn,
    Is the Hermit of Shark Tooth Shoal.

Now Jacob Kaime was the Hermit's name,
   In the days of his pious youth,
Ere he cast a smirch on the Baptist Church
   By betraying a girl named Ruth.

But now men quake at Yukon Jake,
   The Hermit of Shark Tooth Shoal,
For that is the name that Jacob Kaime
   Is known by from Nome to the Pole.

He was just a boy and the parson's joy
   (Ere he fell for the gold and the muck),
And he learned to pray, with the hogs and hay
   On a farm near Keokuk.

But a Service tale of illicit kale—
   And whiskey and women wild—
Drained the morals clean as a soup tureen
   From this poor but honest child.

He longed for the bite of a Yukon night
   And the Northern Lights' weird flicker,
For a game of stud in the frozen mud,
   And the taste of raw red licker.

He wanted to mush along in the slush
   With a team of husky hounds,
And to fire his gat at a beaver hat
   And knock it out of bounds.

So he left his home for the hell-town Nome
   On Alaska's ice-ribbed shores,
And he learned to curse and to drink and worse—
   Till the rum dripped from his pores.

When the boys on a spree were drinking it free
   In a Malamute saloon
And Dan McGrew and his dangerous crew
   Shot craps with the piebald coon:

When the Kid on his stool banged away like a fool
   At a jag-time melody
And the barkeep vowed to the hardboiled crowd
   That he'd cree-mate Sam McGee—

Then Jacob Kaime, who had taken the name
   Of Yukon Jake, the Killer,
Would rake the dive with his forty-five
   Till the atmosphere grew chiller.

With a sharp command he'd make 'em stand
　　And deliver their hard-earned dust,
Then drink the bar dry of rum and rye,
　　As a Klondike bully must.

Without coming to blows he would tweak the nose
　　Of Dangerous Dan McGrew
And becoming bolder, throw over his shoulder
　　The Lady that's known as Lou.

Oh, tough as steak was Yukon Jake—
　　Hardboiled as a picnic egg.
He washed his shirt in the Klondike dirt,
　　And drank his rum by the keg.

In fear of their lives (or because of their wives)
　　He was shunned by the best of his pals;
An outcast he, from the comradery
　　Of all but wild animals.

So he bought him the whole of Shark Tooth Shoal,
　　A reef in the Bering Sea,
And he lived by himself on a sea lion's shelf
　　In lonely iniquity.

But miles away, in Keokuk, Ia.
　　Did a ruined maiden fight
To remove the smirch from the Baptist Church
　　By bringing the heathen Light.

And the Elders declared that all would be squared
　　If she carried the holy words
From her Keokuk home to the hell-town Nome
　　To save those sinful birds.

So, two weeks later, she took a freighter,
　　For the gold-cursed land near the Pole,
But heaven ain't made for a lass that betrayed—
　　She was wrecked on Shark Tooth Shoal!

All hands were tossed in the sea and lost—
　　All but the maiden Ruth,
Who swam to the edge of the sea lion's ledge
　　Where abode the love of her youth.

He was hunting a seal for his evening meal
　　(He handled a mean harpoon)
When he saw at his feet not something to eat,
　　But a girl in a frozen swoon,

Whom he dragged to his lair by her dripping hair,
  And he rubbed her knees with gin.
To his surprise she opened her eyes
  And revealed—his Original Sin!

His eight months' beard grew stiff and weird
  And it felt like a chestnut burr,
And he swore by his gizzard—and the Arctic blizzard—
  That he'd do right by her.

But the cold sweat froze on the end of her nose
  Till it gleamed like a Tecla pearl,
While her bright hair fell like a flame from hell
  Down the back of the grateful girl.

But a hopeless rake was Yukon Jake,
  The Hermit of Shark Tooth Shoal!
And the dizzy maid he rebetrayed
  And wrecked her immortal soul!

Then he rowed her ashore with a broken oar,
  And he sold her to Dan McGrew
For a husky dog and a hot eggnog—
  As rascals are wont to do.

Now ruthless Ruth is a maid uncouth
  With scarlet cheeks and lips,
And she sings rough songs to the drunken throngs
  That come from the sealing ships.

For a rouge-stained kiss from this infamous miss
  They will give a seal's sleek fur,
Or perhaps a sable, if they are able;
  It's much the same to her. . . .

Oh, the North Countree is a hard countree,
  That mothers a bloody brood;
And its icy arms hold hidden charms
  For the greedy, the sinful and lewd.

And strong men rust, from the gold and lust
  That sear the Northland soul,
But the wickedest born from the Pole to the Horn
  Is the Hermit of Shark Tooth Shoal!

EDWARD E. PARAMORE, JR. (1895–1956)

ALEXANDER WOOLLCOTT (1887-1943)

Everybody made fun of him—most people disliked him—and everyone read him. Insolent and fat, he was dubbed "all Woollcott and a yard wide." Howard Dietz ridiculed his weakness for sentimental "little men" and "little women" by calling him "Louisa M. Woollcott," and George Jean Nathan mocked his persistent burbling and bubbling by calling Woollcott "The Seidlitz Powder of Times Square." Self-pampered and petulant—Marc Connelly said that gossip was Woollcott's only form of exercise—he was an excellent storyteller.

Most of his stories were founded on other stories, legends, bits of gossip, stray anecdotes. "Entrance Fee," for example, is a story that Woollcott first heard in France, but he polished and sharpened it until it became the little classic which few anthologists have been able to resist.

ENTRANCE FEE

This, then, is the story of Cosette and the Saint-Cyrien, much as they tell it (and these many years have been telling it) in the smoky *popotes* of the French Army.

In the 90s, when one heard less ugly babel of alien tongues in the sidewalk cafés, the talk at the *apéritif* hour was sure to turn sooner or later on Cosette —Mlle. Cosette of the *Variétés*, who was regarded by common consent as the most desirable woman in France. She was no hedged-in royal courtesan, as her possessive fellow citizens would point out, but a distributed Du Barry, the *chère amie* of a republic.

Her origins were misty. Some said she had been born of fisherfolk at Plonbazlanec on the Brittany coast. Others preferred the tale that she was the love child of a famous actress by a very well-known king. In any case she was now a national legend, and in her pre-eminence the still bruised French people found in some curious way a balm for their wounded self-esteem. Her photographs, which usually showed her sitting piquantly on a café table, were cut from *L'Illustration* and pinned up in every barracks. Every French lad dreamed of her, and every right-minded French girl quite understood that her sweetheart was saying in effect, "Since I cannot hope to have Cosette, will you come to the river's edge at sundown?" Quite understood, and did not blame him.

Everyone had seen the pictures of Cosette's tiny, vine-hung villa at Saint-Cloud, with its high garden wall and its twittering aviary. And even those for whom that wall was hopelessly high took morbid pride in a persistent detail of the legend which said that no man was ever a guest there for the night who could not bring five thousand francs with him. This was in the nineties, mind you, when francs were francs, and men—by a coincidence then more dependable—were men.

The pleasant blend of charm and thrift in Cosette filled the cadets at Saint-Cyr with a gentle melancholy. In their twilight hours of relaxation they talked it over, and all thought it a sorrowful thing that, so wretched is the soldier's pittance, not one of those who must someday direct the great *Revanche* would ever carry into a battle a memory of the fairest woman in France. For what cadet could hope to raise five thousand francs? It was very sad. But, cried one of their number, his voice shaking, his eyes alight, there were a thousand students at Saint-Cyr, and not one among them so lacking in resource that he could not, if given time, manage to raise at least five francs.

That was how the Cosette Sweepstakes were started. There followed then all the anxious distraction of ways and means, with such Spartan exploits in self-denial, such Damon-and-Pythias borrowings, such flagrant letters of per-jured appeal to unsuspecting aunts and godmothers, as Saint-Cyr had never known. But by the appointed time the last man had his, or somebody's, five francs.

The drawing of numbers was well under way when a perplexed instructor stumbled on the proceedings and reported his discovery to the commandant. When the old general heard the story he was so profoundly moved that it was some time before he spoke.

"The lad who wins the lottery," he said at last, "will be the envy of his generation. But the lad who conceived the idea—ah, he, my friend, will some-day be a marshal of France!"

Then he fell to laughing at the thought of the starry-eyed youngster arriv-ing at the stage door of the Variétés with nothing but his youth and his entrance fee. The innocent budget had made no provision for the trip to Paris, none for a carriage, a bouquet, perhaps a supper party. The comman-dant said that he would wish to meet this margin of contingency from his own fatherly pocket.

"There will be extras," he said. "Let the young rascal who wins be sent to me before he leaves for Paris."

It was a cadet from the Vendée who reported to the commandant next afternoon—very trim in his red breeches and blue tunic, his white gloves spot-less, his white cockade jaunty, his heart in his mouth. The commandant said no word to him, but put a little purse of gold *louis* in his hand, kissed him on both cheeks in benediction, and stood at his window, moist-eyed and chuckling, to watch until the white cockade disappeared down the avenue of trees.

The sunlight, latticed by the *jalousies*, was making a gay pattern on Co-sette's carpet the next morning when she sat up and meditated on the day which stretched ahead of her. Her little cadet was cradled in a sweet, dream-less sleep, and it touched her rather to see how preposterously young he was. Indeed, it quite set her thinking of her early days, and how she had come up in the world. Then she began speculating on *his* early days, realized with a pang that he was still in the midst of them, and suddenly grew puzzled. Being a woman of action, she prodded him.

"Listen, my old one," she said, "how did a cadet at Saint-Cyr ever get hold of five thousand francs?"

Thus abruptly questioned, he lost his head and blurted out the tale of the sweepstakes. Perhaps he felt it could do no harm now, and anyway she listened so avidly, with such flattering little gasps of surprise and such sunny ripples of laughter, that he quite warmed to his story. When he came to the part about the commandant she rose and strode up and down, the lace of her peignoir fluttering behind her, tears in her violet eyes.

"Saint-Cyr has paid me the prettiest compliment I have ever known," she said, "and I am the proudest woman in France this day. But surely I must do my part. You shall go back and tell them all that Cosette is a woman of sentiment. When you are an old, old man in the Vendée you shall tell your grandchildren that once in your youth you knew the dearest favors in France, and they cost you not a sou. Not a sou."

At that she hauled open the little drawer where he had seen her lock up the lottery receipts the night before.

"Here," she said with a lovely gesture. "I give you back your money."

And she handed him his five francs.

MICHAEL ARLEN (1895–1956)

Although Michael Arlen was widely read as a piquant recorder of English high life, an "explorer in Mayfair," he was born in Bulgaria of Armenian parents and his name was Dikrân Kuyumjian. Taken to England as a boy, he was educated at Malvern College, and his first book was published when he was barely eighteen. In his early thirties he married the Countess Atalanta Mercati and spent most of his time on the French Riviera, often visiting the United States. After a long illness, Arlen died in New York, June 23, 1956.

He was a popular writer and a tailor's fashion plate while still in his twenties. The short stories in These Charming People *and the sophisticated romance of* The Green Hat *made him a continental celebrity. Critics belittled his style as baroque at the best, vulgar at the worst—George Jean Nathan characterized Arlen as "a purveyor of rented-dress-suit literature"—but W. Somerset Maugham argued that Arlen "gave the persons of his invention his own gaiety, fancifulness, and pleasant wit. He turned London into a Baghdad and made it the scene of adventures as rich with glamor, as fantastic, vivacious, and incredible as those with which Scheherazade beguiled her caliph."*

*"Legend of the Crooked Coronet" completely justifies Maugham's praise.
It is not only romantic and vivacious, but as gay and surprising as a modern
Arabian Night.*

LEGEND OF THE CROOKED CORONET

It is a disagreeable thing to say, and not one to say lightly, but on a day
not long ago a lady was accosted by a man in St. James's Street. This day
is historically memorable because that very morning Herr Hitler had issued
a decree forbidding all good Germans henceforth to eat mutton, on the
ground that sheep look Jewish.

It is true there was a slight haze, for it was a warm afternoon in late
June, but on the whole the visibility was excellent. Therefore the man could
not reasonably excuse himself on the ground that he had mistaken the lady
for what used once to be pompously called a "fallen woman" but is now
known, maybe too enthusiastically, as a "hot number." On the contrary, only
the rudest and most insensitive sort of man could have mistaken the lady
in question for any other than a person of distinction.

Let us not speak of her dress, for anyone can buy the most exquisite frocks.
Her figure was nice, too. But it was her face, carriage, and manner that
permitted the student of the illustrated journals no doubt whatsoever as
to the lady's breeding. Even as she strolled up St. James's Street past Lock's
hat shop he could, as it were, see at her heels a traditional retinue of dogs,
horses, and servants.

The student of the illustrated journals would, in point of fact, have had
no hesitation in recognising the Countess of Quorn and Beaumanoir.

Now though Lady Quorn was not more than thirty-five years old, she had
added to the advantages of birth, beauty, and one of the most distinguished
marriages in England, the reputation of being the most irreproachable of
gentlewomen, the most brilliant of platform speakers in the Conservative
interest, and the most exclusive of hostesses. And she wore these superlatives
with an air that was at once cool and charming.

So that when, as happened several times during the season, she and her
husband stood at the head of the great staircase of Quorn House in Charles
Street to receive their guests at a political or diplomatic reception, it was
willingly conceded even by those the most critical of privilege that here at
last, in a society of casual origins and careless manners, was a pillar of tradition in all but her fair beauty, a Roman matron in all but her youth—in
short, a classical ornament of the Tory party and a lady in the grand manner.

Imagine therefore the audacity of the man who, without any introduction
whatsoever, would thrust his vulgar presence upon this lady. Nor did he
seem in the least ashamed of himself. On the contrary, he was as offhand
as dammit. He neither took his hands out of his pockets, nor his hat off his
head. He was, in a word, extremely rude.

"I want," said he, "to talk to you."

Lady Quorn, who was wondering whether it would be judicious to ask Terry Bruce down to Eves Park for the weekend with or without his charming wife, who bored her to death, was at that moment abreast of Brigg's cane and umbrella shop. And as, even when plunged into the deepest abstraction, her steady blue eyes always looked directly in front of her, she could not fail to note at once that a tall, lean, hawklike man had planted himself immediately in front of her. Therefore, since it was unthinkable that she should move aside, she stopped.

"*What* did you say?"

"I said," said the man, "that I wanted a few words with you. Now you say something."

Now Lady Quorn had a very steady eye with animals and ambassadors. And behold, they quailed before her. But this person showed no signs whatsoever of quailing. She saw before her a man of maybe thirty years of age, a tall athletic figure in a shabby blue suit of a good cut and wearing the honourable tie of her husband's old school. His brown felt hat, which showed all the marks of continuous exposure to the elements over a period of years, was worn so that its turned-down brim obscured his left eyebrow. His face was long, narrow, and tanned, and his nose—which had originally been of the same generic order as her own patrician but decorative affair— had obviously been broken at some time, for it now showed a pronounced twist to one side.

He looked, in fact, a reckless sort of fellow with some pretensions to gentility. And his trousers, she noted with distaste as he stood planted in front of her with his jacket open and his hands in his pockets, were held up by a belt, a transatlantic practice she strongly disapproved of in urban surroundings.

"I think," she said, "you must be mad."

And, her eyes flickering him to one side as she took a step forward to continue her walk, she was arrested again by a really astounding happening. For the man had actually dared to prod her arm sharply. With his thumb.

Her anger was such that for a moment she felt quite dizzy. But she did not want to make a scene in St. James's Street—in the very heart, as they say in thrillers, of Clubland.

"Go," she said, "before I have to call a constable."

"Better hadn't, before you've heard what I have to say."

There was something so infuriating to one of her authority about his contemptuous assurance of manner that, almost forgetting her lifelong habit of restraint with her inferiors, she thought for an instant of slapping his face.

"Do you know," she said icily, "who I am?"

"I couldn't care less," said the hawklike man, "if you were Queen of the May. Now be a good girl, Lady Quorn, and try to be sensible for a change. I am not picking you up——"

"Picking me up?" gasped Lady Quorn. "*Me?*"

"You remind me of my aunt," said the man coldly. "I am not picking you up because I think you are a nice-looking piece but because I want to talk business with you. To make myself a little clearer I shall add two names: Harry and Diana."

We have to respect Lady Quorn. Any other woman might very well have looked frightened, but her eyes expressed only a profound distaste for the company in which she found herself. Thus gentlewomen, they tell us, once went to the guillotine.

"To think," she said, "that a man who was at the same school as my husband could be such a cad."

"This is hardly the time," said the hawklike man, "in which to discuss the faults of the public school system. Would you rather I put my business to you here in St. James's Street, Lady Quorn, or shall we take a taxi and have a jolly ride round the park?"

We have to go on handing it to Lady Quorn. Never in her life had she been talked to in this way. There was something so utterly detestable about this lean and contemptuous stranger that she felt quite giddy with loathing. But there was something more than loathing, too. The man's manner made her—*her*—almost uncertain of herself. And, for perhaps the first time in her life, she felt a twinge of fear.

"Is this," she said, "blackmail?"

"Without gloves, Lady Quorn."

She measured him with cold eyes.

"You may," she said, "call a taxi."

"Let me congratulate you," said the hawklike man. "You are a brave woman."

"I can see nothing brave," said Sheila Quorn, "in getting into a taxi with a worm."

II

In the taxi she sat very upright in her corner. Her heart was beating fast, but you never would have known it. The man, lounging in his corner with his arms crossed on his chest, had the audacity to put up his feet on one of the little seats. Twiddling the toe of one shoe thus prominently displayed— a fidgeting habit which reminded her of her husband in his most irritating moods—he said:

"You will be glad to hear, Lady Quorn, that I have not really had much experience of blackmailing people, for I am by preference a burglar, as my father was before me and my brother is now."

"And was," she asked with distaste, "your charming father caught?"

"No, he went bankrupt, a fate to which all bankers are liable, and one which, I fear, my brother, who is a broker, will not escape for long. Now I daresay, Lady Quorn, you are eager to know why you are being black-mailed. I shall tell you. You are one of the greatest ladies in England. You are admired and respected. To a great name you have added a high reputation as an arbitress of society and a leader of fashion. You are a cherished ornament of the Tory party. You are the idol of the respectable in society and the envy of those who have been found out. Am I right, Lady Quorn?"

She shivered a little, though the afternoon was quite close.

"You are," she said, "the most horrible man I have ever met."

"On the contrary, madam, I am an idealist, as you will see. In seeking to improve the structure of society, it is my mission in life to look behind the surface of things. I seek, probe, and pierce. I penetrate. And then, Lady Quorn, I unveil.

"Now this process has led to some startling and unbecoming results in your case. For what did I see when I unveiled you? Lady Quorn, I was shocked.

"For I saw that you were Dame Jekyll and Mrs. Hyde. Marble without, you were clay within. Behind your unassailable reputation, you live another life. Upheld on the outside by your high position, Lady Quorn, my researches led me to the conclusion that on your real character you wore all the earmarks of a pretty hot number. Madam, we English are snobs, but we are also puritans. We revere our traditions, we fawn upon our betters—but God help them, madam, if they wear their coronets crooked in public places.

"You permit men to fall in love with you. That is not a crime, of course. But you invariably pick on other women's men, and that is a dirty trick. Have I your attention? You are a very secret and a very discreet woman, Lady Quorn, so no one knows of your amorous adventures. Though no doubt some of your friends suspect something of the kind and admire you for getting away with it.

"Now it would be easy for me to share this admiration, for I am as partial as the next man to a beautiful woman, if you were not at heart cold, selfish, greedy, and cruel. Correct me if I am wrong, Lady Quorn, as I may well be, for I am very sentimental. For you a man is an amusement for a few weeks or a few months. To you it doesn't matter that these wretched young men have broken off with their fiancées or wives because you have become the great passion of their lives.

"Let us face the facts. You are beautiful. You are passionate. You are famous. Thus you obsess men, for they are snobs and idiots. And since each one thinks he is the first and only man for love of whom you have been unfaithful to your husband, each has kept your name secret from his wife or his sweetheart. Besides, your reputation stands so very high as a pillar of the conventions and a president of committees that a young man who spoke of you with any familiarity would be put down as a cad and a boaster.

"At a ball recently you took quite a fancy to a presentable young man called Harry Something. He is engaged to be married to a very pretty but not very wise young girl called Diana Something. Harry knows quite a bit about horses, so you asked him down to Eves Park to have a look at your hunters—not on a crowded weekend but on a weekday. He approved of your horses so thoroughly that he has not been able to give a thought to Diana since. In fact, I fancy he has already broken off the engagement.

"Now my expenses in making these momentous enquiries into your private life have been very considerable, Lady Quorn. But I am not a greedy man. So I am going to ask you to promise me to win my approval in the future by being a good girl.

"Let me give you a few pointers as to how to go about it. If in the future you have to have affairs at all, Lady Quorn, you will choose only unattached men whose passion for you will bring no unhappiness to anyone but themselves. But if you continue to have secret meetings with young men like Harry, if you continue to ask young Bruce down to Eves Park without his wife, if, in short, you continue indulging in monkey business—it will cost you, Lady Quorn, one hundred pounds a crack.

"Let me make myself clear. For each and every time that I suspect you on good grounds of having given way to your lower nature with a married or an engaged man, I shall charge you the sum of one hundred pounds. It is on record, after all, that married men have paid much more than that for what is, I believe, known as 'fun' or a 'nice change'—so why, in these days of equality for women, shouldn't you pay too?

"I need hardly say that if you don't I shall make it my business to see that the offended party, that is the wife or fiancée, is given a good hint or series of good hints as to the identity of the intervener.

"In short, Lady Quorn, you continue indulging in monkey business with other people's property and I shall consider it my duty to throw a monkey wrench into your reputation."

The taxi was now on the bridge over the Serpentine for the second time. Glancing at Lady Quorn's cold, severe, and very lovely profile, the hawklike man might have thought she had not heard a word he had said if he had not also noted—rudely leaning forward to do so—the steely brightness of her blue eyes.

She said: "Please stop the taxi."

He did so.

She said: "And get out."

He did so. It was as though she had no knowledge whatsoever of his existence. He stood with one foot on the kerb and the other on the running board of the taxi, looking in at her. She never once glanced in his direction. And when she spoke, her lips scarcely moved.

"What is your name?"

"I am sometimes known as the Cavalier of the Streets." The man looked more than ever hawklike when he smiled. "And sometimes by much shorter names than that. I hope," he added, "that you will give the most careful consideration to what I have said."

She smiled very faintly, never glancing at him.

"I shall not forget you," said Lady Quorn.

III

The man who was sometimes called by much shorter names than the Cavalier of the Streets was not surprised that night to find himself tapped on the shoulder. He had dined in a small restaurant in Greek Street and was walking down Shaftesbury Avenue. He had not gone far when he realised that he was being followed by a beefy-looking man in a bowler hat. He therefore stopped on the kerb at Piccadilly Circus to let the beefy man catch up with him. He stood as though bemused by the tender silhouette of Eros against the bright winking lights of the advertisements.

"I want," said the shoulder-tapper in his ear, "to talk to you, Wagstaffe."

"Mister Wagstaffe," said the hawklike man absently. "Look at that."

"Look at what?"

"The quiet and tender figure of Eros. He is the smallest and the quietest figure in sight, but he is more powerful than us all. Even the worst of us, from a plain-looking chap like me to a really handsome bloke like you, Inspector, have at one time or another been winged by him."

"That'll do," said the Inspector.

"Then you don't want me to tell you about my love life?"

"No, I don't. I want to talk to you."

"If you clear your throat," said the hawklike man, "and take a deep breath, there's no reason why you shouldn't."

"I've got a message for you, my lad," said the Inspector.

"So this isn't a nab?"

"Expecting one, are you?"

"When I begin expecting intelligence from a detective, Bulrose, I'll take to solving crosswords for a living."

"You'll be in prison first, my lad. Want me to spill my message here or shall we go to some quiet place?"

"I have never," said the Cavalier of the Streets, "refused a drink in my life."

They went into a big crowded place nearby where many artists and journalists sat around tables drinking steins of beer in between talking about themselves and thinking about each other. Detective Inspector Bulrose took a deep draught from his glass before addressing his companion.

"Now look here, Wagstaffe, you're in trouble. And you look like being in more trouble."

"Take a look at my figure, Bulrose."

"What's your figure got to do with it?"

"Only that it's trouble that keeps me thin. What about some more beer?"

"You just listen to me first," said Bulrose. "This is straight to you from Superintendent Crust. And *he* had it from someone higher up, maybe from the Commissioner himself, so you can see what trouble you are in. Superintendent says he's sick to death of you, and if he hears any more complaints about a bloke calling himself the Cavalier of the Streets, he's going to jug you. And he means it, Wagstaffe. If he can't pull you in for something you've done, he's going to frame you for something you haven't. So behave yourself. Superintendent told me to say that in spite of knowing you're an incorrigible crook he's got quite a warm spot for you because of the help you've given us in some cases. But you've got to drop irritating and molesting people with this Cavalier of the Streets stuff. Why, only two weeks ago you had the cheek to black that chap Tyre-Temple's eye."

"Why not? I don't like him."

"And who stole Lady Fitzoda's ruby earrings from her bedroom while she was having a bath?"

"She will need more than an ordinary bath to wash away her sins."

"You'd better think of your own, *Mister* Wagstaffe. We've never caught you with the stuff yet, but you can't get away with it every time. Now you listen, my lad. Superintendent says that if you know what's good for you, you'll take a nice long rest at the seaside. I don't know what you've been up to to-day, but Superintendent said that the Commissioner was as mad as hell——"

The hawklike man grinned.

"I'll bet he was. I wonder what she told him."

"What's that?" said the Inspector eagerly. "Who's she?"

"You mind your own business, Bulrose. The Commissioner and I have got some of the same friends in the very highest society, and we naturally couldn't reveal social secrets to mere beer drinkers like you."

"You'd talk the hind leg off a donkey," sighed the Inspector.

"Now you listen to me, Bulrose. Tell Superintendent Crust this from me and he can pass it on to the Commissioner if he wants to. I'll mind my own business, and they can mind theirs. Talking to me about ruby earrings as though I were a common thief!"

"We don't think you're a thief. We darn well know you're the only clever burglar in London."

"Is that so? Then if I'm foolish enough to do something you can gaol me for, I'm ready for gaol. But I don't like being ordered about, when all I'm doing is to behave like a decent citizen."

"Who?" gasped the Inspector. "You?"

"That's me," said the Cavalier of the Streets. "A decent citizen. A respectable subject of the King. Upright and incorruptible. An ally of the police. A friend of the poor. Which reminds me," he said, getting up from the table and taking something out of his pocket, "that here's your pocketbook, which you'll need to pay for the beer. You must have dropped it on the floor. Good night to you, Bulrose. Give my love to the Commissioner, and tell him to keep an eye on his pretty daughter. The aunt she went to dine with last Thursday night wore a silk hat and socks."

IV

Now it can be seen that in Lady Quorn and Beaumanoir beauty and resource were mingled in excellent measure. It was not to the Commissioner that she had made a complaint about the Cavalier of the Streets but to one of her several friends in the Cabinet, who had telephoned to the Home Secretary, who had telephoned to the Commissioner, who had talked to the Assistant Commissioner, who had said a few sharp words to Superintendent Crust, who had passed them on to Inspector Bulrose.

Lady Quorn had not, of course, brought herself into the matter in any way, but had said that an American friend of hers, a young lady for whom she had the highest respect, had recently been troubled a great deal by a rascal calling himself the Cavalier of the Streets.

She had added that this young American lady, who belonged to one of the first families of Philadelphia, was far too shy to make any charge against the wretch, but that really something ought to be done to prevent distinguished foreigners in London from being molested by gangsters. And Lady Quorn was of the opinion that, since so self-confident a rascal must in the past have frequently broken the law, the police should make every effort to protect the amenities of London by speedily proving him guilty of some past misdemeanour and putting him into a safe place where he could no longer annoy people like her charming American friend.

Her influential friend in the Cabinet, whose thoughts about Lady Quorn would have shocked the Archbishop of Canterbury, was able to assure Lady Quorn that everything possible would be done and that the young lady from Philadelphia would no longer be molested.

But Superintendent Crust did not take the same comforting view. In the course of the next few days the poor man was afflicted with several headaches directly attributable to Mr. Wagstaffe, whom he called by names very much shorter than the Cavalier of the Streets.

But Crust knew his business, and he therefore assured the Commissioner, who assured the Home Secretary, who assured the influential member of the Cabinet, who reassured Lady Quorn, who presumably reassured the young lady from Philadelphia, that there was nothing further to worry about.

So about a week later Lady Quorn was disagreeably surprised when one afternoon her butler informed her that a gentleman had called to see her by appointment.

"I am," said her ladyship, "not at home."

She was thinking very rapidly as the butler went towards the door. Then a curious smile flickered over her lovely features, and what was curious about this smile was that it was at the same time childish, wicked, and very attractive.

"I have changed my mind, Jolly. The gentleman has a twisted nose, has he not? Show him into the morning room."

Quite ten minutes passed before she went downstairs. She used the telephone. She used the looking glass. Now Lady Quorn was wearing a hat when Jolly announced the unwelcome visitor, but when she left her room she was not wearing a hat. Her golden burnished hair, which has been described in the illustrated papers as often as the Quorn pearls, of which her throat was never without a rope, need call for no comment here. We can but praise it in passing, and we do so.

The man who called himself the Cavalier of the Streets was standing by the window looking out into Berkeley Square. His head uncovered, his face looked leaner and more hawklike than ever. His black hair was quite decidedly grey at the temples. She was surprised to notice how little out of place he looked in her house, in spite of his casual clothes. She stood very still just within the doorway, a tall, slender, gracious woman. They stared at one another across the room for several seconds, and then his mouth twisted into a smile.

"You seem to be a very dangerous woman, Lady Quorn."

"And aren't you," she asked, "a very reckless man to come here?"

"After you put Scotland Yard on to me?"

"Oh, I don't like being defenceless."

They were standing in front of the empty fireplace. Her wide eyes were bright with laughter. He studied her thoughtfully, and the laughter in her eyes twitched at her mouth.

"With half an eye," he said pleasantly, "I can see that you are up to something, or you wouldn't be so amused."

"And can't you guess, Mr. Cavalier, what it is that is amusing me?"

"The only reason I can imagine for your added radiance——"

"Dear me, are you flattering me?"

"I am deploring you, Lady Quorn. The more desirable you appear, the more urgent I must be in preventing you from turning married men into giddy goats. Maybe what's amusing you is that you have a detective hidden somewhere in this room to catch me in the act of blackmailing you."

She laughed outright. And a dog outside in the hall, hearing her cool and pleasant laugh, barked frantically.

"And are you going to blackmail me?"

"Of course, Lady Quorn. And of course you know why."

She frowned. Fingering her pearls, she continued to frown.

"I don't seem to remember anything of quite that nature since I last saw you."

"Try to think," he suggested.

"Dear me," she said, "it would be so impolite not to remember, wouldn't it?"

"What about," he asked, "the afternoon before last?"

"Oh," she said. "I remember! Terry?"

"Exactly."

"Dear me, of course. Yes, I had tea with him."

"Did you now?" said the Cavalier.

"Terry is such a nice boy, and he was all alone."

"Yes, I gathered that."

"I'm not sure," she said, "that I like the way you said that. He was lonely, you see, and he wanted to be cheered up."

"A cup of tea," he said, "can of course be very cheering."

"I have," she said severely, "the highest respect for Terry's wife."

"I am sure you have, Lady Quorn. It must be a great consolation for her."

"Now you are being sarcastic, and quite unjustifiably. If I can't," she said, "have an innocent cup of tea with a friend, what can I have?"

"Of course," he said, "I can't be quite positive about my facts."

"Well, I should hope not."

"But there is such a thing, Lady Quorn, as circumstantial evidence. I am more or less in the same position as a divorce judge who has to decide whether a love-besotted man and an ardent woman alone together in surroundings that permit them a certain freedom of movement have taken advantage of those surroundings to do no more than have a cup of tea together."

"It is wrong," she said, "to think the worst of people."

"I am afraid, Lady Quorn, that it is no good appealing to the better instincts of a blackmailer."

"I wouldn't dream," she said seriously, "of appealing to your better instincts. It's only that I want fair play, and how can it be fair for me to give you a hundred pounds when my conscience is quite clear?"

"Your conscience?" he said. "A most unreliable witness, Lady Quorn."

"Well, all I know is," she said, "that I am an innocent woman."

"You mean, since I last saw you a week ago?"

"Of course," she said gravely, "only for the last week."

He looked thoughtful. Then, with no effort to conceal his disappointment, he sighed.

"I suppose," he said, "you are quite sure?"

"Oh, quite. Of course, one forgets things sometimes. But about this last week I am quite sure."

"Still," he said, "you will agree that your actions were decidedly misleading."

She sighed. "You are a very suspicious man, aren't you?"

"A blackmailer has to be, Lady Quorn. And besides," he said severely, "it is written that the intention is as bad as the crime."

"That's exactly what I always tell my children. But," she added, "I'm bothered if I am going to pay a hundred pounds for nothing more than an intention. Dear me, if men had to do that, they'd be penniless in no time."

"Well," he said grudgingly, "I suppose that's only fair. Now will you tell me something, Lady Quorn, before I go?"

"But what in the world can I tell a man who already seems to know so much about me?"

"You were very far from amused the last time I saw you. But this time you seem to have had great difficulty in not breaking out into girlish giggles throughout our interview. I wonder why?"

Her level blue eyes were so limpid with laughter that he could not help but smile in return. He took a step back as the very faint perfume from her burnished hair just brushed his nostrils.

"It's quite easy," she said, "to explain. Do you know, I am thirty-five years old, and you are the only person I have ever met in my life who knows me as I am. That is odd, you must agree, and funny too. I never dreamt there would be any man or woman in this world who would ever know the worst of me. You are the only person before whom I do not have to act. You have seen behind the cool façade, but you have seen nothing at all cool there, have you? And so you are the only man in the world who knows that I enjoy the body of love, just as a man does, and not its gentle tender spirit, as nice women are supposed to. That is why this interview has amused me so much. Dear me, how shocked I was at first that anyone had discovered my secret weaknesses. But now all I feel is relieved that I do at last know one person with whom I shall never have to act."

"I can see," he said, "that we are going to be great friends."

"Yes? It's so nice to be natural sometimes. You must come and see me again, Mr. Cavalier."

"But," he said, "it is not easy to believe that you can be acting quite *all* the time. Would these men become so obsessed with the passion for having a cup of tea with you alone if acting was all you had to offer them?"

"Oh, you are being stupid. If I really let myself go as much as I should sometimes like—why, how shocked they would be! Didn't you know that an English lady must never enjoy herself too much—it wouldn't look nice. With foreigners, of course, who aren't really human, a little more latitude may be allowed. But, dear me, those boring Latin experts and their tricks! If I could write," she said, "I would write such a book about the conceit, stupidity and sterling unattractiveness of men as would fill the convents of the world with girls and women clamouring to take the vow of chastity."

"Why, Lady Quorn, anyone would think you disliked men."

"It is the tragedy of women who love men, my friend, that they usually do dislike them. But how can one get round the *impasse?*"

"I am growing really quite sorry for you."

"Rightly, Mr. Cavalier. We must all be sorry for those who try to put a shape to dreams. We dream of lovers equal to the gaieties and the ardours of love—and all we get is a man in search of a mother to protect him, a repentant fool, a jealous bully, or a pathetic child. I wish someone would tell me what flaw there is in men that makes them unworthy of straightforward gifts, of which love should be the first. But no, we cannot give them love and passion with both hands, frankly, we must corrupt our surrender with evasions and retreats, we must act or pretend or tease—else they will not cherish the gift. To think we have been lords of creation these millions of years and have evolved nothing more mature than man as an equal to a woman's love!" The door opened, and she continued in a pleasantly sociable voice: "So you must come and see me again, won't you? I so enjoy your visits."

The butler said: "My lady, the Committee is waiting in the drawing room."

"I shall be there in one moment."

Alone again, she said, coolly smiling: "Well, there is my real life. Sitting or presiding on committees. The rest—all we've been talking about—is nonsense. The leisured classes, they call us. Dear me, what fun life would be if we did not have to work harder at our pleasures than we do at our work." She half extended her hand. "Good-bye, Mr. Cavalier."

She was unsmiling, conventional.

"You have made it impossible for me," he said, "to blackmail you again—almost."

She regarded him so steadily that he blinked. But he did not look away. "Almost?" she said. "And what does that mean?"

"It means," he said, taking her cold hand, "that it is only my concern for the structure of society, which women like you menace, that will compel me to keep an eye on you."

Her bright wide eyes were unfathomable. Withdrawing her hand, she walked towards the door. He stood watching her, a faint smile on his dark face.

"Good-bye, Lady Quorn."

"I know," she said from the door, "that you are a man of courage. But don't force me to send you to prison. The butler will show you out. Good-bye."

v

He had no sooner left the house than he was joined by Detective Inspector Bulrose. That excellent man made no secret of the facts that he had been waiting for him and that he was in an exceedingly bad temper.

"You're a prize juggins, my lad," he said testily. "Now you come along with me."

The hawklike man, balancing himself on his heels as though ready to waste time with the first person who offered him amusement, stared thoughtfully at the Inspector.

"What for, Bulrose?"

"Little innocent, aren't you?" Then suddenly, with a vehemence that flushed his face with crimson, he bawled: "Taxi!"

"What on earth is all this about, Bulrose?"

A taxi driver, who had evidently just finished putting on a spare wheel at the corner of Hill Street, jumped enthusiastically into his cab and drove up beside them. Bulrose testily flung open the door.

"This is a darned serious business, *Mister* Wagstaffe, so don't ask silly questions. Or ask the Superintendent. Jump in."

They were no farther than about eight yards from the door of Lady Quorn's house. Both men turned their backs to the taxi driver as the door was flung open and the slim, elegant figure of a young lady came tripping down the stone steps.

"Now maybe," snapped Bulrose, "you'll know what we want you for."

"Will I indeed?" the other murmured, staring at the approaching figure.

"I suppose," snapped the Inspector, "you're going to say you've never seen *her* before?"

"But you must introduce me, Bulrose. She looks a nice piece."

"Where's your manners?" said the Inspector indignantly. "Calling a friend of Lady Quorn's a 'nice piece,' even though she is American."

The young lady, whose prettiness was of quite an uncommon order, as also was her slim elegance, came tripping towards them. She appeared, like many pretty young ladies, to be more interested in the contents of her vanity bag, in which she was fumbling with her hand, than in her immediate surroundings. And she would no doubt have collided into the two men if, when she was still a yard or two away from them, Bulrose had not taken a step forward and said:

"Beg pardon, miss, is this the man?"

"Sure," said the pretty young lady, looking coldly into the Cavalier's face. Her voice, which was at once soft and racy, would have made the United States Ambassador homesick. "And if," she said, "you will examine his pockets, you'll certainly find the cheque I gave him a few minutes ago."

The Inspector looked with disgust at his prisoner.

"And to think," he said, "I once thought you were almost an intelligent crook. Taking a cheque! Hand it over."

The Cavalier, a bewildered expression on his face, slowly extracted from the right side pocket of his jacket a folded cheque.

"Hand it over," the Inspector repeated. "I suppose you're going to say you've never seen *that* before."

"Oh no," said the Cavalier. "But I'd like to look at it just once again."

Unfolding the cheque, he saw that it was made out to Michael Wagstaffe, Esq., for the sum of one hundred pounds and was signed by Monica Gubbins. Then he handed it to the Inspector, who was about to put it in his pocket, when the pretty young lady cried:

"I'd certainly like it back."

"This is important evidence, miss. You'll get it back all right in due course."

The Cavalier was looking thoughtfully into the girl's face. He noticed she would not meet his eyes.

"You are quite sure, Miss Gubbins," he said, "that you gave me this cheque in Lady Quorn's house?"

"Why, of course!" said the pretty young lady. "What was I to do when you were blackmailing me? And besides, Lady Quorn told me it was the best way out."

"I see," said the Cavalier.

"Miss Gubbins," said the Inspector, "I'm afraid I'll have to trouble you to come along with us and fill in the charge against this man."

"But," said the young lady, "I don't think I'm going to make any charge against him."

Bulrose, pushing back his bowler hat, mopped his flushed brow.

"Ho!" he said bitterly.

The young lady's eyes now met the Cavalier's for the first time. Her lips, he fancied, were twitching faintly.

"Is the Inspector," she asked, "annoyed with me?"

"Oh, not annoyed," said the Cavalier. "Just give him time and he will bust nicely."

"'Course I'm annoyed," said Bulrose indignantly. "I'm sitting down in my office to a cup of tea when along comes an urgent message from Lady Quorn that this crook here has had the impudence to call at her house to see an American lady visiting her ladyship and is no doubt going to try to blackmail her. And when I nab him with the cheque on him—she ain't going to make no charge."

"And what would happen to him," asked the pretty young lady, "if I did make it?"

"Two to three years," said Bulrose persuasively, "hard."

"Then," said Miss Gubbins, turning to the silent Cavalier, "you certainly have to thank Lady Quorn for being given another chance. I owe her so much for her kindness and hospitality that I just couldn't bring myself to refuse her anything at all. And when she asked me to let you off, as you were no doubt just a silly young man driven to crime from reading detective stories or seeing too many gangster pictures, I just had to say I would. Lady Quorn said maybe all you needed to come to your right senses again was a good square meal, and she gave me this ten-shilling note to give you, though of course you mustn't spend it all on going to the movies. But mind, now, this must be a lesson to you never to try blackmailing people again. Do you think, Inspector, that he will go straight after this?"

Bulrose, who appeared to be having some difficulty in controlling his facial muscles, managed to do no more than nod. And the pretty young lady, pressing the ten-shilling note into the Cavalier's numbed hand, walked swiftly away.

Then Detective Inspector Bulrose really got down to business, so that butlers passing by in charge of lap dogs envied him.

"Strike me pink!" he gasped.

Laughing with that profound relish which comes but too rarely in this vale of sorrow, he very nearly choked.

"I wouldn't have missed that," he gasped, "for all the beer in the world. Good as a play, to hear the Cavalier of the Streets being told off for being a bad boy from seeing too many gangster pictures. Which do you like best, Percy, the ones where the villain repents and goes straight for love of a nice pure girl? Superintendent Crust may almost forgive Lady Quorn getting you off when he hears that the biggest crook in London was tipped ten bob to get himself a decent meal."

The hawklike man, staring down at the ten-shilling note in his hand with a queer smile, said not a word. The taxi which Bulrose had hailed was still with them.

"Jerwantme?" said the taxi driver.

"What's that?" said Bulrose, wiping away his tears.

"Jerwantme," said the taxi driver, "or not?"

The Inspector gave him a shilling with a friendly wave of the hand, told the Cavalier to be a good boy in future and see as few gangster films as possible, and, grinning broadly, strode away towards Vine Street to tell his friend, Inspector Mussel, the joke.

The taxi driver, who had been fumbling energetically with his gears while the Inspector was departing, now desisted and looked sympathetically at the silent figure on the kerb.

"Poor old Waggers," he said. "But the main point is that we've got the stuff. It was pretty neat, the way you handed it to me just after I drove up."

The Cavalier, coming suddenly to life, twitched an eyebrow.

"And to think," he said, "I've lived to be called Percy by a flat-footed dick."

But there was a gleam in his dark eyes which might have given Inspector Bulrose food for thought rather than matter for laughter. Approaching so near the taxi driver in his seat that there was no space between their arms, he whispered quickly:

"Hand it back, Pullman."

His obedient subordinate, doing his best to hide his curiosity by whistling, slipped a somewhat bulky handkerchief into the other's hand. The Cavalier, his back to the house behind him, slipped it into his breast pocket.

"Put the car away," he said, "and come to the flat about six. And for pity's sake get yourself a decent shave."

As the taxi driver indignantly changed gears he saw, to his astonishment, his chief mounting the broad steps to Lady Quorn's house.

VI

"I wondered," said Lady Quorn, "if you would come back."

"I can only hope you have missed me. I have," he said, "a bone to pick with you, Lady Quorn."

"Oh, what ingratitude! And after the trouble I went to persuading Miss Gubbins to make no charge against you for the horrible crime of blackmail."

"I don't know how," he said, "to thank you—or forgive you. For entirely owing to you, I have been called Percy by a policeman."

"If you wish," she said, "I will write to the Commissioner and complain on your behalf."

"Are you positive," he said, "that you haven't any complaints to make on your own? Better look in the mirror, Lady Quorn."

Her level eyes rested on him for a long second before she turned to the looking glass over the fireplace.

"I see," she murmured, her reflection in the mirror looking gravely at him.

He was thoughtfully fingering the rope of pearls he had extracted from the handkerchief the taxi driver had returned to him. He held them out to her. She made no movement, her shoulder to him, still gazing at him in the mirror.

"So all that blackmail business," she said, "was just so much nonsense—an excuse to get into my house?"

"Let us call it a background. It was quite sincere. I disapproved of you, Lady Quorn, and I told you why. I only steal from people I disapprove of."

"And give the proceeds to charity?"

"Well, not quite. But I do, I fancy, give as much as any other Christian. You see how modest I am?"

"And why are you returning my pearls?"

"I told you," he said, "that I only stole from people I disapproved of."

"And you have ceased to disapprove?"

"Oh no. But I disapprove of your husband even more for being, as he must be, such an unattractive, useless, and silly man as not to be able to keep the affections of a woman like Sheila Quorn."

"I should like to think, then, that you are returning the pearls because you like me?"

"Yes. And also," he said, "because they are false.

"It was clever of you," he added, absently fingering the pearls, "to slip that cheque into the pocket of an accomplished thief. My vanity is quite concerned, Lady Quorn. How did you do it?"

"Dear me, Cavalier, at one moment you were so near to me that I feared you were about to kiss me."

"And then you would have slapped my face?"

"Oh, it is only frightened women who make small points."

He let the pearls drop with a small crash on to the table, and walked towards the door.

"Cavalier," she said, "would you have returned the pearls if they had been real?"

"I am afraid so," he said from the door. "Is it necessary for me to tell you why? Good-bye, Lady Quorn. But should your husband ever miss his pearl studs, you will know that my disapproval of a complaisant husband has reached its limit."

His hand was on the doorknob.

"My friend," she said, "I have just realised that I know so little about you. Are you, by any chance, engaged or married?"

As he turned from the door he saw she was pressing the bell.
"I am ringing," she said, "for tea."

GABRIEL CHEVALLIER (1895–   )

The Scandals of Clochemerle *by Gabriel Chevallier, born May 3, 1895,
was first published in America in 1937. Ten years later it appeared in a
paper-bound edition, and a moving-picture version of it was made in France.
It is, to its admirers, the best modern expression of true Gallic wit in the
direct line of descent from Rabelais through Anatole France.*

*Clochemerle, a small village in the wine-growing district of Beaujolais, is
a microcosm which erupts in passionate partisanship over an embroiling political maneuver: the decision of the Socialist mayor to build Clochemerle's
first comfort station. Two of the most entertaining episodes in the book are
"A Few Words on the Curé Ponosse"* (who comes to figure importantly in
the trouble because the controversial public convenience happens to be
erected opposite the church) *and "Joyful Acceptance of the Urinal."*

FROM: THE SCANDALS OF CLOCHEMERLE

A FEW WORDS ON THE CURÉ PONOSSE

Thirty years ago, when the Curé Ponosse took up his abode in the town
of Clochemerle, he had come from a somewhat unpleasant parish in the
Ardèche. His period of probation as an assistant priest had done nothing to
educate him in the ways of the world. He was conscious of his peasant origin,
and still retained the blushing awkwardness of a seminarist at odds with the
humiliating discomforts of puberty. The confessions of the women of
Clochemerle, a place where the men are not inactive, brought him revelations
which filled him with embarrassment. As his personal experience in these
matters was of short duration, by clumsily conceived questions he embarked
on a course of study in carnal iniquity. The horrid visions which he retained
as the result of these interviews made his times of solitude, when he was
haunted by lewd and satanic pictures, a heavy burden. The full-blooded temperament of Augustin Ponosse was by no means conducive to the mysticism
prevalent among those who are racked by mental suffering, which itself usually accompanies physical ill health. On the contrary, all his bodily functions
were in splendid order; he had an excellent appetite; and his constitution
made calls upon him which his clerical garb modestly, if incompletely, concealed.

On his arrival at Clochemerle in all the vigor of youth, to take the place of a priest who had been carried off at the age of forty-two by an attack of influenza followed by a chill, Augustin Ponosse had the good fortune to find at the presbytery Honorine, an ideal specimen of a curé's servant. She shed many tears for her late master—evidence this of a respectable and reverent attachment to him. But the vigorous and good-natured appearance of the new arrival seemed to bring her speedy consolation. Honorine was an old maid for whom the good administration of a priest's home held no secrets, an experienced housekeeper who made ruthless inspections of her master's clothes and reproached him for the unworthy state of his linen: "You poor wretched man," she said, "they *did* look after you badly!" She recommended him to wear short drawers and alpaca trousers in summer, as these prevent excessive perspiration beneath the cassock, made him buy flannel underclothing, and told him how to make himself comfortable with very few clothes when he stayed at home.

The Curé Ponosse enjoyed this soothing kindliness, this watchful care, and rendered thanks to heaven. But he felt sad, tormented by hallucinations which left him no peace and against which he fought like St. Anthony in the desert. It was not long before Honorine began to realize the cause of these torments. It was she who first alluded to it, one evening when the Curé Ponosse, having finished his meal, was gloomily filling his pipe.

"Poor young man," she said, "you must find it very hard at your age, always being alone. It's not human, that sort of thing. After all, you *are* a man!"

"Oh dear, oh dear, Honorine!" the Curé Ponosse answered with a sigh, turning crimson, and suddenly attacked by guilty inclinations.

"It'll end by driving you silly, you may depend on it! There have been people who've gone off their heads from that."

"In my profession, one must mortify oneself, Honorine!" the unhappy man replied feebly.

But the faithful servant treated him like an unruly child:

"You're not going to ruin your health, are you? And what use will it be to God if you get a bad illness?"

With eyes cast down, the Curé Ponosse made a vague gesture implying that the question was beyond him, and that if he must go mad from excess of chastity, and such were God's will, he would resign himself accordingly. That is, if his strength held out, which was doubtful. Thereupon Honorine drew nearer to him and said in an encouraging tone:

"Me and the other poor gentleman—such a saintly man he was, too—we fixed it up together. . . ."

This announcement brought peace and balm to the heart of the Curé Ponosse. Slightly raising his eyes, he looked discreetly at Honorine, with completely new ideas in his mind. The servant was indeed far from beautiful, but nevertheless she bore—though reduced to their simplest expression and consequently but little suggestive—the hospitable feminine protuberances. Dismal though these bodily oases might be, their surroundings unflowered and bleak, they were none the less oases of salvation, placed there by Providence in the burning desert in which the Curé Ponosse felt as though he were on the point of losing his reason. A flash of enlightenment came to him. Was it not a seemly act, an act of humility, to yield, seeing that a priest of great experience, mourned by the whole of Clochemerle, had shown him the way? He had only to abandon false pride and follow in the footsteps of that saintly man. And this was made all the easier by the fact that Honorine's rugged form made it possible to concede to Nature only a necessary minimum, without taking any real delight in such frolics or lingering over those insidious joys wherein lies the gravity of the sin.

The Curé Ponosse, having mechanically uttered a prayer of thanksgiving, allowed himself to be led away by his servant, who took pity on her young master's shyness. Rapidly and in complete obscurity came the climax, while the Curé Ponosse kept his thoughts far, far away, deploring and bewailing what he did. But he spent later so peaceful a night, and awoke so alert and cheerful, that he felt convinced that it would be a good thing to have occasional recourse to this expedient—even in the interests of his ministry. As regards frequency, he decided to adhere to the procedure laid down by his predecessor; and, in this, Honorine would be able to instruct him.

However, be that as it might, sinning he undoubtedly was, and confession became a necessity. Happily, after making inquiries, he learned that at the village of Valsonnas, twenty kilometers distant, lived the Abbé Jouffe, an old theological college chum of his. The Curé Ponosse felt that it would be better to make confession of his delinquencies to a genuine friend. On the following day, therefore, he tucked the end of his cassock into his belt and mounted his priest's bicycle (a legacy from the departed) and by a hilly route, and with much labor, he reached Valsonnas.

For some little time the two priests were entirely absorbed by their pleasure at meeting again. But the Curé of Clochemerle could not indefinitely postpone his confession of the object of his visit. Covered with confusion, he told his colleague how he had been treating Honorine. Having given him absolution, the Abbé Jouffe informed him that he himself had been behaving in a similar manner toward his servant, Josépha, for several years past. The visitor then remembered that the door had, in fact, been opened by a dark-haired person who, though she squinted, had a nice, fresh appearance and a pleasant sort of dumpiness. He felt that his friend Jouffe had done better than himself in that respect, for, so far as his own taste was concerned, he could have wished that Honorine were less skimpy. (When Satan sent him voluptuous visions, it was always in the form of ladies with milk-white skins, of liberal charms, and limbs of splendidly generous proportions.) But he banished this envious thought, stained as it was with concupiscence and lacking in charity in order to listen to what Jouffe was explaining to him. This is what he was saying:

"My dear Ponosse, as we cannot entirely detach ourselves from matter, a favor which has been granted only to certain saints, it is fortunate that we both have in our own homes the means of making an indispensable concession to it secretly, without causing scandal or disturbing the peace of souls. Let us rejoice in the fact that our troubles do no injury to the Church's good name."

"Yes," answered Ponosse, "and moreover, is it not useful that we should have some competency in all matters, seeing that we are often called upon to give decisions and advice?"

"Indeed I think so, my good friend, to judge by cases of conscience that have been laid before me here. It is certain that without personal experience I should have stumbled over them. The sixth commandment is the occasion of much disputation and strife. If our knowledge on this point were not, I will not say profound, at least sufficient, we should find ourselves directing some of the souls under our care into a wrong path. Between ourselves, we can say this—complete continence warps judgment."

"It strangles the intelligence!" said Ponosse, remembering his sufferings.

As they drank the wine of Valsonnas, which is inferior to that of Clochemerle (in this respect Ponosse was better off than Jouffe), the two priests felt that an unforeseen similarity in their respective problems could only strengthen the bonds of a friendship which dated from their early youth. They then decided upon certain convenient arrangements, as, for example, to make their confessions to each other in future. In order to spare themselves numerous and fatiguing journeys, they agreed to synchronize their carnal lapses. They allowed themselves, as a general principle, the Monday and Tuesday of each week, as being unoccupied days following the long Sunday services, and chose the Thursday for their confessions. They agreed further to take equal shares in the trouble involved. One week the Abbé Jouffe was to come to Clochemerle to make his own confession and receive that of Ponosse, and the following week it would be the Curé Ponosse's turn to visit his friend Jouffe at Valsonnas for the purpose of their mutual confession and absolution.

These ingenious arrangements proved completely satisfactory for a period of twenty-three years. Their restricted employment of Honorine and Josépha, together with a fortnightly ride of forty kilometers, kept the two priests in excellent health, and this in turn procured them a breadth of view and a spirit of charity which had the very best effects, at Clochemerle as at Valsonnas. Throughout this long period there was no accident of any kind.

It was in 1897, in the course of a very severe winter. One Thursday morning the Curé Ponosse awoke with the firm intention of making the journey to Valsonnas to obtain his absolution. Unfortunately there had been a heavy fall of snow during the night, which made the roads impassable. The Curé of Clochemerle was anxious to start off in spite of this, and refused to listen to his servant's cries and reproaches; he considered himself to be in a state of mortal sin, having taken undue advantage of Honorine for some days past as the result of idleness during the long winter evenings. In spite of his courage and two falls, the Curé Ponosse could not cover more than four kilometers. He returned on foot, painfully, and reached home with chattering teeth. Honorine had to put him to bed and make him perspire. The wretched man became delirious on account of his mortal sin, a condition in which he felt it impossible to remain. In the meantime the Abbé Jouffe, looking out in vain for Ponosse, was in a state of deadly anxiety. He had High Mass the following day and was wondering whether he would be able to celebrate it. Happily, the Abbé of Valsonnas was a man of resource. He sent Josépha to the post with a reply-paid telegram addressed to Ponosse: *Same as usual. Miserere mei by return. Jouffe.* The Curé of Clochemerle replied immediately: *Absolvo te. Five paters five aves. Same as usual plus three. Deep repentance. Misere urgent. Ponosse.* The absolution reached him by telegram five hours later, with "one rosary" as a penance.

The two priests were so delighted with this expeditious device that they considered the possibility of using it constantly. But a scruple held them back: it meant giving too much facility for sin. Further, the dogma of confession, down to its smallest details, goes back to a time when the invention of the telegraph was not even a matter of conjecture. The use they had just made of it raised a point of canon law which would have needed elucidation by an assembly of theologians. They feared heresy, and decided to use the telegraph only in cases of absolute necessity, which arose on three occasions in all.

Twenty-three years after Ponosse's first visit to his friend, the Abbé Jouffe had the misfortune to lose Josépha, then sixty-two years of age. She had kept herself until the end in a good state of bodily preservation, even though her stoutness had increased her weight to over twelve stone, a great one for a person whose height did not exceed five feet two inches. The necessity of dragging about this massive frame had caused her legs to swell, and the growth of fat over her heart prevented that organ from functioning freely. She died of a species of angina pectoris. The Abbé Jouffe did not replace her. To mold a new servant to his habits appeared to him a task beyond his strength. Arrival at an age well past fifty brought peace and calm in its train. He contented himself with a charwoman who came to tidy up the vicarage and prepare his midday meal. In the evening some soup and a piece of cheese were all that he needed. No longer requiring absolution for sins that were hard to confess, he refrained from coming to Clochemerle. This abstention brought disorder into the life of the Curé Ponosse.

Ponosse was now approaching the age of fifty. For a long time past he could quite comfortably have dispensed with Honorine. The faithful servant had reached an age when she might well have retired from service. Unlike Josépha, she had grown continually leaner until she was as thin as a rake. But the Curé Ponosse, always a shy man, was afraid of offending the poor woman by putting an end to relations which he no longer felt to be an overmastering necessity. The example given him by Jouffe decided him. And there was this too—that the journey to Valsonnas was a prolonged agony for the Curé of Clochemerle, who had become very stout and suffered from emphysema. He had to dismount at the bottom of each hill, and the descents made him giddy. So long as his colleague returned his visits he did not lose heart. But when he saw himself condemned to bear alone the burden of all those journeys, he said to himself that the remnants of a former Honorine were not worth all those hours of superhuman effort. He told his servant of his difficulties. She took it very badly, and thought that she had been insulted; which was what the Curé Ponosse had feared. She hissed at him:

"I suppose you'll be wanting young girls now, Monsieur Augustin?"

She called him "Monsieur Augustin" in times of crises. Ponosse set out to calm her.

"As for young girls," he said, "Solomon and David needed them. But the matter is a simpler one for me. I need nothing more, my good Honorine. After all, we are now of an age to lead peaceful lives, to live, in fact, without sin."

"Speak for yourself," Honorine retorted sharply; "*I've* never sinned."

In the mind of the faithful servant, that was the truth. She had always considered as a kind of sacrament anything that her curés had thought fit to administer to her. She continued in a tyrannical tone of voice that made the good priest tremble:

"Do you think I did that because I was a wicked woman, like some low creatures I know at Clochemerle might have done? Like the Putet kind of women with their nasty hanging around? You ought to be ashamed of yourself, Monsieur Augustin, and I don't mind telling you so even if I am a poor nobody. I did it for your health . . . for your *health*, you understand, Monsieur Augustin?"

"Yes, I know, my good Honorine," the curé answered, falteringly. "Heaven will reward you for it."

For the Curé of Clochemerle that day was a difficult one, and it was followed by weeks during which he lived in a state of persecution and surrounded by suspicion. At last, when she had become satisfied that her privilege was not being taken from her in order to be bestowed elsewhere, Honorine grew calm. In 1923 the relations between the Curé of Clochemerle and his servant had been irreproachable for a period of ten years.

JOYFUL ACCEPTANCE OF THE URINAL

The spring of that year was remarkably early, notably mild, and rich with flowers. It was not long before shirts began to be damp from good honest perspiration on chests and backs. As soon as the month of May arrived, men began drinking in the rhythm of summertime, and that, at Clochemerle, is in right liberal measure, and quite beyond the conception of feeble bloodless drinkers in cities and towns. The result of this great overmastering impulse, in the male organisms, was a very sustained renal activity, which demanded a hearty joyous overflow at somewhat frequent intervals. Its proximity to the Torbayon Inn brought the urinal into high favor. Doubtless the drinkers' needs could have found satisfaction in the courtyard of the inn, but it was a gloomy spot of unpleasing odor and badly kept, a cheerless place. It was like a penitence; you had to grope your way, and your footwear was apt to suffer. But crossing the street was the matter of a moment, and the new procedure offered several advantages. There was the novelty of it; you could take a little stroll, and there was the opportunity, as one passed, of a glance at Judith Toumignon, who was always something of a feast to the eye and whose fault-less outlines were a stimulus to the imagination.

Finally, the urinal having two compartments, one usually went there in company; and this procured the pleasure of a little conversation as one pro-ceeded with the business of the moment, which made both the business and the conversation still more agreeable than they would otherwise have been; because one was enjoying two pleasures at the same time. Men who drank with extreme courage and competence, with results to correspond, could but feel happy, one alongside the other, in the enjoyment of two great and in-evitably consecutive pleasures—to drink good wine without stint and then seek relief to its utmost possibility, without haste or hurry, in a fresh well-ventilated place, flushed day and night with a plentiful supply of water. Sim-ple pleasures are these, which the town-bred man, ruthlessly jostled and hurried along on such occasions, can no longer enjoy. At Clochemerle they continued to be fully appreciated. So great was the value placed upon them, so highly were they esteemed, that each time Piéchut passed by his little edifice—as he often did to assure himself that it was not standing idle—if the occupants were men of his own generation they never failed to give him evidence of their satisfaction and content.

The urinal had met with equal favor among the young people, but for very different reasons. Situated in the center of Clochemerle, it marked the point of union between the upper and lower portions of the town, in close proximity to the church, the inn, and the Beaujolais stores, all three of which were important places constantly in the public eye. It was an obvious meeting place. It was also a considerable source of attraction to the lads and younger men, in this way. Monks' Alley was the only available means of access to the vestry for the Children of Mary, and during the month of May they were to be seen there every evening.

These blushing maidens, with their fresh bloom and figures already well developed, were an attractive sight at close quarters. Rose Bivaque, Lulu Montillet, Marie-Louise Richôme, and Toinette Maffigue were those most frequently hailed, or occasionally pushed about, by the Clochemerle youths who, moreover, blushed no less than they, and whose anxiety to be tender only made them coarse. But when there was a whole troop of them they were bold enough. On the other hand, the Children of Mary put on airs of excessive prudishness, though they knew perfectly well what they really wanted—not to stay for the rest of their lives wearing the blue ribbon of maidenhood, but for the youths to feel the same flutter of emotion as they did themselves—though the giggling little hussies had really few doubts on the matter. Grouped in a way which enabled them the better to face the young bloods, they passed them arm in arm, twisting themselves about with an air of seeming indifference, and laughing slyly as they became conscious of a fusillade of burning glances which all but set them on fire. Into the semidarkness of the church they carried with them tender recollections of a face or the tones of a voice which became mingled with the sweet sounds of the hymns. These rude encounters, these clumsy overtures were paving the way for fresh blood, for new stock at Clochemerle.

Two compartments are a meager allowance when there are three or four poor mortals *in extremis* at the same moment, and this happened frequently in a community numbering two thousand eight hundred souls, of whom nearly half were males, who alone are privileged to overflow on the public highway. In these cases of urgency, a return was made to the old expeditious methods, which will always retain their value. The men sought relief against the wall, at the side of the little edifice, in all tranquillity and innocence, seeing no harm or offense therein and no reason whatsoever why they should refrain. Indeed, there were some, of an independent disposition, who even preferred to remain outside.

As for the boys of Clochemerle, they would not have been youths of from sixteen to eighteen years old, with the stupidity characteristic of that restless age, had they not found here an opportunity for certain strange pranks. They vied with each other in making records for height and distance. Applying the processes of elementary physics, they reduced the natural flow and, by thus increasing the pressure, obtained fountainlike effects of a most amusing kind, which compelled them to step backwards. However, these silly pastimes are to be found in every country and at all periods of history; and the men who criticized and blamed them were merely proving the shortness of their own memories. But the good women of Clochemerle, watching from a distance, looked with an indulgent eye at these diversions of a youth insufficiently established in virile functions.

Thus, with simple merriment, life went forward at Clochemerle in the spring of 1923, without needless hypocrisy, but with a certain Gallic fondness for the licentious jest. Piéchut's urinal was the great local attraction. From morning till night there was a moving queue of Clochemerle's inhabitants in Monks' Alley, each man behaving as age or temperament moved him: the young ones impatiently, with lack of watchfulness and care; the men of maturer age with due restraint in their bearing and procedure; the old men slowly, with sighs and great tremulous efforts which produced but a feeble flow, in intermittent showers. But each and all, youths, grown men, and the aged, as soon as they entered the alley made the same precise preparatory gesture directly designed for the beginning of the business; and the same gesture, which finished in the street, on its completion. This latter was deep and prolonged, accompanied by bendings of the knees, which were preliminary to certain rearrangements of a private nature.

This gesture, which has remained the same for forty thousand years—or five hundred thousand—which brings Adam and the Ape Man into close relationship with the men of the twentieth century, this invariable, international, world-wide gesture, this essential, comminatory gesture, this, so to speak, powerfully synthetic gesture, was made by the inhabitants of Cloche-merle without uncalled-for ostentation, but also without absurd dissimula-tion, artlessly and without self-consciousness, as they unreservedly made themselves at home in Monks' Alley. For it would never have occurred to them that any but a strangely distorted mind could have used the alley for un-seemly purposes. But this gesture had an element of provocation, when it was accomplished under the eyes of a personage who imagined that it was aimed at her as a kind of challenge and who, concealed behind her curtain and rooted to the spot by this strange form of enticement, was held fast by its constant repetition. From her window Justine Putet watched these arrivals and departures in the alley. The old maid was spectator of these uninter-rupted performances by men who, believing themselves to be alone, attended to their needs with a fine unconcern. It may well be that, reassured by this conviction of their own solitude, they did not observe every precaution that a scrupulous decency would have demanded.

C. S. FORESTER (1899–   )

Although he is best known for his Captain Horatio Hornblower *series, an unusual combination of excitement and antiquarianism, Cecil Scott Forester is the author of dozens of novels, dramas, travel books, and other smaller works. Born in Cairo, Egypt, he spent his boyhood in a London suburb and studied medicine at Guy's Hospital. He says that laziness and lack of disci-pline made him, like Maugham, give up doctoring and begin writing. After dabbling in verse for a few years, he made his theatrical debut with the sen-sational* Payment Deferred, *which not only starred Charles Laughton but established the actor's reputation. The enormous success of that play was re-peated almost twenty years later when* The African Queen *was transferred to the screen, starring a grim Humphrey Bogart and a gaunt Katharine Hep-burn.*

"The Bedchamber Mystery" is one of Forester's shortest and lightest pieces of writing. It is also one of the most gravely playful—even to the punning title.

THE BEDCHAMBER MYSTERY

Now that a hundred years have passed, one of the scandals in my family can be told. It is very doubtful if in 1843 Miss Forester (she was Eulalie, but being the eldest daughter unmarried, she of course was Miss Forester) and Miss Emily Forester and Miss Eunice Forester ever foresaw the world of 1943 to which their story would be told; in fact it is inconceivable that they could have believed that there ever would be a world in which their story could be told blatantly in public print. At that time it was the sort of thing that could only be hinted at in whispers during confidential moments in feminine drawing rooms; but it was whispered about enough to reach in the end the ears of my grandfather, who was their nephew, and my grandfather told it to me.

In 1843 Miss Forester and Miss Emily and Miss Eunice Forester were already maiden ladies of a certain age. The old-fashioned Georgian house in which they lived kept itself modestly retired, just like its inhabitants, from what there was of bustle and excitement in the High Street of the market town. The ladies indeed led a retired life; they went to church a little, they visited those of the sick whom it was decent and proper for maiden ladies to visit, they read the more colorless of the novels in the circulating library, and sometimes they entertained other ladies at tea.

And once a week they entertained a man. It might almost be said that they went from week to week looking forward to those evenings. Dr. Acheson was (not one of the old ladies would have been heartless enough to say "fortunately," but each of them felt it) a widower, and several years older even than my great-great-aunt Eulalie. Moreover, he was a keen whist player and a brilliant one, but in no way keener or more brilliant than were Eulalie, Emily, and Eunice. For years now the three nice old ladies had looked forward to their weekly evening of whist—all the ritual of setting out the green table, the two hours of silent cut-and-thrust play, and the final twenty minutes of conversation with Dr. Acheson as he drank a glass of old madeira before bidding them good night.

The late Mrs. Acheson had passed to her Maker somewhere about 1830, so that it was for thirteen years they had played their weekly game of whist before the terrible thing happened. To this day we do not know whether it happened to Eulalie or Emily or Eunice, but it happened to one of them. The three of them had retired for the night, each to her separate room, and had progressed far toward the final stage of getting into bed. They were not dried-up old spinsters; on the contrary, they were women of weight and substance, with the buxom contours even married women might have been proud of. It was her weight which was the undoing of one of them, Eulalie, Emily, or Eunice.

Through the quiet house that bedtime there sounded the crash of china and a cry of pain, and two of the sisters—which two we do not know—hurried in their dressing gowns to the bedroom of the third—her identity is uncertain —to find her bleeding profusely from severe cuts in the lower part of the back. The jagged china fragments had inflicted severe wounds, and, most unfortunately, just in those parts where the injured sister could not attend to them herself. Under the urgings of the other two she fought down her modesty sufficiently to let them attempt to deal with them, but the bleeding was profuse, and the blood of the Foresters streamed from the prone figure face downward on the bed in terrifying quantity.

"We shall have to send for the doctor," said one of the ministering sisters; it was a shocking thing to contemplate.

"Oh, but we cannot!" said the other ministering sister.

"We must," said the first.

"How terrible!" said the second.

And with that the injured sister twisted her neck and joined in the conversation. "I will not have the doctor," she said. "I would die of shame."

"Think of the disgrace of it!" said the second sister. "We might even have to explain to him how it happened!"

"But she's bleeding to death," protested the first sister.

"I'd rather die!" said the injured one, and then, as a fresh appalling thought struck her, she twisted her neck even further. "I could never face him again. And what would happen to our whist?"

That was an aspect of the case which until then had occurred to neither of the other sisters, and it was enough to make them blench. But they were of stern stuff. Just as we do not know which was the injured one, we do not know which one thought of a way out of the difficulty, and we shall never know. We know that it was Miss Eulalie, as befitted her rank as eldest sister, who called to Deborah, the maid, to go and fetch Dr. Acheson at once, but that does not mean to say that it was not Miss Eulalie who was the injured sister—injured or not, Miss Eulalie was quite capable of calling to Deborah and telling her what to do.

As she was bid, Deborah went and fetched Dr. Acheson and conducted him to Miss Eunice's bedroom, but of course the fact that it was Miss Eunice's bedroom is really no indication that it was Miss Eunice who was in there. Dr. Acheson had no means of knowing. All he saw was a recumbent form covered by a sheet. In the center of the sheet a round hole a foot in diameter had been cut, and through the hole the seat of the injury was visible.

Dr. Acheson needed no explanations. He took his needles and his thread from his little black bag and set to work and sewed up the worst of the cuts and attended to the minor ones. Finally he straightened up and eased his aching back.

"I shall have to take those stitches out," he explained to the still and silent figure which had borne the stitching stoically without a murmur. "I shall come next Wednesday and do that."

Until next Wednesday the three Misses Forester kept to their rooms. Not one of them was seen in the streets of the market town, and when on Wednesday Dr. Acheson knocked at the door Deborah conducted him once more to Miss Eunice's bedroom. There was the recumbent form, and there was the sheet with the hole in it. Dr. Acheson took out the stitches.

"It has healed very nicely," said Dr. Acheson. "I don't think any further attention from me will be necessary."

The figure under the sheet said nothing, nor did Dr. Acheson expect it. He gave some concluding advice and went his way. He was glad later to receive a note penned in Miss Forester's Italian hand:

Dear Dr. Acheson,
We will all be delighted if you will come to whist this week as usual.

When Dr. Acheson arrived he found that the "as usual" applied only to his coming, for there was a slight but subtle change in the furnishings of the drawing room. The stiff, high-backed chairs on which the three Misses Forester sat bore, each of them, a thick and comfortable cushion upon the seat. There was no knowing which of the sisters needed it.

JOHN COLLIER (1901–   )

John Collier's talent for the macabre—the real macabre—is evidenced by the titles of his books: His Monkey Wife, Presenting Moonshine, Defy the Foul Fiend, Fancies and Goodnights.

Born in London, Collier started writing in his early teens: his first poems appeared in print before he was twenty. Although he received prizes for his poetry, at twenty-nine he turned to prose which blended the fantastic, the satiric, and the sadistic. Soon he became noted as an expert in the odd, the absurd, the slightly mad and generally reprehensible. "Diabolical," "bizarre," "grotesque," "gruesome," and "outrageous" are a few of the adjectives which have been tossed at him—and with good reason. Collier's subjects are, to say the least, strange. He blandly mixes horror with humor; in his hands ordinary people betray unsuspected potentialities which carry them from the eccentric to the incredible. His themes are disturbing, disorderly, and often frightening, but they usually end by being frightfully funny. "In the imaginary world of John Collier," wrote Orville Prescott, "the supernatural is almost natural." In such stories as "Rope Enough" and "Season of Mists" the supernatural (or coincidental) elements are unnaturally logical and logically amoral.

ROPE ENOUGH

Henry Fraser, well assured that almost everything is done by mirrors, was given a job in India. No sooner had he set foot on shore than he burst into a horselaugh. Those who were meeting him asked the cause of this merriment. He replied he was laughing at the mere idea of the Rope Trick.

He emitted similar startling sounds, and gave the same explanation, at a tiffin where he was officially made welcome; likewise on the Maidan, over *chota peg*, in rickshaws, in bazaars, in the Club, and on the polo ground. Soon he was known from Bombay to Calcutta as the man who laughed at the Indian Rope Trick, and he gloried in the publicity.

There came a day, however, when he was sitting in his bungalow, bored to death. His boy entered, and, with suitable salaams, announced that a mountebank was outside, who craved the honour of entertaining the *sahib* with a performance of the Indian Rope Trick. Laughing heartily, Henry consented.

Below, in the dusty compound, stood a native who was emaciated to a degree, and who had with him a spry youngster, a huge mat basket, and a monstrous great sword. Out of the basket he dragged some thirty feet of stout rope, made a pass or two, and slung it up into the air. It stayed there. Henry chuckled.

The boy then, with a caper, sprang at the rope, clutched it, and went up hand over hand, like a monkey. When he reached the top he vanished into thin air. Henry guffawed.

Soon the man, looking upwards with an anxious expression, began to hoot and holler after the boy. He called him down, he ordered him down, he begged him down, he began to swear and curse horribly. The boy, it seemed, took no notice at all. Henry roared.

Now the black, clapping his abominable great scimitar between his teeth, took hold of the rope himself, and went up it like a sailor. He, also, disappeared at the top. Henry's mirth increased.

Pretty soon some yelps and squeals were heard coming out of the empty air, and then a bloodcurdling scream. Down came a leg, thump on to the ground, then an arm, a thigh, a head and other joints, and finally (no ladies being present) a bare backside, which struck the earth like a bomb. Henry went into fits.

Then the black came sliding down, holding on with one hand, fairly gibbering with excitement. He presented to Henry, with a salaam, his reeking blade for inspection. Henry rocked in his chair.

The black, seemingly overwhelmed with remorse, gathered up the fragments of his little stooge, lavishing a hundred lamentations and endearments upon each grisly member, and he stowed them all in the giant basket.

At that moment Henry, feeling the time had come for a showdown, and willing to bet a thousand to one they'd planted the whole compound full of mirrors before calling him out there, pulled out his revolver, and blazed away all six chambers in different directions, in the expectation of splintering at least one of those deceiving glasses.

Nothing of that sort happened, but the black, doing a quick pirouette in alarm, looked down in the dust at his feet, and held up a villainous little snake, no thicker than a lead pencil, which had been killed by one of Henry's stray bullets. He gave a gasp of relief, touched his turban very civilly, turned round again, and made a pass or two over the basket. At once, with a wiggle and a frisk, the boy sprang out, whole, alive, smiling, full of health and wickedness.

The black hastily hauled down the rope, and came cringing up to Henry, overflowing with gratitude for having been saved from that villainous little snake, which was nothing more nor less than a krait—one nip and a man goes round and round like a Catherine wheel for eleven seconds; then he is as dead as mutton.

"But for the heavenborn," said the black, "I should have been a goner, and my wicked little boy here, who is my pride and delight, must have lain dismembered in the basket till the *sahib's* servants condescended to throw him to the crocodiles. Our worthless lives, our scanty goods, are all at the *sahib's* disposal."

"That's all right," said Henry. "All I ask is, show me how the trick is worked, or the laugh will be on me from now on."

"Would not the *sahib*," said the black diffidently, "prefer the secret of a superb hair-restorer?"

"No. No," said Henry. "Nothing but the trick."

"I have," said the black, "the secret of a very peculiar tonic, which the *sahib* (not now, of course, but in later life) might find——"

"The trick," said Henry, "and without further delay."

"Very well," said the black. "Nothing in the world could be more simple. You make a pass, like that——"

"Wait a minute," said Henry. "Like that?"

"Exactly," said the black. "You then throw up the rope—so. You see? It sticks."

"So it does," said Henry.

"Any boy can climb," said the black. "Up boy! Show the *sahib*."

The boy, smiling, climbed up and disappeared.

"Now," said the black, "if the *sahib* will excuse me, I shall be back immediately." And with that he climbed up himself, threw down the boy in sections, and speedily rejoined Henry on the ground.

"All that," said he, scooping up legs and arms as he spoke, "all that can be done by anyone. There is a little knack, however, to the pass I make at this juncture. If the *sahib* will deign to observe closely—like that."

"Like that?" said Henry.

"You have it to perfection," said the black.

"Very interesting," said Henry. "Tell me, what's up there at the top of the rope?"

"Ah, *sahib*," said the black with a smile, "that is something truly delightful."

With that he salaamed and departed, taking with him his rope, his giant basket, his tremendous great scimitar, and his wicked little boy. Henry was left feeling rather morose: he was known from the Deccan to the Khyber Pass as the man who laughed at the Indian Rope Trick, and now he could laugh no more.

He decided to keep very quiet about it, but this unfortunately was not enough. At tiffin, at *chota peg*, at the Club, on the Maidan, in the bazaar, and at polo, he was expected to laugh like a horse, and in India one has to do what is expected of one. Henry became extremely unpopular, cabals were formed against him, and soon he was hoofed out of the Service.

This was the more distressing as in the meantime he had married a wife, strong-featured, upstanding, well groomed, straight-eyed, a little peremptory in manner, and as jealous as a demon, but in all respects a *mem-sahib* of the highest type, who knew very well what was due to her. She told Henry he had better go to America and make a fortune. He agreed, they packed up, and off they went to America.

"I hope," said Henry, as they stood looking at the skyline of New York, "I hope I shall make that fortune."

"Of course," said she. "You must insist upon it."

"Very well, my dear," said he.

On landing, however, he discovered that all the fortunes had already been made, a discovery which very generally awaits those who visit America on this errand, and after some weeks of drifting about from place to place, he was prepared to cut his demand down to a mere job, then to a lesser job, and finally to the price of a meal and a bed for the night.

They reached this extremity in a certain small town in the Middle West. "There is nothing for it, my dear," said Henry. "We shall have to do the Indian Rope Trick."

His wife cried out very bitterly at the idea of a *mem-sahib* performing this native feat in a Middle Western town, before a Middle Western audience. She reproached him with the loss of his job, the poor quality of his manhood, with the time he let her little dog get run over on the bund, and with a glance he had cast at a Parsee maiden at Bombay. Nevertheless, reason and hunger prevailed: they pawned her last trinket and invested in a rope, a roomy grip, and a monstrous old rusty scimitar they discovered in a junk shop.

When she saw this last, Henry's wife flatly refused to go on, unless she was given the star part and Henry took that of the stooge. "But," said Henry, drawing an apprehensive thumb down the notched and jagged edge of the grim and rusty bilbo. "But," said he, "you don't know how to make the passes."

"You shall teach me," she said, "and if anything goes wrong you will have only yourself to blame."

So Henry showed her. You may be sure he was very thorough in his instructions. In the end she mastered them perfectly, and there was nothing left to do but to stain themselves with coffee. Henry improvised a turban and loincloth: she wore a *sari* and a pair of ash trays borrowed from the hotel. They sought out a convenient waste lot, a large crowd collected, and the show began.

Up went the rope. Sure enough, it stuck. The crowd, with a multiple snigger, whispered that everything was done by mirrors. Henry, not without a good deal of puffing, went up hand over hand. When he got to the top, he forgot the crowd, the act, his wife, and even himself, so surprised and delighted was he by the sight that met his eyes.

He found himself crawling out of something like a well, on to what seemed to be solid ground. The landscape about him was not at all like that below: it was like an Indian paradise, full of dells, bowers, scarlet ibises, and heaven knows what all. However, his surprise and delight came less from these features of the background than from the presence of a young female in the nearest of these bowers or arbours, which happened to be all wreathed, canopied, overgrown and intertwined with passion flowers. This delightful creature, who was a positive houri, and very lightly attired, seemed to be expecting Henry, and greeted him with rapture.

Henry, who had a sufficiently affectionate nature, flung his arms round her neck and gazed deeply into her eyes. These were surprisingly eloquent: they seemed to say, "Why not make hey hey while the sun shines?"

He found the notion entirely agreeable, and planted a lingering kiss on her lips, noting only with a dim and careless annoyance that his wife was hooting and hollering from below. "What person of any tact or delicacy," thought he, "could hoot and holler at such a moment?" and he dismissed her from his mind.

You may imagine his mortification when his delicious damsel suddenly repulsed him from her arms. He looked over his shoulder, and there was his wife, clambering over the edge, terribly red in the face, with the fury of a demon in her eye, and the mighty scimitar gripped well between her teeth.

Henry tried to rise, but she was beforehand with him, and while yet he had but one foot on the ground, she caught him one across the loins with the huge and jagged bilbo, which effectually hamstrung him, so that he fell grovelling at her feet. "For heaven's sake!" he cried. "It's all a trick. Part of the act. It means nothing. Remember our public. The show must go on."

"It shall," said she, striking at his arms and legs.

"Oh, those notches!" cried he. "I beg you, my dear, sharpen it a little upon a stone."

"It is good enough for you, you viper," said she, hacking away all the time. Pretty soon Henry was a limbless trunk.

"For the love of God," said he, "I hope you remember the passes. I can explain everything."

"To hell with the passes!" said she, and with a last swipe she sent his head rolling like a football.

She was not long in picking up the scattered fragments of poor Henry, and flinging them down to earth, amid the applause and laughter of the crowd, who were more than ever convinced it was all done by mirrors.

Then, gripping her scimitar, she was about to swarm down after him, not from any softhearted intention of reassembling her unfortunate spouse, but rather to have another hack or two at some of the larger joints. At that moment she became aware of someone behind her, and, looking round, there was a divine young man, with the appearance of a maharaja of the highest caste, an absolute Valentino, in whose eyes she seemed to read the words, "It is better to burn upon the bed of passion than in the chair of electricity."

This idea presented itself with an overwhelming appeal. She paused only to thrust her head through the aperture and cry, "That's what happens to a pig of a man who betrays his wife with a beastly native," before hauling up the rope and entering into conversation with her charmer.

The police soon appeared upon the scene. There was nothing but a cooing sound above, as if invisible turtle doves were circling in amorous flight. Below, the various portions of Henry were scattered in the dust, and the bluebottle flies were already settling upon them.

The crowd explained it was nothing but a trick, done with mirrors.

"It looks to me," said the sergeant, "as if the biggest one must have splintered right on top of him."

SEASON OF MISTS

I was ready for anything when I came to the town of T——. It was already late in the year. Dead leaves crawled like crabs over the asphalt of the deserted esplanade. Winds raced along the corridors of the larger hotels, barging into the wrong rooms.

It is at such a place, and at such a season, that one finds the desperate grass widow, or young things whose natural credulity snaps starvingly at the grossest counterfeit. The illusion of teeming possibilities has gone with the licentious carnival of summer, the masks of coarse sunburn, and him who may be sitting alone among the sand dunes. Ravenous dreams pace the unvisited sitting rooms of villas or stalk between rising waves and falling leaves.

The concealed smile in my smile, and the concealed meaning in my words, would have made me seem a sort of scheme-riddled Machiavelli in the ephemeral mating dance of July. I should have been condemned as heavy going, would-be clever, even unpleasant or dangerous. Now, on the other hand, my slightly involved personality would be as welcome as a jigsaw puzzle in hands already fidgety with boredom. Nevertheless, I had gone so far as to purchase a ready-made sports jacket, and had my black moustache had any objective existence I should have taken the precaution of shaving it off.

I still had a little money. I was not after profit, but pleasure. I desired to intoxicate myself on a real emotion, and I wondered in which of the still-occupied villas, in what sort of absurd drawing room, treading softly in fear of what husband or what aunt, I should perform what drunken antics my chosen potion would inspire in me.

Meticulous in my observance of protective mimicry, I could not of course omit the *snorter* or *quick one* before dinner on my first evening in the hotel. I entered the bar in jaunty style, my mouth already writhing with a classy catch phrase, like the eye socket of a provincial actor in travail with his waggish monocle.

This witticism was never uttered. I thought I saw a golden fish. It was the honey head of the barmaid, bent over a love story, but, as the place had the appearance of the tourist cocktail lounge of a liner sunk two years previously in a hundred fathoms of gray-green ocean, I thought it was a golden fish. I was sharply corrected when she raised a face so dappled with flush and sun gleam that I looked instinctively for the orchard boughs above her head.

All this was disconcerting, and effective in shattering my pose. It happens that these fresh and almost eatable faces have a peculiar effect on me. "Farewell before hail," I thought, "to the sailor's languishing wife, and to the ardent anemia at the Vicarage! I am off."

I ordered one of the far inferior intoxicants that stood ranked behind her, and retired a pace, changing my name to Bert, a young man already doing well, at once cheeky and shy, but probably capable of being serious. One never knew what I could come out with next.

I was wondering about that myself when I saw that she, affecting to take no particular notice of me, had retired into the flowery thicket of her revery. I realized that this must have grown very wild and tangly in the last month or two, because, before she could turn and peep out from it, it swallowed her up entirely, like a prospective sleeping beauty, and indeed she yawned.

I analyzed this yawn with the aloof precision of one of those scientists who are always helping Scotland Yard. I discovered it to be heavy with a supersaturation of sigh, its origin a plaintive protest against the difference between dreams and reality. Though this was only the middle of November, I diagnosed it as a premature December yawn, *and in December they settle for reality*. This emboldened me to act at once.

Affecting to consult my heart, exactly as if it had been a pocket watch, I gasped, bit my lip, and stared at her in wild surmise. You could never tell when I was joking. "Do you believe," I said fervently, "in love at first sight?"

"No, sir," she said severely. "That sort of thing doesn't appeal, thank you."

It was clear she had not been a barmaid more than seven or eight weeks. From behind her professional hauteur she peeped out to watch for its effect, as bewitchingly as if she were a child wearing her mother's terrible hat.

"I'm not fooling," I said (taken down a peg or two, you understand). "The fact is, believe it or not, I'm a bit psychic." On this word, the most useful though not the most beautiful in our language, she raised her eyes to mine, which I had baited with pieces of an old sincerity which I carry about for just such purposes. I put a little in my voice, too, as I added, "Do you know what I thought, the minute I saw you?"

"What?" said she.

"I'll tell you," said I. " 'That girl's tragic,' I thought. 'She's being wasted. There's a sort of bar between her and all sorts of delightful surprises. I wish it could be melted away.' "

"Not really!"

"I did," said I. "Give me your hand. I can read it like a book, probably by your favourite author. Oh, I'm psychic all right. I had a sort of premonition when I came here. I knew I was going to fall desperately in love."

"I know you're kidding," said she, but she offered me her open hand, which proved to be quite illegible.

Nevertheless I spoke with confidence. "You've been thinking of love today. You've been dreaming of a stranger. Now don't deny it, because it's written in your hand. And that's not all."

"What else does it say?" said she.

"Call it Fate," said I solemnly. "Call it Kismet if you like; I can deny you nothing. Or, look here, let's call it Destiny. You can't go back on Destiny, you know. It would absolutely ruin it. It says . . . Guess what!"

"I can't," she said. "Do tell me."

I couldn't guess either. Dumbly I scrutinized her palm. She leaned a little farther over the bar, joining me in the study. Our foreheads touched. I remained conscious, but the shock had dislocated all connection between awareness and volition. With a divine shudder I heard myself reply, "It says we are going to be married."

"Oh," said she. "I don't know about that."

"What?" I cried, hurt to the quick, all caution forgotten. "Is this mutual understanding? Is this two hearts beating as one? Don't let's start off with a rift like this between us."

"I didn't mean it that way," she replied remorsefully.

"Splendid," I said. "Our first little quarrel healed already. And don't we sort of know one another better for it? Aren't we somehow closer? If not, we ought to be. Lean over a little farther."

Fate had evidently triumphed. Her kiss was like cowslips and cream. I was unquestionably in love and felt no longer responsible for my actions.

At that moment, however, a gong sounded in the echoing depths of the hotel. "Better go," she said, already wifely. "Go and get your dinner. I'll be here later on."

I bowed before the importance of Bert's dinner, and went. When I returned the bar was still empty of intruders, and she was still there. I rushed forward, I flung my arms about her, and resumed the kiss that had been so coarsely interrupted.

I had just been struck by the nice thought that perhaps after all it tasted of cream and honeysuckle, rather than cowslips, when I was also struck by a tremendous blow in the face.

"What?" I said, staggering back. "Are you tired of me already? You might at least have broken it more gently."

"I'll call the manager," said she.

"Do so," said I. "Call the boots, too. Call the waiters. Call all the principal residents of T—— on Sea. Let them hear how you promised to marry me before dinner and socked me in the puss for a kiss immediately afterwards."

"Promised to marry you?" she cried. "Before dinner. Oooh! It must have been Bella. Fancy! Bella!"

"What is your name?" said I.

"Nellie," said she.

"That's who it was," said I. "Nellie. You. To the devil with this interfering, designing Bella, who . . ." But, as I spoke, she turned and darted through the door behind her.

I heard some delicious squeals and giggles. "I hope," I thought, "she is giving that abominable Bella a good pinch. Pretending to be her! She had the poor girl all confused." At that moment the door opened again, and out they came, hand in hand.

"I'm Nellie."

"I'm Bella."

"Keep quite still," said I, clowning astonishment. "I must think for a little while about this."

"Look! He's all bowled over."

"Isn't he sweet?"

"Yes, he's a duck. Bella, you *are* lucky."

"Your turn next."

That was the rub. My mind darkened at the thought of a brother-in-law. You know what beasts men are. A thousand intricate jealousies tangled themselves before me. The girls were so exactly alike; they *went together*, as we say. Besides, who can choose between cowslips and honeysuckle?

It was time I said something. "Well!" said I. "By all that's wonderful! I wish old Fred were here tonight!"

"Who's Fred?"

"Fred? You'll like Fred. He's a splendid fellow. We're twins."

"No!"

"Yes, identical twins. More alike than you are. Same looks. Same tastes. Same thoughts. I always know what he's thinking. Listen! He's sort of trying to get through to me now. I bet he knows I'm happy. He does. He's sending congratulations. In waves. He's asking something. What is it, Fred, old boy? Is there what? Oh, *Is there one for me, Bert?* That's what he's trying to say. What shall I tell him, Nellie?"

"Don't know, I'm sure."

"Why don't you bring him along one day?" said Bella.

"I can't," said I. "We're on a very special job. It's just half the time off for each of us. But I'll tell you what; I'll *send* him along."

This was agreed upon. I spent the rest of the evening delightfully, and in the morning bought a new sports coat, brushed my hair differently, and returned as Fred.

I entered the bar, peering through my fingers. "Which are you?" I cried. "I don't want to look at you properly till I know. I might fall in love with the wrong one."

"I'm Nellie."

"Good! To make it absolutely perfect, I'm Fred." With that I dropped my hand. "Good old Bert!" I cried. "Wonderful taste he's got! Wonderful fellow!"

"He's nice. But you're nice, too."

"Do you really think so?"

In short, we were happy. Soon afterwards Bella came in. There was nothing but giggles, comparisons, talk of future joys.

"It really ought to be a double wedding," they said.

"Can't be done," I replied. "Truly. Ask Bert if you don't believe me. He'll tell you it's out of the question."

The next few days passed like lightning. All went twice as merrily as the ordinary marriage bell. I rented two bungalows, semidetached, furnished them from the same store, took a week off for my honeymoon as Bert, and the next week for my honeymoon as Fred.

I then settled down to lives of singular contentment and regularity. One evening Nellie and I would have Bella to dinner, and spend the time saying what a grand fellow Bert was, and the next evening Bella and I would entertain Nellie and do the same for Fred.

It was a full month before I asked myself, which is the happier of the two, Fred or Bert? I was unable to answer. The doubt persisted until it tortured me.

I became a little moody, and sometimes would retire to the next room, under the pretence of a headache, in order to ponder the question over again. On one of these occasions, I went into the hallway to get cigarettes from my overcoat and I heard the girls' voices through the flimsy door of the drawing room. "The darlings!" I thought. "They are discussing their husbands again. This may shed some light on my problem. Bella thinks Bert has the nicer voice. Nellie claims that Fred knows more songs. What is this? Really, Bella! Come, come, Nellie, you flatter me! Bella, what an exaggeration! Nellie, that is a downright lie!"

Soon afterward I heard Nellie go home. I rejoined Bella, who was obviously much exercised in her mind. "Bert," she said, "who is the best swimmer, you or Fred?"

"We never compete, darling, we are so sure we are equal."

"I wonder if you would be if you tried," said Bella, still looking extremely thoughtful.

When I returned to the other bungalow next evening, I found Nellie equally ill at ease. "Tell me something," said she. "Of course I know Bella's my sister, my twin. Nobody could love her more than I do. But tell me, Fred, would you say she was absolutely truthful?"

"Absolutely," said I. "I'd stake my life on it. Bert's life, too. She is incapable of a lie."

"Oh!" said Nellie, lapsing into a deeper revery than before.

It was with a sardonic pleasure that I watched the increasing wistfulness of both my wives. "I have an idea," said I to myself, "that I shall soon learn whether Bert or Fred is the happier."

Sure enough, it was not long before Nellie sent round one evening to ask if Bert would help her move some heavy furniture. I went to her aid, and afterward we sat talking for a while on twins, likenesses, differences, marriage, conventions, love, and what would have happened if Fred had met Bella before I had, and whether what hurts nobody can really be said to be wrong.

It took a long time to resolve all these problems to our complete satisfaction, and I was deprived of a good deal of Bella's company that evening. But this was made up to me on the following day, for she came round to ask if Fred would help her with a leaky tap, and we had an almost identical discussion, which took just as long for its complete resolution.

I was now in a state of extreme and complicated bliss. It was clear that Bert had no reason to envy Fred, and that Fred's happiness was in all respects equal to Bert's. Not only had I two charming wives, but my double domestic happiness was multiplied by a dual and delicious infidelity.

But I was one day in the character of Bert, sitting before the fire, enjoying the more legal of my happinesses with Bella, charmed by her prattle and pleased by the complete restoration of her good spirits, when suddenly I was struck, as if by a thunderbolt, by the thought: "This woman is deceiving me!"

I leapt up with a muttered excuse, and rushed out of the now hateful house. I walked on the shore till late that night, a prey to the most bitter reflections. I had to admit that I was largely responsible, but I at least knew that it made no difference. She had no such excuse; it was she who had blighted our Eden.

I went home long after midnight, slept uneasily, and hurried off in the morning, eager to exchange the pitiful personality of the deceived husband for the roguish character of his betrayer.

As Fred, I returned with a jaunty sneer. Nellie greeted me. "How was Bert," said she, "when you left him?"

"Bert?" said I. "Bert!"

Without another word I went heavily upstairs, and looked at myself in the mirror. The sight maddened me. I itched to get my fingers round my throat. I longed to rush next door and pour out my troubles to my adorable mistress, but I knew in my heart that she was as false as her sister below.

I thought of divorce, working out actions and counteractions on my fingers, and badly spraining two of them in the process. Besides, there was the unsavory publicity.

At last I made up my mind. I hurried off to catch the last train to the town. Arrived there, I wrote two notes, as follows:

"Dear Nellie, I have found you out. I am asking Bert to come for a swim. He will never return. Fred."

"Dear Bella, I know all. Am persuading Fred to take a midnight bathe. He will not come back. Bert."

Having posted my letters, I took my two sports coats to the beach where I left them side by side.

There was just time to get the train for B——, and it was there that I met Mrs. Wilkinson.

JOHN STEINBECK (1902–   )

John Steinbeck was born in 1902 in California and had all his schooling there. Although most of his writing has a local background, it has no kinship with the world of Hollywood glamor, spotlighted swimming pools, and comfortable retirement plans. His is the California of the migrant worker, the poor fruit picker, the Mexican-Americans—the misfits and castoffs, the dregs of society, for whom Steinbeck has a passion of pity as well as pleasure.

Tortilla Flat, published in 1935, a few years before The Grapes of Wrath *and still a favorite, was Steinbeck's first successful book. It is a series of episodes from the life of Danny and his companions, amoral but inherently decent Mexican paisanos who live on the outskirts of Monterey, California. Steinbeck thought of the book as a kind of carefree Arthurian cycle or a sort of modern Gesta Romanorum, "those outrageous tales with monkish morals appended"; but the main issue, he said, was "to present a little known and to me delightful people . . . people of laughter and kindness, of honest lusts and direct eyes, of courtesy beyond politeness."*

"Tortillas and Beans," a self-contained story from the novel, justifies Steinbeck's statement. Here is not merely the skilled craftsman but a writer with easy humor, humility, and a great heart.

FROM: TORTILLA FLAT

TORTILLAS AND BEANS

Señora Teresina Cortez and her eight children and her ancient mother lived in a pleasant cottage on the edge of the deep gulch that defines the southern frontier of Tortilla Flat. Teresina was a good figure of a mature woman, nearing thirty. Her mother, that ancient, dried, toothless one, relict of a past generation, was nearly fifty. It was long since any one had remembered that her name was Angelica.

During the week work was ready to this vieja's hand, for it was her duty to feed, punish, cajole, dress, and bed down seven of the eight children. Teresina was busy with the eighth, and with making certain preparations for the ninth.

On Sunday, however, the vieja, clad in black satin more ancient even than she, hatted in a grim and durable affair of black straw, on which were fastened two true cherries of enameled plaster, threw duty to the wind and went firmly to church, where she sat as motionless as the saints in their niches. Once a month, in the afternoon, she went to confession. It would be interesting to know what sins she confessed, and where she found the time to commit them, for in Teresina's house there were creepers, crawlers, stumblers, shriekers, cat-killers, fallers-out-of-trees; and each one of these charges could be trusted to be ravenous every two hours.

Is it any wonder that the vieja had a remote soul and nerves of steel? Any other kind would have gone screaming out of her body like little sky-rockets.

Teresina was a mildly puzzled woman, as far as her mind was concerned. Her body was one of those perfect retorts for the distillation of children. The first baby, conceived when she was fourteen, had been a shock to her; such a shock, that she delivered it in the ball park at night, wrapped it in newspaper, and left it for the night watchman to find. This is a secret. Even now Teresina might get into trouble if it were known.

When she was sixteen, Mr. Alfred Cortez married her and gave her his name and the two foundations of her family, Alfredo and Ernie. Mr. Cortez gave her that name gladly. He was only using it temporarily anyway. His name, before he came to Monterey and after he left, was Guggliemo. He went away after Ernie was born. Perhaps he foresaw that being married to Teresina was not going to be a quiet life.

The regularity with which she became a mother always astonished Teresina. It occurred sometimes that she could not remember who the father of the impending baby was; and occasionally she almost grew convinced that no lover was necessary. In the time when she had been under quarantine as a diphtheria carrier she conceived just the same. However, when a question became too complicated for her mind to unravel, she usually laid that problem in the arms of the Mother of Jesus, who, she knew, had more knowledge of, interest in, and time for such things than she.

Teresina went often to confession. She was the despair of Father Ramon. Indeed he had seen that while her knees, her hands, and her lips did penance for an old sin, her modest and provocative eyes, flashing under drawn lashes, laid the foundations for a new one.

During the time I have been telling this, Teresina's ninth child was born, and for the moment she was unengaged. The vieja received another charge; Alfredo entered his third year in the first grade, Ernie his second, and Panchito went to school for the first time.

At about this time in California it became the stylish thing for school nurses to visit the classes and to catechize the children on intimate details of their home life. In the first grade, Alfredo was called to the principal's office, for it was thought that he looked thin.

The visiting nurse, trained in child psychology, said kindly, "Freddie, do you get enough to eat?"

"Sure," said Alfredo.

"Well, now. Tell me what you have for breakfast."

"Tortillas and beans," said Alfredo.

The nurse nodded her head dismally to the principal. "What do you have when you go home for lunch?"

"I don't go home."

"Don't you eat at noon?"

"Sure. I bring some beans wrapped up in a tortilla."

Actual alarm showed in the nurse's eyes, but she controlled herself. "At night what do you have to eat?"

"Tortillas and beans."

Her psychology deserted her. "Do you mean to stand there and tell me you eat nothing but tortillas and beans?"

Alfredo was astonished. "Jesus Christ," he said, "what more do you want?"

In due course the school doctor listened to the nurse's horrified report. One day he drove up to Teresina's house to look into the matter. As he walked through the yard the creepers, the crawlers, and the stumblers were shrieking one terrible symphony. The doctor stood in the open kitchen door. With his own eyes he saw the vieja go to the stove, dip a great spoon into a kettle and sow the floor with boiled beans. Instantly the noise ceased. Creepers, crawlers and stumblers went to work with silent industry, moving from bean to bean, pausing only to eat them. The vieja went back to her chair for a few moments of peace. Under the bed, under the chairs, under the stove the children crawled with the intentness of little bugs. The doctor stayed two hours, for his scientific interest was piqued. He went away shaking his head.

He shook his head incredulously while he made his report. "I gave them every test I know of," he said, "teeth, skin, blood, skeleton, eyes, co-ordination. Gentlemen, they are living on what constitutes a slow poison, and they have from birth. Gentlemen, I tell you I have never seen healthier children in my life!" His emotion overcame him. "The little beasts," he cried. "I never saw such teeth in my life. I *never* saw such teeth!"

You will wonder how Teresina procured food for her family. When the bean threshers have passed, you will see, where they have stopped, big piles of bean chaff. If you will spread a blanket on the ground, and, on a windy afternoon, toss the chaff in the air over the blanket, you will understand that the threshers are not infallible. For an afternoon of work you may collect twenty or more pounds of beans.

In the autumn the vieja and those children who could walk went into the fields and winnowed the chaff. The landowners did not mind, for she did no harm. It was a bad year when the vieja did not collect three or four hundred pounds of beans.

When you have four hundred pounds of beans in the house, you need have no fear of starvation. Other things, delicacies such as sugar, tomatoes, peppers, coffee, fish, or meat may come sometimes miraculously, through the intercession of the Virgin, sometimes through industry or cleverness; but your beans are there, and you are safe. Beans are a roof over your stomach. Beans are a warm cloak against economic cold.

Only one thing could threaten the lives and happiness of the family of the Señora Teresina Cortez; that was a failure of the bean crop.

When the beans are ripe, the little bushes are pulled and gathered into piles, to dry crisp for the threshers. Then is the time to pray that the rain may hold off. When the little piles of beans lie in lines, yellow against the dark fields, you will see the farmers watching the sky, scowling with dread at every cloud that sails over; for if a rain comes, the bean piles must be turned over to dry again. And if more rain falls before they are dry, they must be turned again. If a third shower falls, mildew and rot set in, and the crop is lost.

When the beans were drying, it was the vieja's custom to burn a candle to the Virgin.

In the year of which I speak, the beans were piled and the candle had been burned. At Teresina's house, the gunny sacks were laid out in readiness.

The threshing machines were oiled and cleaned.

A shower fell.

Extra hands rushed to the fields and turned the sodden hummocks of beans. The vieja burned another candle.

More rain fell.

Then the vieja bought two candles with a little gold piece she had kept for many years. The field hands turned over the beans to the sun again; and then came a downpour of cold streaking rain. Not a bean was harvested in all Monterey County. The soggy lumps were turned under by the plows.

Oh, then distress entered the house of Señora Teresina Cortez. The staff of life was broken; the little roof destroyed. Gone was that eternal verity, beans. At night the children cried with terror at the approaching starvation. They were not told, but they knew. The vieja sat in church as always, but her lips drew back in a sneer when she looked at the Virgin. "You took my candles," she thought. "Ohee, yes! Greedy you are for candles. Oh, thoughtless one!" And sullenly she transferred her allegiance to Santa Clara. She told Santa Clara of the injustice that had been done. She permitted herself a little malicious thought at the Virgin birth. "You know, sometimes Teresina can't remember either," she told Santa Clara viciously.

It has been said that Jesus Maria Corcoran was a greathearted man. He had also that gift some humanitarians possess of being inevitably drawn toward those spheres where his instinct was needed. How many times had he not come upon young ladies when they needed comforting. Toward any pain or sorrow he was irresistibly drawn. He had not been to Teresina's house for many months. If there is no mystical attraction between pain and humanitarianism, how did it happen that he went there to call on the very day when the last of the old year's beans was put in the pot?

He sat in Teresina's kitchen, gently brushing children off his legs. And he looked at Teresina with polite and pained eyes while she told of the calamity. He watched, fascinated, when she turned the last bean sack inside out to show that not one single bean was left. He nodded sympathetically when she pointed out the children, so soon to be skeletons, so soon to die of starvation.

Then the vieja told bitterly how she had been tricked by the Virgin. But upon this point, Jesus Maria was not sympathetic.

"What do you know, old one?" he said sternly. "Maybe the Blessed Virgin had business someplace else."

"But four candles I burned," the vieja insisted shrilly.

Jesus Maria regarded her coldly. "What are four candles to Her?" he said. "I have seen one church where She had hundreds. She is no miser of candles."

But his mind burned with Teresina's trouble. That evening he talked mightily and piteously to the friends at Danny's house. Out of his great heart he drew a compelling oratory, a passionate plea for those little children who had no beans. And so telling was his speech that the fire in his heart ignited the hearts of his friends. They leaped up. Their eyes glowed.

"The children shall not starve," they cried. "It shall be our trust!"

"We live in luxury," Pilon said.

"We shall give of our substance," Danny agreed. "And if they needed a house, they could live here."

"Tomorrow we shall start," Pablo exclaimed. "No more laziness! To work! There are things to be done!"

Jesus Maria felt the gratification of a leader with followers.

Theirs was no idle boast. Fish they collected. The vegetable patch of the Hotel Del Monte they raided. It was a glorious game. Theft robbed of the stigma of theft, crime altruistically committed—— What is more gratifying?

Now food began to accumulate in the house of Teresina. Boxes of lettuce lay on her porch, spoiled mackerel filled the neighborhood with a strong odor. And still the flame of charity burned in the friends.

If you could see the complaint book at the Monterey Police Department, you would notice that during this time there was a minor crime wave in Monterey. The police car hurried from place to place. Here a chicken was taken, there a whole patch of pumpkins. Paladini Company reported the loss of two one-hundred-pound cases of abalone steaks.

Teresina's house was growing crowded. The kitchen was stacked high with food. The back porch overflowed with vegetables. Odors like those of a packing house permeated Tortilla Flat. Breathlessly the friends dashed about at their larcenies, and long they talked and planned with Teresina.

At first Teresina was maddened with joy at so much food, and her head was turned by the compliment. After a week of it, she was not so sure. The baby was down with colic, Ernie had some kind of bowel trouble, Alfredo's face was flushed. The creepers and crawlers cried all the time. Teresina was ashamed to tell the friends what she must tell them. It took her several days to get her courage up; and during that time there arrived fifty pounds of celery and a crate of cantaloupes. At last she had to tell them. The neighbors were beginning to look at her with lifted brows.

She asked all of Danny's friends into her kitchen, and then she informed them of the trouble, modestly and carefully, that their feelings might not be hurt.

"Green things and fruit are not good for children," she explained. "Milk is constipating to a baby after it is weaned." She pointed to the flushed and irritable children. See, they were all sick. They were not getting the proper food.

"What is the proper food?" Pilon demanded.

"Beans," she said. "There you have something to trust, something that will not go right through you."

The friends went silently away. They pretended to themselves to be disheartened, but they knew that the first fire of their enthusiasm had been lacking for several days.

At Danny's house they held a conference.

This must not be told in some circles, for the charge might be serious.

Long after midnight, four dark forms who shall be nameless, moved like shadows through the town. Four indistinct shapes crept up on the Western Warehouse Company platform. The watchman said, afterward, that he heard sounds, investigated, and saw nothing. He could not say how the thing was done, how a lock was broken and the door forced. Only four men know that the watchman was sound asleep, and they will never tell on him.

A little later the four shadows left the warehouse, and now they were bent under tremendous loads. Pantings and snortings came from the shadows.

At three o'clock in the morning Teresina was awakened by hearing her back door open. "Who is there?" she cried.

There was no answer, but she heard four great thumps that shook the house. She lighted a candle and went to the kitchen in her bare feet. There, against the wall, stood four one-hundred-pound sacks of pink beans.

Teresina rushed in and awakened the vieja. "A miracle!" she cried. "Come look in the kitchen."

The vieja regarded with shame the plump full sacks. "Oh, miserable dirty sinner am I," she moaned. "Oh, Holy Mother, look with pity on an old fool. Every month thou shalt have a candle, as long as I live."

At Danny's house, four friends were lying happily in their blankets. What pillow can one have like a good conscience? They slept well into the afternoon, for their work was done.

And Teresina discovered, by a method she had found to be infallible, that she was going to have a baby. As she poured a quart of the new beans into the kettle, she wondered idly which one of Danny's friends was responsible.

ERSKINE CALDWELL (1903–   )

Born in the tiny town of White Oak in Georgia on December 17, 1903, son of a Presbyterian preacher, erratically educated, Erskine Caldwell was a professional football player, occasional cottonpicker, stagehand, and salesman of building lots three feet under water before he was recognized as a serious writer. More than a hundred short stories and novelettes had been rejected when, nearing thirty, he wrote Tobacco Road, *which became a sensation. When it was followed by* God's Little Acre, *Caldwell was hailed as a sociological critic, the champion of underprivileged people trapped by their devotion to a waste land which they themselves had laid waste. It was much later that Caldwell's remarkable talent for comedy was appreciated as fully as his social protests; it was not until Caldwell was in his late forties that his publishers issued* The Humorous Side of Erskine Caldwell.

Meanwhile Caldwell had published some seventeen volumes, all of which had been extraordinarily successful—the paper-back editions alone sold more than thirty-four million copies—but his literary status still perplexed the critics. Although Caldwell has been compared to Twain, Caldwell is neither a satirist nor a playful comedian. His humor is both grotesque and naturalistic. The people he writes about may be naïve to the point of carefree primitivism, but their author records their brutalities as well as their irresponsibilities with a detachment which is, in itself, an indictment of their background.

OVER THE GREEN MOUNTAINS

Was reading a piece in the Boston paper last night about the smartest people in the whole country coming from the State of Maine. Said at the time, and I'm still here to say it: you can take your pick of any ten men in the whole Union, and I'll back one Varmonter of my own choosing against them any day. Take ten men from any of the states you can find them in, and all of them put together won't have the smartness that my lone Varmonter has got. Have lived in the State of Maine all my life, ninety-odd years of it, but I've always said that if you want some smartness you shall have to go to Varmont to get it. Varmont is where it comes from.

Now, you take the farmers. Varmont farmers is that smart they can't keep from making money while the farmers in other places is all losing money. And here is why they are so smart: not so long ago there was a Varmont farmer over here, riding around in his big auto having a good time and laughing at us farmers here because we hadn't made enough money to retire and maybe take a trip to Florida on, in even years. I asked this Varmont farmer how it was he had made so much money running a farm.

And this is what he told me: "Friend," he said, "the secret of making money out of a farm is this: Sell all you can; what you can't sell, feed to the hogs; what the hogs won't eat, eat yourself."

After he finished telling me that, he drove off laughing in his big auto to look at some more Maine farmers working and sweating in the fields because they ain't got sense enough to make money to retire on, and maybe take a winter trip to Florida, in even years.

That sporting farmer wasn't the first Varmonter I'd known, though. I used to know another one when I was a young man on the Penobscot.

This was a young fellow we called Jake Marks, one of them old-time Varmonters who used to come over here to the State of Maine driving teams of oxen before the railroads was built across the mountains. This Jake Marks was a smart one, if there ever was a Varmonter who warn't. He used to drive his oxen over here, hauling freight back and forth all the time. It was a long haul in them days, when you stop to think how slow them brutes travel, and Jake had a lot of mountain to cross coming and going. I don't recall how long it took him to make one of his trips, but it was quite a time in them days when there warn't no state roads, only trails wide enough for a yoke of oxen.

Jake was a real young man at that time, I should say about twenty-five, maybe twenty-seven. He warn't married then, neither. But pretty soon he took a liking to a young and handsome filly who cooked his meals for him at the house in Bangor where he put up while he was changing cargo between trips. She was just the kind of young filly that Jake wanted, too. She used to come into the room where he sat waiting for his meal and make herself real frisky in his presence. Jake, he was tormented something awful by the way she cut up in front of him, and he used to have to get up out of his chair sometimes and walk real fast around the house three-four times to get control over himself.

But this Jake Marks was a cautious man, and he never undertook a deal until he had thought it out a lot beforehand and saw that he had everything on his side. Then, when he had thought it all through, he turned loose and went after whatever it was he wanted like a real Varmonter. All them old-time Varmonters was like that, I guess; anyway, the ones who used to drive ox freights over here to the State of Maine was, and Jake was just like all the rest of them.

This young filly of Jake's got so she pestered him about marrying of her all the time he was resting up between trips. Jake, he wanted her, all right. That was one thing he was wanting all the time he was over here. But Jake, he was taking his own good time about it, I'm telling you. He was figuring the thing out like all them Varmonters who drove ox freights did. He had to be real certain that everything was on his side before he made any signs. He took the rest of the season for figuring the thing out, and he didn't make motions of a move toward the young filly that year at all.

The next spring when the frost had thawed out of the ground and when he could make his first trip of the year over the mountains, Jake he called at the house where this young filly stayed and told her to get ready to be married to him when he got back to Bangor on his next trip. That suited the young filly first-rate. She had been uneasy all winter about Jake, taking too much at heart all the gossip that was talked about them Varmont ox freighters. But when Jake told her to get ready for marrying, she knew he would keep his promise right down to the last letter and come and marry her like he said he would.

So, Jake he went back to Varmont with his freight, promising to be ready to marry the young filly the same day he got back to Bangor on his next trip.

And just as he promised, Jake came back to get married to the young filly.

He went straight to the house where she stayed, and there she was all waiting for him. Jake told her to get ready right away for the marriage, and then he went out to find a preacher somewhere. When he got back to the house with the preacher, he called her down to the room where all the guests had gathered to see the ceremony performed.

The minute she stepped into the room where Jake and the rest of the people was, Jake took one look at the young filly and told her to go back upstairs to her room and take off her dress. Well, that was all right and proper, because in those days there was a law in the State of Maine to the effect that a man could make what was called a shift marriage. That was to say, the man could make the woman take off the dress she was wearing while the ceremony was being performed, and in that case he could not be held legally responsible for her past debts and would not have to pay them for her if he didn't have a mind to. Well, Jake he had heard all about this shift law in Maine, and he was taking full advantage of its benefits. That was what he had been figuring out all the time he was driving them slow-footed oxen back and forth between Bangor and Varmont. Jake, he warn't no man's fool. Jake, he was a Varmonter.

After a while Jake's young filly came downstairs dressed according to this here shift law. She had on what women wore under their dresses in those days, and that was all she had on. But Jake, he warn't satisfied, not completely. He told her to go back upstairs and take off everything she had on. Jake, he was a hardheaded ox freighter from Varmont, all right. He had figured all this out while he was driving them slow-footed oxen back and forth across the mountains.

In a little while his young filly came into the room again where Jake and the preacher and all the guests was, and she didn't have nothing on, except that she had a bedsheet wrapped around her, which was a good thing, I tell you. She was a handsome-looking filly if there ever was one.

They all got ready again for the ceremony, the preacher telling them where to stand and what to say to the questions he was getting ready to ask them. Then, just when they was beginning to get married, Jake he told his young filly to drop the bedsheet on the floor. Now, Jake he warn't taking no chances over here in the State of Maine. That shift law said that if a woman was married without her dress on, her husband couldn't be held liable for her past debts, and Jake he figured that if the young filly didn't have nothing at all on her, there wouldn't be a chance in the whole world for to dun him for what she might owe, while if she had clothes on that he didn't know the true and legal names of, a storekeeper might try to say her underclothes was her overdress. Jake he was thinking that he might by chance get cheated out of his rights to the full benefits of the shift law if he didn't take care, and Jake he warn't after taking no chances whatsoever over here in the State of Maine when he was so far away from Varmont. He was as cautious where he sat his foot as the next ox freighter from Varmont.

"Drop the bedsheet on the floor," Jake he told the young filly again.

The young filly was getting ready to turn loose the bedsheet and let it drop on the floor like Jake told her to do, when the preacher he grabbed the bedsheet and held to it tight around her so she wouldn't show none of her naked self to him and Jake and the rest of the people in the house.

"No! No! No!" he yelled, getting red in the face and shaking his head at Jake. "That won't do, my man—that won't do at all! That would be indecent here before all of us! That can't be done! I'll never allow it!"

But the preacher he didn't know Jake Marks. Jake was one of them Varmont ox freighters, and he was as hardheaded about what he wanted as the next one to come along. Jake he told the young filly again to drop the bedsheet on the floor, and to drop it quick if she wanted to get married.

The handsome young filly was getting ready to let go of it like Jake said to, because she was that crazy about Jake she would have stood on her head right then and there if Jake had told her to do it, but just when she was getting ready to let go of it, the preacher he grabbed the bedsheet again and held it fast with both hands.

The preacher started in trying to argue with Jake about it being indecent for the handsome young filly to stand there naked while she was being married, but Jake he had his head set on getting the full benefits of the shift law and he wouldn't give in an inch.

Then the preacher said he warn't going to perform the ceremony if that was what Jake was set on doing, and Jake he told the preacher he warn't going to get married at all without the bedsheet being dropped on the floor so that none of the cloth was touching the young filly.

Everybody got excited when Jake said that, and the people talked back and forth for an hour or more, arguing first on Jake's side, because they knew the law on the books, and then on the preacher's side, because they realized how it might upset the preacher if the handsome young filly stood there naked like Jake was set on having her do. The young filly didn't care which way the ceremony was done, just so long as Jake married her. She was willing to drop the bedsheet for Jake the minute the preacher let her. She was all excited about getting married, just like Jake had been all the time.

After a while the preacher gave in to Jake just a little. He saw what a fool he was, trying to argue with a Varmont ox freighter.

"If she'll go inside the closet and shut the door so nobody can see her nakedness, I'll perform the ceremony," the preacher told Jake.

"That's all right by me," Jake said, "but I'll be compelled to have some witnesses on my side in case anybody tries to dispute me about us being married under the shift law or not."

They finally settled that part when the preacher agreed to allow two of the older women to go in the closet with the young filly, just to make sure that everything was done in a legal manner. The preacher he didn't like to have Jake going in a closet with the naked filly, but he was pretty well worn out by that time after arguing for nearly two hours with a Varmont ox freighter, and he said he would have to allow Jake to go in the closet, too.

Jake went in the closet where the filly and the two older women were.

"Now, you just look once, Jake," the preacher said, shaking his head back and forth, "and then you shut your eyes and keep them shut."

Jake was in the closet saying something to the young filly, but nobody in the room could hear what it was. The preacher he reached over and made a bit of a crack in the door while he was marrying them so he could hear their answers to the questions. And all that time Jake he was in there striking matches to make sure that the young filly was not putting the bedsheet on again, and to be certain that he was getting the full benefits of the shift law.

When it was all done, the preacher he took the money Jake handed him and went off home without waiting to see what shape the young and handsome filly was in when the closet door was opened. When they came out into the room, the bedsheet was all twisted up into a knot; Jake handed it to her, and she didn't lose no time in getting upstairs where her clothes were. Jake he had told her to hurry and get dressed, because he wanted to get started with his ox freight back to Varmont.

They started home to Varmont right away, the handsome young filly all dressed up in her wedding clothes and sitting on top of the freight cargo while Jake he walked along beside the wagon bellowing at the oxen.

When Jake came back to Bangor on his next trip, a storekeeper tried to present him a bill for a hundred and forty dollars. The storekeeper told Jake that the young filly had bought a lot of dresses and things just before she got married, and he wanted to know if Jake had married her under the shift law.

Jake just laughed a little, and started unloading his cargo.

"Well, was you married that way, or the other way?" the storekeeper asked him.

"You tell me this first," Jake said, "and then I'll answer your question. Does the State of Maine have a shift law on the books?"

"Well, yes; but the shift law says that the woman has to—"

"Never mind about explaining it to me," Jake said. "If the shift law is on the statute books, then that's the law I married her with!"

MEDDLESOME JACK

Hod Sheppard was in the kitchen eating breakfast when he heard one of the colored boys yell for him. Before he could get up and look out the window to see what the trouble was, Daisy came running into the room from the garden house in the field looking as if she had been scared out of her wits.

"Hod! Hod!" she screamed at him. "Did you hear it?"

He shook her loose from him and got up from the table. Daisy fell down on the kitchen floor, holding on to his legs with all her might.

"Hear what?" he said. "I heard one of the niggers yelling for me. That's all I heard. What's the matter with you, Daisy?"

Just then Sam, the colored boy, called Hod again louder than ever. Both Hod and Daisy ran to the back door and looked out across the field. The only thing out there they could see was the yellow broom sedge and the dead-leafed blackjack.

"What's all this fuss and racket about, anyway?" Hod said, looking at Daisy.

"I heard something, Hod," she said, trembling.

"Heard what? What did you hear?"

"I don't know what it was, but I heard it."

"What did it sound like—wind, or something?"

"It sounded like—like somebody calling me, Hod."

"Somebody calling you?"

She nodded her head, holding him tightly.

"Who's calling you! If I ever find anybody around here calling you out of the house, I'll butcher him. You'd better not let me see anybody around here after you. I'll kill him so quick——"

Sam came running around the corner of the house, his overall jumper flying out behind, and his crinkly hair jumping like a boxful of little black springs let loose. His eyes were turning white.

"Hey there, you Sam!" Hod yelled at him. "Quit your running around and come back here!"

"Sam heard him, too," Daisy said, standing beside Hod and trembling as if she would fall apart. "Sam's running away from him."

"Heard what—heard who! What's the matter with you, Daisy?"

Daisy held Hod tighter, looking out across the broom sedge. Hod pushed her away and walked out into the back yard. He stood there only a minute before the sound of Sam's pounding feet on the hard white sand grew louder and louder. Sam turned the corner of the house a second later, running even faster than he had before. His eyes were all white by that time, and it looked as if his hair had grown several inches since Hod had last seen him.

Hod reached out and caught Sam's jumper. There was a ripping sound, and Hod looked down to find that he was holding a piece of Sam's overall. Sam was around the house out of sight before Hod could yell at him to stop and come back.

"That nigger is scared of something," Hod said, looking in the doorway at Daisy.

"Sam heard him," Daisy said, trembling.

Hod ran to Daisy and put both hands on her shoulders and shook her violently.

"Heard who!" he yelled at her. "If you don't tell me who it was around here calling you, I'll choke the life out of you. Who was around here calling you? If I catch him, I'll kill him so quick——"

"You're choking me, Hod!" Daisy screamed. "Let me loose! I don't know who it was—honest to God, I don't know who it was, Hod!"

Hod released her and ran out into the yard. Sam had turned and was running down the road toward the lumber mill a mile away. The town of Folger was down there. Two stores, the post office, the lumber mill, and the bank were scorching day after day in an oval of baked clay and sand. Sam was half-way to Folger by then.

"So help me!" Daisy screamed. "There he is, Hod!"

She ran into the kitchen, slamming and bolting the door.

Out behind the barn Amos Whittle, Sam's father, was coming through the broom sedge and blackjack with his feet flying behind him so fast that they looked like the paddles on a water mill. He had both hands gripped around the end of a rope, and the rope was being jerked by the biggest, the ugliest, and meanest-looking jack that Hod had ever seen in his whole life. The jack was loping through the broom sedge like a hoop snake, jerking Amos from side to side as if he had been the cracker on the end of a rawhide whip.

"Head him, Mr. Hod!" Amos yelled. "Head him! Please, sir, head him!"

Hod stood looking at Amos and the jack while they loped past him. He turned and watched them with mouth agape while they made a wide circle in the broom sedge and started back towards the house and barn again.

"Head him, Mr. Hod!" Amos begged. "Please, Mr. Hod, head him!"

Hod picked up a piece of mule collar and threw it at the jack's head. The jack stopped dead in his tracks, throwing out his front feet and dragging his hind feet on the hard white sand. The animal had stopped so suddenly that Amos found himself wedged between his two hind legs.

Hod walked towards them and pulled Amos out, but Amos was up and on his feet before there was any danger of his being kicked.

"Where'd you get that jack, Amos?" Hod said.

"I don't know where I got him, but I sure wish I'd never seen him. I been all night trying to hold him, Mr. Hod. I ain't slept a wink, and my old woman's taken to the tall bushes. She and the girls heard him, and they must have thought I don't know exactly what, because they went off yelling about being scared to hear a sound like that jack makes."

The jack walked leisurely over to the barn door and began eating some nubbins that Hod had dropped between the crib and the stalls. One ear stood straight up, and the other one lay flat on his neck. He was the meanest-looking jackass that had ever been in that part of the country. Hod had never seen anything like him before.

"Get him away from here, Amos," Hod said. "I don't want no jack around here."

"Mr. Hod," Amos said, "I wish I could get him away somewhere where I'd never see him again. I sure wish I could accommodate you, Mr. Hod. He's the troublesomest jack I ever seen."

"Where'd you get him, Amos? What are you doing with him, anyway?"

Amos glanced at Hod, but only for a moment. He kept both eyes on the jack.

"I traded that old dollar watch of mine for him yesterday, Mr. Hod, but that jack ain't worth even four bits to me. I don't know what them things are made for, anyhow."

"I'll give you fifty cents for him," Hod said.

"You will!" Amos shouted. "Lord mercy, Mr. Hod, give it here! I'll sure be glad to get rid of that jack for four bits. He done drove my wife and grown girls crazy, and I don't know what mischief he'll be up to next. If you'll give me fifty cents for him, I'll sure be much obliged to you, Mr. Hod. I don't want to have nothing more to do with that jackass."

"I don't want him around, either," Hod said, turning to look through the kitchen window, "but I figure on making me some money with him. How old is that jack, Amos?"

"The man said he was three years old, but I don't know no way of telling a jack's age, and I don't aim to find out."

"He looks like he might be three or four. I'm going to buy him from you, Amos. I figure on making me a lot of money out of that jack. I don't know any other way to make money these days. I can't seem to get it out of the ground."

"Sure, sure, Mr. Hod. You're welcome to that jack. You're mighty much welcome to him. I don't want to have nothing more to do with no jackass. I wish now I had my watch back, but I reckon it's stopped running by now, anyhow. It was three years old, and it never did keep accurate time for me. I'll sure be tickled to get four bits for that jack, Mr. Hod."

Hod counted out fifty cents in nickels and dimes and handed the money to Amos.

"Now, you've got to help me halter that jack, Amos," Hod said. "Get yourself a good piece of stout rope. Plowlines won't be no good on him."

"I don't know about haltering that jack, Mr. Hod. Looks like to me he's never been halterbroke. If it's all the same to you, Mr. Hod, I'd just as lief go on home now. I've got some stovewood to chop, and I got to——"

"Wait a minute," Hod said. "I'll get the rope to halter him with. You go in the house and wake up Shaw. He's in the bed asleep. You go in there and get him up and tell him to come out here and help us halter the jack. Ain't no sense in him sleeping all morning. I'm damned tired of seeing him do it. When he comes home, he ought to get out and help do some work about the place."

Shaw was Hod's brother who had been at home seven or eight days on leave from the Navy. He was getting ready to go back to his ship in Norfolk in a day or two. Shaw was two years younger than Hod, and only a few years older than Daisy. Daisy was nineteen then.

"I'd sure like to accommodate you, Mr. Hod," Amos said, "but the last time you sent me in to wake up Mr. Shaw, Mr. Shaw he jumped out of bed on top of me and near about twisted my neck off. He said for me never to wake him up again as long as I live. Mr. Hod, you'd better go wake up Mr. Shaw your own self."

Hod reached down and picked up a piece of stovewood. He walked towards Amos swinging the stick in his hand.

"I said go in the house and get him up," Hod told Amos again. "That sailor had better stop coming here to stay in bed half the day and be all the time telling Daisy tales."

Amos opened the kitchen door and went into the house. Hod walked towards the barn where the jack was calmly eating red nubbins by the crib door.

When Hod reached the barnyard gate, the jack lifted his head and looked at him. He had two or three nubbins of red corn in his jaws, and he stopped chewing and crunching the grains and cobs while he looked at Hod. One of the jack's ears lay flat against the top of his head and neck, and the other one stood straight up in the air, as stiff as a cow's horn. The jack's ears were about fourteen or sixteen inches long, and they were as rigid as bones.

Hod tossed the piece of stovewood aside and walked to the opened gate for a piece of rope. He believed he could halter the jack by himself.

He started into the barnyard, but he had gone no farther than a few steps when boards began to fly off the side of the barn. The mare in the stall was kicking like a pump gun. One after the other, the boards flew off, the mare whinnied, and the jack stood listening to the pounding of the mare's hoofs against the pine boards.

When Hod saw what was happening to his barn, he ran towards the jack, yelling and waving his arms and trying to get him to the leeward side of the barn.

"Howie! Howie!" he yelled at the jack.

As long as the mare got wind of the jack, nothing could make her stop kicking the boards off the barn from the inside. Hod jumped at the jack, waving his arms and shouting at him.

"Howie! Howie!"

He continued throwing up his arms to scare the jack away, but the jack just turned and looked at Hod with one ear up and one ear down.

"Howie! You ugly-looking son of a bitch! Howie!"

Hod turned around to look towards the house to see if Shaw and Amos were coming. He turned just in time to see Amos jumping out the window.

"Hey there, Amos!" Hod yelled. "Where's Shaw?"

"Mr. Shaw says he ain't going to get up till he gets ready to. Mr. Shaw cussed pretty bad and made me jump out the window."

The jack began to paw the ground. Hard clods of stableyard sand and manure flew behind him in all directions. Hod yelled at him again.

"Howie! Howie! You flop-eared bastard!"

The jack stopped and turned his head to look at Amos on the other side of the fence.

"Mr. Hod," Amos said, "if you don't mind, I'd like to have a word with you."

Hod yelled at Amos and at the jack at the same time.

"Mr. Hod," Amos said, "if I don't go home now and chop that stovewood, me and my folks won't have no dinner at all."

"Come back here!" Hod shouted at him.

Amos came as far as the gate, but he would not come any farther.

Suddenly the jack lifted his head high in the air and brayed. It sounded as if someone were blowing a trumpet in the ear.

The bray had no more than died out when the mare began pounding the boards with both hind hoofs, the boards flying off the side of the barn faster than Hod could count them. He turned and looked to see what Amos was doing, and over his head he saw Daisy at the window. She looked as if she had completely lost her mind.

The jack brayed again, louder than ever, and then he leaped for the open barnyard gate. Hod threw the rope at him, but the rope missed him by six feet. The jack was through the gate and out around the house faster than Hod could yell. Amos stood as if his legs had been fence posts four feet deep in the ground.

The jack stopped at the open bedroom window, turned his head towards the house, and brayed as if he were calling all the mares in the entire county. Daisy ran to the window and looked out, and when she saw the jack no more than arm's length from her, she screamed and fell backward on the floor.

"Head him, Amos! Head him!" Hod yelled, running towards the jack.

Amos's feet were more than ever like fence posts. He was shaking like a tumbleweed, but his legs and feet were as stiff as if they had been set in concrete.

"Where in hell is that God damn sailor!" Hod yelled. "Why in hell don't he get up and help me some around here! If I had the time now, I'd go in there with a piece of cordwood and break every bone in his head. The son of a bitch comes home here on leave once a year and lays up in bed all day and stays out all night running after women. If that seagoing son of a bitch comes here again, I'll kill him!"

"Yonder goes your jack, Mr. Hod," Amos said.

Daisy stuck her head out of the window again. She was looking to see where the jack was, and she did not look at Hod. She was standing there pulling at herself, and getting more wild-eyed every second. She disappeared from sight as quickly as she had first appeared.

"Come on, you black bastard," Hod said; "let's go after him. I ought to pick up a stick and break your neck for bringing that God damn jack here to raise the devil. He's got the mare kicking down the barn, and Daisy is in there acting crazy as hell."

They started out across the broom sedge after the loping jack. The jack was headed for Folger, a mile away.

"If I ever get my hands on that jack, I'll twist his neck till it looks like a corkscrew," Hod panted, running and leaping over the yellow broom sedge. "Ain't no female safe around a sailor or a jack, and here I am running off after one, and leaving the other in the house."

They lost sight of the jackass in a short while. The beast had begun to circle the town, and he was now headed down the side of the railroad tracks behind the row of Negro cabins. They soon saw him again, though, when the jack slowed down at a pasture where some horses were grazing.

A hundred yards from the cabins they had to run down into a gully. Just as they were crawling up the other side, a Negro girl suddenly appeared in front of them, springing up from nowhere. She was standing waist-high in the broom sedge, and she was as naked as a pickaninny.

Hod stopped and looked at her.

"Did you see a jack?" he said to her.

"White folks, I saw that jack, and he brayed right in my face. I just jumped up and started running. I can't sit still when I hear a jackass bray."

Hod started off again, but he stopped and came back to look at the girl.

"Put your clothes back on," he said. "You'll get raped running around in the sedge this close to town like that."

"White captain," she said, "I ain't hard to rape. I done heard that jackass bray."

Hod turned and looked at Amos for a moment. Amos was walking around in a circle with his hands in his pockets.

"Come on," Hod told him, breaking through the broom sedge. "Let's get that jack, Amos."

They started towards the pasture where the jack had stopped. When the jack saw them coming, he turned and bolted over the railroad tracks and started jogging up the far side of the right-of-way towards Folger. Hod cut across to head him off and Amos was right behind to help.

There were very few men in town at that time of day. Several storekeepers sat on Coca-Cola crates on the sidewalk under the shade of the water-oak trees, and several men were whittling white pine and chewing tobacco. The bank was open, and RB, the cashier, was standing in the door looking out across the railroad tracks and dusty street. Down at the lumber mill, the saws whined hour after hour.

The jack slowed down and ran into the hitching yard behind the brick bank. When Hod saw that the jack had stopped, he stopped running and tried to regain his breath. Both he and Amos were panting and sweating. The August sun shone down on the dry baked clay in the oval where the town was, and remained there until sunset.

Hod and Amos sat down in the shade of the depot and fanned themselves with their hats. The jack was standing calmly behind the bank, switching flies with his tail.

"Give me back my fifty cents, Amos," Hod said. "You can have that God damn jack. I don't want him."

"I couldn't do that, Mr. Hod," Amos pleaded. "We done made the trade, and I can't break it now. You'll just have to keep that jack. He's yours now. If you want to get shed of him, go sell him to somebody else. I don't want that jack. I'd heap rather have my old dollar watch back again. I wish I'd never seen that jack in all my life. I can do without him."

Hod said nothing. He looked at the brick bank and saw RB looking out across the railroad tracks towards the stores where the men were sitting on upturned Coca-Cola crates in the water-oak shade.

"Sit here and wait," Hod said, getting up. "I've just thought of something. You sit here and keep your eyes on that jack till I come back."

"You won't be gone long, will you, Mr. Hod? I don't mind watching your animal for you, but I'd sure hate to have to look at that jack any more than I'm compelled to. He don't like my looks, and I sure don't like his. That's the ugliest-looking creature that's ever been in this country."

"Wait here till I get back," Hod said, crossing the tracks and walking towards the brick bank.

RB saw Hod coming and he went back inside and stood behind his cashier's cage.

Hod walked in, took off his hat, and leaned his arm on the little shelf in front of the cage.

"Hello, RB," he said. "It's hot today, ain't it?"

"Do you want to deposit money, or make a loan?"

Hod fanned himself and spat into the cuspidor.

"Miss it?" RB asked, trying to see through the grill.

"Not quite," Hod said.

RB spat into his own cuspidor at his feet.

"What can I do for you?" he said.

"Well, I'll tell you, RB," Hod said. "It's like this. You've got all this money here in the bank, and it ain't doing you much good where it is. And here I come with all my money tied up in livestock. There ain't but one answer to that, is there?"

"When did you get some livestock, Hod?" he asked. "I didn't know you had anything but that old mare and that gray mule."

"I made a trade today," Hod said, "and now just when my money is all tied up in livestock, I find a man who's willing to let me in on a timber deal. I need fifty dollars to swing my share. There ain't no use trying to farm these days, RB. That's why I'm going in for livestock and timber."

"How many head of stock do you own?"

"Well, I've got that mare, Ida, out there at my place, but I ain't counting her. And likewise that old mule."

"How many others do you own?"

"I purchased a high-class stud animal this morning, RB, and I paid out all my ready cash in the deal."

"A bull?"

"No, not exactly a bull, RB."

"What was it then?"

"A jackass, RB."

"A jackass! Who in hell wants to own a jackass, Hod? I can't lend the bank's money on a jackass."

"You're in the moneylending business, RB, and I've got an animal to mortgage. What else do you want? I'm putting up my jack, and you're putting up your money. That's business, RB. That's good business."

"Yes, but suppose you force me to foreclose the mortgage—I'd have the jack, and then maybe I couldn't find a buyer. Jackass buyers are pretty scarce customers, Hod. I don't recall ever seeing one."

"Anybody would give you a hundred dollars for a good high-class jack, RB. If you knew as much about farming and stock raising as you do about banking, you'd recognize that without me having to tell you."

"What does a jackass look like?"

"A jack don't look so good to the eye, RB, but that's not a jack's high point. When a jack brays——"

RB came running around from behind his cage and caught Hod by the arm. He was so excited that he was trembling.

"Is that what I heard last night, Hod?"

"What?"

"A jackass braying."

"Wouldn't be surprised if you did. Amos was out exercising him last night, and he said the jack brayed almost all night long."

"Come back here with me," RB said, still shaking. "I'm going to let you have that loan, and take a mortgage on that jack. I want to have a hand in it. If I'll let you have the loan, will you let me take the jack home and keep him at my house for about a week, Hod?"

"You're more than welcome to him, RB. You can keep him all the time if you want to. But why do you want to keep a jack at your house? You don't breed mules, do you?"

RB had Hod sign the papers before he replied. He then counted out five ten-dollar bills and put them into Hod's hand.

"This is just between me and you, Hod," he said. "Me and my wife haven't been on speaking terms for more than a month now. She cooks my meals and does her housework, but she's been mad at me about something and she won't say a word or have anything to do with me. But last night, sometime after midnight, we were lying there in the bed, she as far on her side as she could get without falling out, and all at once I heard the damnedest yell I ever heard in all my life. It was that jackass braying. I know now what it was, but I didn't know then. That jack was somewhere out in the sedge, and when he brayed, the first thing I knew, my wife was all over me, she was that scared, or something. That sounds like a lie, after I have told you about her not speaking to me for more than a month, and sleeping as far on her side of the bed as she could get without falling on the floor, but it's the truth if I know what the truth is. That jack brayed just once, and the first thing I knew, my wife was all over me, hugging me and begging me not to leave her. This morning she took up her old ways again, and that's why I want to stable that jack at my house for a week or two. He'll break up that streak of not talking and not having anything to do with me. That jack is what I am in need of, Hod."

Hod took the money and walked out of the bank towards the depot where Amos was.

"Where's the jack, Hod?" RB said, running after him.

"Out there behind your bank," Hod said. "You can take him home with you tonight when you close up."

Amos got up to meet Hod.

"Come on, Amos," Hod said. "We're going home."

Amos looked back over his shoulder at the jack behind the bank, watching him until he was out of sight. They walked through the broom sedge, circling the big gully, on the way home.

When they reached the front yard, Hod saw Sam sitting under a chinaberry tree. Sam got up and stood leaning against the trunk.

"What are you doing here?" Hod asked him. "What are you hanging around here for? Go on home, Sam."

Sam came forward a step, and stepped backward two.

"Miss Daisy told me to tell you something for her," Sam said, chewing the words.

"She said what?"

"Mr. Hod, Miss Daisy and Mr. Shaw went off down the road while you was chasing that jack. Mr. Shaw said he was taking Miss Daisy with him back to the navy yard, and Miss Daisy said she was going off and never coming back."

Hod went to the front porch and sat down in the shade. His feet hung over the edge of the porch, almost touching the ground.

Amos walked across the yard and sat down on the steps. He looked at Hod for several minutes before he said anything.

"Mr. Hod," he said, chewing the words worse than his son had before him, "I reckon you'd better go back to Folger and get your jack. Looks like that jack has a powerful way of fretting the womenfolks, and you'd better get him to turn one in your direction."

AUGUST AFTERNOON

Vic Glover awoke with the noonday heat ringing in his ears. He had been asleep for only half an hour, and he was getting ready to turn over and go back to sleep when he opened his eyes for a moment and saw Hubert's woolly black head over the top of his bare toes. He stretched his eyelids and held them open in the glaring light as long as he could.

Hubert was standing in the yard, at the edge of the porch, with a pine cone in his hand.

Vic cursed him.

The colored man once more raked the cone over Vic's bare toes, tickling them on the underside, and stepped back out of reach.

"What do you mean by standing there tickling me with that dad-burned cone?" Vic shouted at Hubert. "Is that all you can find to do? Why don't you get out in the field and do something to them boll weevils? They're going to eat up every boll of cotton on the place if you don't stop them."

"I surely hated to wake you up, Mr. Vic," Hubert said, "but there's a white man out here looking for something. He won't say what he's looking for, but he's hanging around waiting for it."

Vic sat up wide awake. He sat up on the quilt and pulled on his shoes without looking into the yard. The white sand in the yard beat the glare of the sun directly into his eyes and he could see nothing beyond the edge of the porch. Hubert threw the pine cone under the porch and stepped aside.

"He must be looking for trouble," Vic said. "When they come around and don't say anything, and just sit and look, it's trouble they're looking for."

"There he is, Mr. Vic," Hubert said, nodding his head across the yard. "There he sits up against that water-oak tree yonder."

Vic looked around for Willie. Willie was sitting on the top step at the other end of the porch, directly in front of the strange white man. She did not look at Vic.

"You ought to have better sense than to wake me up while I'm taking a nap. This is no time of the day to be up in the summertime. I've got to get a little sleep every now and then."

"Boss," Hubert said, "I wouldn't never wake you up at all, not at any time, but Miss Willie just sits there high up on the steps showing her pretty and that white man has been out there whittling on a little stick a long time without saying nothing. I'm scared about something happening when he whittles that little stick clear through, and it's just about whittled down to nothing now. That's why I waked you up, Mr. Vic. Ain't much left of that little whittling stick."

Vic glanced again at Willie, and from her he turned to stare at the stranger sitting under the water-oak tree in his front yard.

The piece of wood had been shaved down to paper thinness.

"Boss," Hubert said, shifting the weight of his body uneasily, "we ain't aiming to have no trouble today, is we?"

"Which way did he come from?" Vic asked, ignoring the question.

"I never did see him come from nowhere, Mr. Vic. I just looked up, and there he was, sitting against that water oak out yonder and whittling on that little stick. I reckon I must have been drowsy when he came, because when I opened my eyes, there he was."

Vic slid down over the quilt until his legs were hanging over the edge of the porch. Perspiration began to trickle down his neck as soon as he sat up.

"Ask him what he's after, Hubert."

"We ain't aiming to have no trouble today, is we, Mr. Vic?"

"Ask him what he wants around here," he said.

Hubert went almost halfway to the water-oak tree and stopped.

"Mr. Vic says what can he do for you, white folks?"

The man said nothing. He did not even glance up from the little stick he was whittling.

Hubert came back to the porch, the whites of his eyes becoming larger with each step.

"What did he say?" Vic asked him.

"He ain't said nothing yet, Mr. Vic. He acts like he don't hear me at all. You'd better go talk to him, Mr. Vic. He won't give me no attention. Appears to me like he's just sitting there and looking at Miss Willie on the high step. Maybe if you was to tell her to go in the house and shut the door, he might be persuaded to give some notice to what we say to him."

"Ain't no sense in sending her in the house," Vic said. "I can make him talk. Hand me that stillyerd."

"Mr. Vic, I'm trying to tell you about Miss Willie. Miss Willie's been sitting there on that high step showing her pretty and he's been looking at her a right long time, Mr. Vic. If you won't object to me saying so, Mr. Vic, I reckon I'd tell Miss Willie to go sit somewhere else, if I was you. Miss Willie ain't got much on today, Mr. Vic. Just only that skimpy outside dress, Mr. Vic. That's what I've been trying to tell you. I walked out there in the yard this while ago to see what he was looking at so much, and when I say Miss Willie ain't got much on today, I mean she's got on just only that skimpy outside dress, Mr. Vic. You can go look yourself and see if I'm lying to you, Mr. Vic."

"Hand me that stillyerd, I said."

Hubert went to the end of the porch and brought the heavy iron cotton-weighing steelyard to Vic. He stepped back out of the way.

"Boss," Hubert said, "we ain't aiming to have no trouble today, is we?"

Vic was getting ready to jump down into the yard when the man under the water oak reached into his pocket and pulled out another knife. It was about ten or eleven inches long, and both sides of the handle were covered with hairy cowhide. There was a spring button in one end. The man pushed the button with his thumb, and the blade sprang from the case. He began playing with both knives, throwing them up into the air and catching them on the backs of his hands.

Hubert moved to the other side of Vic.

"Mr. Vic," he said, "I ain't intending to mess in your business none, but it looks to me like you got yourself in for a peck of trouble when you went off and brought Miss Willie back here. It looks to me like she's got up for a city girl, more so than a country girl."

Vic cursed him.

"I'm telling you, Mr. Vic, you ought to marry yourself a wife who hadn't ought to sit on a high step in front of a stranger, not even when she's wearing something more than just only a skimpy outside dress. I walked out there and looked at Miss Willie, and, Mr. Vic, Miss Willie is as bare as a plucked chicken, except for one little place I saw."

"Shut up," Vic said, laying the steelyard down on the quilt beside him.

The man under the water oak closed the blade of the small penknife and put it into his pocket. The big hairy cowhide knife he flipped into the air and caught it easily on the back of his hand.

"Mr. Vic," Hubert said, "you've been asleep all the time and you don't know like I do. Miss Willie has been sitting there on that high step showing off her pretty a long time now, and he's got his pecker up. I know, Mr. Vic, because I went out there myself and looked."

Vic cursed him.

The man in the yard flipped the knife into the air and caught it behind his back.

"What's your name?" he asked Willie.

"Willie."

He flipped the knife again.

"What's yours?" she asked him, giggling.

"Floyd."

"Where are you from?"

"Carolina."

He flipped it higher than ever, catching it underhanded.

"What are you doing in Georgia?"

"Don't know," he said. "Just looking around."

Willie giggled, smiling at him.

Floyd got up and walked across the yard to the steps and sat down on the bottom one. He put his arms around his knees and looked up at Willie.

"You're not so bad-looking," he said. "I've seen lots worse-looking."

"You're not so bad yourself," Willie giggled, resting her arms on her knees and looking down at him.

"How about a kiss?"

"What would it be to you?"

"Not bad. I reckon I've had lots worse."

"Well, you can't get it sitting down there."

Floyd climbed the steps on his hands and feet and sat down on the next to the top step. He leaned against Willie, putting one arm around her waist and the other under her knees. Willie slid down the step beside him. Floyd pulled her to him, making a sucking sound with his lips.

"Boss," Hubert said, his lips twitching, "we ain't aiming to have no trouble today, is we?"

Vic cursed him.

Willie and Floyd moved down a step without loosening their embrace.

"Who is that yellow-headed sapsucker, anyhow?" Vic said. "I'll be dad-burned if he ain't got a lot of nerve—coming here and fooling with Willie."

"You wouldn't do nothing to cause trouble, would you, Mr. Vic? I surely don't want to have no trouble today, Mr. Vic."

Vic glanced at the eleven-inch knife Floyd had stuck into the step at his feet. It stood on its tip, twenty-two inches high, while the sun was reflected against the bright blade and made a streak of light on Floyd's pants leg.

"Go over there and take that knife away from him and bring it to me," Vic said. "Don't be scared of him."

"Mr. Vic, I surely hate to disappoint you, but if you want that white folk's knife, you'll just have to get it your own self. I don't aim to have myself all carved up with that thing. Mr. Vic, I surely can't accommodate you this time. If you want that white folk's knife, you'll just be bound to get it your own self, Mr. Vic."

Vic cursed him.

Hubert backed away until he was at the end of the porch. He kept looking behind him all the time, looking to be certain of the exact location of the sycamore stump that was between him and the pine grove on the other side of the cotton field.

Vic called to Hubert and told him to come back. Hubert came slowly around the corner of the porch and stood a few feet from the quilt where Vic was sitting. His lips quivered and the whites of his eyes grew larger. Vic motioned for him to come closer, but he would not come an inch farther.

"How old are you?" Floyd asked Willie.

"Fifteen."

Floyd jerked the knife out of the wood and thrust it deeper into the same place.

"How old are you?" she asked him.

"About twenty-seven."

"Are you married?"

"Not now," he said. "How long have you been?"

"About three months," Willie said.

"How do you like it?"

"Pretty good so far."

"How about another kiss?"

"You just had one."

"I'd like another one now."

"I ought not to let you kiss me again."

"Why not?"

"Men don't like girls who kiss too much."

"I'm not that kind."

"What kind are you?"

"I'd like to kiss you a lot."

"But after I let you do that, you'd go away."

"No, I won't. I'll stay for something else."

"What?"

"To get the rest of you."

"You might hurt me."

"It won't hurt."

"It might."

"Let's go inside for a drink and I'll show you."

"We'll have to go to the spring for fresh water."

"Where's the spring?"

"Just across the field in the grove."

"All right," Floyd said, standing up. "Let's go."

He bent down and pulled the knife out of the wood. Willie ran down the steps and across the yard. When Floyd saw that she was not going to wait for him, he ran after her, holding the knives in his pocket with one hand. She led him across the cotton field to the spring in the pine grove. Just before they got there, Floyd caught her by the arm and ran beside her the rest of the way.

"Boss," Hubert said, his voice trembling, "we ain't aiming to have no trouble today, is we?"

Vic cursed him.

"I don't want to get messed up with a heap of trouble and maybe get my belly slit open with that big hairy knife. If you ain't got objections, I reckon I'll mosey on home now and cut me a little firewood for the cookstove."

"Come back here!" Vic said. "You stay where you are and stop making moves to go off."

"What is we aiming to do, Mr. Vic?"

Vic eased himself off the porch and walked across the yard to the water oak. He looked down at the ground where Floyd had been sitting, and then he looked at the porch steps where Willie had been. The noonday heat beat down through the thin leaves overhead and he could feel his mouth and throat burn with the hot air he breathed.

"Have you got a gun, Hubert?"

"No, sir, boss," Hubert said.

"Why haven't you?" he said. "Right when I need a gun, you haven't got it. Why don't you keep a gun?"

"Mr. Vic, I ain't got no use for a gun. I used to keep one to shoot rabbits and squirrels with, but I got to thinking hard one day, and I traded it off the first chance I got. I reckon it was a good thing I traded, too. If I had kept it, you'd be asking for it like you did just now."

Vic went back to the porch and picked up the steelyard and hammered the porch with it. After he had hit the porch four or five times, he dropped it and started out in the direction of the spring. He walked as far as the edge of the shade and stopped. He stood listening for a while.

Willie and Floyd could be heard down near the spring. Floyd said something to Willie, and Willie laughed loudly. There was silence again for several minutes, and then Willie laughed again. Vic could not tell whether she was crying or laughing. He was getting ready to turn and go back to the porch when he heard her cry out. It sounded like a scream, but it was not exactly that; it sounded like a shriek, but it wasn't that, either; it sounded more like someone laughing and crying simultaneously in a high-pitched, excited voice.

"Where did Miss Willie come from, Mr. Vic?" Hubert asked. "Where did you bring her from?"

"Down below here a little way," he said.

Hubert listened to the sounds that were coming from the pine grove.

"Boss," he said after a little while, "it appears to me like you didn't go far enough away."

"I went far enough," Vic said. "If I had gone any farther, I'd have been in Florida."

The colored man hunched his shoulders forward several times while he smoothed the white sand with his broad-soled shoes.

"Mr. Vic, if I was you, the next time I'd surely go that far, maybe farther."

"What do you mean, the next time?"

"I was figuring that maybe you wouldn't be keeping her much longer than now, Mr. Vic."

Vic cursed him.

Hubert raised his head several times and attempted to see down into the pine grove over the top of the growing cotton.

"Shut up and mind your own business," Vic said. "I'm going to keep her till the cows come home. Where else do you reckon I'd find a better-looking girl than Willie?"

"Boss, I wasn't thinking of how she looks—I was thinking of how she acts. That white man came here and sat down and it wasn't no time before she had his pecker up."

"She acts that way because she ain't old enough yet to know who to fool with. She'll catch on in time."

Hubert followed Vic across the yard. While Vic went toward the porch, Hubert stopped and leaned against the water oak where he could almost see over the cotton field into the pine grove. Vic went up on the porch and stretched out on the quilt. He took off his shoes and flung them aside.

"I surely God knowed something was going to happen when he whittled that stick down to nothing," Hubert was saying to himself. "White folks take a long time to whittle a little piece of wood, but when they whittle it down to nothing, they're going to be up and doing before the time ain't long."

Presently Vic sat upright on the quilt.

"Listen here, Hubert——"

"Yes, sir, boss!"

"You keep your eye on that stillyerd so it will stay right where it is now, and when they come back up the path, you wake me up in a hurry."

"Yes, sir, boss," Hubert said. "Are you aiming to take a little nap now?"

"Yes, I am. And if you don't wake me up when they come back, I'll break your neck for you when I do wake up."

Vic lay down again on the quilt and turned over on his side to shut out the blinding glare of the early afternoon sun that was reflected upon the porch from the hard white sand in the yard.

Hubert scratched his head and sat down against the water oak, facing the path from the spring. He could hear Vic snoring on the porch above the sounds that came at intervals from the pine grove across the field. He sat staring down the path, drowsy, singing under his breath. It was a long time until sundown.

JOHN O'HARA (1905–   )

An ardent explorer of his particular territory and a hater of pomposity in any field, John O'Hara has been termed "the voice of the hang-over generation" who was "the Boswell of the post-Scott Fitzgerald era." After a catch-as-catch-can newspaper career, he had a smashing success with his first novel, Appointment in Samarra, which was followed by the even more sensational Butterfield 8.

Although O'Hara continued to write pungent and often provoking novels, he also published short stories which were praised by the critics for their social documentation, and enjoyed by uncritical readers for their penetration. His Pal Joey series, centering about night-club entertainers, flesh peddlers, and other semi-illiterates, was enlarged into a musical comedy that, unlike its genre, did not try to make a hero out of a heel.

JOEY AND THE CALCUTTA CLUB

Pal Ted: Well, Chum, the poor man's Bing Crosby is still making with the throat here in Chi. but if the present good fortune keeps up I ought to be getting the New York break pretty soon. The trouble is up to now the good fortune has been keeping so far up it is up in the stratuspere out of sight. But never out of mind, kiddy. Never out of mind. N.Y. is where I belong N.Y. or Hollywood or will settle for both. However have been off the bread line and working steady but you do not see me on the caviare line yet and was always a one to have the ambition to starve to death within reach of caviare if you get what I mean. If I have to starve to death it would be this way, namely, have about 5 lbs. of caviare and filet mignon & champagne etc. but me too God damn lazy to reach for it. Maybe to make it perfect I would be firsting my attentons on like Hedy La Marr instead of just plain lazy and would be so busy would forget to eat. That is the manner in which I would prefer to starve to death.

Well, speaking of the charming opposite sex I have a little spot of annecdotes (I dote on annecdotes) to tell you which may amuse the chappies around Lebuses and give them all my best excepting those that I would not say I would not spit on them as I can hardly wait to spit on them. Well this is the story and not only a story but also a good thing to keep in mind in case you get in the same situation some time yourself.

Shortly after I got started working here, a little mouse came in one nite with a party of six and naturally began asking for request nos. and in that way I got aquainted and also thru knowing one of the guys on the party. It was not a spending party, strictly cufferoo. The guy is a fellow named Quinn on one of the local papers here in Chi. and covers nite clubs, etc. and signs his initials L. Q. to reviews he gives the spots here & there but mostly in the Loop etc. So Quinn asked me to join them and I did and this mouse with them named Jean Benedict looks like 10000 other dames on the line of some Bway show except when she opens her trap she has an accent that is so British even Sir Nevile Chamberlin would not be able to understand her. I knew she was strictly U.S.A. by appearance but the accent is so good I think what is the angle. What gives, I asked her, altho not in so many words. I inquired how she happen to have the accent and she said a lot of people inquire of her the same thing and it is easily explained. She is half American and her father is British. Well she sounded so refined I wanted to say a few one syllable words to her to note the effect to see if she would know what I meant. Well I did not, not that nite. About three nites later. The 1st nite all she did was say why didn't I call her up at her flat and drop in for a gin and "it." I said the "it" was o. k. with me if we were both talking about the same thing and she put on the act as if not getting "it" and then said priceless. Oh, how wrong she was when she said priceless but am getting ahead of my story.

Well on acc't of a certain other obligation which I mentoned in my prevous letter I could not give my full attenton to Miss Benedict but will just say in passing if I would of given her any more attenton at the rate I was going I would now not be cutting paper dolls. Oh no. I would not be able to lift a paper doll. However let me suffice it to say that I moved in & during the course of our more dull conversatons I accertain that Miss Benedict is living with this other mouse whom I do not meet. They are sharing this flat. Also she tells me her dear mother and dear papa are in dear old London. I never asked her that. All I asked her was did she live alone, etc. and now I recall it she certanly did jump at the chance to explain about the old man and the mother. I should of known that the English have more reserve about personal affairs but I guess I had good reason to forget all about reserve in connecton with Miss B. Anyway she gave me the routine about father & mother being in London that day and two days later when "love dropped in for tea" meaning me, she kept standing by the window and looking out and when I would say anything to her she would act like as if she did not hear me and then I finally said pardon me but remember me I am yr. pal Joey, the fellow that just came in about 15 mins. ago and didnt we meet at the club etc. She said "I apologize" but she was upset and maybe it would be better if I did not stay but went out to a picture that day as she was not herself. I must say the girl is an actress because I honestly tho't I squeezed it out of her that her check from her old man was late and she said no doubt because of the way things have been in dear old London. She said she always got her check of $300 by the 7th of the month, sometimes earlier. But here it was the 10 or 11 of the month and no check and no letter either. The check always came with a letter and she worried about if they sent her father off on some misson for the gov't and it was so important he was not allowed to leave her know he was even going away. He was some important fellow in the office that runs India and maybe they sent him there. It was not only the money but what if it was an important dangerous misson? What about her mother, I inquired? Well, she said that was where she swore me to secrecy and told me that her mother was an American but also had a lot to do with India, also some kind of an agent but American in name only so as to keep her passport. Well of course all this went on for a half an hr. and eventually I was a sucker for the touch. I admit it. I let her have $75.

Well I gave her my oath I would not tell about her people being sort of spies against India but even so would not of told anybody about it as I did not want it to get around that I went for a $75 touch as you get the reputaton of being a soft touch like that and pretty soon girls from all over the country are waiting at yr. dressing room and also I had this "other obligaton" if *she* heard I was putting out 75 here and there she would take back her car and maybe even get me the bounceroo from this spot. So I kept quite but one nite soon after I happen to see Quinn and went over to thank him for a nice menton and he started out by asking me how was Miss Benedict. I played dumb and he said, "Oh, I tho't you were in. I took for granted you were in and how did you happen to miss that as I was given to understand that you are a young man that moved right in." Well imagine, I burned and said "Listen, wise guy not only am I in but the nite you bro't her here she slipped me her phone no. with you sitting at the table." I could of cut my throat when I realized what I said, insulting the guy after he gave me the good notice but instead he did not get sore. On the contrary he replied, "Ah, then perhaps you will join our little club. What did she take you for?" I said for nothing. And he said "Oh, you can level with me, do you mean to say she did not put the touch on you for a little, like a yard?" So I admitted it and then he told me. It seems that I was a member of quite a club, and a paid up member too. Miss B. took Quinn for 50 and another guy for 50 and another for 75 and one guy for around 300, a middle aged fellow that sold religous articles to churches and did not want any trouble. So Quinn said we ought to form a club called the Calcutta Club after the town over in India. Well I saw the humor of it but I would of liked to give Miss B. a kick in the stomach if she came along at the time.

Well I put it down to experience and tho't no more of it till about two wks. later Quinn came in and told me he had a propositon, not his but Miss B's. It seems what she did was take our India money and move out and get a more expensive flat by herself without the girl friend and after she moved in she was there about two weeks and met some guy from Milwaukee that tho't she was right and so much so that this guy was already talking wedding bells even before he moved in. She had him thinking it made her sick to see a woman smoke and she never went out to nite spots but always had a good book around. How she picked him up I dont know but he was going for everything. He had no suspicons aroused because at the time she was absolutely staying away from the spots. Well she only had two wks. to go she told Quinn before the rent was due and that meant only two wks. to work on the prospect from Milwaukee, so the propositon she put to Quinn was if we would stake her to the next month's rent and she felt sure that was all she would need. He asked me what I tho't of it and he said frankly he had no $50 to throw away but he would rather throw the 50 away on a chance of getting the 100 back and he advised me to do the same. He won me over but I told him on one conditon, namely, how did we know there was this sucker from Milwaukee and so it was agreed that if she could produce him and convince us then we would put up the ready. So that was how it was and a nite or two later she came in the club and him with her and I took one quick gander at him and was convinced but to make sure I stopped at the table suddenly like I just recognized him and said, "I beg yr. pardon but havent we met. I am sure I met you in Milwaukee last yr." and the way he got red and said no I knew he was from Milwaukee and I also knew something Miss B. did not know as smart as she was, namely, he was dumb but not that dumb that he would marry her, but was willing to put up the rent etc. Well that was o. k. She pretend to go to the little girls rm. and I had a talk with her and told her I was in favor of the propositon and would tell the other members of the club I was and she would have the front money. But I also told her that Mr. Milwaukee was not going to marry her if I knew human nature and she said to me, "Joey, darling, I could almost like you for being so intelligent, if for nothing else." She said "I told Quinn that Chubby (the nickname for the Milwaukee guy) did not move in but he did move in but Quinn is a dope and I had to tell him a good story. What I want the front money for is so Chubby will get expensive ideas and not get the idea that he is only going for coffee and cakes dough." Then she gave me a little kiss on the cheek and said "that will have to be all for the present but we shall see what we shall see." So the boys all got their dough back last wk. including me but I got mine in three 50 dollar bills inclosed in a gold clip with a watch on it. You have to admire a girl like that from Buffalo, N.Y. where she is from. That is how English she is. She has relatons in Canada. Anyway she is a very smart little operator and I predict great things for her. She got me putting on a little wt. as Chubby likes caviare and she always keeps some in the frigidair for him but all we singers put on wt. like Caruso, McCormick, Crosby, etc.

YRS.

PAL JOEY

GIOVANNI GUARESCHI (1908–   )

The Little World of Don Camillo *revolves about a continuing feud between Don Camillo, the town's devout but unorthodox priest, and Peppone,
the town's Communist mayor. The little stories which describe this little
world are both tender and ribald, irreverent yet full of a spirited faith in
men of good well. The author, Giovanni Guareschi, is an artist, journalist,
and editor who informs us that the locale of his book is almost any village
in the valley of the Po River in northern Italy.*

*At the end of his introduction, Guareschi adds this final word as a kind of
explanation:* "If there is a priest anywhere who feels offended by my treatment of Don Camillo, he is welcome to break the biggest candle over my
head. And if there is a Communist who feels offended by Peppone, he is
welcome to break a hammer and sickle on my back. But if there is anyone
who is offended by the conversations of Christ, I can't help it; for the one
who speaks in this story is not Christ but my Christ—that is, the voice of
my conscience." *Full of irrepressible humor mixed with physical fun, Don
Camillo is one of the liveliest and most lovable priests in modern fiction.*

FROM: THE LITTLE WORLD OF DON CAMILLO

A BAPTISM

One day Don Camillo, perched high on a ladder, was busily polishing St.
Joseph's halo. Unexpectedly a man and two women, one of whom was Peppone's wife, came into the church. Don Camillo turned around to ask what
they wanted.

"There is something here to be baptized," replied the man, and one of
the women held up a bundle containing a baby.

"Whose is it?" inquired Don Camillo, coming down from his ladder.

"Mine," replied Peppone's wife.

"And your husband's?" persisted Don Camillo.

"Well, naturally! Who else would be the father? You, maybe?" retorted
Peppone's wife indignantly.

"No need to be offended," observed Don Camillo on his way to the sacristy.
"I've been told often enough that your party approves of free love."

As he passed before the high altar Don Camillo knelt down and gave a
discreet wink in the direction of Christ. "Did you hear that one?" he murmured with a happy grin. "One in the eye for the Godless ones!"

"Don't talk rubbish, Don Camillo," replied Christ irritably. "If they had
no God why should they come here to get their child baptized? If Peppone's
wife had boxed your ears it would have served you right."

"If Peppone's wife had boxed my ears I should have taken the three of
them by the scruff of their necks and . . ."

"And what?" Christ asked severely.

"Oh, nothing; just a figure of speech," Don Camillo hastened to assure Him, rising to his feet.

"Don Camillo, watch your step," Christ said sternly.

Duly vested, Don Camillo approached the baptismal font. "What do you wish to name this child?" he asked Peppone's wife.

"Lenin, Libero, Antonio," she replied.

"Then go and get him baptized in Russia," said Don Camillo calmly, replacing the cover on the font.

The priest's hands were as big as shovels, and the three left the church without protest. But as Don Camillo tried to slip into the sacristy he was stopped by the voice of Christ. "Don Camillo, you have done a very wicked thing. Go at once and bring those people back and baptize their child."

"But, Lord," protested Don Camillo, "You really must bear in mind that baptism is a very sacred matter. Baptism is . . ."

"Don Camillo," Christ interrupted him, "are you trying to teach me the nature of baptism? Didn't I invent it? I tell you that you have been guilty of gross presumption, because if that child were to die at this moment it would be your fault if it failed to attain Paradise!"

"Lord, let us not be melodramatic! Why in the name of Heaven should it die? It's as pink and white as a rose!"

"That doesn't mean a thing!" Christ pointed out. "What if a tile should fall on its head or it suddenly had convulsions? It was your duty to baptize it."

Don Camillo raised his hands in protest. "But, Lord, think it over. If it were certain that the child would go to Hell, then we might stretch a point. But since he might easily manage to slip into Heaven, in spite of his father, how can You ask me to risk anyone getting in there with a name like Lenin? I'm thinking of the reputation of Heaven."

"The reputation of Heaven is my business," shouted Christ angrily. "What matters to me is that a man should be a decent fellow, and I care less than nothing whether his name be Lenin or Button. At the very most, you should have pointed out to those people that saddling children with fantastic names may be a nuisance to them when they grow up."

"Very well," replied Don Camillo. "I am always wrong. I'll see what I can do."

Just then someone came into the church. It was Peppone, alone, with the baby in his arms. He closed the church door behind him and bolted it. "I'm not leaving this church," he said, "until my son has been baptized with the name that I have chosen."

"Look at that," whispered Don Camillo, smiling as he turned to Christ. "Now do You see what these people are? One is filled with the holiest intentions, and this is how they treat you."

"Put yourself in his place," Christ replied. "One may not approve of his attitude but one can understand it."

Don Camillo shook his head.

"I have already said that I do not leave this place unless you baptize my son!" repeated Peppone. After laying the bundle containing the baby upon a bench he took off his coat, rolled up his sleeves, and came toward the priest threateningly.

"Lord," implored Don Camillo. "I ask You! If You think one of Your priests should give way to the threats of a layman, then I must obey. But if I do and tomorrow they bring me a calf and compel me to baptize it, You must not complain. You know very well how dangerous it is to create precedents."

"All right, but in this case you must try to make him understand . . ."

"And if he hits me?"

"Then you must accept it. You must endure and suffer as I did."

Don Camillo turned to his visitor. "Very well, Peppone," he said. "The baby will leave the church baptized, but not with that accursed name."

"Don Camillo," stuttered Peppone, "don't forget that my stomach has never recovered from that bullet I stopped in the mountains. If you hit low I go after you with a bench."

"Don't worry, Peppone; I can deal with you entirely in the upper stories," Don Camillo assured him, landing a quick one above his ear.

They were both burly men and their blows whistled through the air. After twenty minutes of speechless and furious combat, Don Camillo distinctly heard a voice behind him.

"Now, Don Camillo! A left to the jaw!" It came from Christ above the altar. Don Camillo struck hard and Peppone crashed to the ground.

He remained there for about ten minutes; then he sat up, got to his feet, rubbed his jaw, shook himself, put on his jacket and reknotted his red handkerchief. Then he picked up the baby. Fully vested, Don Camillo was waiting, steady as a rock, beside the font. Peppone approached him slowly.

"What are we going to name him?" asked Don Camillo.

"Camillo, Libero, Antonio," muttered Peppone.

Don Camillo shook his head. "No; we will name him Libero, Camillo, Lenin," he said. "After all, the Camillo will cancel out Lenin any day."

"Amen," muttered Peppone, still massaging his jaw.

When all was done and Don Camillo passed before the altar, Christ smiled and remarked: "Don Camillo, I have to admit that in politics you are my master."

"And in boxing," replied Don Camillo with perfect gravity, carelessly fingering a large lump on his forehead.

OUT OF BOUNDS

Don Camillo used to go back and measure the famous crack in the church tower, and every morning his inspection met with the same result: the crack got no wider but neither did it get smaller. Finally he lost his temper, and the day came when he sent the sacristan to the Town Hall.

"Go and tell the mayor to come at once and look at this damage. Explain that the matter is serious."

The sacristan went and returned.

"Peppone says that he will take your word for it that it is a serious matter. He also said that if you really want to show him the crack, you had better take the tower to him in his office. He will be there until five o'clock."

Don Camillo didn't bat an eye; all he said was, "If Peppone or any member of his gang has the courage to turn up at Mass tomorrow morning, I'll fix them. But they know it and probably not one of them will come."

The next morning there was not a sign of a "red" in church, but five minutes before Mass was due to begin the sound of marching was heard outside the church. In perfect formation all the "reds," not only those of the village but also those of the neighboring cells, including the cobbler, Bilo, who had a wooden leg, and Roldo dei Prati who was shivering with fever, came marching proudly toward the church led by Peppone. They took their places in the church, sitting in a solid phalanx with faces as ferocious as Russian generals.

Don Camillo finished his sermon on the parable of the good Samaritan, with a brief plea to the faithful.

"As you all know, a most dangerous crack is threatening the church tower. I therefore appeal to you, my dear brethren, to come to the assistance of the house of God. In using the term 'brethren,' I am addressing those who came here with a desire to draw near to God, and not certain people who come only in order to parade their militarism. To such as these, it can matter nothing should the tower fall to the ground."

The Mass over, Don Camillo settled himself at a table near the door, and the congregation filed past him. Each one, after making the expected donation, joined the crowd in the little square in front of the church to watch developments. And last of all came Peppone, followed by his battalion in perfect formation. They drew to a defiant halt before the table.

Peppone stepped forward proudly.

"From this tower, in the past, the bells have hailed the dawn of freedom and from it, tomorrow, they shall welcome the glorious dawn of the proletarian revolution," Peppone said to Don Camillo, as he laid on the table three large red handkerchiefs full of money.

Then he truned on his heel and marched away, followed by his gang. And Roldo dei Prati was shaking with fever and could scarcely remain on his feet, but he held his head erect, and the crippled Bilo as he passed Don Camillo stamped his wooden leg defiantly in perfect step with his comrades.

When Don Camillo went to the Lord to show Him the basket containing the money and told Him that there was more than enough for the repair of the tower, Christ smiled in astonishment.

"I guess your sermon did the trick, Don Camillo."

"Naturally," replied Don Camillo. "You see You understand humanity, but I know Italians."

Up to that point Don Camillo had behaved pretty well. But he made a mistake when he sent a message to Peppone, saying that he admired the military smartness of the men but advising Peppone to give them more intensive drilling in the rightabout-face and the double, which they would need badly on the day of the proletarian revolution.

This was deplorable and Peppone planned to retaliate.

Don Camillo was an honest man, but in addition to an overwhelming passion for hunting, he possessed a splendid double-barreled gun and a good supply of cartridges. Moreover, Baron Stocco's private preserve lay only three miles from the village. It presented a permanent temptation, because not only game but even the neighborhood poultry had learned that they were in safety behind the fence of wire netting.

It was therefore not astonishing that on a certain evening Don Camillo, his cassock bundled into an enormous pair of breeches and his face partly concealed beneath the brim of an old felt hat, should find himself actually on the business side of the baron's fence. The flesh is weak and the flesh of the sportsman particularly so.

Nor was it surprising, since Don Camillo was a good shot, that he brought down a fine rabbit almost under his nose. He stuffed it into his game bag and was making a getaway when he suddenly came face to face with another trespasser. There was no alternative but to butt the stranger in the stomach with the hope of knocking him out and thereby saving the countryside the embarrassment of learning that their parish priest had been caught poaching.

Unfortunately, the stranger conceived the same idea at the same moment. The two heads met with a crack that left both men side by side on the ground seeing stars.

"A skull as hard as that can only belong to our beloved mayor," muttered Don Camillo, as his vision began to clear.

"A skull as hard as that can only belong to our beloved priest," replied Peppone, scratching his head. For Peppone, too, was poaching on forbidden ground and he, too, had a fine rabbit in his game bag. His eyes gleamed as he observed Don Camillo.

"Never would I have believed that the very man who preaches respect for other people's property would be found breaking through the fences of a preserve to go poaching," said Peppone.

"Nor would I have believed that our chief citizen, our comrade mayor . . ."

"Citizen, yes, but also comrade," Peppone interrupted, "and therefore perverted by those diabolical theories of the fair distribution of all property, and therefore acting more in accordance with his known views than the reverend Don Camillo, who, for his part . . ."

This ideological analysis was suddenly interrupted. Someone was approaching them and was so near that it was quite impossible to escape without the risk of stopping a bullet, for the intruder happened to be a gamekeeper.

"We've got to do something!" whispered Don Camillo. "Think of the scandal if we are recognized!"

"Personally, I don't care," replied Peppone with composure. "I am always ready to answer for my actions."

The steps drew nearer, and Don Camillo crouched against a large tree trunk. Peppone made no attempt to move, and when the gamekeeper appeared with his gun over his arm, Peppone greeted him:

"Good evening."

"What are you doing here?" inquired the gamekeeper.

"Looking for mushrooms."

"With a gun?"

"As good a way as another."

The means whereby a gamekeeper can be rendered innocuous are fairly simple. If one happens to be standing behind him, it suffices to muffle his head unexpectedly in an overcoat and give him a good crack on the head. Then advantage can be taken of his momentary unconsciousness to reach the fence and scramble over it. Once over, all is well.

Don Camillo and Peppone found themselves sitting behind a bush a good mile away from the baron's estate.

"Don Camillo!" sighed Peppone. "We have committed a serious offense. We have raised our hands against one in authority!"

Don Camillo, who had actually been the one to raise them, broke out into a cold sweat.

"My conscience troubles me," continued Peppone, watching his companion closely. "I shall have no peace. How can I go before a priest of God to ask forgiveness for such a misdeed? It was an evil day when I listened to the infamous 'Muscovite doctrine,' forgetting the holy precepts of Christian charity!"

Don Camillo was so deeply humiliated that he wanted to cry. On the other hand, he also wanted to land one good crack on the skull of his perverted adversary. As Peppone was well aware of this, he stopped talking for a moment. Then suddenly he shouted, "Accursed temptation!" and pulled the rabbit out of his bag and threw it on the ground.

"Accursed indeed!" shouted Don Camillo and, hauling out his own rabbit, he flung it far into the snow and walked away with bent head. Peppone followed him as far as the crossroad and then turned to the right.

"By the way," he said, pausing for a moment, "could you tell me of a reputable parish priest in this neighborhood to whom I could go and confess this sin?"

Don Camillo clenched his fists and walked straight ahead.

When he had gathered sufficient courage, Don Camillo went before the main altar of the church. "I didn't do it to save myself, Lord," he said. "I did it simply because, if it were known that I go poaching, the Church would have been the chief sufferer from the scandal."

But Christ remained silent. Now whenever this happened Don Camillo acquired a fever and put himself on a diet of bread and water for days and days, until Christ felt sorry for him and said: "Enough."

This time, Christ said nothing until the bread and water diet had continued for seven days. Don Camillo was so weak that he could remain standing only by leaning against a wall, and his stomach was rumbling from hunger.

Then Peppone came to confession.

"I have sinned against the law and against Christian charity," said Peppone.

"I know it," replied Don Camillo.

"What you don't know is that, as soon as you were out of sight, I went back and collected both the rabbits. I have roasted one and stewed the other."

"Just what I supposed you would do," murmured Don Camillo. And when he passed the altar a little later, Christ smiled at him, not so much because of the prolonged fast as because Don Camillo, when he murmured "Just what I supposed you would do," had felt no desire to hit Peppone. Instead he had felt profound shame, recalling that on that same evening he himself had had a momentary temptation to do exactly the same thing.

"Poor Don Camillo," whispered Christ tenderly. And Don Camillo spread out his arms as though he wished to say that he did his best and that if he sometimes made mistakes it was not deliberately.

"I know, I know, Don Camillo," replied the Lord. "And now get along and eat your rabbit—for Peppone has left it for you, nicely cooked, in your kitchen."

WILLIAM J. LEDERER (1912-   )

When William J. Lederer wrote All the Ship's at Sea—*the apostrophe is important—he knew what he was writing about. He had seen service as secretary to the columnist Heywood Broun, reporter on the New York Times, factory worker in a radio plant, and enlisted man in the Navy, where he was advanced to the rank of commander and chief of Magazine and Book Division, Office of Public Information. According to a confidential report from Lederer's secretary, he was always "in sixteen different kinds of trouble and always wiggling out in a blaze of glory—the kind of guy who stubs his toe on a rock and finds a thousand dollar bill under it." "The Skipper's Pink Panties," while dubiously autobiographical, discloses the author's trouble-making and laugh-rousing propensities.*

THE SKIPPER'S PINK PANTIES

When Captain Burke received orders to China, I pulled strings to go with him. No luck. The Bureau of Navigation said "—Ensign Lederer needs more seasoning before a tour in the Orient."

The day Captain Burke left, we nearly cried. Especially as the *Fortune's* new skipper, Captain "Bullet Head" Poindexter, didn't measure up to the recent standard. A huge man with a small head and a high-pitched voice, he made it clear from the start that everything in the ship revolved about him.

As a shiphandler and a tactician, Captain Poindexter carried out his duties in a sound manner. In his human relations he fell into an error too common to military men: he believed because he was a military expert that, ipso facto, he also had a greater knowledge of philosophy, art, sex, philology, etc., than any person beneath him in rank.

Captain Poindexter enjoyed stating a theory at mealtime and then, with big words, ramming it down the throats of his, in his opinion, untutored junior officers. He usually memorized articles in the encyclopedia before coming to the wardroom.

When he learned that I was the ship's radical—that is, a believer in the New Deal—Captain Poindexter (an Old Guard Republican) addressed his mealtime discussions in my general direction. Before many months went by I violently disputed the Old Man's theories. Frankly, his mind operated slowly; and ruining his theories was easy. Often I embarrassed him; the more I argued the more annoyed he became. It became a fad with me to foul up the captain's pompousness, and I used every sophistry and dirty trick in the book.

For example, once, after a lengthy wrangle, the captain angrily concluded with his clincher argument. "Irregardless, Lederer, the fact remains that Americans are better farmers than Chinese. Max Store in his book, *The Orient in Rebellion*, clearly proves this."

"Captain," I said smugly, "I'm afraid there's no such word as irregardless. And as for Mr. Store, he never saw a Chinese farmer in his life. No one who knows *anything* about the Orient would accept a word——"

The Old Man exploded. "I'm sick and tired of your shyster arguments and sharp practices. Now listen to me. I don't want you ever to open your mouth in this wardroom again. Do you understand? That's an order! As long as I'm commanding officer, you keep your mouth shut. Shut tight."

"Aye, aye, sir."

"Except," continued the skipper, "if I tell a joke. And then, by God, you lean back in your chair and laugh and laugh and laugh."

We ensigns all agreed that I won that round.

I soon found out that actually I had lost it. Captain Poindexter wasn't kidding. The next day, when I made a remark at lunch, he ordered me to my room for two days for failing to carry out his orders. A week later he showed me the first draft of my fitness report.

"Although this young officer carries out his duties well," the report read, "he has an inclination to be unco-operative with the commanding officer. He has applied for duty in China. His commanding officer has recommended that this not be approved until Ensign Lederer acquires more social maturity. His perspective on respect due a senior officer is slightly warped."

The fitness report, if sent in, could easily ruin my career. Furthermore, upon thinking the thing over, I concluded that the captain had a lot of truth on his side. I decided to woo the guy scientifically.

I bought *How to Win Friends and Influence People* and read it carefully. It seemed that the way to gain back the Old Man's friendship was to ask him his advice on personal questions and, later, when the opportunity arose, let him beat me in a discussion.

Meanwhile, I got into a bit of trouble somewhere else. I told a young lady at a dance that her petticoat was showing; she, having a couple of drinks under her girdle, felt offended and slapped me. She told an admiral that I had been fresh with her. He reprimanded me.

Here, I thought, was the time to seek Captain Poindexter's counsel.

The next morning, at breakfast, I brought up the problem.

"Captain, sir, I'm in some personal trouble and would very much appreciate your advice on the matter."

There came a long silence, during which time I didn't know whether he'd send me to my room again for talking, or help me out.

"What's your trouble?" he said finally.

"Sir," I said, dropping my eyes and trying to look contrite, "last night I went to a dance. I noticed that one girl's petticoat hung down. I went up to her politely, trying to be helpful, and told—"

"Petticoat!" roared the skipper looking up from his pork chop and scrambled eggs. "Did I hear you say petticoat?"

"Yes, sir."

He put his hand to his head and opened his mouth as if he had seen a ghost. "Petticoat! You mean a slip, man, a slip! Women haven't worn petticoats for thirty years."

I said nothing.

"Do you know the difference between a petticoat and a slip?"

"No, sir."

"Good heavens! Can there be an officer on my ship as dumb as that?" The captain warmed to his subject.

"Do you know what a redingote is?" he asked.

"No, sir."

"What's a dirndl?"

"I don't know, sir."

"A jabot?"

"I don't know, sir."

"An officer on my ship!" moaned the captain. "Is it possible?"

The Old Man waved for Abe to bring him another pork chop. While waiting for it, he continued working me over.

"Mr. Lederer, are you familiar with Article 912, U.S. Navy Regulations?"

"No, sir. But I'll look it up."

"Don't bother. I'll tell you—it says that I, as your commanding officer, am responsible for your professional training. And, by gad, mister, I'm going to see that the regulations are carried out."

"I appreciate it, sir."

He continued. "No one's going to say I neglected my duty. Being a good officer is more than conning a ship and shooting the guns. It also embraces knowing your way around in society."

The skipper's pork chop arrived.

"It's evident to me," said the Old Man, "that you haven't had much experience with women. A petticoat!"

"I'll admit I'm pretty shy, sir."

"Shy! You just haven't been around. How old are you?"

"Twenty-six, sir."

"And you don't know a blessed thing about undergarments. Lederer——"

"No, sir. I'm pretty ignorant on that subject."

"I want you to go out with a woman over this weekend," Captain Poindexter chuckled. His chuckle turned into a belly laugh. "Oh ho! What a situation. Ho, ohhh, ho!"

"Aye, aye, sir," I said, smiling.

"Mister, this is no joking matter. I'm ordering you to take a woman out this weekend."

"Aye, aye, sir."

"And bring back a hunk of her underwear to prove it. Bring back her step-ins. You know what step-ins are, I hope."

"Yes, sir."

"Very well, mister. Go ashore in the first liberty boat and carry out your orders. Good hunting, son," he said, running into another belly laugh.

That afternoon, after going ashore, I looked up a married classmate and explained the problem. His wife bought a cheap pair of pink step-ins for me. I sprinkled some sand on them, wrapped them up in a damp towel, and threw the bundle in the back of my car. I would bring the panties out to the ship on Monday.

However, the next evening, Sunday, I turned the matter over in my mind and decided that it wouldn't be dignified showing the underclothes on the ship in front of my shipmates. I telephoned the captain's home to ask him if I could bring my trophy to his house.

Mrs. Poindexter answered.

"No, Mr. Lederer, the captain isn't home. He went fishing over the weekend. Can I take a message?"

"No, ma'am, it's nothing important, thank you."

It occurred to me that the captain might appreciate my being nice to his wife, so I invited her to come to the open-air movies with me at the Strand, a couple of miles down the beach from Coronado. She accepted. We saw the late showing of *The Baroness and the Butler* and I left her at her home about 11 P.M.

"When you see the captain tonight, Mrs. Poindexter," I said as I left her porch, "please tell him I got what he ordered. He'll know what I mean."

"He won't be back this evening. He won't be back until the morning and he's going straight out to the ship."

Leaving the captain's home, I went to the club and turned in, returning to the *Fortune* at 0745 the next morning, clutching the towel with my precious panties wrapped in it.

The officer of the deck stopped me as I reached the main deck.

"The Old Man left word to send you below pronto. He's got a mob down there."

"A mob?"

"Yeh, looks like the skippers and execs from every ship in the squadron came over to inspect your loot. The Old Man's putting you on the spot, too. He's told them the whole story about ordering you to go out with a gal and bring back her pants. Now you better hurry; it's only ten minutes until quarters."

"He's done me dirt," I muttered on my way to the wardroom.

The officer of the deck hadn't exaggerated. The place was so jammed with senior officers that I couldn't get beyond the entrance.

The buzz of many voices stopped as I appeared.

"Well, sir," the Old Man greeted me sternly, "have you carried out your orders?"

I took the pink garment from the towel and held it up.

Cheers resounded throughout the wardroom.

"Gentlemen," said the captain, "I'm proud to announce that Ensign Lederer has carried his mission to a successful conclusion, as you can see. His courage, resourcefulness, determination and, may I say, good taste, reflect credit upon himself and upon the naval service——"

"Speech! Speech!"

"—And now, perhaps, we can persuade him to tell us just how he obtained such a beautiful and useful piece of apparel. Yes, tell us about it, son."

More cheers.

I hesitated.

"Come on, mister," said Captain Poindexter, "speak up."

"Aw gosh," I said, "there was nothing to it. I just carried out your orders." Everyone shouted.

"You seen your duty and you done it all right!"

"You can come over to my ship as supply officer any time you want," said one of the skippers, laughing and enthusiastically pumping my hand.

"Give us the pitch on your technique."

I didn't know what to do; but here, at least, was my opportunity to show the Old Man that I was co-operative.

I looked at him. He nodded for me to go ahead.

"Well, if you insist," I said, "it was like this. Last night we were driving along the beach——"

I paused for effect.

A half dozen destroyer captains hung on every syllable. I decided to lay it on thick.

"There was a big moon," I continued. "The surf thundered on the beach, and yellow lights twinkled from nearby cottages. The top of the car was down and the summer breeze blew through my companion's hair——"

"Well," laughed someone, "at last we've got the girl in the picture."

Captain Poindexter held up his hand.

"Give him a chance, he'll tell us the story."

The situation worried me. What I had intended as a funny yarn looked as if it might get out of hand. I glanced at my watch; it was three minutes until morning quarters. If I could stall for just that long, then the meeting would break up of its own accord. I continued.

"'What a wonderful night,' my girl said to me. 'Let's stop for a while and look at the moon. We have plenty of time.'"

My audience laughed. Only a minute and a half to go until quarters.

"I stopped the car," I went on. "We put our heads back and looked at the big silvery moon. It seemed as if it were about to drop into the ocean——"

"Never mind the build-up," called the heckler. "Let's get down to business. How did you get the drawers?"

"What's the babe's name and telephone number?" asked another.

I bit my lip.

"Go ahead," said Captain Poindexter, "give us the dope on this little rendezvous. You're among shipmates. Let your hair down and tell all."

The wardroom buzzer sounded.

Hopefully I thought that it might be the signal for morning quarters. But no, thirty seconds to go yet. The buzzer gave notice that the squadron commodore (a grand guy, my old instructor at Annapolis) had come aboard. Captain Poindexter made a move to meet him, but before he could reach the passageway the commodore descended the ladder leading to the wardroom. Seeing me standing apparently alone in the entrance, he greeted me.

"Good morning, Lederer; hey, didn't I see you driving on the beach about midnight last night with——"

He paused to catch his breath, and everyone in the wardroom nearly fell out of his shoes waiting for the rest of the sentence.

"—with Mrs. Poindexter? That was Mrs. Poindexter, wasn't it?"

I didn't say anything. The blood rushed to my head and I felt like running and hiding in the bilges. The commodore stood there waiting for an answer.

"Yes, sir," I answered, "that was Mrs. Poindexter."

Captain Poindexter opened his mouth a few times, but no sound came out.

I twisted my cap in my hands.

Slowly, one by one, the officers from other ships found excuses for leaving. Quarters sounded. Frantically I fumbled through my pockets for the sales slip on the panties. Finally, I found it and thrust it into the captain's hand. He looked at it for a few seconds and went into his cabin.

He didn't talk much to anyone for a while, and never referred to the incident. Two days later he called me into his cabin.

"Do you still want to go to China?"

"Yes, sir."

"That's all," he said, nodding toward the door.

The following Monday I received dispatch orders to report to the Commander-in-Chief, Asiatic Fleet, Shanghai, China.

IRA WALLACH (1913–   )

Ira Wallach has been a parodist from the beginning. His first book was deceptively entitled How To Be Deliriously Happy, *a definite take-off on* How To *books and something of a fraud insofar as it did not teach its readers how to make friends or a million dollars, how to influence people or achieve lifelong peace. This was followed by two books in which no living author was safe, as one parody outdid the other:* Hopalong-Freud and Other Modern Literary Characters *and* Hopalong-Freud Rides Again.

"The Keeper of the Gelded Unicorn," from the first of these two collections, is a burlesque of the big bosom-and-boudoir historical novel, for which so many pine forests have been laid waste. "God's Little Best Seller," from the second, is a killing onslaught that is also a critical satire on the ever so Deep South stories of Erskine Caldwell. A not too pretentious social documentarian, Wallach offers the latter story as another chronicle of the rise and fall of the Southern mattress.

THE KEEPER OF THE GELDED UNICORN

"A hogshead of fine wine!"

The barmaid, her eyes wide with admiration, looked at the man who had shouted his order with such an air of confident gaiety. He was tall, lean, bronzed, with broad shoulders, slender hips, eyes that blazed like live coals, dark unruly hair, and a twinkle in the corner of a mouth which could, at

times, be stern enough to strike terror into the hearts of the greatest swords-
men on the Continent and in very England itself.

"Come, maid, God wot, 'sblood, marry!" he called. "Did you not hear me,
maid? A hogshead of fine wine!" He pinched her lightly and took her to
bed, after which she brought the wine, her eyes tender and moist with devotion.

Two public letter writers whispered in a corner. Outside, the cry of the
fishwives could be heard over the shouts of the children laughing and clapping
as the dancing bear performed in the streets thick with cutpurses.

The barmaid slipped into the kitchen where her father awaited. "Who is
that young gentleman of noble mien, Father?" she asked.

Old Robin, keeper of the inn, took one look and gasped. "The Keeper of
the Gelded Unicorn!" he whispered. "The finest sword in England! 'Tis
said he was born a foundling and raised in the court of the Duc D'Ambert
who lacked a son. The streets of London are paved with the hearts he has
broken, cemented by the blood he has spilled. But he is ever a friend to the
poor, and a sworn enemy to Guise, the Earl of Essence!"

The barmaid's eyes filled with limpid tears. "Then he is not for me,
father!"

Old Robin shook his head sadly. "God wot, no, daughter," he said. "Good
Brogo, the blacksmith's half-witted son, will make you a fine husband."

At that moment Guise, the Earl of Essence, successor to many proud
titles, strode into the inn, followed by his retinue. Guise might have been
called handsome had not cruelty, avarice, and dissipation left their telltale
marks on his countenance.

The barmaid hastened to serve him. Guise narrowed his eyes. "A fine
ankle," he murmured. His courtiers smirked as Guise fondled the barmaid's
left rump. In a moment a shining blade lay across the table.

"Aha! Meeting in rump session with your retinue! Wouldst cross blades
now, my lord Guise?"

Guise looked up into a pair of burning eyes. Slowly, he removed his hand
from the barmaid's rump. "Your time will come, Warren of Hastings," he
spat, addressing the Keeper of the Gelded Unicorn by his true name, known
only to those few who suspected from his demeanor that in his blood ran
the cold skill of the English, the wild ferocity of the Scotch border chiefs,
the lilting carefree spirit of the Irish, and the soft and murmurous tenderness
of the Latin.

Abruptly, Guise rose and left with his retinue. The barmaid approached
the table and put her hand timidly upon that of Warren of Hastings. "You
should not have done it, my lord," she murmured.

He snapped his fingers. "What if I do start the Thirty Years' War!" he
exclaimed in his carefree manner.

England, in the Year of Our Lord 1746, was torn by dissension. The
Queen's faction, headed by Warren of Hastings with the loyal aid of France's

Count D'Même-Chose, was plotting an anti-Spanish alliance with the Holy Roman Empire and the Palatinate. The King's faction, led by Guise, Earl of Essence, sought instead an alliance with the Saracen, and the Earl was ready to go so far as to sign a secret treaty with the Czar. Richelieu, disturbed by the development of events, vacillated between the two, and only the Huguenots, tied as they were by bonds of kinship and blood to Austro-Hungary, and influenced by the sinister figure of Oliver Cromwell, followed an unswerving path. No one knew in which direction the Winter King would turn, and over all loomed the shadow of Napoleon. Into this maelstrom grimly strode Philip IV of Spain. Lenin remained noncommittal. Little wonder that heads rolled in the Tower, and that, on the streets of London, Warren of Hastings, at the head of his faithful band, often clashed with the hired cutthroats and Pomeranian mercenaries brought to England by Guise, the Earl of Essence.

Through a dark street, disguised only by a cloak over his face, Warren of Hastings sped toward the palace. Two public letter writers whispered in a corner. The cry of the fishwives could be heard over the shouts of the children laughing and clapping as the dancing bear performed in the streets thick with cutpurses. In a few moments, Warren of Hastings was in the Queen's bedchamber where he took the cloak from his face and murmured, "My lady!"

She walked toward him slowly, her dark hair gleaming under a caul of tinsel, her arms outstretched. "Warren of Hastings," she whispered, "swordsman, warrior, balladier, courtier, pamphleteer, lover, poet, and patriot!"

He seized her roughly, importunately, and drew her to the window, where he laid his cheek athwart her heaving bosom. She yielded momentarily, then turned her face to the darkening sky. "Not now," she whispered, "not now." Then, "Marry," she said, "notice yon white clouds."

"Not so white as thy teeth," he replied, "nor half so regular."

Again she freed herself from his embrace. "God wot, Warren, even now my Earl of Guise is approaching Duncanfayne with a horde of Pomeranians. 'Tis said they will lay siege to Duncanfayne this night!"

Warren of Hastings leaped back, his hand instinctively clutching his sword's hilt. "Duncanfayne, where my lady has hidden her treasures!"

She nodded quietly, and only a tear betrayed her thoughts.

"And my liege, the King?" asked Warren of Hastings.

"Carousing with Gisette of Lyons." She said it without bitterness, although a trace of irony hardened her voice. "Little does he know that Gisette of Lyons is in the pay of Richelieu!"

"More fool he!" murmured Warren of Hastings.

"Sir!" cried the Queen, stirred to sudden wrath, "you are speaking of our lord, the King!"

Warren of Hastings dropped to his knees and pressed her hand against his lips. "Forgive me, dear lady," he pleaded. "I forgot myself."

"I forgive you," she said, forcing his head against the pillow.

"Even now Warren of Hastings, the Keeper of the Gelded Unicorn, is closeted in the Queen's chamber while we march on Duncanfayne," spat Guise as he rode his charger through the murky night, followed by a horde of Pomeranians.

Across the channel rose a faint glow from the fire whereon Joan of Arc was burning. Hammel de Vyl, the Earl's companion and master spy, smiled a dry smile. "More fool he," muttered Hammel.

The Earl snarled lightly. "Is all prepared?" he asked.

Again Hammel laughed, but with no trace of humor. "The guards are bribed, the moat is down, the bridge is up, and our agent has spavined all the spears in Duncanfayne. Warren of Hastings wots not of this."

"Well done, Hammel de Vyl," remarked the Earl, tossing him a bag of doubloons.

The four-master leaned to the wind, the night foam spraying her bow. "Wet the sails, ye slobberers!" shouted the captain, his teeth trembling in the gale. "Jettison the cargo!"

The sailors sprang to, and overboard went casks, barrels of sprawns, cauls of lichen, two farthingales, and a huge tusk of billingsgate. Leaning against the mainmast, his feet on the mizzen, his face turned to the flying spray, was Warren of Hastings. Near him stood the faithful Edward Masterfield, a youth whose courage and sword most closely matched those of Warren himself.

"God wot, Edward," cried Warren, "little does Guise reck that we shall cut him off at Duncanfayne by sea this night!"

"More fool he," said Edward, his mouth making a grim line as his forefinger tested the edge of his sword.

From the crow's-nest far aloft came a sudden call, "Land ahoy!" All eyes turned to the starboard where, across the bow, faintly glimmered the lights from the storm-tossed battlements of Duncanfayne.

Within an hour's time the good ship *Aphrodite* had tied up alongside and a group of silent men, their faces in their cloaks, slipped ashore.

In bloodstained Duncanfayne, Guise, the Earl of Essence, and Hammel de Vyl saw victory within their grasp. Then the Queen would sing a different tune indeed! Richelieu and the Winter King would have to retreat, and the counsel of the Earl of Essence would carry new weight in Venice before the whole province went to the Doges! Even the crown—it was not impossible, nay, it was probable—might revert to the Earl himself, once the King had become sufficiently involved in his wild dream of an *entente* with Bruit van Hooten of Holland!

The Earl himself led his men to the gates of the treasury. But suddenly the door swung open, a strong hand reached out and pulled the Earl within. The door immediately slammed shut against his Pomeranian followers.

Bewildered, the Earl looked about. The floors were strewn with the Queen's jewelry. Upon the table four candles gave the vault its only light. Lined against the walls were the followers of the Queen's faction, and there in the center, his merry eyes still twinkling, stood Warren of Hastings, Keeper of the Gelded Unicorn.

"'Sblood!" cried Guise.

"How now, Guise," answered Warren, brushing back an unruly lock of curly hair.

"God wot!" retorted the Earl.

"Marry!" laughed Warren in rejoinder. "Shall we try the temper of our swords?"

Guise blanched. "Your men," he said, indicating the band that stood against the walls.

"My retinue will not interfere, will you, retinue?"

"Nay, God wot!" they cried as one man.

"Then, have to!" shouted Warren, unsheathing his blade.

The Earl leaped back and bared his sword to the candlelight. For a moment they fenced cautiously. Then the swords locked at the hilt and the two faces met and almost touched. "I shall carve thee for a roast," hissed Guise.

"Let us see who does the roasting and who does the eating," rejoined Warren between clenched teeth.

They separated. The blades flashed. The Earl advanced, taking the offensive. Skillfully, Warren parried the quick thrusts as he retreated around the table. At that moment he caught the eye of Edward Masterfield and turned to smile. It was a mistake of overconfidence, for in that very moment of turning, Guise's swift blade thrust in, cut through doublet, lumpkin, ruffle, and wattles, drawing a thin line of blood upon Warren's shoulder.

"'Sblood!" cried Warren of Hastings. Quickly he turned to the offensive and brought the duel to the Earl, his lightning blade catching the fine glints of the candlelight. Another bold thrust forward, and bright steel cut flesh on Guise's thigh. Guise withdrew, but Warren was relentless. A few sudden parries, a feint, an *entrechat*, and to the hoarse cry of "Long live the Queen!" a slender blade shot forward and pierced the Earl's throat.

Warren sighed. "Now open the doors," he ordered his men. The doors swung wide. The Pomeranians advanced, but catching sight of the Earl, now dead, they fell back with a cry of horror, and crossed the Channel.

"A good night's work," murmured Edward Masterfield weakly, as he drew a Pomeranian arrow, shot by a fleeing malcontent, from his abdomen.

It was a gay and lighthearted Warren of Hastings who brought the jewels to the Queen's chamber. Although she had lost neither whit nor tittle of her regal bearing, her eyes spoke for her as she said, "You may kiss me, Warren of Hastings."

Wilder and wilder grew Warren's passion. He heard her murmurous, "No, no," but he was his heart's puppet, and he could not deny his Irish, English, Scotch, or Latin blood. In the bed he drew her still closer as they lay in murmurous and ecstatic silence.

Outside the palace two public letter writers whispered in a corner. The cry of the fishwives could be heard over the shouts of the children laughing and clapping as the dancing bear performed in the streets thick with cut-purses.

"And now, beloved lady," cried Warren of Hastings, "on to the War of the Roses!"

Her eyes filled with tears. "Honor will always take thee further afoot than love," she sighed.

"God wot," he replied, bowing his head. Through the window the sun rose on the battlements and on the triumphant standards of the Queen.

Warren of Hastings silently arose from bed and removed his hat.

England was safe.

GOD'S LITTLE BEST SELLER

Georgia has more girls with erect breasts than any other state in the Union, and that's a fact.

That's what Luke was thinking. Luke examined the third step on the porch, the broken step. He always said he was going to fix that step. "Bring me a little closer to the Lord," he said, "when the step is fixed." He shaded his eyes and looked over the field. Out on the new ground Spike was planting a cotton seed for the twelfth time. This time it ought to stay down.

"Spike!" Luke hollered, wiping the sweat off his forehead with his shirt-sleeve. He put the shirtsleeve back in his pocket.

Spike laid the cotton seed to one side and ambled toward the porch. Then Tucker came out of the house and sat down next to Luke on the second step. "Look here, now, boys," Luke said, "we ain't agoin' to give up. We been fixin' this step for nine years now, and I got a feelin' in my bones we're gonna fix it for good this year, and that's a fact.

Tucker hefted the broken end of the plank.

"Get the car, boys," Luke told them. "We're gone to Wrightstown now and get us a nail."

Spike walked silently around the house and began filling the tires with air. He didn't have no pump so he just blew them up with his mouth. When the tires were full Spike got up off his knees. "Ain't no sense gone to Wrightstown afore we eat, is there, boys?"

"They ain't," said Tucker, "and that's a fact."

They went single file into the kitchen where Effie, Luscious Lil, and Gloria Mundy were cooking the grits. Luke stared at his daughters. "God sure give me a handsome set of girls," he said to himself. He shook his head admiringly. "Luscious Lil," he said out loud, "every time I look at your rising beauties I get a feelin'!"

"Aw, Paw!" Luscious Lil hid her face in the hominy grit pot. "Aw, Paw!"

"Never mind that 'Aw, Paw,' stuff. If I gotta say it, I gotta say it. Looks like God give me three fine girls with erect breasts, that's what it looks like, it does, and that's a fact. But them rising beauties—makes me feel like loping around the house!"

"Aw, Paw," said Luscious Lil, crawling behind the stove.

"Yes, sir," Luke said, "the Lord sure was good to me, giving me three daughters with——"

"Eat your grits, Paw," said Tucker. "We ain't never gonna get that nail without we get to Wrightstown before sundown."

Luke ate his grits silently. While they were eating, the door creaked open and Philo Butts waddled in. Philo Butts was the local coke salesman, but he didn't like to sell cokes on hot days. He wiped his flushed red face with a pocket towel. Then he looked at Luscious Lil. His eyes had a hound-dog look.

"I shore would like to marry with you, Luscious Lil," he said plaintively.

"Set down and eat some grits, Philo," said Luke.

Philo pulled out a chair and sat down. He ate with one hand. The other was under the table, feeling around Luscious Lil's garter. He got his fingers under the garter.

"That's my garter you got your fingers under," said Luke. "Luscious Lil don't wear no garters."

"They ain't much use without stockings," said Luscious Lil.

Philo sighed. It was too hot to take his hand away, so he left it there. Then Luscious Lil stuck her tongue out at Philo. "Stupid!" she said. Then she got undressed and wouldn't pass the coffee pot to Philo. Philo was flustered. He couldn't eat his grits nohow.

"Stop teasing Philo," Effie said, "and pass him the coffee pot." She rumpled Philo's hair. "Why don't you let Philo alone?"

Luke looked up. "The Lord sure gave me three beautiful daughters with——"

"Come on, Paw," said Tucker. "We got to get to Wrightstown."

They all started out for the car. On the way Bledsoe, the hired man from the Flacksey place down near to Euphoria, came ambling by. "Still fixing the third step, Luke?" he asked, his eyes on Effie. Effie stared back at him, her lips quivering a little, the corners of her mouth wet.

"We aim to have it all done this year," said Luke, "and that's a fact."

Effie smiled and Bledsoe smiled back. "Wait a moment, Paw," Effie said. "I got to talk to Bledsoe a bit."

She took Bledsoe by the arm and led him away. Luke, Spike, Tucker, Philo, Luscious Lil, and Gloria Mundy, sat down on the running board.

In a little while, Tucker scratched his head. "Wonder what's keeping Effie?" he asked. "Maybe we better all take a look."

They got up slowly and walked around the barn. Effie and Bledsoe were lying on the ground near Effie's clothes which lay in a heap next to the well.

Luke shook his head. "You hadn't oughta leave your clothes in the damp, Effie," he complained. They all stood around in a circle. "Imagine that!"

Luke was querulous. "Just when we was getting ready to go Wrightstown."

"Go away, Paw, and you and Tucker and Spike, too," said Luscious Lil, pushing them.

"Why, what's the matter with you, Luscious Lil?" asked Luke.

"Effie don't like the menfolk around at a time like this. You ought to be ashamed of yourself, Paw."

"Me? Why should I be ashamed of myself? Effie ain't thin-skinned like you."

"Go away, Paw," insisted Luscious Lil.

Luke turned silently and went back to the car with the boys. Effie came along in a few minutes and got on to the front seat. Bledsoe stood with one foot on the running board while the others got in. He was staring at Luscious Lil. Luscious Lil's lips quivered a little. The corners of her mouth were wet.

"Better hurry up, Paw," said Tucker, "or we ain't never gonna get out of here."

The car's exhaust blew a cloud of dust in Bledsoe's face. Luscious Lil drove fast. The back door of the car rattled and threatened to break the piece of wire that held it to the body. Luke looked around at his family. "The Lord sure was good to me," he said to himself, watching Luscious Lil's rising beauties. Luke got down on the floor of the car and barked. "Aw, Paw!" said Luscious Lil, pressing her cheek against the dashboard.

"Better watch the road, Luscious Lil," Tucker warned.

Twenty minutes later they reached Jessamyn's house in Wrightstown. Jessamyn was Luke's other daughter. She was married to Brad, and Brad worked in the mill when the mill was working. But there was no work now, and Brad was sitting on the porch, thinking. He was thinking he couldn't live away from the mill, and he was thinking of all the girls he could see from the mill windows, girls with wide mouths and erect breasts and flowery eyes and erect breasts. The men were lean and hard and they waited around the shut gates of the mill where they could see the girls with their erect breasts, not like in the country, but then Brad could never be a country man, never leave Wrightstown or the mill, with its big window from which he could look out and see the girls pass with their wide mouths and their erect breasts. Brad glowered. Jessamyn greeted Luke and the girls, but Brad didn't say anything. A girl passed by on the street, and Brad watched her pass with her wide mouth and her e.b.'s.

Brad finally looked up. "Hello, folks," he said.

"Come to town to get a nail," Luke explained.

"You still on that plank?" Brad asked. "Nine years and still at it?"

"Thought maybe you and Jessamyn'd come out and help us hammer," Luke said. "We're almost done. We sure could use you now to help a mite, and that's fact."

Brad rose slowly. He turned to Jessamyn. "Supper ready?" he asked.

She nodded. They all went to the kitchen. After supper they sat on the porch and watched the sun go down. Brad didn't look at the sun. He looked at the dark silhouette of the mill.

Luke yawned. Then he rose and turned to Turner and Spike. "Guess it's too late to get that nail tonight," he said. "Let's go."

The boys nodded and followed Luke to the car. Luke looked back. "Coming, girls?"

Effie said, "Think we'll stay over, Paw. Pick us up tomorrow when you come back for the nail."

Luke and the boys drove off.

An hour later the girls walked inside the house. Jessamyn picked up her knitting. Suddenly Brad turned to Luscious Lil. There was something in his face that frightened Jessamyn. Brad looked drunk but he wasn't.

"I got a feelin' inside me," he muttered, staring at Luscious Lil, "and goddam, it's the mill and me, and something that said to me all the time, I got to have Luscious Lil. Your paw is right, Luscious Lil. Your paw is absolutely right. I'm mighty powerful now. Nothing is gonna stop me, nothing, and that's as sure as God made little green apples. Don't move none, Luscious Lil!"

Luscious Lil stood silently, her mouth half open, her body shaking like a hog's ear in a high wind.

Brad went on as though he didn't care if anyone were listening or not. "I've waited for this, Luscious Lil. And now I'm gonna do it. I'm gonna take all the basting outen your dress, and all the basting outen your underwear, and I'm gonna take all the nails outen your shoes, and I'm gonna do it all with my teeth!"

He moved toward her. She stood trembling, waiting. She knew she couldn't move if she wanted to. Effie said, "Philo Butts is gonna kill you, Brad." Jessamyn was knitting. She dropped a stitch.

Brad just walked toward Luscious Lil. He leaned over her shoulder. Then he bared his teeth and suddenly, in a spurt of violence, he tore at the basting. Thread by thread the dress dropped off. The shoes took longer. Finally Brad got the last nail between his teeth and the soles flopped off. Silently, he lifted Luscious Lil and carried her to the couch.

Gloria Mundy crawled around the floor while Effie played solitaire. "Put the black ten on the red jack," said Jessamyn, looking up from her knitting. There was a beautiful expression on her face.

A few neighbors dropped in and looked around. "See you got company," one of them said. He was a lean young fellow with a double thumb. Gloria Mundy crawled over to him and clutched convulsively at his trouser cuff. He leaned over and dragged her to the next room. There was a lot of noise and Jessamyn had to shout when she asked, "You folks want me to freeze some ice cream?"

"That'd be nice," Brad murmured. Luscious Lil sat up. She knew now that Paw was right, and Paw and Brad knew something nobody else knew and never would know, and that was that a man has to feel with all his power and not care what or who or when or whatever or however or if or why, if it stands in the way, and that's the way it was with Brad. And that was why she would never forget Brad.

Effie ran out at solitaire and then she helped turn the freezer. When the ice cream was done they looked up and saw Philo Butts standing in the doorway. Philo was staring at Brad and leveling a shotgun at him. "You hadn't ought to have done it, Brad," he said, "and that's a fact."

Brad tried to hide behind Effie, but Effie was in the kitchen dishing out the ice cream. The explosion rattled the wood walls of the house. Luscious Lil screamed. Just then Luke and Spike and Tucker came in the door. Luke stared at Brad, lying next to the ice-cream freezer. "Strawberry?" he asked.

Luscious Lil, Effie, Gloria Mundy, and Jessamyn kneeled beside Brad's body and wept. They put their arms about each other and they laid their heads against each other's shoulders. Then the women's auxiliary came in with their erect breasts, and kneeled by Brad's body and wept.

Luke turned to Philo. "The sheriff's gonna hear about this come Sunday," he said. "Better take a walk, Philo. Sun's down and walking won't be so hard."

Philo took the shotgun and stood in the doorway.

"All my life I wanted to keep the peace," said Luke. "God blessed me with three fine daughters—"

"Four, Paw," said Tucker.

"—four fine daughters with erect breasts. Guess the Lord had to give me the sorrows, too." Luke sat down slowly like a tired man. "Tucker," he said, "I guess we might as well stay on in Wrightstown and pick up the nail in the morning."

Philo opened the door and started into the darkness. Luscious Lil stood up, Jessamyn next to her. "Wait for us," Luscious Lil whispered to Philo. He waited. Luscious Lil and Jessamyn got down on the floor, crawled over to Philo, and hooked on to his legs. Luke looked at Philo, sympathy in his eyes. "That's gonna make for hard walking," he said, "and that's a fact."

Luke heard the door close. From outside he could hear the faint swoosh-swoosh of Luscious Lil and Jessamyn dragging in the street as they clung to Philo's legs.

In the morning Spike and Tucker went over to the general store and fetched a nail. Effie waited on the porch for them. When they returned, they all got in the car. Effie drove. In twenty minutes they were back and they started hammering at the nail like crazy. "We'll get it fixed this year," Luke swore.

"Hello, Effie." The voice came from the porch. Effie saw that it was Bledsoe. Her mouth was wide and moist, and she had erect shoulders. Bledsoe walked down the farm a piece to the tree at the edge of the new ground, and Effie followed.

"What's Effie doing now?" asked Luke complainingly.

"Aw, let her alone, Paw," said Tucker.

"God was mighty good to me," said Luke. "He give me four beautiful daughters with——"

"Pass the hammer, Paw," said Tucker.

Luke looked at the new nail. This time, he promised himself, this year they'd get that third plank in, and that's a fact.

JEAN DUTOURD (1920–   )

The Best Butter, winner of the Prix Interalliée, is perhaps the most bizarre novel to come out of the war. It is a story of Paris during the German occupation, and concerns a "typical" French shopkeeper, M. Poissonard, who amasses a fortune by shrewd activities in the black market. This venal theme is treated with such satirical wit, written in so devastatingly lucid a style, that the author, Jean Dutourd, has been compared to Balzac, Voltaire, and Zola.

The most endearing if exasperating character in The Best Butter *is the twenty-six-year-old student, Léon Lécuyer, who escapes from a German prison camp because "when one's a prisoner, one must escape. It is one's duty." Making his way back to Paris, he hides in his mother's flat. Soon all the neighborhood knows he is there. Mme. Poissonard, to ingratiate herself with the Germans, informs the authorities. But when the military police knock on Mme. Lécuyer's door, Léon escapes through the bedroom window in his underpants, and flees over the roofs of Paris—which is how and where we find him at the beginning of the following excerpt from* The Best Butter.

FROM: THE BEST BUTTER

LÉON LOSES HIS VIRGINITY

We must now turn back and pay some attention to Léon Lécuyer, whom we left on a rooftop. It is not exactly warm in October at five in the morning. At a height above sixty feet the wind blows strong. Lélé ran like a hare. Clad in nothing but his underpants, with his elbows close to his sides, he sped between the chimney pots, leaped from roof to roof, straddled crevasses, and slithered up and down slopes. "Always on the run," he thought gloomily. "When shall I be able to take up arms again and face the foe?" This reflection reveals an inexhaustible fund of silliness.

No one can run indefinitely. After a quarter of an hour's gallop, Léon collapsed out of breath against a lightning conductor. The lead roof thundered as he fell, but he was so exhausted that he had not the strength left to take cover behind a nearby chimney. A window opened and a voice cried:

"Is anybody there?"

As one can imagine, Léon made no reply. Crouching out of sight in an angle of the roof, he did not run much risk.

"I'm sure there's someone there," pursued the voice. "Who is it? Answer me. Is it the roof mender?"

"Yes, it's the roof mender," said Léon. "Don't worry."

"You might make less noise," said the voice. "You woke me up."

It was the voice of a young woman. Léon's romantic heart gave a lurch. He edged forward. At the same time a head appeared, a solitary head, projecting like a ball around the sloping roof: small blue eyes, plump cheeks, and tangled yellow hair.

"Well, I never!" said the head. "Whoever saw such a sight!"

Suddenly Léon felt chilly.

"I'm cold," he said plaintively.

"That doesn't surprise me," said the head. "At least put your jacket on."

"I haven't any clothes," said Lélé.

"I haven't seen many roof menders like you in my life!" cried the head.

Léon, standing and gripping the lightning rod in one hand like a spear, was a weird spectacle. Letting himself slide along the incline of the roof, he reached his questioner. Her face was comely; her flannel nightdress could not entirely conceal the charm of her body.

"Well," she said, "what's wrong?"

"I'll explain. Let me in. I promise I won't molest you . . . I'm not what you think. My name is Léon Lécuyer."

The room, furnished with a brass bedstead, a pitch-pine wardrobe, and two cardboard suitcases, was pretty disheartening. The gray wallpaper was yellowing and covered with damp patches. A faded blue eiderdown drew the eye, flaccid as a jellyfish on the shore of blankets.

"And my name," said the young woman, pulling on a dressing gown, "is Emilienne, like in the song. I work downstairs, for Monsieur and Madame Bloncourt on the third floor. It's not a bad place, you know: there's no children. And now, what are you up to? You ought to have a number tied on your back, running a race over the roofs like that! You wouldn't be walking in your sleep by any chance?"

Whereupon Emilienne burst into delicious laughter. This girl was not without charm. All at once Léon blushed: he was more or less naked in a woman's bedroom. He felt ashamed of his skinny body and thin, hairy legs. He was covered with goose pimples and thought lovingly of the nice warm bed standing there empty. But how could he find his way into this bed?

"All the same," continued Emilienne, as if echoing his thoughts, "whatever would my boy friend say if he saw you like this, here in my room in your underpants? Take a blanket from the bed, you'll be warmer."

Léon, who had the most extraordinary ideas about women, was rather saddened to learn that this girl of twenty-six or -seven apparently had a lover. A virgin himself, he saw virginity all about him.

"I'm going back to sleep," said Emilienne. "I don't have to be up till eight o'clock. But you still haven't told me what you were doing on the roof."

"Nothing!"

"I'd make you a cup of tea, only I've run out of spirits for my stove."

Emilienne, in her brass bed, reflected by the mirror of the pitch-pine wardrobe, made a sublime picture. Léon sorrowfully reflected that this girl was not for him. She loved another and, as far as he could judge, was faithful to him. What was he to do? In *La Nuit et le Moment* by Crébillon *fils*, a naked man slips without a word of warning into a woman's bed and, after a brief struggle, remains there; but that is fiction. Should Léon take it into his head to act thus, Emilienne would scream the house down.

"You ought to try and get a couple of hours' sleep, M'sieu Lécuyer," said Emilienne. "It would set you up."

"Perhaps I could lie down on your bed," said Léon in a shaky voice. "On top, of course. May I?"

Emilienne remained silent. No reply means consent. Léon, in the grip of a powerful emotion, stretched himself out on the blue eiderdown.

"Why not get inside?" murmured Emilienne.

"Well!" thought Léon. "That's pretty familiar. Why not? Obviously I'd be better off in the bed. And since she wants me to . . ."

"What cold feet you've got!" said Emilienne.

"Oh! I'm so sorry!" cried Léon in embarrassment, drawing back so far that he nearly fell out of the bed.

"Why did you keep the blanket on? Chuck it out!"

The blanket chucked out, Emilienne snuggled up against Léon. The idea that he was going to sleep clasping a woman in his arms filled him with joy. "What a simple creature!" he thought; "what abandon! What a girl! She trusts me. She knows I won't try to take advantage of her." Only he was tormented by the idea that his body might commit some involuntary indiscretion which would alarm his hostess. The latter closed her eyes; sleep had already recaptured her. Léon, immobile as a stone, gazed admiringly at this round face, which seemed to him more beautiful than the Mona Lisa. With infinite precaution he put his lips to it. God knows what dream had Emilienne in its toils: although the kiss barely brushed her forehead, she abruptly raised her head, gave a weird moan, and Léon's lips met hers. However explicit this girl's behavior, it took another quarter of an hour for Léon to realize that the death knell of his virginity had sounded.

At a quarter past seven the earsplitting din of the alarm clock dragged the two lovers out of a heavy sleep. Léon sat up, stiff and aching in an unfamiliar and wonderful way. His eyes roved around the dreary maid's room which seemed to him the perfect setting for voluptuousness: then, looking down at Emilienne, a smile at once conceited and shy spread over his lips.

Emilienne had difficulty in opening her eyes. A curl quivered above her left eyebrow.

"Jojo," she murmured. "I love you. You're my man, Jojo!" Then, suddenly awake, she cried: "Let's have a kiss, darling, so I've the courage to get out of bed."

Léon, his heart pierced to the core by this untimely reference to Jojo, coldly kissed Emilienne's cheek; but she, hot-blooded by nature, seized him round the waist and purred:

"We've still got ten minutes."

Those ten minutes went by in a flash. Léon was astonished at himself. "How easy it is!" he thought. "How could I have waited twenty-six years? What is life without love? I have a mistress!" These reflections rather marred his pleasure.

Emilienne jumped out of bed. As she was entirely naked, Léon was able to confirm that she was quite well built and on the plump side; but he watched her furtively, afraid to offend her modesty by staring too openly. It was he, Léon, who was modest.

"All set," said Emilienne. "I'm going down now. You can have a long nap. If anyone knocks, don't answer; but nobody will. There's only Jojo who might come, and I'd be surprised if he did."

"You haven't got a book you could lend me?" asked Léon on intimate terms with a woman for the first time in his life and feeling extremely pleased with himself.

"I've some *Lisez-moi bleu* in the cupboard. Just dig them out. And there's *Confidences*, too. Make yourself comfy. I'll come up directly I get a moment. I'll bring you something to eat. You must be hungry, my little cabbage."

Emilienne gone, Léon folded his hands behind his head and gave the ceiling a broad smile. Life takes delightful turns. In three hours he had changed his whole personality. He felt important; he was participating at last in the ways of the world! "I am a man," he thought. "I am no longer a backward adolescent. I have possessed the body of a woman; I occupy her mind. What a splendid creature this Emilienne is! She has asked nothing of me. I seduced her straightaway. And with a woman's generosity she gave me all. She's going to bring me food, perhaps clothes. I only had to appear, a hunted prisoner, abandoned by all, alone in the world, for her to love me at once. O woman! all tender heart and sweet pity! Perhaps she was waiting for me. She's a housemaid, of course, but she hasn't a housemaid's heart. And she is intelligent. Only an intelligent woman could give herself like that, readily, without demur. Ah! Emilienne, Emilienne! Should I love you? You love me, without a doubt: a woman does not give herself without love. There are accents which do not deceive, and those accents you had. What am I to do? I cannot leave her in my debt; I will ask her to marry me. Why shouldn't I marry this admirable girl? Because she is not of my class? I hate my class. I've always been a Socialist."

He got up and went to study his features in the spotted mirror on the wardrobe door. "So someone loves this face," he told himself with a mixture of astonishment and pride. "Someone desires this body," he continued, passing his hands over his skinny limbs. "Perhaps I'm handsome after all. If not handsome, at least attractive." He had completely forgotten his escape from Pomerania, the defeat of France, and his steeplechase over the roofs. He could only picture a future all pink and voluptuous in Emilienne's company. "Of course, there's this Jojo; but that's not serious. Jojo's a mistake. Her first love, I suppose. The man who revealed the life of the senses to her. I shall meet him. I'll make him understand he must sacrifice himself. I shall defend our happiness. I am not a bleating sheep to be led to the slaughterhouse. It seems to me I've proved that."

Despite this intense meditation, he began to feel bored. Looking for something to read in the cupboard, he found, besides weekly magazines, half a dozen cheap novels signed by such absurd names as Max du Veuzit, Jean de la Hire, Claude Fleurange, and Roby. The presence of these works, instead of irritating, touched him. He made plans to educate, Emilienne. Intellectually she was a child, who sinned only through ignorance. Léon would draw her up a list of good authors, from the *Chanson de Roland* down to the present day. After the wedding, he would take her to concerts and exhibitions of painting.

The magazine *Confidences*, in which singers and actresses described their amorous experiences, captivated Léon, who read a dozen numbers of it straight off. This prose, which he would have despised the day before, charmed him; it expressed genuine emotions. Toward ten o'clock, Emilienne knocked on the door. She brought two sandwiches, which Léon devoured, and some red wine.

"I say, you *were* hungry," she said. "Doesn't surprise me, after a night like that. D'you know, we're in luck, my employers have gone and are lunching out."

Whereupon she raised her arms in the air, her dress flew off, and the next moment she was in the bed. At noon, Léon asked:

"Where am I?"

"What a silly question! In my room, of course!"

"I mean, what street?"

"Why, don't you know? This is the Rue Poncelet. Number ninety-six."

"Rue Poncelet!" exclaimed Léon. "Then . . . then I went in a circle on the roofs. I thought I'd gone at least a mile. Rue Poncelet indeed! Only a step from the Rue Pandolphe."

"Oh yes, I know the Rue Pandolphe. That's where I do my shopping."

"How amazing," said Léon. And he fell silent.

"D'you know the *Bon Beurre* in the Rue Pandolphe?" pursued Emilienne, made shy by the idea that her lover might know the same people as she did, and immediately cooling in her attitude. "The *Bon Beurre's* our dairy. That's where I go to fetch the milk every morning. I was around there just now."

"It's really amazing," repeated Léon.

"Then in that case, you live around here," said Emilienne, who had recovered her aplomb. "It's funny I've never seen you. But after all . . . you still haven't told me . . ."

Léon brooded for a moment over the smallness of the world and the setbacks of fate; then he said gravely:

"Listen, Emilienne . . ."

"Ah no!" cried Emilienne. "Don't call me Emilienne. I don't like that name. Call me Milou. Only my employers say Emilienne."

"Listen, Milou. Yes, I live around here. I know the *Bon Beurre* well, and Florentin the butcher, too. . . ."

"That's right! Florentin. He's our butcher, and then there's the *Boulangerie-Patisserie des Ternes* where I get the cakes; and Rasepion the shoemaker: and the *Charcuterie des Gourmets* . . ."

"I live in the Impasse du Docteur-Barthès with my mother."

"You don't say!"

Léon then told the story of his tribulations. He enjoyed this; Emilienne learned that she had to do with a brave man, holder of a medal with two escapes to his credit. "How she must admire me!" he thought. "For her I'm a true adventurer, a hero out of a novel."

"Well," declared Emilienne, "to think I thought you were just an overgrown kid! You've had a tough time, my poor dear. But you're a nice boy all the same. Give your Milou a kiss to console her for all your troubles."

This reaction did not enchant Léon. He had been counting on wild excitement and (why not?) tears. He would also like to have discussed Jojo and made his proposal of marriage.

"And anyway," resumed Emilienne, "you can't stay here forever. Wait, I've an idea. There's an old suit of my boy friend's in one of my cases. You put it on and tonight, when it's dark, you can make your getaway. How's that?"

"What a woman!" thought Léon; "she can rise to every occasion." However, the prospect of wearing the castoffs of the abhorred Jojo was torture to him.

"Love me?" asked Emilienne, squirming in the bed.

"Now's the moment," thought Léon, "to speak up."

"Listen," he said, "let's fly together." (Readers cannot fail to have noticed the pompous way in which this young man speaks to himself and to others. It is the effect of living in solitude and overindulgence in the mediocre authors studied at the Sorbonne.)

"Where to?" asked Emilienne.

"To the Free Zone. We'll get married there."

"You want to marry me?"

"Yes, Emilienne."

"Are you crazy?" said Emilienne. "It takes two to get married. *I* don't know *you*. I've never set eyes on you till today. And Jojo? What would he say? It's easy to see you've never met him."

"As a matter of fact, I've been planning to have a word with him," replied Léon in a rather overblustering voice.

"Don't do that!" cried Emilienne in alarm. "He'll wallop me, and you too. He's very jealous—— That'd be the last straw!"

These words wounded Léon. The proofs of love she had lavished on him since six o'clock that morning did not prevent *him* from being jealous. "There's women for you," he thought bitterly. "I've been more intimate with this one than with any other, and yet she dares to pretend she doesn't know me! O woman! Abyss of duplicity! She deceives Jojo with me; she will deceive me with someone else; and after that she will tell both Jojo and me that she loves us!"

Léon, as one can see, was making progress in the knowledge of human beings. Emilienne did not believe him capable of standing up to Jojo. It was intolerable.

"So you prefer Jojo to me?" he said.

"The idea! We've been together for three years. What else do you expect?"

This psychology, albeit elementary, completely baffled Léon. He saw everything in a romantic light. In matters of sentiment, he could not conceive that there was any room for good sense and placidity.

"And what does this excellent Jojo do," he arrogantly demanded, "for him to be handled so gently?"

"He's a plumber."

Emilienne was quite the most irresponsible creature in the world. It never seemed to occur to her that Léon was suffering; harsh as they were, his words left her unmoved. Worse still, she came up to him and planted a series of little kisses under his chin.

"You know," she said, "Madame hasn't given me the whole day off. So don't let's waste our time squabbling. I shall have to go down again in half an hour."

When Emilienne returned to her employers' apartment, she left Léon in deep perplexity. His emotions had lost their acridity, but they were neither so exalted nor so agreeable. Truth to tell, he no longer thought of Emilienne with love. The latter had laid out Jojo's suit on a chair. As he put it on, Léon discovered that solitude and silence, after considerable exertion, are not so painful after all. He decided to renounce his marriage for the time being. This "for the time being" was a polite gesture to himself. He would flee to the unoccupied zone of France and there he would see . . . Alas! it was cruel to imagine Emilienne enjoying in Jojo's embrace sensual delights which he could picture to himself only too clearly. While meditating in this fashion, he whistled the andante from Beethoven's *Fifth Symphony*, which he had enjoyed so many times at concerts at the Châtelet. He believed that this romantic music reflected the torments of his soul.

The mirror showed him a grotesque image. Jojo's suit was at once too wide and too short. On him, the jacket looked like some ample bolero, and the trousers came to an end four inches above his ankles. The outfit, of cheap cloth and unsupported by any shirt, tie, or shoes, made Léon a sorry sight.

As he was inspecting himself, he was overcome by giddiness. With a heavy head, sagging body, and trembling legs, he fell onto the bed and was asleep almost immediately. He dreamed of the Rue Pandolphe. He was walking down it after curfew. All was dark except the dairy, *Au Bon Beurre*, which glimmered like phosphorus. The shop, reconstructed in marble, resembled the Parthenon. Entering this sanctuary, Léon saw a throne of gold encrusted with precious stones, and on it Mme. Poissonard, in a brocade gown and a tiara. She smiled at him, but there was something venomous about that smile. "A diabolical smile," murmured a mysterious voice, while another, doubtless the voice of reason, replied: "Diabolical! What can be diabolical about this honest tradeswoman's smile?" Léon shrugged his shoulders. "And what will it be for Monsieur Lécuyer?" said Mme. Poissonard. "It will be prison, banishment, and death!" she added in such a bantering tone of voice that it was impossible to believe in such a terrible verdict. At this moment M. Poissonard, seated on a second throne which had escaped Léon's notice, opened his mouth and exclaimed: "Monsieur Lécuyer, a small parcel, at the desk!" Léon's stomach contracted with hunger and he paid less heed to this preposterous announcement, even though he could sense that there was something prophetic about it, than to the food stacked in the temple. The walls were covered with hams hung up like votive offerings; there were great clusters of salamis, anthills of butter, slabs of chocolate as big as Veronese pictures, cheeses as vast as the rose windows of a cathedral. An ungovernable lassitude rooted Léon to the floor; his leaden arms refused to reach out towards this tantalizing provender. The two enthroned Poissonards regarded his impotence, nodding their heads. A third figure rose up out of the shadows: a boy of about fifteen—nearer fourteen than fifteen. His face, unfamiliar to Léon, nevertheless struck some chord in his memory: it had Mme. Poissonard's eyes and her husband's mouth, like an offspring embodying their fusion in one flesh, but Léon did not know of any son of theirs of that age; moreover, the boy was dressed in the oddest way, in a long gown; his dour and obtuse face was that of an angel subjected to the most unjust punishments of God. From a far corner of the temple came choking sobs. In spite of the darkness, Léon recognized his mother, his own mother, wringing her hands; like him, she seemed to be bound by invisible chains. Deeply upset by these demonstrations, he tried to move in order to drag the old lady outside, but an agonizing pain shot through his head: the angel had struck him with a rod of gold. He had twisted about in his sleep. His forehead had knocked against one of the brass bedposts.

Once awake, he tried to analyze this dream according to the methods of Dr. Freud. But, however earnestly he applied these, he could find no trace of any repressed homosexual passion, infantile traumatism, or incest tendency. Strictly speaking, the presence of the hams signified necrophilia or sadomasochism, but that did not satisfy him. It was hard to conclude a mother fixation merely from the fact that Mme. Lécuyer had been there. "Could it be that I coveted Madame Poissonard," he wondered as a last resort, "and that my subconscious was punishing me in this way?" But, remembering that woman as he had last seen her on Christmas leave in 1939, he had to admit that no fantasy of such a nature had ever crossed his mind. Mme. Poissonard smelled of sour milk; she was fat and white; her pudding face, her pointed nose, her frizzy black hair and acid voice aroused no desire.

"My dream means nothing at all," declared Léon. "I must have been too hot. Or hungry. Anyway, it's never a good thing to sleep in the afternoon."

His head ached. The dream made him melancholy. A wholehearted Socialist, a graduate in higher studies at the Sorbonne, nurtured on the Fathers of Free Thought, Léon believed in neither God nor the devil, and yet he was filled with a vague terror, as if this inexplicable dream was a premonition. Toward six o'clock, the return of Emilienne dispelled these gloomy imaginings. She brought "one of Monsieur's old shirts and a pair of shoes he'd thrown out." Outside it was as dark as one could wish for.

"Here," she said. "Put these on. Now's the moment to slip away. Here's a ticket for the underground. You haven't any money either? Let's see what we can do."

She took a mock leather handbag out of the closet and rummaged inside it. Léon, who could only respond to generosity by greater generosity, insisted on giving her an I O U. Emilienne accepted this more easily than he had expected. She also suggested that Mme. Lécuyer might reimburse her.

"That way, I can give her your news. She must be feeling anxious, the poor thing!"

Léon would have liked their parting to be marked by some emotional extravagance. An afternoon of solitude had restored all his ardor, but Emilienne astonished him by her coolness. She turned her mouth away from his kiss and, when he put his hands on her thighs, disengaged herself with a pretty, sinuous twist of her body.

"Hands off!" she said.

In fourteen hours a love had been born, had flared up and died away. Emilienne seemed impatient for him to go. This unseemly haste saddened Léon.

He couldn't help asking: "Do you love me, Emilienne?"

The stupidity of the question, its incongruity, struck him. He had put it in a tremulous voice. There was a lump in his throat. He could not explain his emotion.

"Of course I love you," said Emilienne shortly. "If I didn't love you, you wouldn't be here. And now, off with you!"

Human nature is full of resources. Léon, who was tearful as he went down the stairs, was surprised to find himself humming outside. The sound of his footsteps in the deserted Rue Poncelet filled him with gaiety. They were the steps of a conqueror, not of a fugitive. The faint scent of lavender exuded by M. Bloncourt's old shirt combated the rather fierce smell of Jojo's suit.

Léon promised himself to go after the war and pay a courtesy call on this M. Bloncourt, and astound him with a description of his exploits. He owed him some slight return.

In the underground he stared at the German soldiers with an irony which quite escaped them. "After all," he thought, "it hasn't been such a bad day. I've escaped, I've seduced a pretty woman, and I've got money and clothes for my pains." His mind strayed to the point where at the Gare de Lyon he was quite seriously comparing himself with Casanova. Where does the abuse of reading not lead? But no matter! He was happy; that alone excuses everything.

RAY BRADBURY (1920–   )

Although the stories in The Martian Chronicles, The Illustrated Man, Fahrenheit 451, *and* The Golden Apples of the Sun *reveal a preoccupation with the complexities of time, space, and the intimidating future, Ray Bradbury is much more than a gifted writer of science fiction. His fecund imagination, poetic and often profound, explores the dark territories of the human mind as avidly as the mysterious galaxies. Born in Waukegan, Illinois, in 1920, he supported himself by selling newspapers after graduating from high school in Los Angeles. He had begun writing at twelve; while still in his twenties he was hailed as one of the most brilliant storytellers of his generation, particularly in a field which few people were taking seriously. His sometimes fantastic, sometimes whimsical, and always extraordinary tales were collected in several volumes, dramatized for television, and reprinted in more than sixty anthologies. "En la Noche" exhibits another extension of Bradbury's range: his half-poignant, half-humorous understanding of a group of tired tenement dwellers.*

EN LA NOCHE

All night Mrs. Navarrez moaned, and these moans filled the tenement like a light turned on in every room so no one could sleep. All night she gnashed her white pillow and wrung her thin hands and cried, "My Joe!" The tenement people, at 3 A.M., finally discouraged that she would *never* shut her painted red mouth, arose, feeling warm and gritty, and dressed to take the trolley downtown to an all-night movie. There Roy Rogers chased bad men through veils of stale smoke and spoke dialogue above the soft snorings in the dark night theater.

By dawn Mrs. Navarrez was still sobbing and screaming.

During the day it was not so bad. Then the massed choir of babies crying here or there in the house added the saving grace of what was almost a harmony. There was also the chugging thunder of the washing machines on the tenement porch, and chenille-robed women standing on the flooded, soggy boards of the porch, talking their Mexican gossip rapidly. But now and again, above the shrill talk, the washing, the babies, one could hear Mrs. Navarrez like a radio tuned high. "My Joe, oh, my poor Joe!" she screamed.

Now, at twilight, the men arrived with the sweat of their work under their arms. Lolling in cool bathtubs all through the cooking tenement, they cursed and held their hands to their ears.

"Is she *still* at it!" they raged helplessly. One man even kicked her door. "Shut *up*, woman!" But this only made Mrs. Navarrez shriek louder. "Oh, ah! Joe, Joe!"

"Tonight we eat out!" said the men to their wives. All through the house, kitchen utensils were shelved and doors locked as men hurried their perfumed wives down the halls by their pale elbows.

Mr. Villanazul, unlocking his ancient, flaking door at midnight, closed his brown eyes and stood for a moment, swaying. His wife Tina stood beside him with their three sons and two daughters, one in arms.

"Oh God," whispered Mr. Villanazul. "Sweet Jesus, come down off the cross and silence that woman." They entered their dim little room and looked at the blue candlelight flickering under a lonely crucifix. Mr. Villanazul shook his head philosophically. "He is still on the cross."

They lay in their beds like burning barbecues, the summer night basting them with their own liquors. The house flamed with that ill woman's cry.

"I am stifled!" Mr. Villanazul fled through the tenement, downstairs to the front porch with his wife, leaving the children, who had the great and miraculous talent of sleeping through all things.

Dim figures occupied the front porch, a dozen quiet men crouched with cigarettes fuming and glowing in their brown fingers, women in chenille wrappers taking what there was of the summer-night wind. They moved like dream figures, like clothes dummies worked stiffly on wires and rollers. Their eyes were puffed and their tongues thick.

"Let us go to her room and strangle her," said one of the men.

"No, that would not be right," said a woman. "Let us throw her from the window."

Everyone laughed tiredly.

Mr. Villanazul stood blinking bewilderedly at all the people. His wife moved sluggishly beside him.

"You would think Joe was the only man in the world to join the Army," someone said irritably. "Mrs. Navarrez, *pah!* This Joe-husband of hers will peel potatoes; the safest man in the infantry!"

"Something *must* be done." Mr. Villanazul had spoken. He was startled at the hard firmness of his own voice. Everyone glanced at him.

"We can't go on another night," Mr. Villanazul continued bluntly.

"The more we pound her door, the more she cries," explained Mr. Gomez.

"The priest came this afternoon," said Mrs. Gutierrez. "We sent for him in desperation. But Mrs. Navarrez would not even let him in the door, no matter how he pleaded. The priest went away. We had Officer Gilvie yell at her, too, but do you think she listened?"

"We must try some other way, then," mused Mr. Villanazul. "Someone must be—sympathetic—with her."

"What other way is there?" asked Mr. Gomez.

"If only," figured Mr. Villanazul after a moment's thought, "if only there was a *single* man among us."

He dropped that like a cold stone into a deep well. He let the splash occur and the ripples move gently out.

Everybody sighed.

It was like a little summer-night wind arisen. The men straightened up a bit; the women quickened.

"But," replied Mr. Gomez, sinking back, "we are all married. There is no single man."

"Oh," said everyone, and settled down into the hot, empty river bed of night, smoke rising, silent.

"Then," Mr. Villanazul shot back, lifting his shoulders, tightening his mouth, "it must be one of *us!*"

Again the night wind blew, stirring the people in awe.

"This is no time for selfishness!" declared Villanazul. "One of us must *do* this thing! That, or roast in hell another night!"

Now the people on the porch separated away from him, blinking. "*You* will do it, of course, Mr. Villanazul?" they wished to know.

He stiffened. The cigarette almost fell from his fingers. "Oh, but I——" he objected.

"You," they said. "Yes?"

He waved his hands feverishly. "I have a wife and five children, one in arms!"

"But none of us are single, and it is your idea and you must have the courage of your convictions, Mr. Villanazul!" everyone said.

He was very frightened and silent. He glanced with startled flashes of his eyes at his wife.

She stood wearily weaving on the night air, trying to see him.

"I'm so tired," she grieved.

"Tina," he said.

"I will die if I do not sleep," she said.

"Oh, but, Tina!" he said.

"I will die and there will be many flowers and I will be buried if I do not get some rest," she murmured.

"She looks very bad," said everyone.

Mr. Villanazul hesitated only a moment longer. He touched his wife's slack hot fingers. He touched her hot cheek with his lips.

Without a word he walked from the porch.

They could hear his feet climbing the unlit stairs of the house, up and around to the third floor where Mrs. Navarrez wailed and screamed.

They waited on the porch.

The men lit new cigarettes and flicked away the matches, talking like the wind, the women wandering around among them, all of them coming and talking to Mrs. Villanazul, who stood, lines under her tired eyes, leaning against the porch rail.

"Now," whispered one of the men quietly, "Mr. Villanazul is at the top of the house!"

Everybody quieted.

"Now," hissed the man in a stage whisper, "Mr. Villanazul taps at her door! Tap, tap."

Everyone listened, holding his breath.

Far away there was a gentle tapping sound.

"Now, Mrs. Navarrez, at this intrusion, breaks out anew with crying!"

At the top of the house came a scream.

"Now," the man imagined, crouched, his hand delicately weaving on the air, "Mr. Villanazul pleads and pleads, softly, quietly, to the locked door."

The people on the porch lifted their chins tentatively, trying to see through three flights of wood and plaster to the third floor, waiting.

The screaming faded.

"Now, Mr. Villanazul talks quickly, he pleads, he whispers, he promises," cried the man softly.

The screaming settled to a sobbing, the sobbing to a moan, and finally all died away into breathing and the pounding of hearts and listening.

After about two minutes of standing, sweating, waiting, everyone on the porch heard the door far away upstairs rattle its lock, open, and, a second later, with a whisper, close.

The house was silent.

Silence lived in every room like a light turned off. Silence flowed like a cool wine in the tunnel halls. Silence came through the open casements like a cool breath from the cellar. They all stood breathing the coolness of it.

"Ah," they sighed.

Men flicked away cigarettes and moved on tiptoe into the silent tenement. Women followed. Soon the porch was empty. They drifted in cool halls of quietness.

Mrs. Villanazul, in a drugged stupor, unlocked her door.

"We must give Mr. Villanazul a banquet," a voice whispered.

"Light a candle for him tomorrow."

The doors shut.

In her fresh bed Mrs. Villanazul lay. He is a thoughtful man, she dreamed, eyes closed. For such things, I love him.

The silence was like a cool hand, stroking her to sleep.